GUN DIGEST BOOK OF
GUN ACCESSORIES & SERVICES

Edited by Joseph J. Schroeder

Robert S.L. Anderson, Associate Editor

DBI Books, Inc. Northfield, Ill.

Editorial Staff

Editor
Joseph J. Schroeder

Associate Editor
Robert S.L. Anderson

Cover Photography
John Hanusin

Associate Publisher
Sheldon L. Factor

Publisher
Milton P. Klein

Cover case by Norbert Ertel.

Listings, descriptions and prices contained herein are not advertising, and neither the publication nor the publisher offers the merchandise and services described for sale, nor do they recommend purchase of any particular item of merchandise or service. Prices contained herein were furnished by the manufacturers and vendors listed; all are subject to change—they are included here as a guide only.

The editors and publisher have exercised all reasonable care in the preparation and assembly of the material in this book. However, no responsibility for the accuracy or correctness of the information contained herein is assumed.

ISBN 0-695-81313-7 **Library of Congress Catalog Card Number 79-54269**

Table of Contents

Introduction

The *Gun Digest Book of Gun Accessories & Services* has been designed to be both the most comprehensive book of its kind and also the most usable. Within its pages literally thousands of items and services have been organized into 19 appropriate divisions, each with its contents grouped and arranged in some sort of logical sequence.

The introduction to each section, found on its title page, not only describes the contents of that section but also outlines, when appropriate, the organization of that section. As a number of items in the book could logically fit properly in more than one of its sections, the section introductions also provide suggestions as to where else to look when a particular type of item is not found where it seemingly should be. The introduction also suggests convenient sources for items in that section.

With every item or service in the book a company or individual's name is provided. Without exception, every one of those names is listed, along with complete mailing address and often telephone number, in the directory at the very end of the book. Although many items can be most conveniently purchased from local shops or the large mail order specialty houses, a large number of the things and most of the services described are available only from the source listed in the directory. When writing for information, particularly to the smaller firms or to individuals, including a self addressed, stamped envelope will greatly increase your chance for a prompt reply. When telephoning, remember that an engraver or smith's time is his livelihood and it's a courtesy to keep your calls as short as possible.

Prices are included whenever they were available. A great deal of effort was put into making these prices as accurate and current as possible, but all are subject to change and should thus be taken only as a guide until confirmed. In many cases, of course, a range of prices is shown. Prices for many services can vary widely so both the service and its price should be agreed on in writing by both parties before work is begun.

The coverage of this first edition of the *Gun Digest Book of Gun Accessories & Services* is very broad, yet much thought and effort went into putting it into a practical, user-oriented format. To that end, the editors would deeply appreciate any criticisms or suggestions as to how future editions may be made even more useful than this one is.

Pistol Customizing Accessories

In this section almost all of the many items we've included are those that the average gun enthusiast can add to his pistol or revolver himself. Most will, of course, require the use of some tools. With few exceptions the tools needed will be found in the average household.

Some of the items in this chapter do require more than average ability and knowledge to properly install; a few (generally so noted) actually do require the services of a skillful smith with a well equipped shop. For the most part, however, such items will be found in Section 8, *Custom Guns & Gunsmithing Services*.

Pistol and revolver grips lead off this section of the book. They're among the most attractive, useful and universal of all pistol and revolver accessories—and there are plenty of good ones on the market. Next come sights and barrel ribs, then action accessories, barrels and conversion kits. A variety of other pistol accessories will be found throughout the section.

Finally, not all pistol customizing accessories do, indeed, appear in this section. In organizing the book there were any number of times where an item clearly fit into more than one section, or, conversely, didn't quite clearly fit anywhere. As a result, you're likely to find some pistol customizing accessories in Section 7, *Gun Parts: Replacement & Obsolete,* or in Section 8, *Custom Guns & Gunsmithing Services*. Sights, of course, are all found in Sections 3 (iron) and 4 (scopes).

To purchase any of the things you'll find in this chapter start with your local gunshop first. You will often be surprised at some of the low demand items he does stock, and if he doesn't have exactly what you asked for he may have a perfectly adequate substitute. In addition, your request will put him on notice that there is a demand so the next time you ask, you may well find he now stocks it. If you can't find it locally, the larger mail order supply houses probably can help you. Some items are available only from the maker and will generally be noted as such. When writing any supplier, a self-addressed, stamped envelope will often greatly expedite a reply.

SMITH & WESSON GRIPS

Available for K- or N-Frame revolvers, smooth or checkered target stocks. These are the oversized target stocks currently preferred by many shooters for general field use. (Sold only in pairs.)

Price: K-frame (walnut checkered only) $17.88; K-frame goncalo alves (smooth or checkered) $18.70; N-frame walnut (checkered only) $20.08; N-frame goncalo alves (smooth or checkered) $20.90.

From Smith & Wesson.

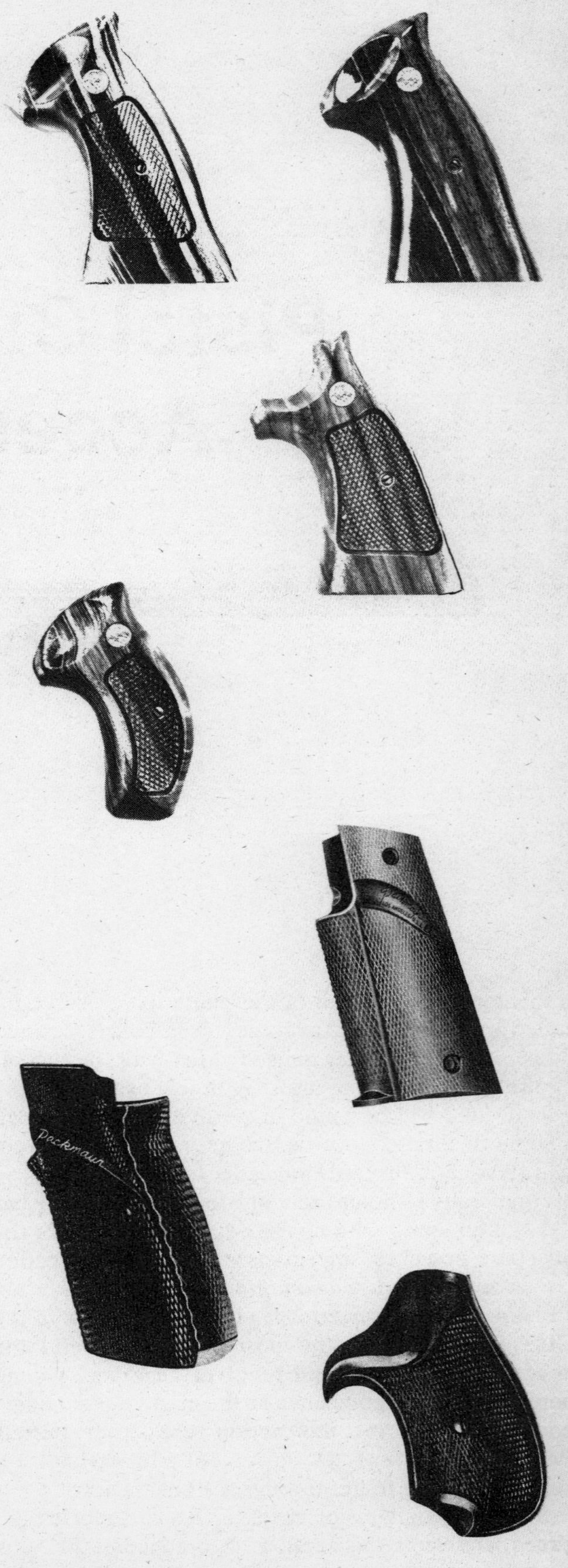

SMITH & WESSON GRIPS

Available for K- or N-Frame revolvers. These oversized target grips feature a more generous cut out on the left grip panel to facilitate the use of speed-loaders.

Price: K-Frame walnut (checkered only) $17.88, K-Frame goncalo alves (smooth or checkered) $18.70; N-Frame walnut (checkered only) $20.08; N-Frame goncalo alves (smooth or checkered) $20.90.

From Smith & Wesson.

SMITH & WESSON GRIPS

"Banana-Style" target stocks for small (J) frame revolvers. Checkered walnut shown but also available in smooth or checkered goncalo alves as well.

Price: checkered walnut $15.13; Smooth or checkered goncalo alves $16.50.

From Smith & Wesson.

PACHMAYR SIGNATURE GRIPS FOR COLT .45 AUTO

These grips feature a wrap-around design. Fit either right or left hand. Won't crack, chip or break. Designed for all Colt .45 autos that have the regular government frame.

Price: $17.50.

From Pachmayr Gun Works.

PACHMAYR SIGNATURE GRIPS FOR AUTO PISTOLS

Available for S&W, Walther PP/PPKS, Browning H.P. and H&K P9S autos. Features wraparound construction; won't crack, chip or break.

Price: $22.50.

From Pachmayr Gun Works.

PACHMAYR PRESENTATION GRIPS (COMPAC) FOR SMALL FRAME REVOLVERS

This is a compact version of the full sized Presentation grips. Won't crack, chip or break. Available for most small-frame Smith & Wesson, Colt and Charter Arms handguns.

Price: $12.75.

From Pachmayr Gun Works.

Prices shown are subject to change.

PACHMAYR PRESENTATION GRIPS (COMPAC) FOR MEDIUM SIZE ROUND BUTT REVOLVERS

Won't crack, chip or break. Available for most medium framed Smith & Wesson and Ruger handguns.

Price: $12.75.

From Pachmayr Gun Works.

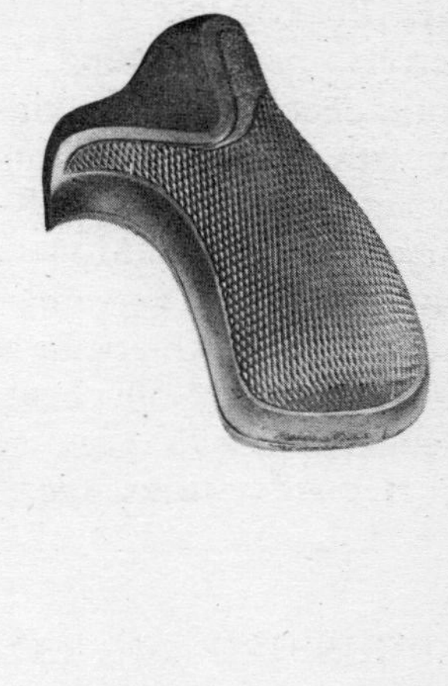

PACHMAYR PRESENTATION GRIPS FOR S/A REVOLVERS

Made of a special neoprene compound along with steel insert. Won't crack, chip or break. Available for the newer Colt and Ruger S/A revolvers.

Price: $12.75.

From Pachmayr Gun Works.

CUSTOM HANDGUN GRIPS

Made for the Smith & Wesson Model 39 auto. Available in a wide selection of woods and two styles of grip—plain and combat (combat shown).

Price: Walnut $8.50; zebrawood $11; rosewood $11; goncalo alves $11; cocobolo $11.50; macassar ebony $15. (For 50¢ more you can get the combat grip, as shown, in any of the above woods.)

From Jean St. Henri.

CUSTOM HANDGUN GRIPS

Available in a wide selection of wood for the Smith & Wesson Model 59.

Price: Walnut $8; zebrawood $10; rosewood $10; goncalo alves $10; cocobolo $11; macassar ebony $14. (For 50¢ more you can get a combat-style grip in any of the above woods. Plain grip shown.)

From Jean St. Henri.

CUSTOM HANDGUN GRIPS

Available in a wide selection of wood for the Browning High-Power 9mm auto. These grips have a reinforcing inset laminated on the inside to prevent splitting or warping.

Price: Walnut $14, zebrawood $16; rosewood $16; goncalo alves $16; cocobolo $17; macassar ebony $19.00.

From Jean St. Henri.

CUSTOM HANDGUN GRIPS

This set of grips is made for the Star PD .45 auto and come in walnut, zebrawood, rosewood, goncalo alves, cocobolo or macassar ebony. (Goncalo alves shown.)

Price: Walnut $12; zebrawood $13; rosewood $13; goncalo alves $13, cocobolo $14; macassar ebony $16.50.

From Jean St. Henri.

See the Directory for complete company addresses.

HANDGUN GRIPS

Herrett's new Shooting Master grips are available in smooth, checkered and skip-checkered designs. They come with finger grooves and are made for the Ruger New Security Six, S&W K- or N-Frame guns, Colt Python and Officer Model revolvers. Shown is the fine-line checkered version for the Ruger New Security Six. Made from American walnut.

Price: Smooth $25.50; checkered (shown) $27.50; skip checkered $29.75

From Herrett's Stocks, Inc.

HANDGUN GRIP FOR T/C SINGLE SHOT

Herretts new Hunter grip for the Thompson Center Contender is made of selected walnut, has finger grooves and is designed for left-, right- or two-handed hold.

Price: $23.75.

From Herrett's Stocks, Inc.

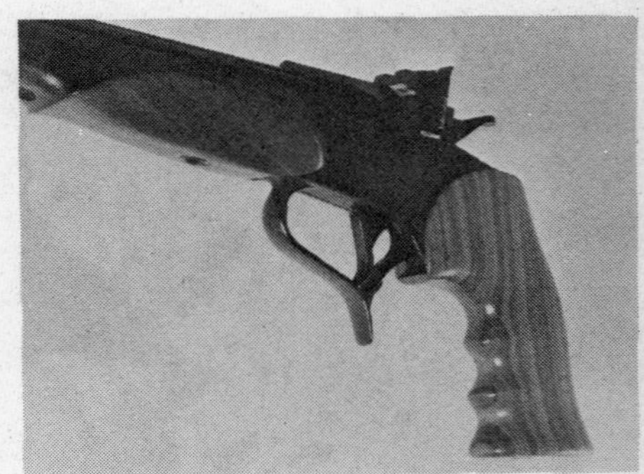

HANDGUN STOCKS

Herretts Stocks offers a wide selection of auto and revolver grips for just about every popular handgun. They are available smooth or checkered; and, special features, such as deluxe checkered finger grooves and figured walnut are available at extra cost.

Prices: Contact manufacturer or see your local dealer.

From Herrett's Stocks, Inc.

CUSTOM GRIPS

Walnut Grips for most S&W Colt and Ruger handguns (plus others). Grips are ready to install.

Prices:

1. S&W #7K (K-Frame)	$20.95
2. Ruger #411 (Super Black Hawk)	25.85
3. S&W #007 (K-Frame)	20.95
4. S&W #77S (N-Frame)	34.50
5. S&W #7KTR (K-Frame)	22.20
6. S&W #521 (Mdls. 52&39)	34.50
7. Walther #073 (P-38)	22.20
8. Ruger #8 (Std. Auto)	13.55
9. Colt #811 (D-Frame)	22.20

From Sile, Inc.

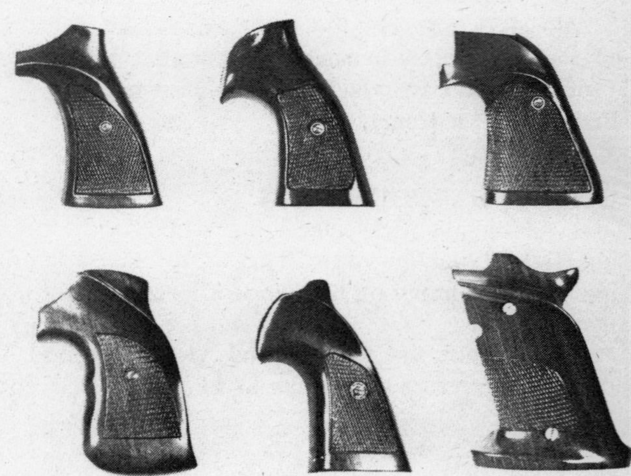

CUSTOM HANDGUN STOCKS

For Colt and Smith & Wesson K- and N-frame revolvers. Come in oil finished walnut and other more exotic woods.

Price: $24.95; sedjua, partridge and Indian rosewood $10 more.

From Schiermeier.

Prices shown are subject to change.

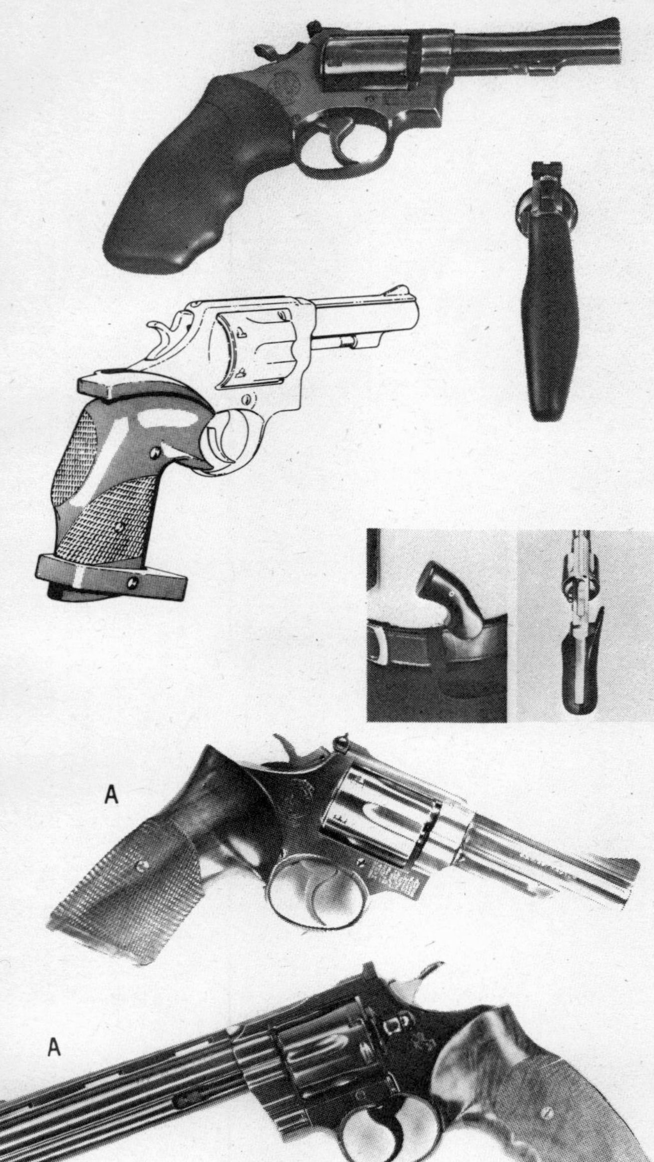

CUSTOM HANDGUN GRIPS

Currently available for S&W K-frame revolvers. They are made of high impact black urethane plastic. Feature palm swell, finger grooves and left-grip relief for speed loaders.

Price: $11.45

From Bullet Industries.

CUSTOM TARGET GRIPS

Available for most Smith & Wesson and Colt revolvers. These new grips have been designed to meet ISU specs and come with right-hand thumb rest and adjustable palm support.

Price: $34.95

From Fitz Grips.

CUSTOM HANDGUN GRIP

Called the "Hip-Grip," this particular item eliminates the need for a holster. It's available for many Colt, S&W and Charter Arms revolvers.

Price: $10.95

From Barami Corporation.

A **CUSTOM HANDGUN GRIPS**

Available for most popular revolvers and automatics. These are strictly custom-quality grips. The standard wood is walnut but a very broad range of exotic wood is also available.

Prices: Revolvers $65; S/A factory grips $45; automatics $45; one-piece style Colt SAA $75. For 20 Lines per inch checkering add $35; 22 LPI $40; 24 LPI $45; 26 LPI $50. (Delivery time is 12-16 weeks.)

From Robert H. Newell.

CUSTOM S/A REVOLVER GRIPS

Available in ivory, carved, inlaid or smooth. Engraving cost can vary with each request for a specific design or amount of coverage. If carved ivory catches your eye, write for a price quotation.

Price: About $100 for smooth, plain ivory; rare wood grips available at a much-reduced price over ivory.

From Iron Age Craftsworks (Jim Kelso).

LEFT HAND GRIPS FOR DOMINO SP602 and OP601 AUTOS

Target shooters have flocked to the Domino pistols in recent years. Now you can get a set of factory left-hand grips. Shown nearby (on the left) is left-hand grip for the Domino OP 601; on the right are left-hand grips for the Domino SP 602.

Price: OP601 $120; SP602 $109.

From Mandall Shooting Supplies, Inc.

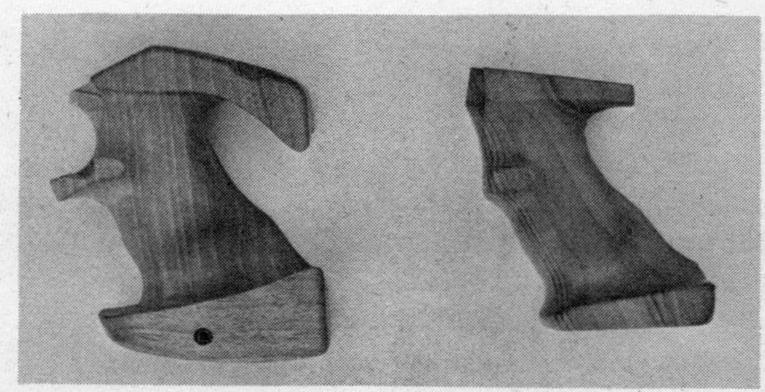

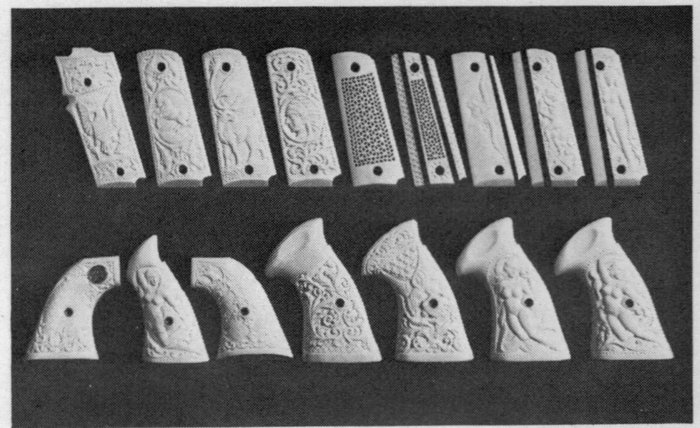

CUSTOM IVORY GRIPS

Art Jewel's custom ivory grips are hand made and feature high relief on both grips. (Art Jewell also offers a wide selection of rosewood grips as well-carved or plain.) All grips—rosewood or ivory—are available for most popular autos and revolvers.

Prices: For the Ivory, contact your local dealer; rosewood (shown nearby) $25.95 smooth, $28.95 carved.

From Art Jewel Enterprises.

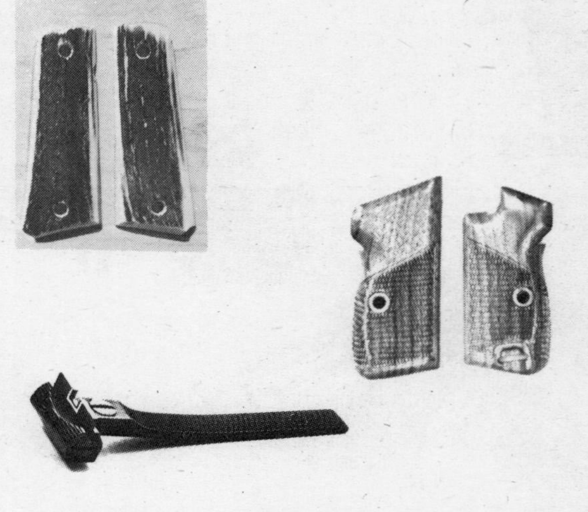

GENUINE STAG GRIPS

Available for most S&W, Colt and Ruger handguns. These grips are highly sought after and, often times, hard to find. Shown nearby are grips for a Smith & Wesson K-Frame and a Colt .45 auto.

Price: $24.95

From Lock Stock & Barrel (Larry W. Carpenter).

SIG P-210 PISTOL GRIPS

Nicely made, checkered walnut grips.

Price: $105 per pair.

From Mandall Shooting Supplies, Inc.

SMITH & WESSON ADJUSTABLE REAR SIGHT

This sight is fully adjustable for windage and elevation and is made for J-, K- and N-frame revolvers. Comes in blue only.

Price: $16.75; with white-outline blade $18.50.

From Smith & Wesson.

SMITH & WESSON FULLY ADJUSTABLE SIGHT FOR MODELS 59/39

This is the new S&W replacement rear sight for the models 59 or 39 autos. Unlike original factory sights, this replacement is *fully* adjustable for windage and elevation. (Not available with white-outline notch.)

Price: $16.75.

From Smith & Wesson.

SMITH & WESSON REAR SIGHT LEAFS

Available for most S&W adjustable sights. Come in either white outline or plain.

Price: plain $2.25; white outline $5.

From Smith & Wesson.

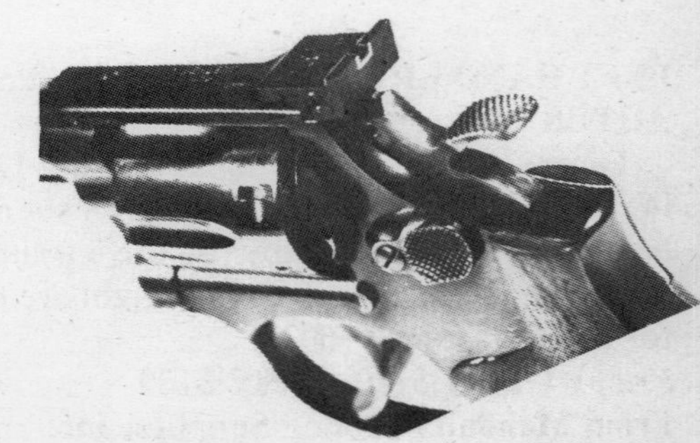

ADJUSTABLE REAR SIGHT

For K- and N-Frame S&W, Dan Wesson, Ruger and Colt revolvers; also Colt Gold Cup and Browning autos. Has 20 clicks of elevation and 16 clicks of windage. The sight blade and windage spindle are precision cast for strength. (K-Frame S&W version shown.)

Price: Plain $32; white outline $35.

From Austin Behlert Custom Gun Shop.

RAISED HANDGUN RIB

Poly Choke's custom rib kit includes everything you'll need to install your rib in just a few minutes. No fitting, cutting or machining. At press time we were advised that ribs are available for some Colt, Smith & Wesson and Ruger products; and, that new models of the Poly Choke Pistol Rib were being developed. (Write Poly Choke to see if they have a rib for your particular handgun.) Shown nearby is a Ruger Super Blackhawk complete with rib. (Vent and solid models available for some guns.)

Price: $14.95.

From Poly Choke.

CUSTOM SIGHT/RIB COMBO

Available for the Walther PP series autos. The rib uses the S&W Kit sight milled into the rear of the rib which has a ramp-type blade pinned into the front. No ribbing of the slide is required and the added sight height is only ¼″.

Price: $55

From Austin Behlert Custom Gun Shop.

REVOLVER FRONT SIGHTS AND RAMPS

The ramp is available with a variety of blade heights and types. The ramp is ⅜″ high and the blade heights vary according to customer need.

Price: Ramp $12.95; Blades $4.50 plain, $9.95 with insert—blades are cross-pinned and can be easily changed.

From Austin Behlert Custom Gun Shop.

RED RAMP INSERT KIT

The home hobbyist can, according to the manufacturer, install this one himself. A complete set of instructions comes with each kit. Available in red, yellow, orange or white.

Price: $19.95.

From Lee's Red Ramps.

ADJUSTABLE CLARK (RUGER) REAR SIGHT

Easy to install, the Clark rear right is designed to replace all Ruger adjustable rear sights. Comes with large, flat rear blade with deeper sight notch. Improved sight picture, better click adjustments. (Also available to fit base on current production model Mark I Ruger auto).

Price: $16.50; White-outline blade $3.50 extra.

From James E. Clark.

SMITH & WESSON HANDGUN ACCESSORIES

The following list of miscellaneous S&W accessories and prices represents some of the most sought-after Smith & Wesson handgun accessories currently available. Included are barrels, magazines, counterweight, triggers, hammers—a literal potpouri of S&W accessories. All prices are suggested retail. (Most of the listed Accessories you can install yourself; others may require gunsmith installation.)

Prices:

Adjustable Olympic counterweights for Model 41 $27.60
Counterweights for Model 52 18.30
Magazines for Model 41 & 52 8.35
Magazines for Model 39 7.05
Magazines for Model 59 10.00
New 7″ Model 41 Barrel with sights (No muzzle brake provision) 59.65
5½″ Heavy Barrel with sights, for Model 41 68.95
Oversize trigger guard for Model 41 9.35
.22 Magnum chamber insert for use with .22 Long Rifle rim fire cartridges in Model 53 1.65
K-38 Single Action Kit 36.60
Halfmoon clip for .45 A.C.P. cartridges .60
Sight-adjustment screwdriver 1.65
Grip adapter (small, medium or large frame revolvers) 2.60
Mahogany Presentation Cases are available for all large frame revolvers with target sights 28.00
Butt Swivel with pin. (Blue or nickel) 2.35
Target Hammer Assembly 15.75
Target Trigger Assembly 13.55
Smooth Combat Trigger Assembly 13.55

From Smith & Wesson.

1911 COLT MAINSPRING HOUSING

Available in 20 or 30 lines per inch checkering. Nicely done. Comes in either flat or arched configuration. Chromed or blued.

Price: Arched, 30- or 20-lines per inch $27.50; flat $25.

From Victor Bortugno.

DOMINO REPLACEMENT SEAR UNIT

These units come in two separate weights—"light and standard." Designed as a drop-in replacement to meet ISU specs.

Price: $75

From Mandall Shooting Supplies Inc.

DETONICS .45 SUBSTITUTE RECOIL SPRING

In the nearby photo the original Detonics recoil spring is on the top. Below is the Seecamp dual-spring version. Makes for easier slide retraction and loading, and considerable compression at battery.

Price: $30

From L. W. Seecamp Co.

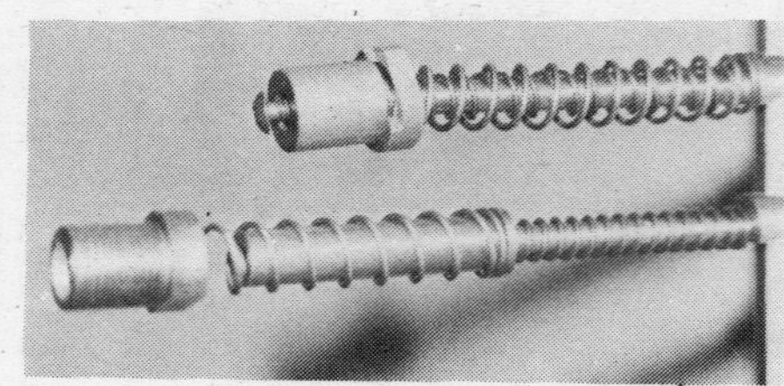

SINGLE-UNIT BACKSTRAP FOR COLT AUTOS

For combat competition. Solid blued steel one-piece backstrap eliminates grip safety feature. Available for all models of the Colt .45 auto.

Price: $30

From L. W. Seecamp Co.

COVERED MAINSPRING HOUSING FOR COLT .45 AUTO

Checkered Neoprene covered mainspring housing is designed to be used with Pachmayr's Presentation Grips for the Colt .45 Auto. Provides a non-slip, cushioned backstrap. Style A requires machining of frame; Style B and Style C drop into your existing frame, no alteration necessary.

Price: $9.75.

From Pachmayr Gun Works.

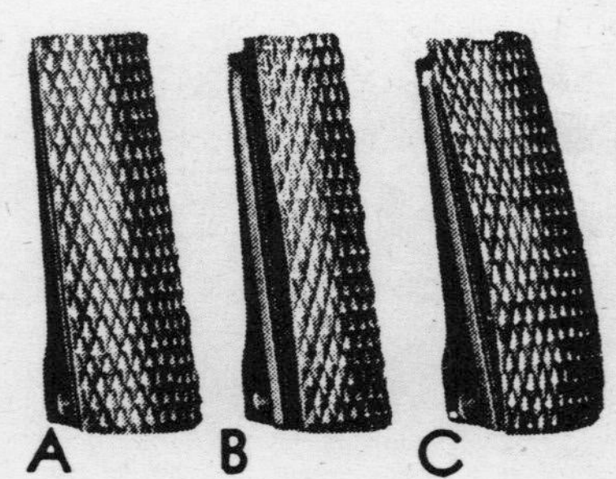

Prices shown are subject to change.

LEFT-HAND SLIDE STOP

Available for the Smith & Wesson Models 59/39, Browning High Power, Star PD and Colt autos (shown). Easy to install.

Price: Blue $55; electroless nickel or satin chrome $57.50.

From Austin Behlert Custom Gun Shop.

EXTENDED SLIDE STOP

Available for the Smith & Wesson Models 59/39, Browning High Power and the Star PD (shown). Gives better leverage for the thumb. Does not interfere with the holster and does not protrude beyond normal grip thickness. (Grip modification may be necessary.)

Price: Blue $24.95; nickel, satin chrome or chromalloy $28.50.

From Austin Behlert Custom Gun Shop.

CARTRIDGE ADAPTERS FOR THE THOMPSON CENTER CONTENDER

Each adapter is made of the finest steel and allows the user to fire other rim- or center-fire rounds in his favorite T/C single-shot handgun.

See the following list to find your adapter:

.22 LR in .22 Hornet TC	.22 LR in .218 Bee TC
.22 LR in .221 Fireball TC	.22 WMR in .218 Bee TC
.22 WMR in .221 Fireball TC	.25 ACP in .256 Win Mag
.22 LR in .222 Rem TC	.25 ACP in .25-35
.22 WMR in .222 Rem TC	.30 Carbine in .30-30
.22 LR in .223 Rem TC	.32 ACP in .30 Herrett
.22 WMR in .223 Rem TC	.32 ACP in .30 Herrett
.22 LR in .22 Jet TC	9mm in .357 Herrett
.22 WMR in .22 Jet TC	9mm in .35 Remington

Price: $11.95 each

From Sports Specialties, Inc.

STAINLESS STEEL AUTO PISTOL BARRELS

Available for all Colt .45 autos and the Browning High Power. Where applicable, bushing comes with barrel. The Bar-Sto barrels are precision made and have gained an excellent reputation for accuracy. They are available in .45 ACP, .38 Super, .38/.45 and 9mm. The list below contains prices; those items with an asterisk take 6-12 weeks for delivery and any required fitting may be done by a competent gunsmith. (Shown nearby is the Browning 9mm High Power Barrel.)

Prices:

.45 ACP (Government Model & Commander)	$65.00
.45 ACP (Gold Cup)	65.00
.45 ACP Match Target (Must be fitted)	75.00
.45 ACP Match Target Gold Cup (Must be fitted)	75.00
.45 ACP 6″ Match Target (Must be fitted)	150.00
.38 Super (Headspaced on case mouth)	65.00
9mm (Government Model & Commander)	65.00
.38/.45* (For all Models)	90.00
.45 ACP 6″* Match Target (Compensator Cuts at muzzle)	175.00
¾″ extra length barrel for Commander	90.00
Browning HI-Power barrel, 9mm	90.00

From Bar-Sto Precision Machine

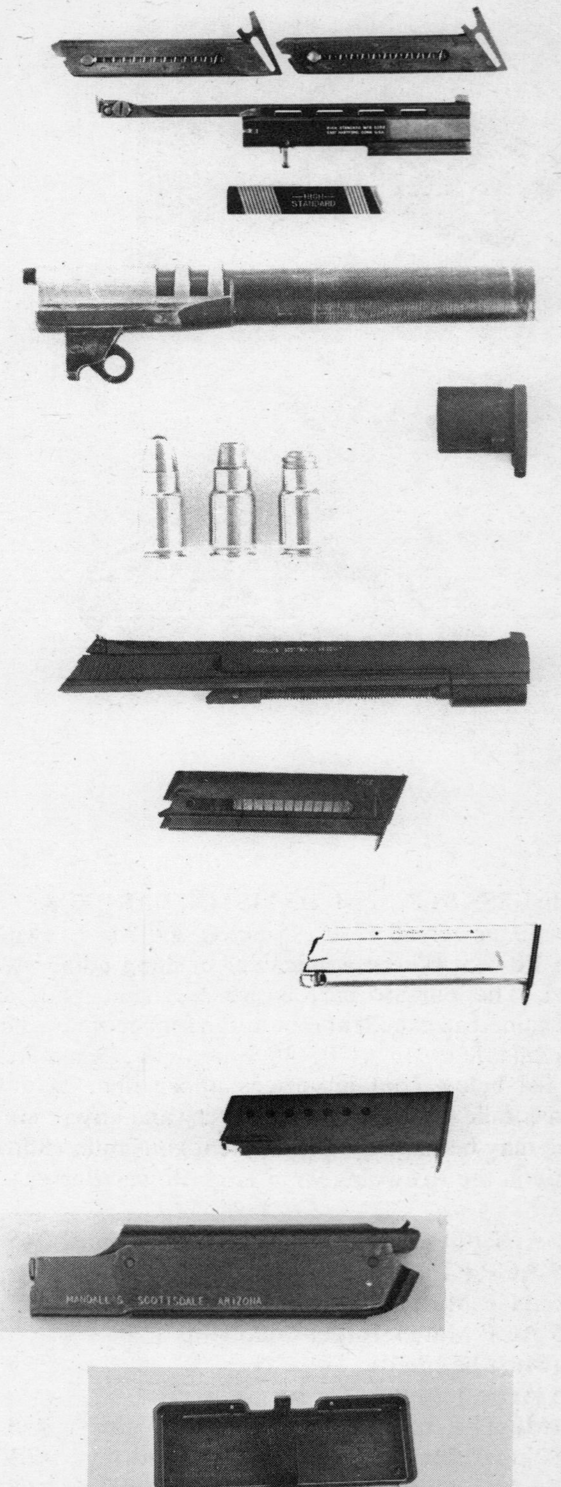

HIGH STANDARD .22 SHORT CONVERSION KIT

The kits are available for the High Standard Victor, Trophy or Citation model autos. While they are designed primarily for the competitive shooter, they will come in handy for the general handgunner who's looking for less noise and expense in his rimfire shooting.
Price: Victor Kit $130; Trophy/Citation Kit $105.
From High Standard.

.38/.45 CONVERSION UNIT

The barrel for this unit is a new one, made by Colt. Available for all versions of the 1911 Colt .45 ACP. Converts the big .45 into a .38 caliber. This is a wildcat cartridge for which dies are available from most major die houses, including Whitney sales.
Price: $62.50 standard; $62.50 Commander, $69 Mark IV; chrome moly barrel bushing $9.
From Whitney Sales.

SIG-210 SERIES RIMFIRE CONVERSION UNIT

Converts any 9mm or 7.65mm SIG 210 auto into a rimfire plinker or paper puncher. Consists of magazine, barrel, recoil spring and slide. Handles all .22 Long Rifle ammo.
Price: $650.
From Mandall Shooting Supplies, Inc.

SIG P-210 RIMFIRE MAGAZINE

Designed as a component part of the .22 LR conversion. This is sold as a spare, extra magazine.
Price: $105
From Mandall Shooting Supplies Inc.

SIG P-210 9mm MAGAZINE

This is simply a spare magazine for the P-210 Auto. Hard to find.
Price: $55
From Mandall Shooting Supplies Inc.

IGI DOMINO MAGAZINE

Replacement magazine available in either .22 Short or .22 Long Rifle.
Price: $49.95
From Mandall Shooting Supplies Inc.

MAGAZINE WALLET

The Case-Gard Magazine Wallet holds one loaded pistol magazine. It keeps out unwanted moisture and dust. Designed to carry .45 ACP magazines, S&W 39/59 magazines plus all models of Astra, Llama, Star, Sterling and Walther magazines. Comes in dark brown.
Price: $2.95.
From MTM Molded Products Company.

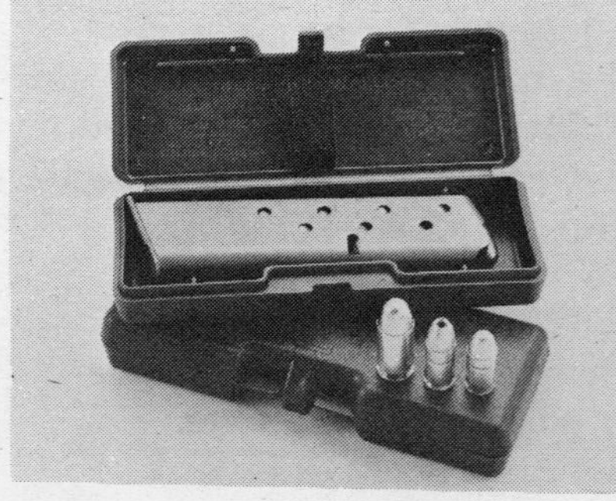

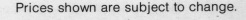

Prices shown are subject to change.

Rifle & Shotgun Customizing Accessories

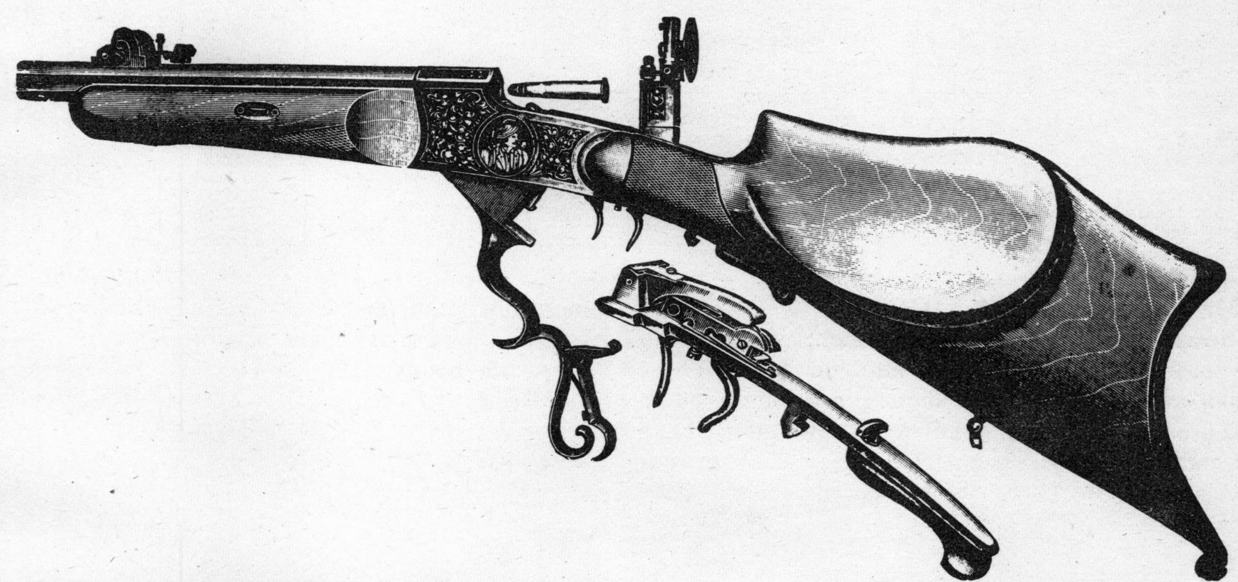

Rifle and shotgun customizing is certainly one of the most popular do-it-yourself gun enthusiast's activities. Such efforts vary from simple decorative additions to butt plates or pistol grip caps to complete restyling of military surplus actions into fine quality sporting arms.

For the most part the accessories found in this section are those which the average gun buff with reasonable ability with tools and a modest but adequately stocked tool kit can install himself. Some require the services of a better than average craftsman but are still within the capabilities of many home workshops, while a very few may require professional advice or even assistance.

For the user's convenience, we've arranged the contents of this section into two parts, Shotguns (first) and Rifles, and each of the parts into the following groups and order:

- Stocks and Stock Blanks
- Recoil Pads, Butt Plates and Pistol Grip Caps
- Sling Swivels
- Barrel Bedding Materials
- Actions
- Barrels
- Chokes or Muzzle Brakes

Other rifle and shotgun accessories appear through-out the section. Sights, of course, are found in Sections 3 and 4.

A good many of the items shown in the following pages are available only from the makers or—in some cases—the larger gunsmith supply houses. However, it always pays to consult with local gunshops with a specific request, as many have a surprisingly diverse stock.

CUSTOM DOUBLE AND OVER/UNDER STOCKS

Shown nearby is an L.C. Smith double Barrel shotgun completely re-stocked by Fajen. Made to original style with beavertail forearm and original checkering pattern. Stocks are available for just about every popular foreign or domestic double or over/under—past or present. Available to your dimensions in a wide variety of grades of walnut.

Prices: See below:

From Reinhart Fajen.

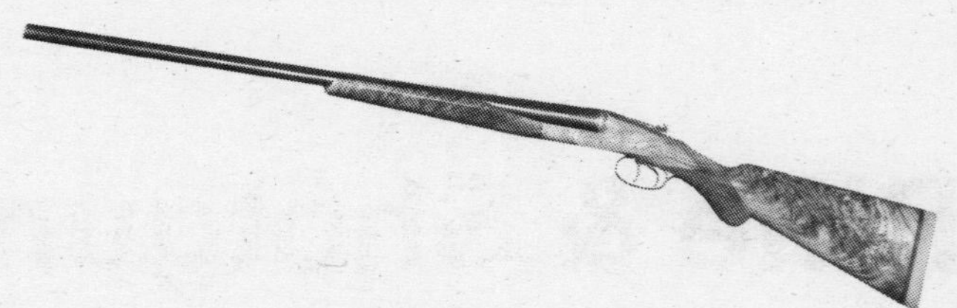

	Shaped and Machine Inletted Semi-finished		Custom Fitted to Customer's Gun Hand Fitted		Finished & Checkered	
FIELD — MONTE CARLO TRAP STRAIGHT TRAP STYLES						
Supreme	$ 32.50		$145.00		$191.00	
Semi-fancy	42.50		155.00		201.00	
Fancy	61.50		180.00		232.00	
Extra Fancy	88.00		212.00		270.00	
Walnut/Maple Lam.	75.00		199.00		256.00	
Cherry/Maple Lam.	72.00		196.00		253.00	
	ARISTOCRAT REGENT	**FOREARM**	**ARISTOCRAT REGENT**	**FOREARM**	**ARISTOCRAT REGENT**	**FOREARM**
Supreme	$ 38.50	$ 20.00	$168.50	$100.00	$221.00	$135.00
Semi-fancy	49.50	27.00	179.50	106.00	232.00	141.00
Fancy	70.00	34.00	205.00	120.00	262.00	160.00
Extra Fancy	96.50	43.00	236.00	135.00	298.00	182.00
Walnut/Maple Lam.	85.00	43.00	225.00	135.00	287.00	182.00
Cherry/Maple Lam.	82.00	42.00	223.00	134.00	285.00	181.00

PUMP/AUTO SHOTGUN STOCKS

Shown nearby is a Winchester Model 12 shotgun with a set of finished and checkered shotgun stocks. These stocks are available for just about every popular pump and auto shotgun you can find in the new and used gun racks at your local gun shop. They are available to your dimensions in a wide variety of grades of walnut. Always specify gauge when ordering.

Prices: See below:

From Reinhart Fajen.

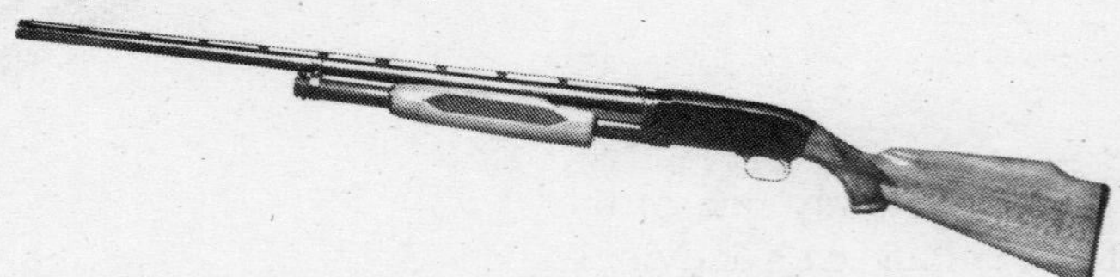

	100% Shaped 90% Machine Inletted Semi-finished		Custom Fitted to Customer's Gun Hand Fitted		Finished & Checkered	
	MONTE CARLO TRAP STRAIGHT TRAP	**SPORTSMAN ARISTOCRAT REGENT**	**MONTE CARLO TRAP STRAIGHT TRAP**	**SPORTSMAN ARISTOCRAT REGENT**	**MONTE CARLO TRAP STRAIGHT TRAP**	**SPORTSMAN ARISTOCRAT REGENT**
Utility	$ 18.00	$ 21.50				
Supreme	20.00	23.50	$ 42.50	$ 62.00	$ 77.00	$108.00
Semi-Fancy	30.50	34.00	53.00	72.50	87.50	118.50
Fancy	45.50	51.00	73.00	96.00	113.50	147.00
Extra Fancy	69.00	77.00	103.00	127.00	149.00	184.00
Walnut/Maple Lam.	58.00	61.50	92.00	111.50	138.00	168.50
Cherry/Maple Lam.	55.00	59.50	89.00	109.50	136.00	165.50
	FIELD STYLE	**FOREARM**	**FIELD STYLE**	**FOREARM**	**FIELD STYLE**	**FOREARM**
Utility	$ 15.00	$ 11.00				
Supreme	17.00	12.00	$ 39.50	$ 29.00	$ 74.00	$ 58.00
Semi-fancy	27.50	18.00	50.00	35.00	84.50	64.00
Fancy	42.50	25.00	70.00	47.50	110.50	82.00
Extra Fancy	66.00	32.00	100.00	60.00	146.00	94.50
Walnut/Maple Lam.	55.00	32.00	89.00	60.00	135.00	94.50
Cherry/Maple Lam.	52.00	31.00	86.00	59.00	133.00	93.50

Prices shown are subject to change.

SHOTGUN STOCKS

The following shotgun stocks are made from European Walnut, are hand checkered and are delivered as shown.

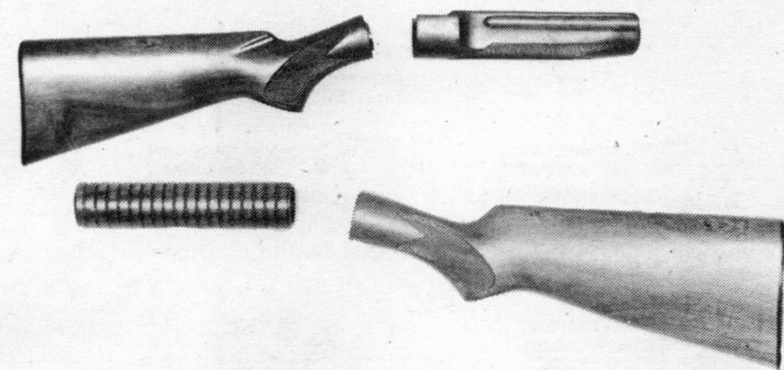

Price: Winchester 12 Trap Stock & Forend $82.60
Remington Model 11 Stock & Forend 67.75
Winchester 97 Stock & Forend 67.75
Winchester 12 Stock & Forend 67.75

From Sile.

"TRIPLE MAGNUM" SKEET RECOIL PAD

Designed for fast shouldering and pointing. Really eliminates the "kick." Comes in black only, leather finish. Three Sizes are available; small, medium and large.

Price: $14.75

From Pachmayr Gun Works.

"TRIPLE MAGNUM" TRAP RECOIL PAD

This Pachmayr offering is designed to distribute the recoil force over the entire pad surface. Patented sponge inserts in each end absorb recoil energy and counteract the tendency of the butt to jump downward when fired. In black only; sizes small, medium and large.

Price: $14.75

From Pachmayr Gun Works.

TRAP SHOOTER'S RECOIL PAD

Pachmayr's Model 550 recoil pad is made specifically for the Trap shooter. It's available in three face designs; screen, leather textured and pigeon shooter. (The pigeon shooter design has a rounded heel with slightly different contour.) Available in medium or large sizes. Comes in either red, brown or black.

Price: $9.75

From Pachmayr Gun Works.

FIELD-TYPE PAD

Pachmayr's lightweight Field recoil pad comes checkered as shown. Comes in three sizes and colors; small, medium and large; red, brown or black.

Price: $7.75

From Pachmayr Gun Works.

SLIP-ON RECOIL PAD

Easy-on, easy off. Handy items to have when it comes time to lengthen a stock on a borrowed gun. Can be used in addition to regular pad. Comes in three sizes; small, medium and large. Color: brown.

Price: $4.80

From Pachmayr Gun Works.

See the Directory for complete company addresses.

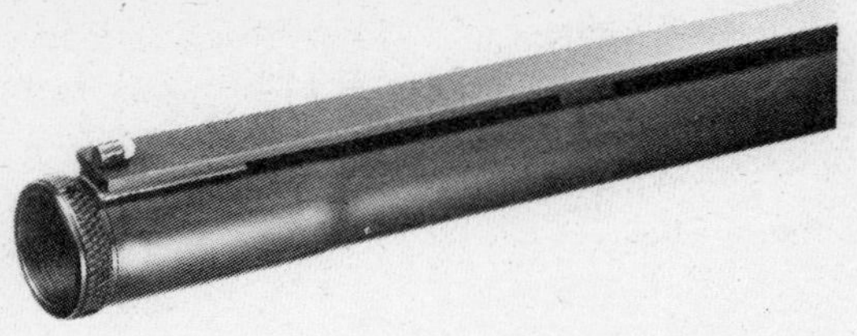

ADJUSTABLE CHOKE

The Cutts Compensator has been around for years—it's a favorite with shotgunners. The Cutts is available in 12 or 20 gauge only and comes complete with adapter, wrench and choke tube of your choice.

Price: $41.50; $53.50 with fully adjustable tube; Spare tubes $11 each. Your gunsmith can install it.

From Lyman.

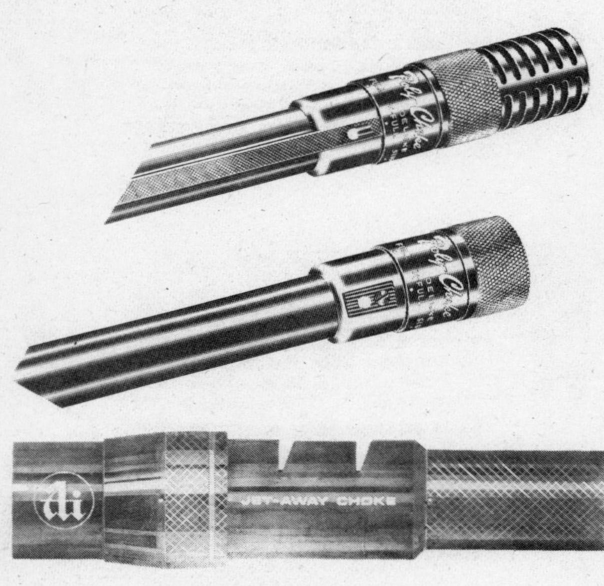

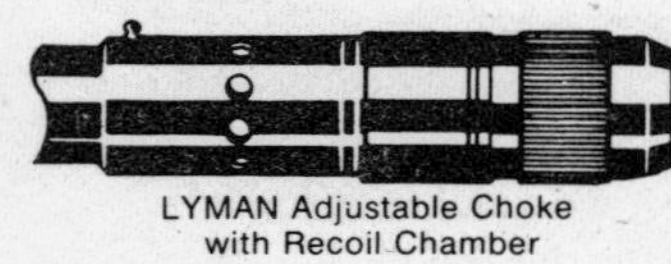

LYMAN Adjustable Choke with Recoil Chamber

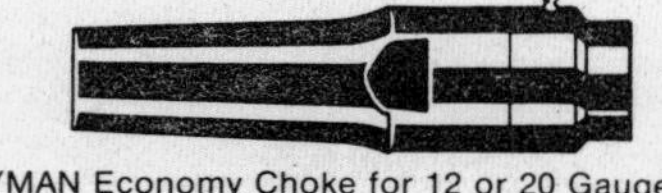

LYMAN Economy Choke for 12 or 20 Gauge

SCREW-IN CHOKE

Wide range of chokes are available and installation costs vary from gun to gun when a ribbed barrel is converted.

Price: For installation on barrel without rib, $60.

From Stan Baker.

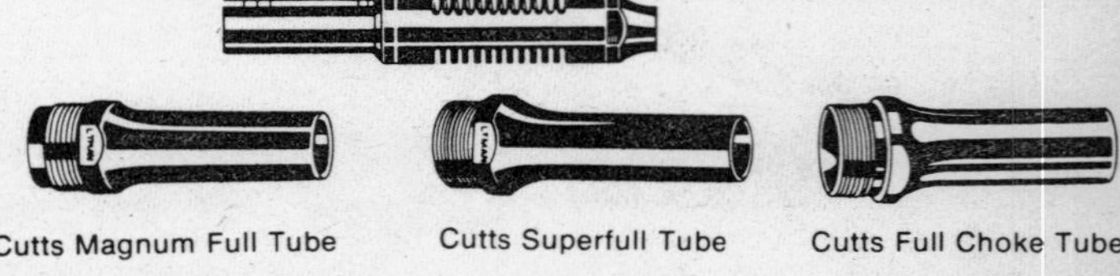

Cutts Magnum Full Tube   Cutts Superfull Tube   Cutts Full Choke Tube

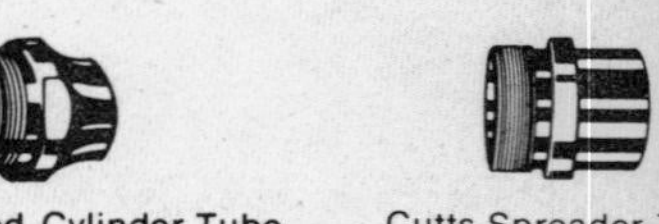

Cutts Modified Tube   Cutts Improved Cylinder Tube   Cutts Spreader Tub

Cutts Adjustable Tube

ADJUSTABLE SHOTGUN CHOKE

Available in either vented or non-vented configuration. Each choke offers nine individual settings including extra-full and slug. Ventilated model reduces recoil by as much as 20%. Your gunsmith can install it.

Price: $39.95 for the vented model; $32.95 for the standard model. Available for most popular chokes.

From Poly Choke Company.

ADJUSTABLE CHOKE

Patterns are controlled through venting of gas and by moving sleeve back (for dense patterns) or forward (for more open patterns). Available in 10, 12, 16 and 20 gauge.

Price: 10 gauge, $50; others, $35.

From Arms Ingenuity Company.

ADJUSTABLE CHOKE

Made for 12 or 20 gauge, the Lyman Adjustable Choke comes with three specific choke settings which can be selected with a turn of the hand.

Price: $30.50 with adjustable tube and wrench. Your gunsmith can install it.

From Lyman.

ADJUSTABLE CHOKE

Called the Economy Choke, it comes available for 12 or 20 gauge and allows you to change your shotguns patterning to suit a variety of needs. Your gunsmith can install it.

Price: $16.50 with tube of your choice; Adjustable tube $25; extra tubes $11.

From Lyman.

Prices shown are subject to change.

FLUSH MOUNT SHOTGUN SLING SWIVELS

An inletted receptacle in the buttstock and a special magazine cap adapter permits the use of a sling with most pump and automatic shotguns without disturbing the gun's lines when the sling is removed.

Price: $6.95

From Michaels of Oregon.

SLING SWIVELS FOR BROWNING 2000

Front sling swivel mounts to an adapter which is attached in the gas port vent of the fore-end cap; a wood screw base is provided for the butt mounting. Quick release swivels permit fast, easy removal of the sling while hunting.

Price: $6.95

From Michaels of Oregon.

SWIVEL SET FOR SHOTGUNS

Available in 12, 16 or 20 gauge only. Stock swivel should be professionally installed or the experienced handyman can do it himself. Front swivel (shown) installs in seconds by the purchaser.

Price: $7

From Williams Gun Sight.

SLUG SIGHTS

The Williams 5-D peep sight can be seen along with that firm's special ramp-and-bead front sight. The fully adjustable peep sight is screw-mounted to this Winchester Model 12 receiver. The front sight is easily installed by the purchaser.

Price: Front Ramp Sight with Gold Bead $5.65; 5-D peep sight $12.50.

From Williams Gun Sight.

MAGAZINE EXTENSION AND LIGHT MOUNT

Choate's magazine extension is designed for police use and increases magazine capacity to 7 shots. Available for a number of different repeater shotguns. The flashlight mount and light are a separate, easily detachable, unit.

Price: Flashlight and mount, $25; magazine extension, $20.

From Choate Machine and Tool.

SHOTGUN SIGHT

Called the Accu-Point, this front shotgun sight mounts easily to most steel shotgun ribs (gunsmith installation recommended). Forces shooter to keep his head down on the stock; when he sees the blaze-orange dot he knows he's ready to shoot.

Price: About $17.

From the W. R. Weaver Co.

SHOTSHELL ADAPTER

Suitable for most break-open shotguns. Converts 12-gauge shotgun into a .410 instantly.

Price: $18.85

From Savage Arms.

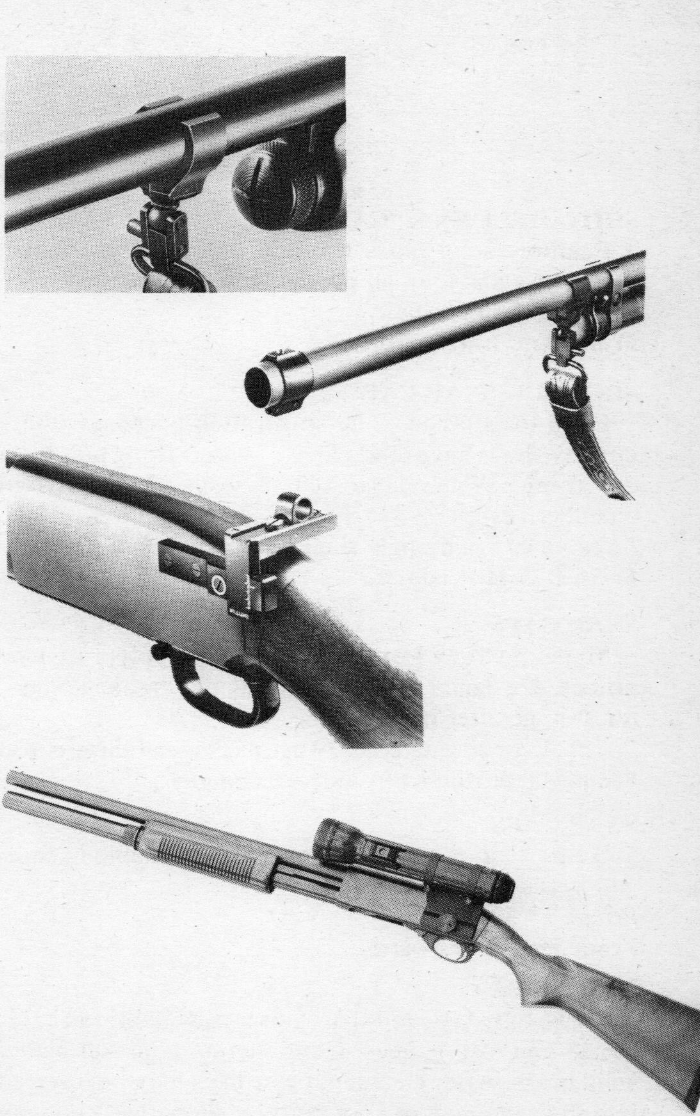

See the Directory for complete company addresses.

RECOIL REDUCER

Helps reduce flinching and barrel whip normally associated with recoil. Manufacturer advises a 50% reduction in recoil with single unit. Double unit (shown) removes even more. Seven ounces per unit.
Price: $24 per unit.
From Edwards Recoil Reducer.

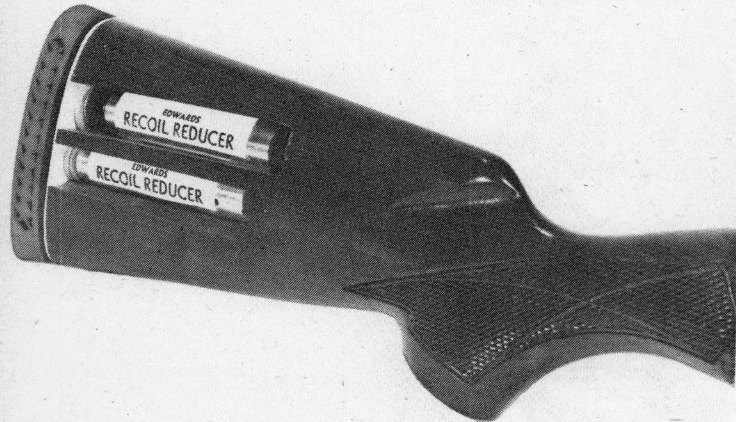

SHOTSHELL SNAP CAPS

Features solid brass rim and tube, and are nickel plated. Available in all popular bore sizes.
Price: $13.50 per pair.
From Wm. Larkin Moore.

SHOTGUN SNAP-CAP

Used for storage or demonstration purposes, these dummy shells have inert caps to protect firing pins from dry firing. When lubricated they also help prevent chamber rust.
Price. $3.25 per single shell; $5.75, the pair.
From D & H Products.

SNAP CAPS

Made of strong Lexan with a durable polypropylene primer. Designed to prevent firing pin breakage; and, for storage after cleaning.
Price: 12 or 20 gauge, $2.39 per package of three caps.
From MTM Molded Products Company.

SNAP CAPS

Helps keep moisture out of bore. Available in shotgun bores all but 16 gauge.
Price: $3.50 each.
From Jesse B. Edwards.

SNAP CAPS

These fully nickeled snap caps are available in 12, 16, 20, 28 and .410 gauges. Construction is nickel plated solid brass. After cleaning, these caps may be inserted into the chambers of your favorite shotguns. You may dry fire without fear of damaging firing pins.
Price: $15 per pair.
From Bill McGuire & Associates.

SHELL CATCHER

No tools are needed to install. It's available for the Remington 1100 only. Made for 12, 20, 28 and .410 gauges only.
Price: $29.95
From Morton International Enterprises.

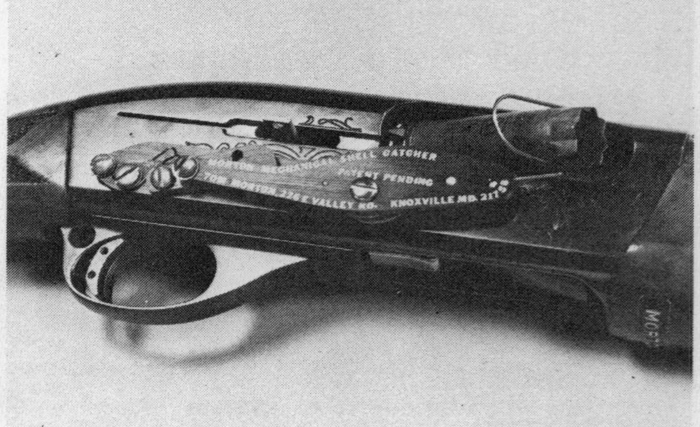

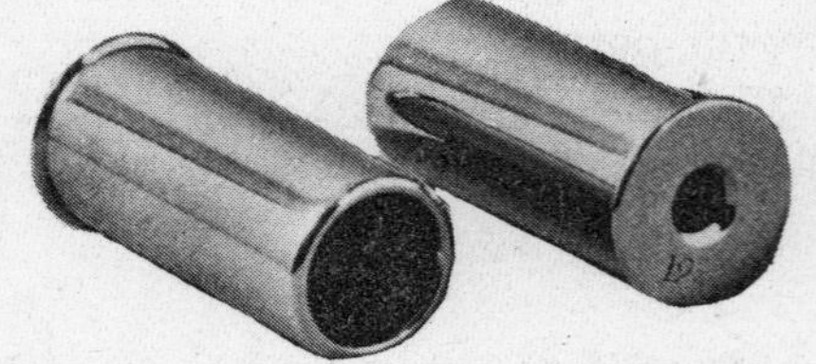

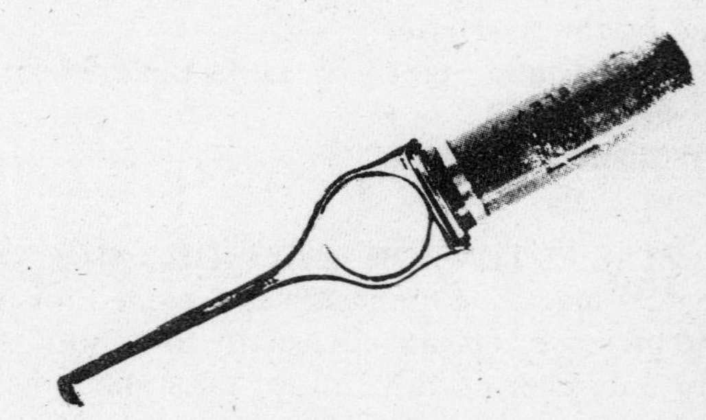

STUCK CASE EXTRACTOR

Nickel plated. For the removal of shotshell cases or portions of blown cases, from shotgun chambers.
Price: $9.
From Wm. Larkin Moore.

Prices shown are subject to change.

FIBERGLASS STOCKS

Stocks made of this material are impervious to water and won't warp. Stocks are available inletted (about $75-$100) or completely finished and painted (about $210-$250). Models of stocks available are the Benchrest, Hunting/Silhouette and the Prone Position Stock (for small or large bore) with adjustable cheek piece. Also available is a Marine-style M-14 stock that sells for $250 complete with hardware.
From Gale McMillan.

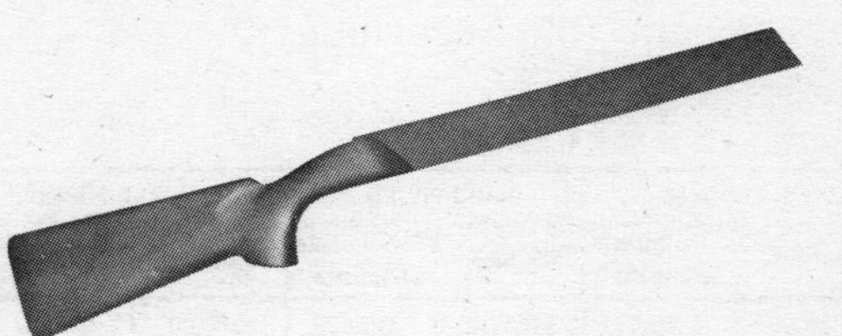

FIBERTHANE RIFLE STOCKS

No voids inside stock. Aluminum tube used internally to add rigidity. Come primer painted ready for bedding and final painting. Shown is the Silhouette Stock. Available for most modern rifles.

Prices:

F-100 "Fiberthane" FRP Benchrest Stock - Weight 2.0 pounds $85.00
F-200 "Fiberthane" FRP Sporter Stock - Weight 1.75 pounds $85.00
F-300 "Fiberthane" FRP Silhouette Stock - Weight 2.0 pounds $85.00

From H-S Precision, Inc.

FIBERGLASS STOCKS

Available in a number of styles, from top to bottom:

BERGER BENCH REST
This pattern is made for a Rem. 40X, Witchita, Shilen DGA, Hart, etc. It has a full 3-inch wide flat forearm as well as 3-inch wide rear section.
Weight: 2 lbs. 4oz. *Price:* $75.00

HUNTER BENCH
Made to conform to Hunter Bench rules. 2¼-inch wide slightly oval forearm. This is also a good off-hand or Varmint stock. Made to fit the Rem. 40X, Rem. Varmint Special, or 700 short. The barrel channel will accept a full heavy barrel.
Weight: 1 lb. 7 oz. *Price:* $72.50

WINCHESTER MODEL 70 CLASSIC
This is a Model 70 Winchester pre- and post-64 Classic stock.
Weight: 1 lb. 5 oz. *Price:* $72.50

B.P.G.
This is a pistol-grip-less bench rest stock that has won so many championships. Will fit Rem 40X, XP100, Shilen DGA, Hart and other custom actions.
Weight: 1 lb. 10 oz. *Price:* $67.50

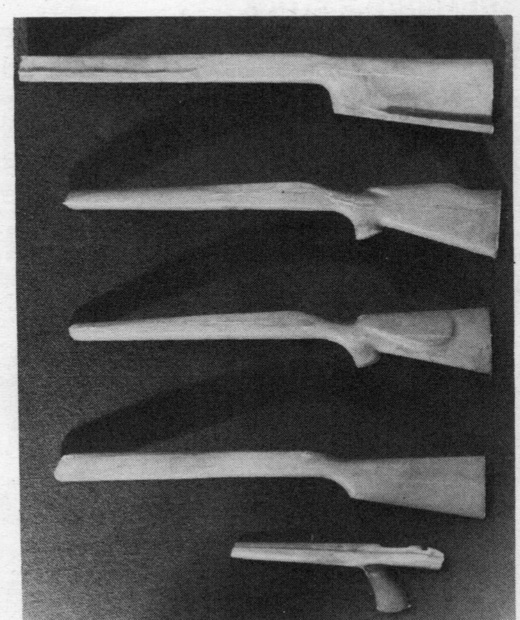

XP-100 PISTOL STOCK
Made to fit the XP-100 with standard trigger linkage. It will take a larger-than-standard barrel.
Weight: 12 oz. *Price:* $65.00

These stocks are ready to be sanded and painted as they come from the maker. The glass bedding serves as the "final inletting." If desired, the manufacturer will fit and finish a stock to your barreled action and hardware for about $230. (Left hand stocks available for Remington 700 ADL or BDL).
From Brown Precision.

See the Directory for complete company addresses.

SILHOUETTE RIFLE STOCK

Fajen's "Silhouette" and "Thumbhole Silhouette" stock are available for the 98 Mauser, Mark-X Mauser, 40X Remington, M70 Win. (Pre- & Post-64), M77 Ruger, Wichita Classic, 700 Remington (long & short), 54 Anschutz, 64 Anschutz, 580 Remington, 581 Remington and Winchester Model 52. Shown is the "Thumbhole Silhouette" design with a Remington 700 barreled action. Comes in either walnut, laminated walnut or walnut/maple laminate. Overall dimensions conform to Silhouette Rifle regulations.

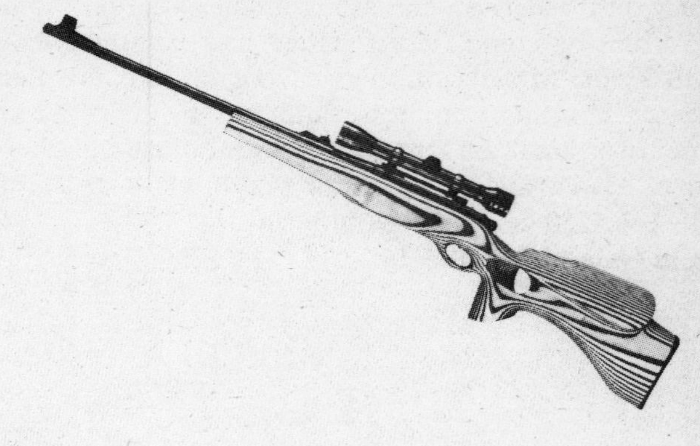

Prices:

	SEMI FINISHED		HAND FITTED		COMPLETELY FINISHED	
	"Silhouette"	"Thumbhole Silhouette"	"Silhouette"	"Thumbhole Silhouette"	"Silhouette"	"Thumbhole Silhouette"
Supreme	$ 55.00	$ 60.00	$151.00	$156.00	$218.00	$213.00
Walnut Lam.	137.00	142.00	247.00	252.00	333.00	338.00
Wal/Maple Laminated	137.00	142.00	247.00	252.00	333.00	338.00

From Reinhart Fajen.

THUMBHOLE STOCK

Called the Thumbhole Varminter, the Fajen stock has a 2-inch wide forearm that will handle light, medium and heavy barrels. Available in a good selection of walnut, laminates and degrees of completion.

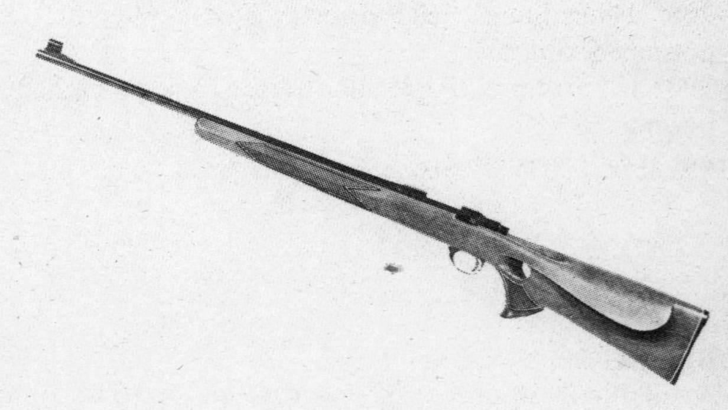

Prices & Grades:

	100% Shaped 90% Machine Inletted Semi-finished	Custom Fitted to Customer's Gun Hand Fitted	Finished & Checkered
Supreme	$ 36.00	$123.00	$184.00
Supreme Deluxe	42.00	129.00	190.00
Semi-fancy	60.00	147.00	208.00
A Fancy	70.00	164.00	236.00
AA Fancy	82.00	176.00	248.00
AAA Fancy	120.00	220.00	298.00
Walnut Laminated	103.00	203.00	287.00
Walnut/Maple Lam.	103.00	203.00	287.00
Cherry/Maple Lam.	98.00	198.00	282.00

From Reinhart Fajen.

CUSTOM STOCK

This is a thumbhole design that may be shot in a conventional manner, if so desired. Stock comes ready for sanding and final (minimal) amount of inletting. Delivery time 1-4 weeks; 3-6 weeks for lefthanded stocks. Available in most woods. Shown is an Exhibition Grade stock.

Prices:

Economy Grade (Maple, etc.)	$27.95
Standard Grade	36.95
Select Grade	39.95
Semi-fancy Grade	44.95
Laminated: ⅛″ Walnut, 1/24″ Maple	99.50
Grade A	55.95
Grade AA	71.95
Grade AAA	93.95
Exhibition Grade	110.00 to 125.00
⅛″ Walnut & ⅛″ Walnut	98.50

From Richards Micro-Fit Stocks.

Prices shown are subject to change.

CUSTOM STOCKS

Most woods available; the following prices are approximate, write for exact quote.

Prices:

Stockmaking—1. Bolt action, 1-piece rifle stock: From $350. 2. 2-piece rifle or shotgun stocks: From $375.

Checkering (20, 22 & 24 LPI)—1. Basic Pattern (similar to Ruger 77): $50. 2. Wrap-around forend/grip panels: $75. 3. Full coverage, Fleur-de-lis: $100.

All From Fred D. Speiser.

TWO-PIECE RIFLE STOCKS

Available for Winchester 94, Savage 99, Remington pump and auto rifles and several popular single shot rifles as well. Shown nearby is a Winchester 94 that's wearing the best wood money can buy, complete with best checkering and carving. These two-piece stocks are available in a wide variety of grades of walnut.

Prices: See Below.

	100% Shaped 90% Machine Inletted Semi-finished		Custom Fitted to Customer's Gun Hand Fitted		Finished & Checkered	
	FIELD	ISSUE	FIELD	ISSUE	FIELD	ISSUE
Utility	$ 15.00	$ 18.00				
Supreme	17.00	20.00	$ 39.50	$ 62.00	$ 74.00	$108.00
Semi-fancy	27.50	30.50	50.00	72.50	84.50	118.50
Fancy	42.50	45.50	70.00	96.00	110.50	147.00
Extra Fancy	66.00	69.00	100.00	127.00	146.00	184.00
Walnut/Maple Lam.	55.00	58.00	89.00	111.50	135.00	168.50
Cherry/Maple Lam.	52.00	55.00	86.00	109.50	133.00	165.50
	SPORTSMAN ARISTOCRAT CLASSIC	FOREARM	SPORTSMAN ARISTOCRAT CLASSIC	FOREARM	SPORTSMAN ARISTOCRAT CLASSIC	FOREARM
Utility	$ 21.50	$ 11.00				
Supreme	23.50	12.00	$ 62.00	$ 29.00	$108.00	$ 58.00
Semi-Fancy	34.00	18.00	72.50	35.00	118.50	64.00
Fancy	51.00	25.00	96.00	47.50	147.00	82.00
Extra Fancy	77.00	32.00	127.00	60.00	184.00	94.50
Walnut/Maple Lam.	61.50	32.00	111.50	60.00	168.50	94.50
Cherry/Maple Lam.	59.50	31.00	109.50	59.00	165.50	93.50

From Reinhart Fajen.

SPORTER STOCKS FOR MILITARY RIFLES

The Fajen "Sportsman" stock is available in a wide variety of grades of walnut. Shown nearby is an M-1 carbine and Springfield 1903 A3—both are wearing finished and checkered Supreme Grade Stocks. (Checkering is at 18 lines per inch).

Prices:

	Semi-finished	Hand Fitted	Finished & Chkrd
Utility	$ 22.95 (when available)		
Supreme	28.00	$ 97.00	$160.00
Supreme Deluxe	40.00	108.00	171.00
Semi-fancy	55.00	124.00	185.00
A Fancy	66.00	142.00	210.00
AA Fancy	80.00	155.00	222.00
AAA Fancy	122.00	205.00	280.00
Walnut Laminated	112.00	195.00	270.00
Walnut/Maple Lam.	112.00	195.00	270.00
Cherry Maple Lam.	107.00	190.00	265.00

From Reinhart Fajen.

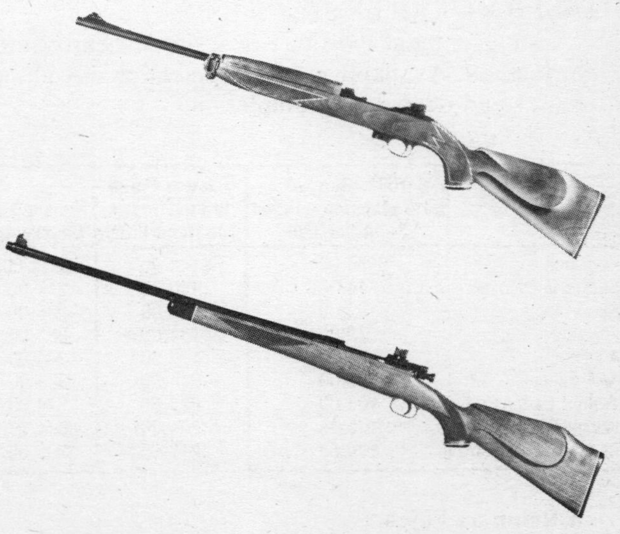

CARBINE STOCK CONVERSION KIT

The "Tommy-Gun" look—vertical hand grips fore and aft. Quick detachable butt stock on the Mark IV Kit, which is shown. (Mark I Kit is like the Mark IV except there's no provision for a quick-detachable stock). The Mark II Kit has no butt stock.

Prices: Mark I, $45; Mark II, $39.50; Mark IV, $49.50.

From Commando Arms, Inc.

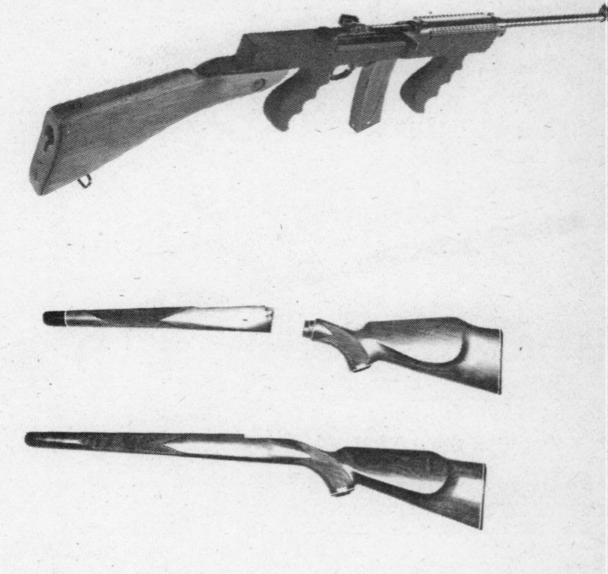

CUSTOM RIFLE STOCKS

The following stocks are made of walnut, are fully inletted, finished and sport hand checkering. Stocks are ready to install

Prices:

1. Enfield 4 & 5/1, 2, 3* $80.10
2. Mauser Mark 10 $80.10

From Sile.

SEMI-FINISHED STOCKS

Stocks are cut from green walnut blanks and fully shaped and inletted. They are then kiln-dried to 6-percent moisture content. Available for Winchester M70 (Post- and Pre-64); 1917 Enfield, FN and M98 Mauser; Springfield '03 and A-3; Sako Vixen and Forester; Savage 110 short action (right and left) and Weatherby Mark V.

Price: $25

From The Crane Creek Company.

SEMI-FINISHED STOCK

Full Mannlicher design with handguard. Available in walnut (top), or maple (below).

Write direct for prices.

From Columbia Precision Woodworking.

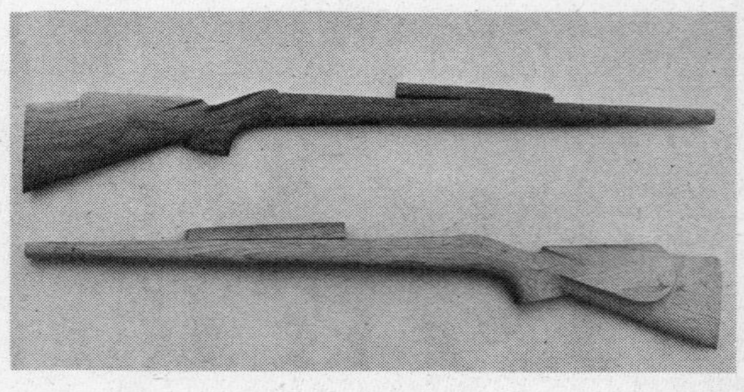

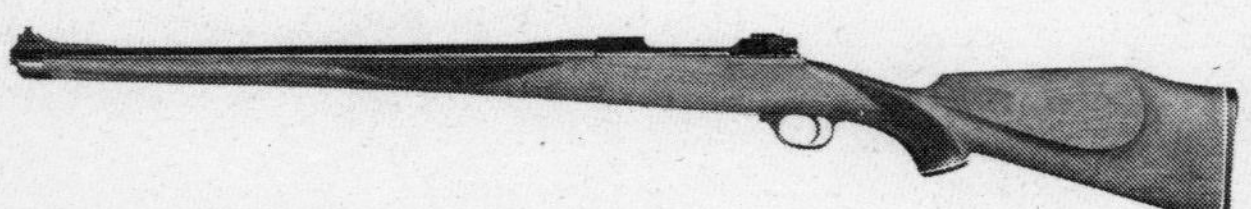

MANNLICHER RIFLE STOCK

Available for most sporting rifles; shown nearby is an 03 Springfield. Available in a good selection of walnut, laminates and degrees of completion.

Prices & Grades:

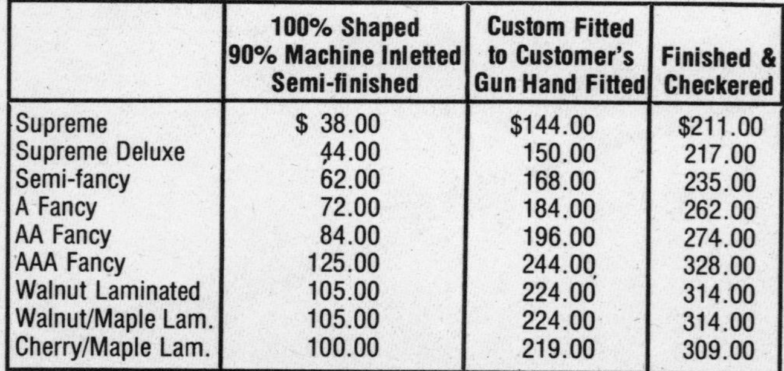

	100% Shaped 90% Machine Inletted Semi-finished	Custom Fitted to Customer's Gun Hand Fitted	Finished & Checkered
Supreme	$ 38.00	$144.00	$211.00
Supreme Deluxe	44.00	150.00	217.00
Semi-fancy	62.00	168.00	235.00
A Fancy	72.00	184.00	262.00
AA Fancy	84.00	196.00	274.00
AAA Fancy	125.00	244.00	328.00
Walnut Laminated	105.00	224.00	314.00
Walnut/Maple Lam.	105.00	224.00	314.00
Cherry/Maple Lam.	100.00	219.00	309.00

From Reinhart Fajen.

STOCK MAKING SERVICE

Unique new pantograph can reproduce any stock to one-ten-thousandth of an inch accuracy. Service is available for all types of gun stocks; and, a broken stock may also be duplicated once repaired by Hoenig & Rodman.

Prices: Start at about $150—suggest you write for exact quote. (This is not a semi-inletting service—when stock is finished all metal will fit stock to above quoted accuracy figure).

From Hoenig & Rodman.

Prices shown are subject to change.

CUSTOM ENGLISH & BASTOGNE WALNUT BLANKS

Bill Dowtin has a reputation for providing some of the finest walnut blanks available. Each blank is air-dried and special care is taken to dry them out slowly and evenly. Each blank is also weighed every 3 months and turned for more even air circulation. Shown nearby are two full rifle blanks and one bullstock blank.

Prices: We suggest you write the firm.

From Custom Rifles by Bill Dowtin.

CUSTOM WALNUT BLANKS

These blanks are of some of the best walnut available to the trade. Shown nearby are "Standard," "XX" and "XXX" blanks. These blanks are properly dried and ready for use by your gunsmith.

Prices: In California English Walnut the "Standard" $35; "XX" $150; "XXX" $250.

From Don Allen.

STOCK BLANKS

Johnson Wood Products offers a number of different types of suitable stock-blank woods. They also offer semi-inletted blanks for many action styles. Grades of American walnut are as follows and the nearby photo shows pieces of *Special Selection Grade* walnut (above *"Rare Exhibition" Grade)*.

Prices: Sporter length rifle stock blank:

Select	$10.00
Semi-Fancy	$20.00
Exhibition	$50.00
Rare Exhibition	$75.00 (and up)

(Selected Mannlicher rifle blanks 40 to 44 inches are $10 above respective grade sporter blank).

From Johnson Wood Products.

CUSTOM STOCK WOODS

Paulsen Gunstocks offers a wide selection of quality stock making wood. Available woods: American Black Walnut, Claro Walnut, Bastogne Walnut, Circassian Walnut, Wild Black Cherry, Butternut, Myrtle, Maple and others. Availability is, of course, subject to the strains of demand—we urge you to contact this outfit directly to see what's available. A good selection of grades is also available.

Price: From as low as $25 to $50 on up to several hundred dollars, depending upon your choice of wood and grade.

From Paulsen Gun Stock & Shooters Supply.

QUALITY STOCK WOOD

Some nice walnut is available from this source with prices ranging from $10 to $300.

From Jack Burres.

See the Directory for complete company addresses.

INDIAN EBONY WOOD

This Indian ebony is not subject to checking like the African variety. Normally hard to get in the U.S., this wood is offered in appropriately-sized blocks for use as fore-end tips, butt plates, grip caps. Your gunsmith can fashion these to order.

Price: Fore-end Tip Block 1½x1½x2⅛ inches $2 each; 2x2x3 $3; Butt plate/grip cap block ½x1½x8 $5; Butt plate or butt extension block 1x2¾x6 $7.

From Philip D. Letiecq.

STOCK FINISHING KIT

Includes walnut stain and filler specially formulated to permit matching existing finishes on touch up and repairs. Stock finish provides an attractive, hard, lustrous refinishing for a complete stock yet is easy to apply and fast drying. Kit includes sandpaper, steel wool, patches.

Price: $3.75

From Williams Gun Sight.

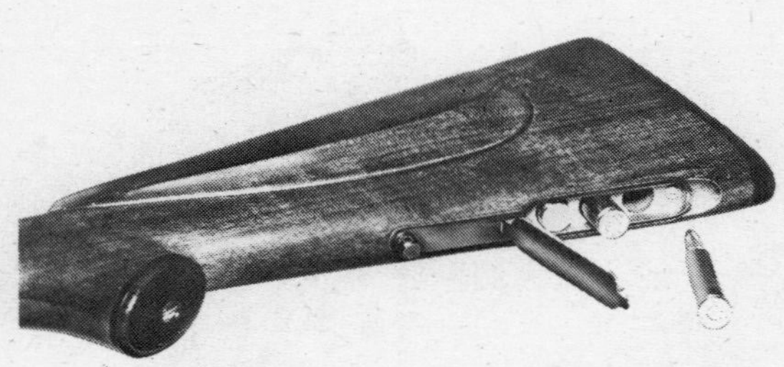

CARTRIDGE TRAP

The Fajen Cartridge Trap is big enough to take magnum rifle cartridges; holds 3 rounds of ammo and comes complete with sling swivel stud. This hinged trap comes in blued steel. May be professionally installed by a competent gunsmith.

Price: $35; $60 if installed by Fajen on one of their Semi-Finished stocks.

From Reinhart Fajen.

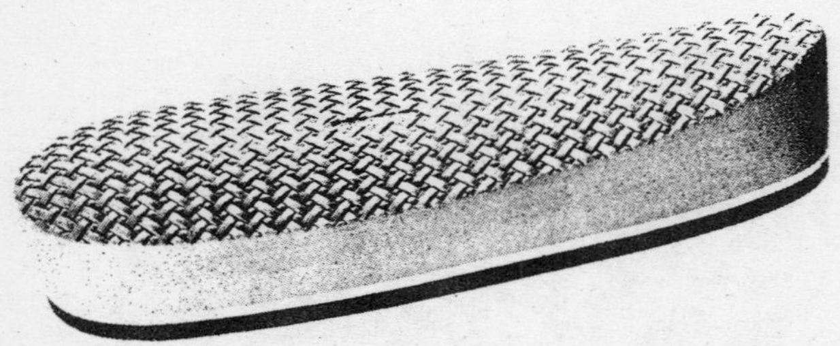

WHITE-LINE PRESENTATION RECOIL PAD

This Pachmayr pad is designed expressly for heavy magnum rifles. It features a basket-weave face and smooth sides. Available in three thicknesses; .600″, .800″ and 1-inch. Comes in red, brown or black; small medium or large. Available with plain black base on special order.

Price: $9.75

From Pachmayr Gun Works.

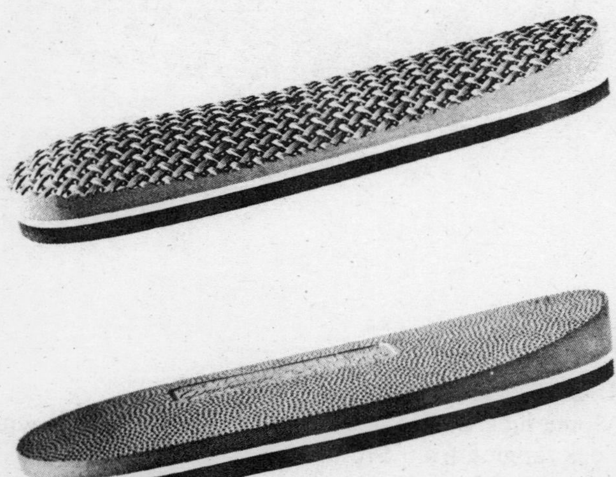

PRESENTATION RECOIL PAD

Pachmayr's Presentation recoil pad features a basketweave face. Available with plain black base on special order.

Price: $7.50

From Pachmayr Gun Works.

RECOIL PAD

Pachmayr's White-Line recoil pad adds a touch of functional grace to any rifle. One size fits all. Comes in red, brown and black.

Price: $7.25

From Pachmayr Gun Works.

Prices shown are subject to change.

TRAP BUTT PLATE

Blued as shown, and made of chrome-moly steel, this trap butt plate is checkered 20-lines to the inch and is for professional fitting. Opening is large enough to accommodate ammo shown or sectioned cleaning rod.
Price: $24.95
From Albright Products.

CUSTOM GRIP CAP

Bill Dyer, Engraver, makes this custom grip cap out of nickel silver along with a gold initial of your choice. The cap is most attractive—a nice touch for your favorite sporting rifle.
Price: Write maker direct.
From Bill Dyer, Engraver.

TRAP-TYPE GRIP CAP

These steel caps come in the white, ready for installation by a competent gunsmith. Handy for holding extra front sight blade or other items.
Price: $49.95
From London Guns.

CUSTOM GRIP CAPS

Two styles are available—plain and trap type. Both are in the white.
Price: Plain $25; trap $50.
From Hoenig & Rodman.

CUSTOM GRIP CAP

Each cap is nicely blued and contains an animal-head inset. The inset is in sterling silver and has been designed by Sid Bell. A total of 29 separate animal-head designs are available for either rifle or shotgun.
Price: Write direct
From Philip D. Letiecq.

CUSTOM GRIP CAP

This cap comes with screws and is in the white as shown. It's made of steel and is ready for final fitting and bluing by your gunsmith.
Price: $20
From Dave Talley.

CUSTOM GRIP CAP

Available in polished ($7.95), which is shown, or unpolished ($3) form.
From Lenard M. Brownell.

STOCK PAD

Allows the shooter to vary the comb height of any rifle or shotgun. Several spacers included with each pad. Velcro fasteners allow quick adjustment or removal.
Price: $31.49 with 11 varying heights; $10.95 with 6 varying heights.
From Meadow Industries.

See the Directory for complete company addresses.

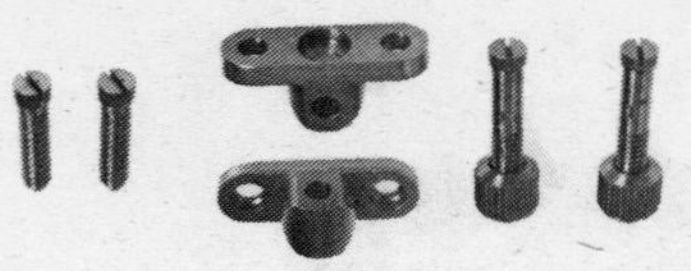

Q.D. SWIVEL BASES

These custom bases are in the white as shown. They are machined from cold drawn, bar stock. Screws have machine-cut threads with milled narrow slots. Ready to be polished, blued and installed by your gunsmith.
Price: $25 per set.
From Dave Talley.

BARREL BAND SWIVEL MOUNT

Each band comes in the white and is ready to be sweated in place by your own gunsmith. Style "SD" fits standard Q.D. swivels; Style "W" fits old-style Winchester Q.D. swivels; Style "H" fits English hook swivels. Barrel bands are tapered .010 per inch. I.D. dimensions are nominal and are taken at the band's midpoint. Sizes available: .630, .655, .680, .705, .730, .755, .780, .805, .830, .855, .880 and .905.
Prices: $17.45 for "SD" & "W" Styles; $22.45 for "H" Style.
From London Guns.

QUICK DETACHABLE SLING SWIVELS

Fit all guns with factory installed QD bases such as Ruger M77, Browning BAR. Specify for use with 1- or 1¼-inch sling.
Price: $3.99 (swivels only); $4.19 (with front and rear QD bases); $1.49 (QD base set only).

As above, but with universal adapter to install on magazine cap of most pump and automatic shotguns.
Price: $7.49

As above, but for tube magazine .22 rifles, Winchester 64, 94, Marlin 36,336 (specify).
Price: $7.29 (specify make and model).

As above, but with split magazine tube band to mount on most tubular magazine rifles and shotguns (specify make and model) without dissembly.
Price: $7.49

As above, but with special adapter that replaces fore-end bolt on Remington Model 742 BDL or pre-1968 Model 760A (specify).
Price: $7.29
From Herter's.

QD SLING SWIVELS

Quick disconnect sling swivels for a variety of sporting rifles. Specify for 1″ or 1¼″ sling.
Price: For Winchester 94, Marlin 336, .650″ barrels: $8.75. For Ruger 10-22, 44, M-1 carbine: $7.25. For Remington 81 (10-36 threads), guns with mag. caps (10-32 threads): $6.95.
From Williams Gun Sight.

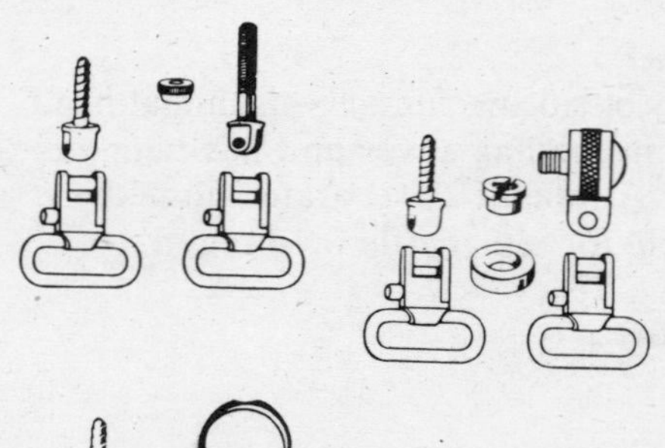

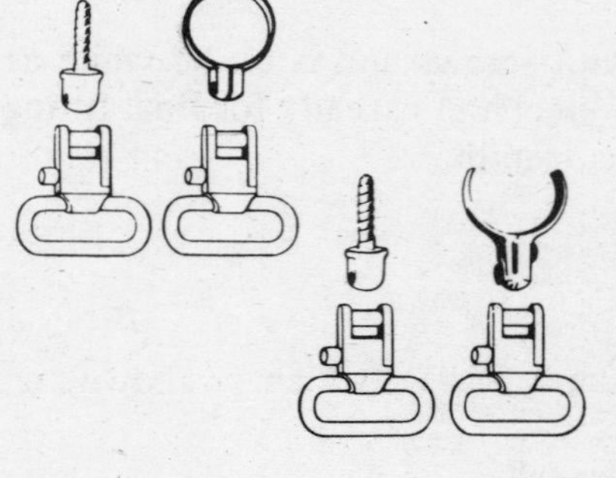

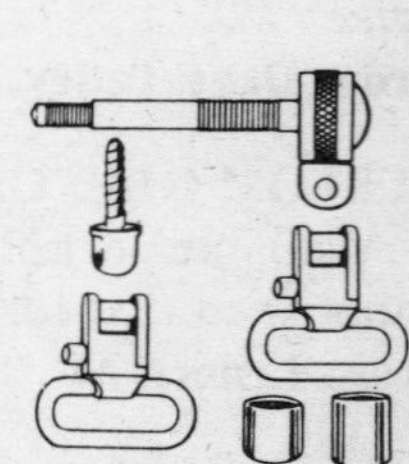

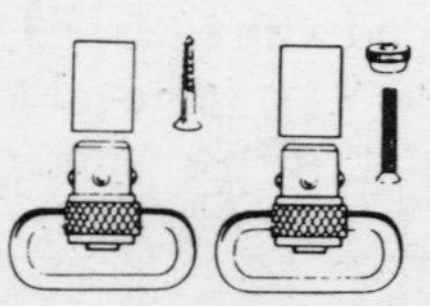

Prices shown are subject to change.

LEVER ACTION SLING SWIVEL SET

Adjustable front swivel clamps to magazine tube of Marlin 336, Winchester 94, other tubes or barrels from .650″ to .680″; rear swivel screws into stock.
Price: \$6.75 (specify 1″ or 1¼″ sling).
From Williams Gun Sight.

PUSH-BUTTON DETACHABLE SLING SWIVELS

Attractive low-profile swivels fit most makes and models of rifle or shotgun. Bases are flush with stock and fore-end wood.
Price: \$4.19 (specify 1- or 1½-inch sling).
From Herter's.

Q.D. SLING SWIVELS

When it comes to sling swivels, Uncle Mike's offers, perhaps, the broadest selection currently available for rifles or shotguns. They are made of blued steel durable, and work as advertised—they have a good reputation with shooters and hunters.
Price: From \$5.25 to \$8.95 depending upon the model of gun.
From Michael's of Oregon.

RIFLE BARREL-BAND SWIVELS

Available for 1-inch or 1¼-inch slings—rotates completely. No tools are needed to install it. Comes in varying sizes to accommodate your particular gun (be sure to specify).
Price: \$2.95
From the Phil Judd Company.

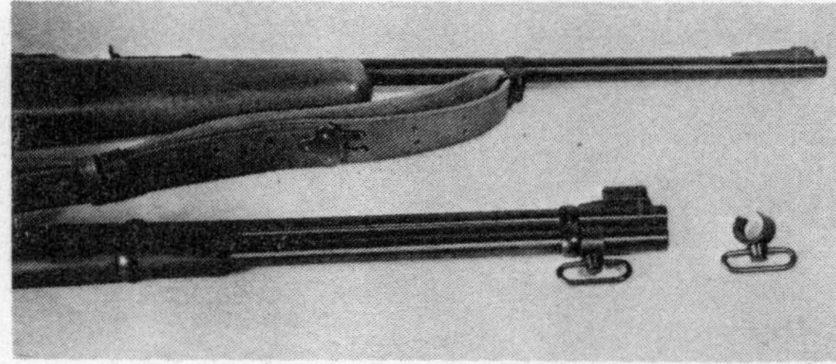

"BISONITE" RIFLE BEDDING KIT

Kit comes with steel or aluminum-filled bedding compound, release agent measuring cup, and complete instructions. Contains material for bedding one or two rifles.
Price: \$7.95 (aluminum filled); \$8.50 (steel filled).
From H-S Precision.

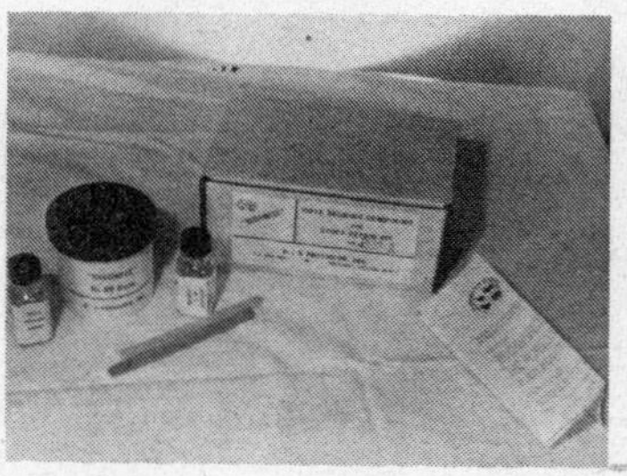

"ACCU-BED" RIFLE BEDDING KIT

One-gun bedding kit is designed for ease of use, with no weighing or measuring required. Available in either liquid or paste form (specify), with steel or aluminum filler.
Price: \$4.95 (aluminum); \$5.50 (steel).
From H-S Precision.

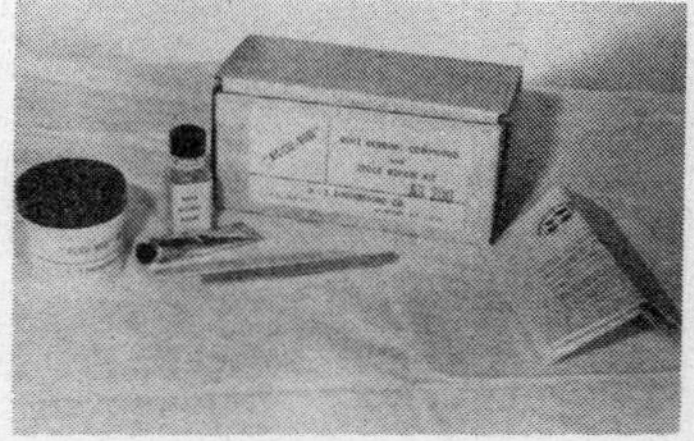

P.O. ACKLEY REBARRELING SERVICE

Many shooters are hesitant to give up a good gun just because the barrel has gone bad or been damaged through an unavoidable accident. The P.O. Ackley shop offers a complete rebarreling service; and, will even duplicate the contours of your original barrel.

Prices:

.22 - .45	$90.00
.17 - .20	$ 5.00 extra
Duplication of old barrel	$10.00 extra
Blueing of barrel	$10.00 extra
Building of recoil lugs	$20.00 extra
Rebarreling of single shots	$20.00 extra
Returning old barrel	$ 5.00 extra

From P.O. Ackley Barrels.

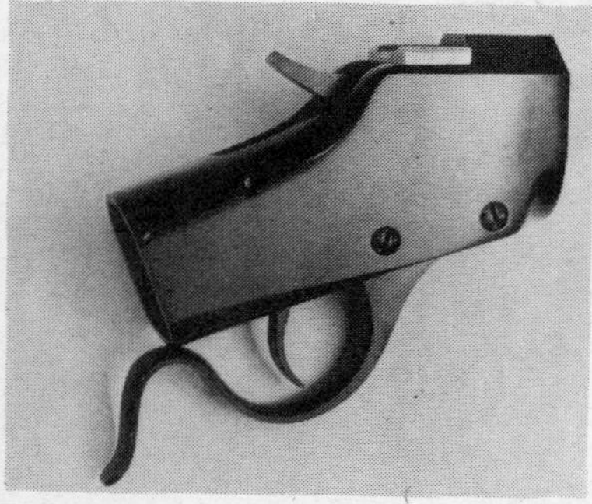

FALLING BLOCK ACTIONS

Complete, ready-to-barrel and stock actions are offered. Action shown is the Model J, for .22 Hornet through .45-70. Accessory Schuetzen, International Match and loop levers are available in addition to the standard lever illustrated.

Prices: (Model J Action, complete): $185. Levers: $40 (Schuetzen); $38 (International Match); $37 (loop).

From Falling Block Works.

BARRELED ACTION

A commercial Mauser-type action with adjustable trigger and side safety. All-steel contoured trigger guard, hinged floorplate. In-the-white.

Price: $84.95

From Federal Firearms.

BARRELED ACTION

Atkinson stainless steel barrels are available fitted to new Remington 700 actions or Wichita BR actions. All calibers available.

Prices:

A. Rem 700 ADL/SST-100 Stainless Steel Barrel $340.00

B. Rem 700 ADL/Mag/SST-100 Stainless Steel Barrel $350.00

C. Rem 700 BDL/SST-100 Stainless Steel Barrel $365.00

D. Rem 700 BDL/Mag/SST-100 Stainless Steel Barrel $375.00

E. Wichita BR/SST-100 Stainless Steel Barrel, Canjar LP Trigger, with trigger guard and lug $490.00

From H. S. Precision.

BARRELED ACTIONS

These are barreled Mauser-type actions that are available in most popular standard calibers—magnum calibers are $10 and $20 more depending upon caliber requested. Premier Grade barrels cost an additional $3. All are in-the-white.

Prices:

1. Santa Barbara Federal Barreled Action	$115
2. Mark X Federal Barreled Action	$130
3. Mark X Federal Barreled Action with adjustable trigger.	$140
4. Sako Federal Barreled Action	$198

From Federal Firearms.

CUSTOM ACTIONS

Series of custom bolt actions are available in five sizes. From top to bottom: DGA Magnum-Length repeater, $330; DGA Medium-Length Repeater, $315; DGA Medium-Length Single Shot, $315; BP Medium-Length Single Shot, $315 and the BP Short-Length Single Shot, $315. Top three actions feature non-glare, blue-black trigger guards while the bottom two come in the white.

From Shilen Rifles, Inc.

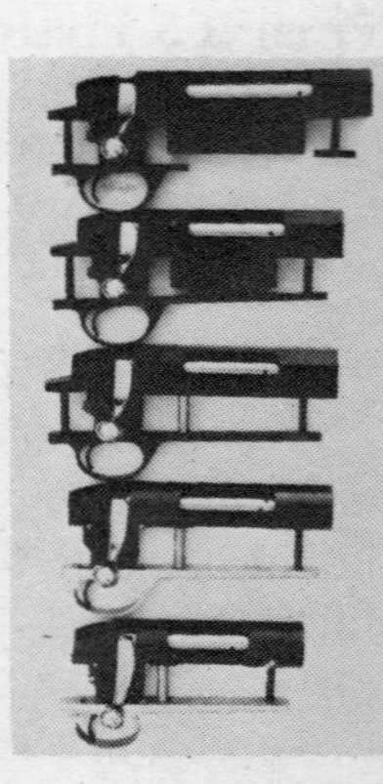

DOUGLAS BARRELS

Douglas barrels have an excellent, well-deserved reputation for accuracy. These barrels are available in most popular calibers in either rough blank, finished (turned and polished) or completely finished (turned, threaded, crowned, polished, chambered and cut to length) styles. As you will notice in the nearby chart, barrels carry numbers running from "1" through "9"—this indicates the weight of the barrel. "Featherweight" is the lightest with barrel weight increasing as the numbers ascend. The prices shown are for standard grade barrels—add $5 for premium grade; $20 for air gauging and $35 for stainless.

Prices:

CUSTOM BARRELS

Made exclusively from Douglas blanks. A wide variety of calibers are available. Barrels are in-the-white or blued. Classic tapered octagon barrels are also available. The maker advises he strives for total quality and will not be rushed; hence, a 12- to 14-week waiting period on regular barrels; and, a 6-month wait for tapered octagon barrels.

Write direct for prices.

From W. C. Strutz.

Barrel No. or Type (See Reverse Side for Further Detail Information)	Rough Turned to Approx. Size (PRET)		Finished Turned & Polished (FT)		Turned, Threaded Chambered, Cut to Length, Crowned & Polished (FTC)	
	*M-S	*ENF.	*M-S	*ENF.	*M-S	*ENF.
FEATHERWEIGHT	50.00	N.A.	53.50	N.A.	69.00	N.A.
NO. #1	47.50	50.00	49.00	55.75	63.75	70.75
NO. #2 THRU #3	39.50	45.75	44.25	50.75	59.50	66.50
NO. #4 THRU #7	41.00	47.00	46.25	52.75	61.25	68.00
NO. #8	42.25	48.25	48.00	54.50	63.00	69.75
BENCHRESTER & #9	55.25	55.25	61.00	61.00	74.75	74.75
BASIC — SHORT	32.75	37.00	N.A.	N.A.	N.A.	N.A.
BASIC — MEDIUM	34.00	38.50	N.A.	N.A.	N.A.	N.A.
BASIC — LONG	35.00	40.00	N.A.	N.A.	N.A.	N.A.

*M-S & Enf. refers to breech diameter shown on barrel chart below. The basic barrel is rough turned to straight cylinder shape 1⅛" to 1³⁄₁₆" diameter and comes in three lengths: 26" — 27½" — 30" to finish at 24", 26" and 28".

P.O. ACKLEY BARREL BLANKS

These blanks are currently offered in calibers ranging from .17 to .45 in full round, rough tapered and contoured and semi-polished configurations. They are made of 4140 chrome moly steel, drilled and reamed slowly, then button rifled.

Price:

.22 - .45 Full round $50.00
Rough tapered $55.00
Contoured and semi polished ..$60.00
Chambered ....$10.00 extra
Threaded ....$ 5.00 extra
.17 - .20 Caliber ....$ 5.00 extra

From P.O. Ackley Barrels.

BARRELS

Diamond-lapped barrels in-the-white. Available in all popular calibers. For Premier Grade barrel add $3.

Price: $38.45

From Federal Firearms.

CUSTOM BARREL BLANKS

William H. Hobaugh makes barrel blanks in calibers ranging from .224 to .45—special twists to order, no extra change. The steel used is 4140 chrome moly. Sporter, featherweight, target/varmint and benchrest blanks are available. Write for full list of services. May be installed by your gunsmith.

Prices:

Basic Sporter Blank: 25" overall $50.00
Featherweight Blank: 25" overall 52.50
Featherweight Blank: 27" overall 52.00
Target/varmint Blank: 29" overall 55.00
Benchrest Blank: 31" overall 57.50
Barrels of 1⅜" Stock: to your specs up to 27" long 57.50
Sporter Barrels w/integral magnum lug 60.00
Chrome Moly Barrel: installed, chambered, blued, on your action—up to 26" barrel length 110.00

From The Rifle Shop.

.30 Carbine/.30-06

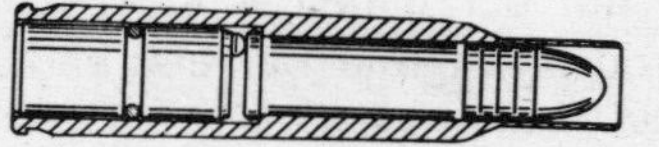

.22LR/.222 Remington

CARTRIDGE ADAPTORS

Allows the use of other ammo of correct caliber in centerfire rifles. Each adapter is made of the best steel. Adapters are also available to allow the use of rimfire ammo in .22 centerfires such as the .222 Remington. (Shown nearby are two examples.) For available adapters see below:

.22 L.R. in .220 Swift
.22 L.R. in .221 Fireball
.22 L.R. in .222 Remington
.22 L.R. in .222 Remington Magnum
.22 L.R. in .223
.22 L.R. in .225 Winchester
.22 L.R. in .22-250
.22 Magnum in .220 Swift
.22 Magnum in .222 Remington
.22 Magnum in .222 Remington Magnum
.22 Magnum in .223
.22 Magnum in .225 Winchester
.22 Magnum in .22-250
.22 Hornet in .220 Swift
.22 Hornet in .22-250
.22 Hornet in .225 Winchester
.30 Carbine in .30-06
.30 Carbine in .308 Winchester
.30 Carbine in .30-30
.30 Carbine in .300 Savage
.30 Carbine in .300 Winchester Magnum
.32 ACP in .30-06
.32 ACP in .30-30
.32 ACP in .308 Winchester
.32 ACP in .300 Savage
.32 ACP in 8mm Mauser
.32 ACP in .300 Winchester Magnum

Prices: Each of above $11.95.
From Sports Specialties.

REPLACEMENT BOLT HANDLE

These handles are machined from low-carbon bar stock and come in the white as shown. They are designed to replace military or commercial bolt handles and may be used as the basis for a custom handle, if so desired. May be installed to your specifications by a competent gunsmith.
Price: $6.95 each.
From Dave Talley.

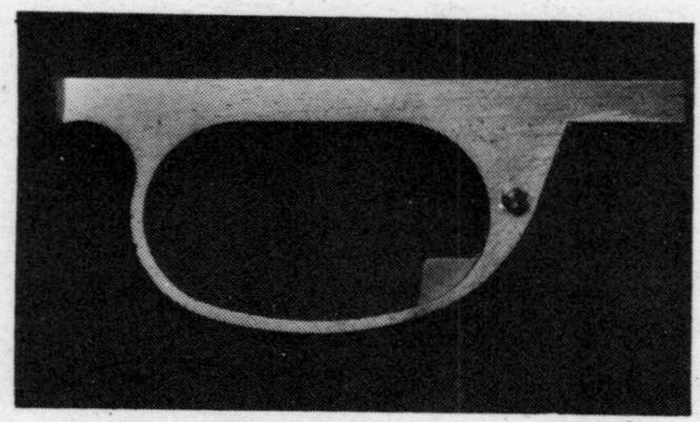

PRE-64 MODEL 70 QUICK RELEASE TRIGGER BOW

These bows come in the white as shown and are designed primarily as a replacement unit for Pre-64 Model 70 rifles. May be installed by your gunsmith.
Price: $50
From Don Allen.

BOLT HANDLE

Ready for your gunsmith to install, polish and blue. Nearby you'll see the bolt as shipped.
Price: $2.75
From Lenard M. Brownell.

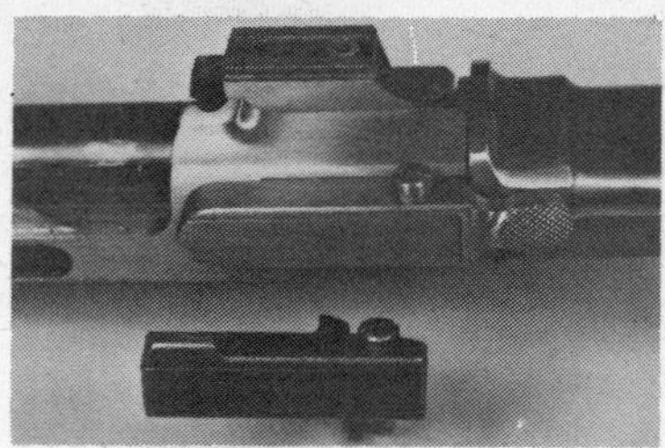

MAUSER BOLT STOP

Custom conversion from military to style shown. Available as a complete unit or customer can send bolt stop for exchange. Front end round (as shown) or left square as desired.

Prices: Not available at time of publication.

From Lenard M. Brownell.

CUSTOM TRIGGER GUARD FOR MDL. 52 WINCHESTER

Made of solid steel and milled, not stamped. All hand work. Features miniature floorplate (hinged) and hand checkered release.

Price: Write direct.

From N. B. Fashingbauer.

PRE-64 MODEL 70 QUICK RELEASE TRIGGER BOW & FLOOR-PLATE ASSEMBLY

This entire assembly comes in the white as shown. It replaces trigger guard assemblies on Pre-64 Model 70 bolt action rifles; or, it can be used as a basic component for a custom rifle.

Price: $100

From Don Allen.

STEEL FLOORPLATE/TRIGGER GUARD FOR 600 SERIES REMINGTONS

Made of steel and comes blued. Contoured to fit the stock cutout at the rear end and to be flatter than the original. Will fit any Remington 600, 660 or Mohawk 600.

Price: $27.95

From Neil A. Jones.

CUSTOM TRIGGER GUARDS

Lightweight Springfield and Mauser trigger guards are cast from special alloy aluminum, anodized a deep lustrous black. Hinged, button release floorplates in black, gold, or silver are figured with a running deer (Springfield) or antelope head (Mauser).
Specify action.

Price: $29.95 (specify bottom plate finish).

Figured floor plates (only) as described above, for Springfield or Mauser military actions.

Price: $13.95

From Michaels of Oregon.

MAGNUM DROP MAGAZINE FOR MAUSER 98's

These all steel magazines hold five .375 H&H cartridges. Comes in the white with follower. (Also avail-

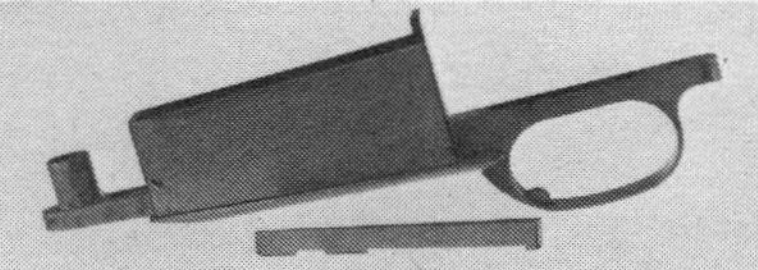

able as unfinished castings adaptable to M70's, Enfields, Springfields, and others—less follower.)

Prices: Complete with Follower $150; Unfinished Casting $60.

From London Guns.

MAUSER RIFLE FLOOR PLATE RELEASE

Add a push button floor plate release to your Mauser bolt rifle action with this easily-installed, blued tool steel release button.

Price: $4.95

From The Sight Shop.

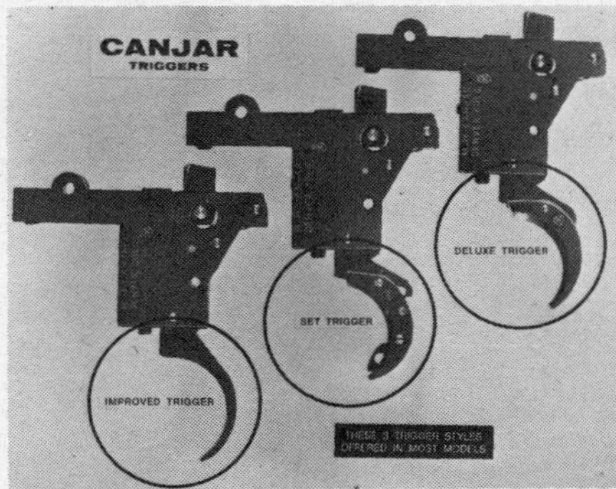

ADJUSTABLE TRIGGERS

Available for most brands of modern sporting rifles. Three styles: Improved, Set and Deluxe. Upper section of all three styles are mechanically the same—the difference is in the trigger shoe area and their width and functions.

Prices: Range depending upon the model of trigger and the gun they're going to be put on. As an example, for the Remington 700 the prices run: Set, $75.88; Deluxe, $58.82; Improved, $53.58.

From M. H. Canjar Co.

LIGHT PULL TRIGGER

Designed as a reasonably-priced competition-type trigger, these units have an adjustment range between 2 and 12 ounces. Suitable for silhouette, bench rest, free rifle competition and some types of varmint shooting where the rifle is carefully handled. Available for most Remingtons and Winchester's Model 52 target rifles.
Price: About $65.
From M. H. Canjar Co.

ADJUSTABLE TRIGGER

For Remington rifles. Features a ¼-inch trigger, all steel construction and may be used with your existing safety. Available with ⅜-inch trigger ($2.50) and outside adjustment ($3). Model R. (See chart nearby for further information).
Price: $35
From Timney Manufacturing Co.

ADJUSTABLE TRIGGERS

Fully adjustable. The "Super Liteweight" model features machined steel parts in an alloy housing. Integral safety. Available for most bolt action rifles. (See chart nearby for further information.)
Price: Model FD $32.
From Timney Manufacturing Co.

ADJUSTABLE TRIGGER

For the Husqvarna and Interarms Mark X rifles. Features machined parts, alloy housing and 3/16-inch trigger. Model H is shown. (See Master Chart nearby for further information.)
Price: $30
From Timney Manufacturing Co.

ADJUSTABLE TRIGGER

Fits most military bolt actions and is fully adjustable. Alloy housing, machined steel working surfaces, 3/16-inch trigger. Model SP. (See chart nearby for further information).
Price: $20
From Timney Manufacturing Co.

RIFLE MODEL NUMBER	RIFLE OR MFG. NAME	ADDITIONAL DATA	ORDER TIMNEY TRIGGER . . .		
			MODEL SP	MODEL TS	MODEL FD
SO3-A3	SPRINGFIELD	ALL MODELS EXCEPT .22 CALIBER	X	X	X
SM2-22	SPRINGFIELD	.22 CALIBER ONLY	X	X	X
M98-FN	MAUSER	THOSE WITH 2" TRIGGER GUARDS	X	X	X
M98-K	MAUSER	THOSE WITH 1¾" TRIGGER GUARDS	X	X	X
M98-B	MAUSER	BROWNING 400's J. C. HIGGINS M50's	X	X	X
M95-6	MAUSER	SWEDISH 94's SPANISH 95's	X	X	X
MS-98	MAUSER	MEXICAN M98 SHORT ACTIONS	X	X	X
M91-4	MAUSER	SPANISH M93's	X	X	X
M91-4K	MAUSER	SWEDISH M94's MODEL G33/50	X	X	X
M91-S	MAUSER	ARGENTINE M 91's	X	N/A	N/A
E1-4	ENFIELD	5 SHOT MAGAZINES N/A FOR BRITISH 303	X	X	N/A
E1-5	ENFIELD	6 SHOT MAGAZINES N/A FOR BRITISH 303	X	X	N/A
600 700	REMINGTON	PRESENT SAFETY USED IN INSTALLATION		MODEL R	
721 722	REMINGTON	PRESENT SAFETY USED IN INSTALLATION		MODEL R40X	
L461• L579•L61	SAKO	VIXEN-FORRESTER FINNBEAR		MODEL SA	
70	WINCHESTER	MODEL 70 ONLY!		MODEL W7	
6.5 MM 7.7 MM	JAP	JS-WITH SAFETY J-WITH SAFETY	MODEL J		MODEL JS
ALL	HUSQVARNA	INTEGRAL SAFETY			MODEL H
MARK X	prior to 1977 INTERARMS	INTEGRAL SAFETY			MODEL HX

CUSTOM TRIGGERS

Available for most military bolt actions, in single stage or speedlock configurations. All operating parts hardened and honed.
Prices: Range from $14.50 to $18.50 depending upon type of gun and style of trigger. Shown is a typical Enfield type EW single-stage trigger ($14.50).
From Dayton Traister Company.

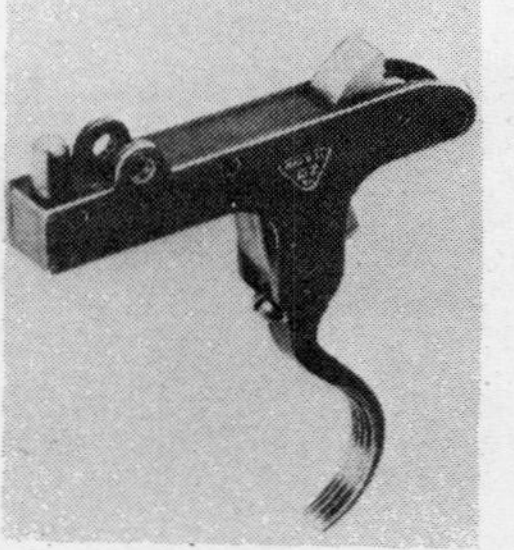

Prices shown are subject to change.

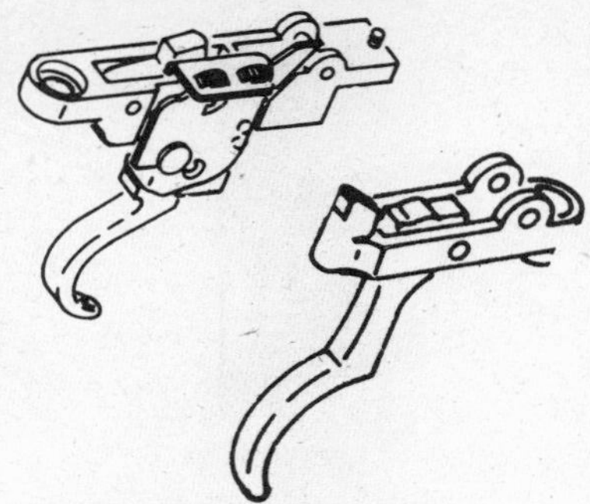

MAUSER RIFLE TRIGGERS

Convert Mauser 98 trigger to fully adjustable let off with an easily installed replacement trigger assembly (top). To change Mauser actions from standard two-stage Military to single stage, use the trigger and sear assembly below.
Prices: $9.95 (adjustable); $4 (single stage).
From Sherwood.

TRIGGER SHOES

Williams Guide trigger shoes are precision machined, fit snugly over the standard trigger of most current and many earlier revolvers and auto pistols to provide greater control and better feel to the shooter. Easily fitted in minutes with hex wrench (provided).
Price: $4.70 (Specify make and model).
From Williams Gun Sight.

TRIGGER SHOE

Each shoe is made of solid, blued steel, has a grooved face and comes with a miniature Allen wrench for quick installation by the shooter. These shoes are favored by varmint hunters and bench resters alike. They're available for most popular rifles, pistols and shotguns; and they simply slip over your existing trigger providing a wider, better bearing surface for the trigger finger.
Price: $3
From Flaig's Lodge.

MARTINI EXTRACTOR

Martini Cadet rifle extractors will not extract rimless cartridges. However, the spring-loaded claw in Snapp's replacement extractor permits converting the Cadet to rimless as well as rimmed cartridges.
Price: $25
From Snapp's Gun Shop.

HAMMER EXTENSION

Permits easier cocking of external hammer rifles, pistols and shotguns when a scope is mounted over the action. Specifically designed for the H&R Topper, Marlin 36, 336 and 39 rifles, Ruger Blackhawk, Savage 24 shotgun/rifles, T/C Contender, Winchester 94 and 9422, Browning BLR and BL-22. The extension mounts quickly to the hammer with an Allen-head set screw.
Price: $3.95 (specify make and model gun).
From Michaels of Oregon.

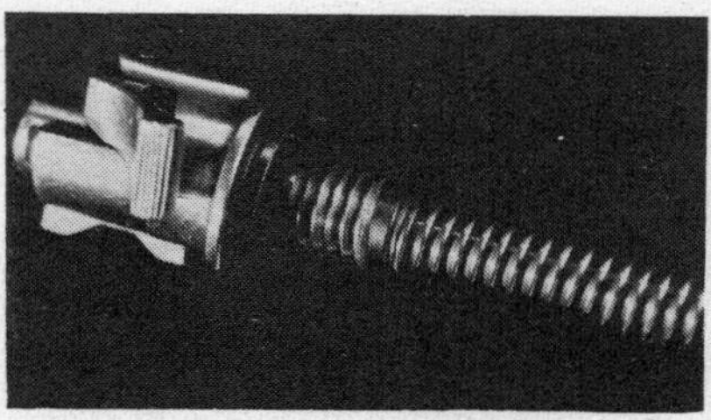

MODEL 70 TYPE SAFETY FOR MAUSER 98's

These safeties are much easier to use than the standard version. May be installed by your gunsmith.
Price: $55
From Don Allen.

"GIANT HEAD" RIFLE AND SHOTGUN SAFETIES

Larger than standard push button safeties are safer, surer to use, than factory original safeties. Both right and left hand versions are offered for most current Winchester, Ruger 44 and 10-20 (Left hand only), Remington 11, Savage 270, Ithaca 37.
Price: $4.45 (Winchester, Ruger); $5.50 (others).
From Williams Gun Sight.

See the Directory for complete company addresses.

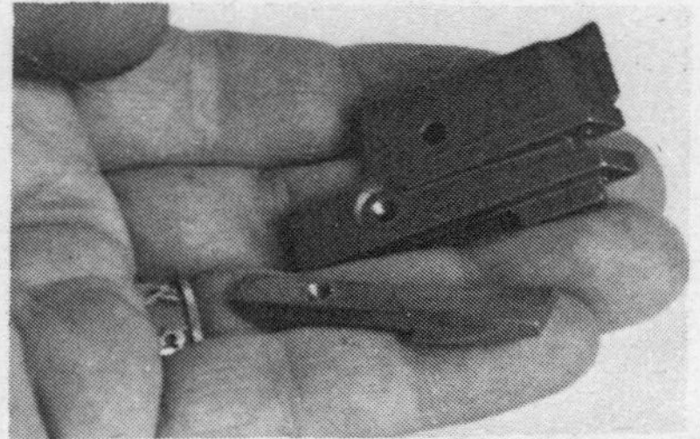

MODEL 92 CONVERSION CARTRIDGE GUIDES

Reliable feed is a major problem when the Winchester Model 92 rifle is converted to .357 Magnum, a problem neatly resolved when the original guides are replaced with Snapp's .357 guides.

Price: $30 (per set).

From Snapp's Gun Shop.

CUSTOM BARREL BAND

Machined from steel and available for all rifles, but must be bored to correct barrel taper. This is a sweat-on band.

Price: $25

From Hoenig & Rodman.

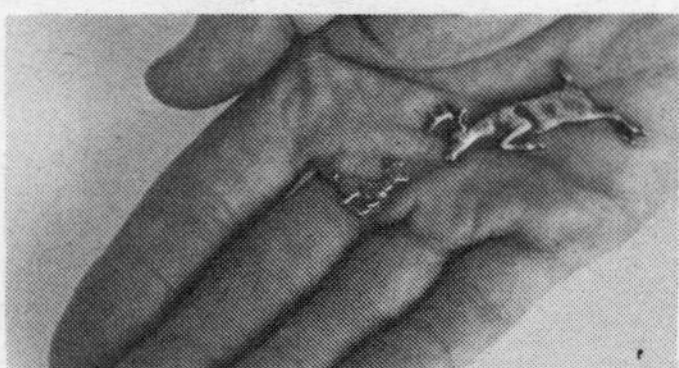

SID BELL SILVER OR GOLD GAME ANIMALS

These beautifully done running and leaping deer figures are designed to be either soft soldered or epoxied in place on flat sided receivers like the Winchester 94 or the Marlin 336. They serve to add a quiet, yet elegant touch of class to otherwise plain, flat receivered rifles or deerslayer type shotguns.

Prices: Silver, large leaping deer: $20.00; Small running deer in silver: $8; gold $35.

From Sid Bell Originals.

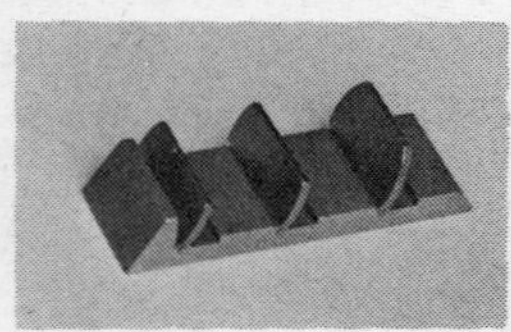

BRITISH STYLE EXPRESS SIGHT AND BASES

Each sight comes in the white with one standing and three folding leaves. These sights will require the services of a competent gunsmith for regulating and installation. Small or large dovetail bases are also available.

Prices: Sight $49.95; Base $19.95.

From London Guns.

CUSTOM CLAW-STYLE SCOPE MOUNT

This mount is specifically made for Mauser 98's with 1″ rings. Scope pivots to rear to detach; comes blued.

Price: $150 per set.

From London Guns.

MINI-14 FLASH SUPPRESSOR AND FRONT SIGHT UNIT

From left to right: Prong-type, cage and night firing units. They all are machined from steel and appropriately blued. Should be installed by a gunsmith.

Price: Prong, $26; cage $26; night firing $30.

From Choate Machine and Tool.

BIPOD

This spring-loaded bipod is made from high-strength aluminum alloy. Quickly attaches to any Q.D. swivel base. Legs are simply folded down and adjusted for desired length. When not being used, the legs are folded up parallel to barrel.

Price: $27.75

From Harris Engineering.

SIG-STG-57 ACCESSORIES

Original factory (SIG) extras.

Prices: Bayonet, $125; roll-up cleaning kit, $75; magazines, $75; leather sling, $30; Web sling, $15.

From Mandall Shooting Supplies, Inc.

SIG-AMT ACCESSORIES

These are original accessories from the manufacturer, SIG.

Prices: Bipod, $125; Magazines in 20, 10 or 5-shot, $75; Flash hider, $125; Front sight key $125; Cloth sling, $15; Stock-housed cleaning accessories $15; Upper handguard wood, $55.

From Mandall Shooting Supplies, Inc.

Prices shown are subject to change.

Metallic Sights

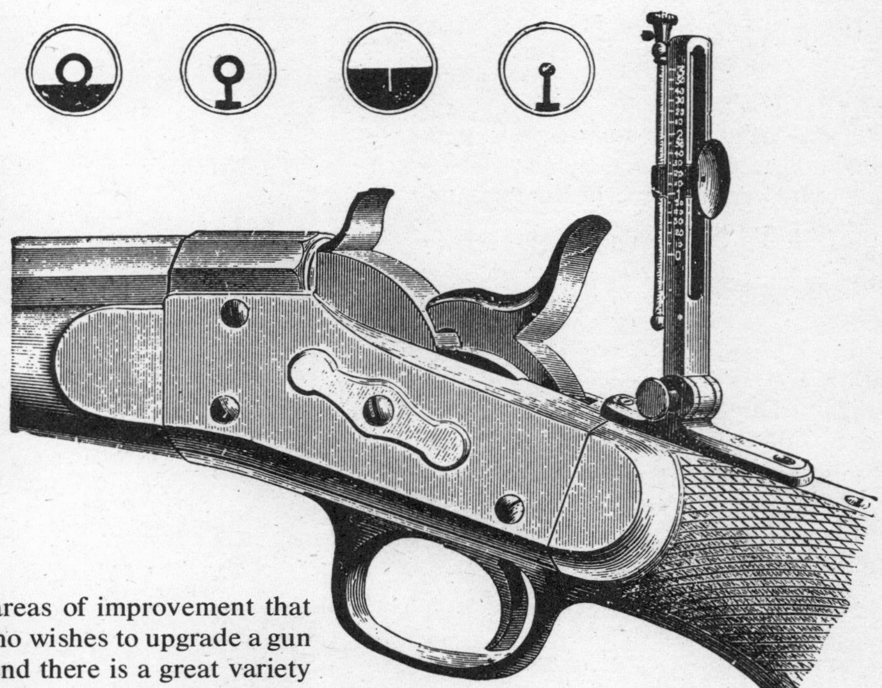

Sights are one of the first areas of improvement that occur to a gun enthusiast who wishes to upgrade a gun in his battery, and to that end there is a great variety available in today's marketplace. For the most part, replacement metallic sights will require little sophistication on the part of the installer; they're designed to mount in the same place and with the same hardware as the sights they replace. In some cases, however, some rudimentary—or occasionally even rather demanding—machine shop work will be needed.

Open sights appear first on the following pages, followed by peep, custom and other specialized types. Metallic sights from the larger makers are often carried in gun shop and mail order house inventories, but for the smaller makers you'll generally have to go direct. When writing for additional information, a self-addressed, stamped envelope will often expedite a reply.

FULLY ADJUSTABLE FOLDING LEAF SIGHTS

Marble's folding leaf sights come in dovetail or mounting block style as seen nearby. They feature screw adjustments for both windage and elevation; plus, a white-diamond insert blade and reversible "U" or "V" notches.

Price: From about $6.60 for the dovetail; $9.60 for the same sight with base.

From Marble Arms.

ADJUSTABLE RIFLE SIGHT

Marble's Rear Sporting Sight fits a wide variety of sporting rifles. It features step adjustable elevation, drift adjustable windage and a diamond insert blade that's reversible for either "U" or "V" notches. Available in full buckhorn, semi-buckhorn or flat top.

Price: $6.80, flat top; $6.80 semi-buckhorn; $7.70, buckhorn.

From Marble Arms.

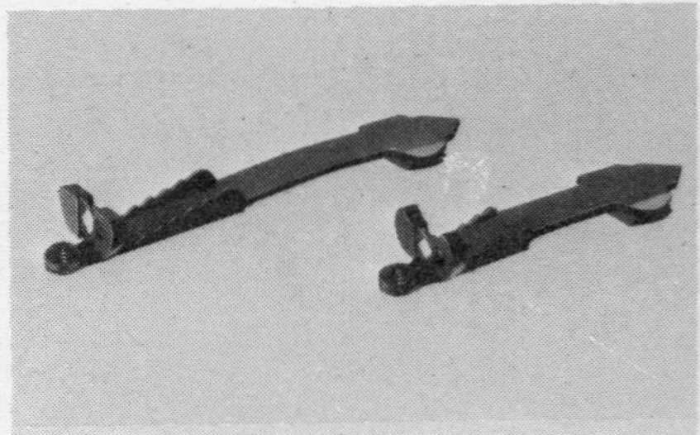

OPEN REAR SIGHT

The Williams Guide open sight screws on the barrel and is fully adjustable for windage and elevation. Fits all popular rifles and is made of durable alloy. Four blade styles are available.

Price: $8.30

From Williams Gun Sight.

OPEN REAR SIGHT

The Williams Dovetail Open Sight is designed to fit any standard rifle dovetail. It's made of the toughest aluminum alloy and is screw-adjustable for windage and elevation. Four blade styles available.

Price: $6.90

From Williams Gun Sight.

REAR SIGHT BLADES

The blades shown are ready to install in any Williams Guide open sight. From left to right: square notch, U-notch, V-notch and "B"-style.

Price: $2.35 each.

From Williams Gun Sight.

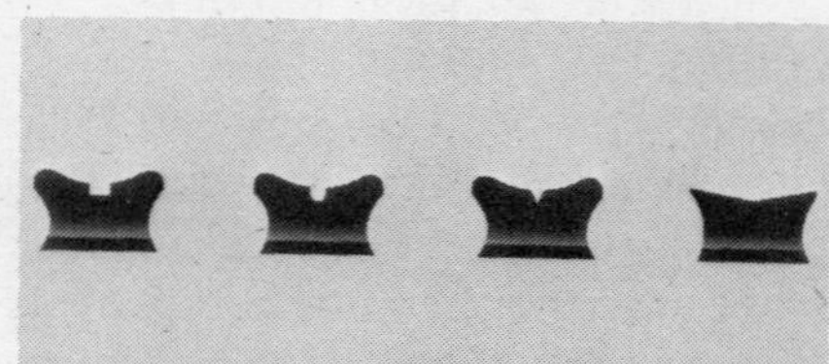

FOLDING LEAF SIGHT

The Lyman No. 16 Folding Leaf rear sight comes in 3 heights: .400″ high, elevates to .500″; .345″ high, elevates to .445″; and .500″ high, elevates to .600″. Folds up or down at the flick of a finger.

Price: $6.50

From Lyman Products Corp.

LYMAN No. 16
Folding Leaf Sight

Prices shown are subject to change.

LYMAN Hunting Front Sights No. 3 (1/16″ bead) and No. 28 (3/32″ bead)

HUNTING FRONT SIGHTS

Lyman bead front hunting sights are equipped with a standard ⅜″ dovetail, choice of white or gold bead and come in variety of heights. The 1/16″ bead is popular but many hunters prefer the wide 3/32″ bead for fast shooting.

Prices: No. 3 - 1/16″ bead, base width F (17/32″) (½ oz.) $5.50
No. 28 - 3/32″ bead, base width F (17/32″) (½ oz.) 5.50
No. 31 - 1/16″ bead, base width A (11/32″) (½ oz.) 5.50
No. 37 - 3/32″ bead, base width A (11/32″) (½ oz.) 5.50

From Lyman Products Company.

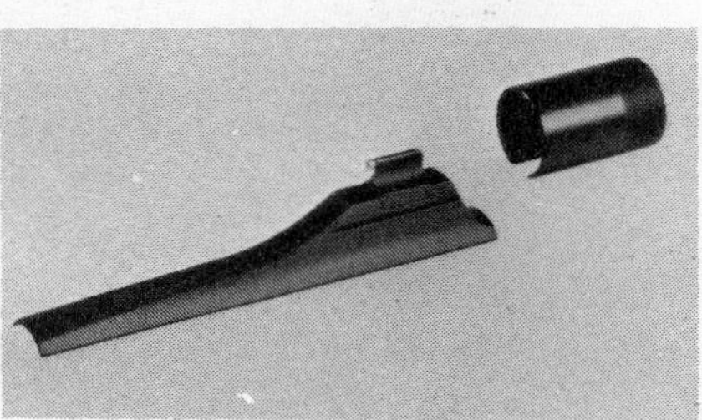

FRONT SIGHT, RAMP & HOOD

Ramp is available in either sweat-on or screw-on models and is checkered to reduce reflection. The detachable hood helps protect front sight blade during storage or transportation.

Price: $6.95 for the ramp; $1.65 for the hood; $4.25 for the blade.

From Marble Arms.

FRONT SIGHT BLADES

Shown nearby, from left to right, are Marble's standard blade front sight, sheared front sight, contour front sight and standard front sight. All come in 1/16″ bead only, except for the contour model, which is also offered in 3/32″ bead.

Price: Standard front, $4.25; contour, $4.80; sheared, $5.25; standard blade, $6.

From Marble Arms.

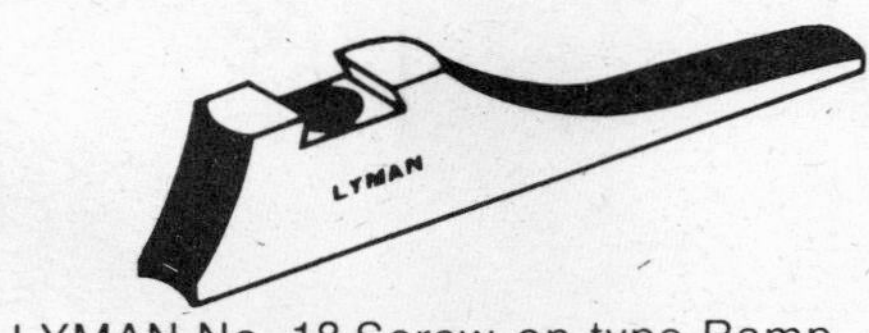

LYMAN No. 18 Screw-on type Ramp

FRONT SIGHT RAMP

Lyman's No. 18 screw-on type ramp is ruggedly built and comes in low ramp, medium ramp and high ramp sizes.

Price: $7.50; complete with sight, $13.

From Lyman Products Company.

RAMP FRONT SIGHT

Williams ramp and front sight combo are an attractive and practical purchase for either the hunter or target shooter. Ramp is checkered to eliminate glare.

Price: Ramp, $7.75; with hood, $9.30; sight blade, $4; specify gun when ordering or purchasing from your local gun shop.

From Williams Gun Sight.

See the Directory for complete company addresses.

FRONT TARGET SIGHT

The Lyman 17A target front sight is designed for use with dovetail mounting. Good range companion to the Lyman 57/66 receiver sight. Comes with 7 inserts that lock into place with a threaded cap. Available in 5 different sight heights ranging from .360″ to .532″.
Price: $12
From Lyman Products Company.

LYMAN Series 17A
Target Front Sight

GLOBE FRONT SIGHT

The Redfield International Small Bore front sight comes with six clear, distortion-free inserts and 6 skeleton inserts in vinyl insert holder. For the target shooter.
Price: $32.40
From Redfield.

International
Small-Bore Front

OLYMPIC FRONT SIGHT

Redfield's Olympic front sight comes with 10 inserts and is a top companion for any target-type aperture sight.
Price: $22.60
From Redfield.

Olympic Front

BIG-BORE FRONT SIGHT

The Redfield International Match Big-Bore front sight is specifically made for .30-caliber shooting events. Same as the Small Bore sight except for shortened tube to meet I.S.U. requirements. Comes with the same inserts—12 in all—as the Small Bore sight.
Price: $32.40
From Redfield.

ADJUSTABLE HANDGUN SIGHTS

MMC's adjustable pistol sights are designed to easily replace original, non-adjustable factory versions. In most cases, these sights require little or no gunsmithing when it comes to installation. Available for Ruger Standard Auto, High Standard automatics, Walthers, Browning Hi-Power, Colt 1911 and 1911 A1 autos, the S&W models 39 and 59 and other popular handguns. (S&W Model 39/59 sight shown.)
Available with white outline rear leaf.
Prices: Range from about $25 to $47, depending on the model desired. The S&W Model 39/59 shown, sells for $45 plain; $47.50 with white outline leaf.
From Miniature Machine Company.

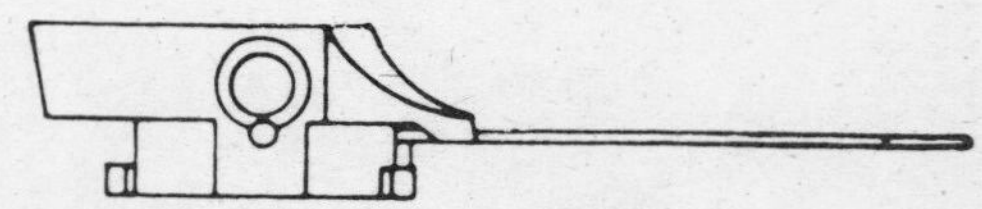

Prices shown are subject to change.

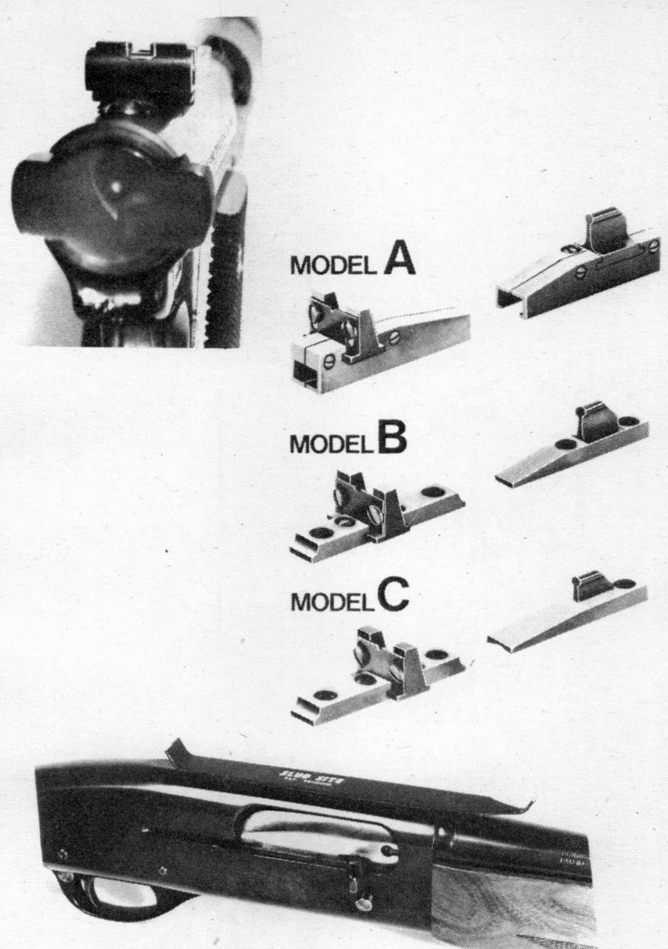

WHITE OR GOLD OUTLINED SIGHT LEAF

Omega Sales is currently offering a white or gold outlined rear sight leaf for Colts, Rugers and the Interarms Virginia single action that has a provision for an adjustable sight blade. The insert blades serve as a sighting aid in poor or low light conditions.
Price: $5.95
From Omega Sales.

QUICK CHANGE ADJUSTABLE SHOTGUN SIGHT

Available for vent ribbed (Model A), solid ribbed (Model B) and plain (Model C) barrel shotguns. Comes with built-in windage and elevation adjustment. Can be mounted in minutes by the purchaser. For 12, 16 and 20 gauge shotguns, most popular makes.
Price: From $14.95 to $18.95, depending on style of sight and gun sight is to be mounted on.
From Accura-Site Co., Inc.

SHOTGUN SLUG SIGHT

The Slug Site is a handy combo front/rear sight unit that attaches itself to your gun's receiver with a pressure sensitive adhesive strip. It works.
Price: $7.95
From Slug Site Co.

LYMAN Shotgun Sights

SHOTGUN SIGHT BEADS

No. 10 (front) is a press-fit type bead sight; No. 10D (front) is a screw-in type front sight; No. 11 is a middle-rib bead that's designed to be press-fitted into place.
Price: No. 10, $2; No. 10D, $2.50; No. 11, $2.
From Lyman Products Company.

XPERT FRONT SIGHTS

Poly BEAD

XPERT MID RIB SIGHTS

BEV-L-BLOK

SHOTGUN SIGHT BEADS

Poly Choke's shotgun beads are available in four styles. From top to bottom: the Xpert front sight, available in 3-56 and 6-48, 3/32″ or 5/32″ shank length; the Poly Bead which comes in ⅛″ bead, 3-56 or 6-48, short, medium or long shank; Xpert mid rib beads in tapered carrier (ivory only) or 3-56 threaded shank (gold only); Bev-L-Blok ramp in high or low size with 6-48 tap size only.
Price: Xpert front sight, $1.50 in gold or ivory — blaze orange, $2.50; Poly Bead $1.25; Xpert Mid Rib Bead $1.50; Bev-L-Blok $1.50 for gold or ivory — $2.50 for blaze orange.
From Poly Choke.

APERTURE SIGHT

Williams' Foolproof series of peep sights are made for just about every popular sporting rifle. They are available in either high- or low-sight line models. The FP sight shown, features micrometer adjustment knobs.

Price: $22.10; with Twilight aperture, $22.75; with target knobs (as shown), $26.20.

From Williams Gun Sight.

APERTURE SIGHT

This inexpensive Williams sight is called the "5-D" and is fully adjustable for windage and elevation. It fits most big game rifles, .22s. Like other Williams peep sights, the 5-D is also available with the Twilight aperture.

Price: $12.50; with Twilight aperture, $13.15.

From Williams Gun Sight.

APERTURE SIGHT FOR WIN. .375 BIG BORE 94

The Williams FP-94 375 peep sight, as shown, comes with their Twilight aperture which helps define targets under poor light conditions. Fully, and easily adjustable for windage and elevation. Made of the toughest aluminum alloy.

Price: About $23.

From Williams Gun Sight.

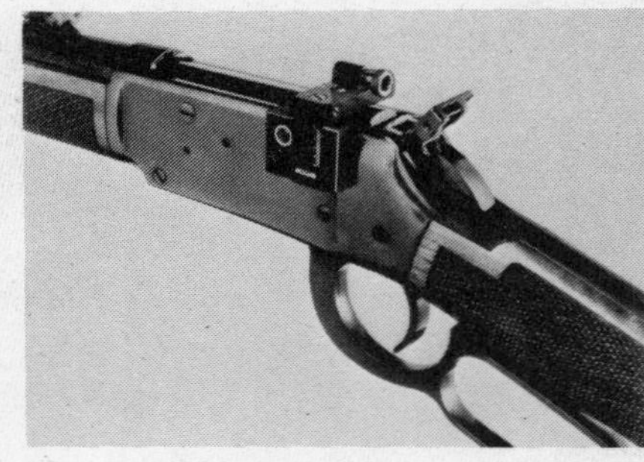

APERTURE SIGHTS

The Lyman Models 57 and 66 are identical except for the fact that the 57 is for round receivers while the 66 is for flat receivers. Features audible ¼-minute click adjustment for elevation and windage, quick-release slide and a set of aperture discs (2)—one for hunting, one for target.

Price: $28

From Lyman Products Corp.

LYMAN
Series 66
Universal Sight

LYMAN
Series 57
Universal Sight

Prices shown are subject to change.

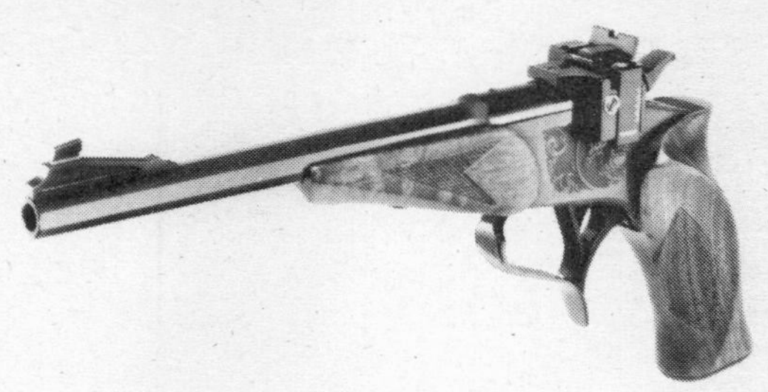

T/C REAR SIGHT

This Williams Foolproof Sight is available with square notch leaf or aperture (leaf shown). The sight is fully adjustable for windage and elevation. Made of the toughest aluminum alloy.

Price: $24 (leaf); $22 (aperture).

From Williams Gun Sight.

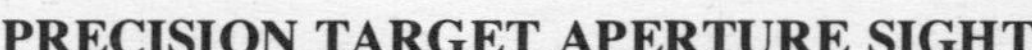

PRECISION TARGET APERTURE SIGHT

Redfield's Palma Metallic Target Sight is one of the last American made precision peep sights available to competitive shooters. Windage and elevation adjustment are crisp and have ¼-M.O.A. capability. The "clicks" are also adjustable for a hard or soft feel—shooters' choice. Repeatability error is limited to .001-inch per click. Precision made.

Price: $144.30; adjustable filter adapter, $4.40; SI disc ⅞" x .046", $2.60; SI disc ⅞" x .093", $2.60; Sure-X disc, $13.20.

From Redfield.

ADJUSTABLE APERTURE

The Merit adjustable aperture fits most popular peep sights. The size of the aperture itself is fully adjustable by turning the knurled eyepiece. Quickly adapts your rifle for a variety of shooting conditions. Deluxe model has internal click-spring.

Price: $24; deluxe, $30.

From Merit Gunsight Co.

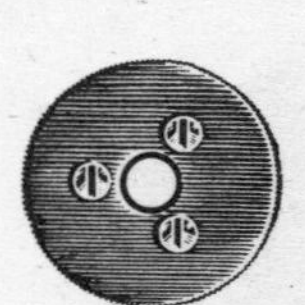

SIGHT DISC ADAPTER

Special adaptor permits Redfield discs to be used in Anschutz sights, others using the same thread combination.

Price: $4.50

From K.W. Kleinendorst

UNERTL TUBE SIGHT

Unertl's tube sight is used in conjunction with a full telescope height front sight, properly raised so the front sight will appear well centered when sighted in at 100 yards. For 50 or 200 yards, the front sight will appear low or high, but will be well within the field of the tube. Eye-piece end is threaded to fit almost all standard sighting discs. Comes with ¼-minute target-type mounts. Perfect for competition shooting.

Price: $60

From the John Unertl Optical Company.

Section 4

Telescopic Sights & Mounts

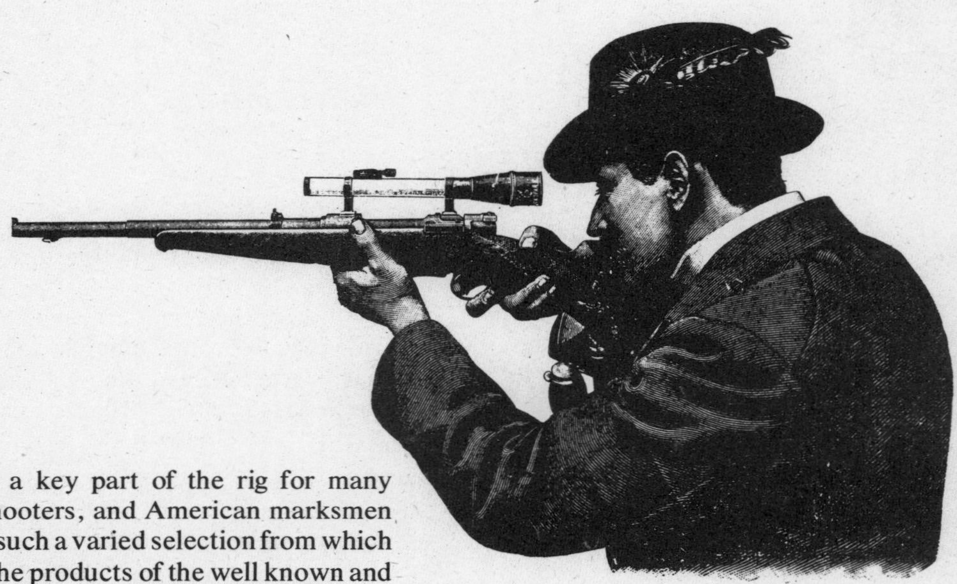

Telescopic sights are a key part of the rig for many hunters and target shooters, and American marksmen are fortunate to have such a varied selection from which to choose. Between the products of the well known and respected American makers and the imports from some of the rest of the world's most highly regarded optical manufacturers, there's virtually a scope (and appropriate mount) for every need and every pocketbook.

Because of the number of offerings in most scope maker's stables, this section has been arranged alphabetically by maker with scopes first, then mounts. Though the individual descriptions and accompanying illustrations provide a good starting point for making a buying decision, the tabular information found in the various manufacturer's charts will usually provide the best point-by-point comparison. When possible it's always best to examine a scope—preferably mounted on a rifle—before buying one. As most gun shops handle one or more scope lines, your favorite shop should be the first stop on your trip toward buying a scope once you've carefully determined exactly what you want and how you're going to be using it.

BURRIS 1¾X to 5X VARIABLE POWER SCOPE

This Fullfield, Hi-Lume Burris scope offers the shooter a field of view that ranges from 70 to 27 feet at 100 yards depending upon the power selected. This scope is ideally suited for brush country shooting. It's fully fog and dust proofed. Fully adjustable for windage and elevation.

Price: Plex or Crosshair reticle $139.95; Post and Crosshair $144.95; 1- or 3-inch Dot $149.95.

From the Burris Company.

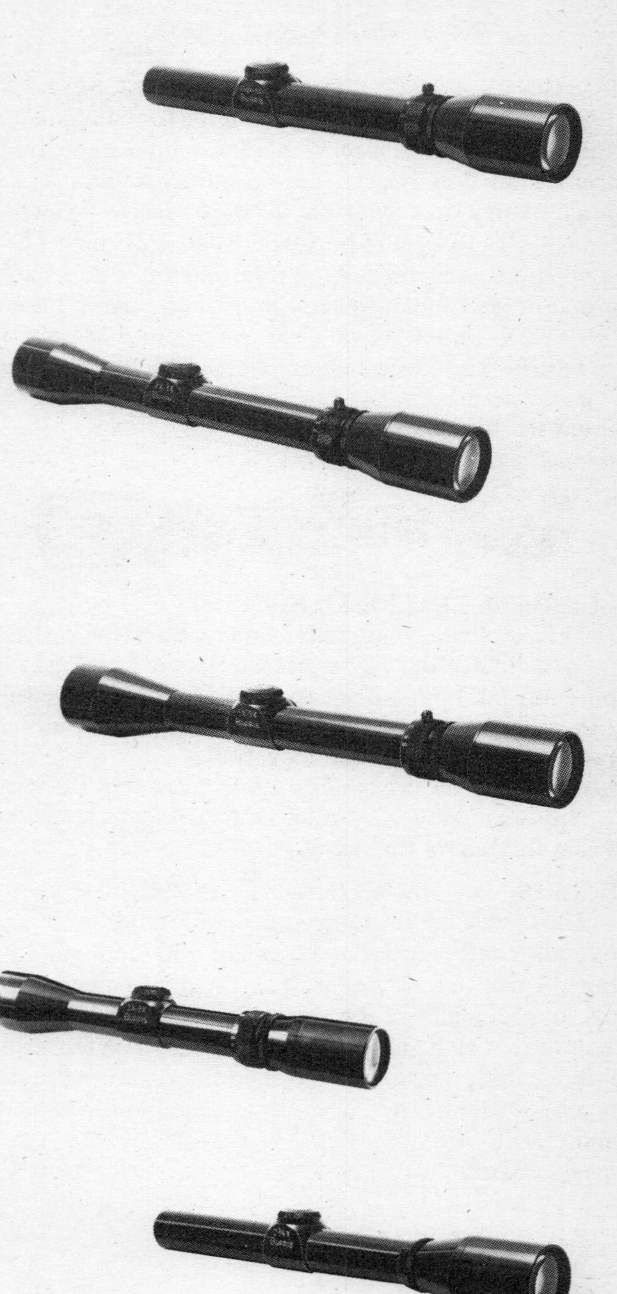

BURRIS 2X TO 7X VARIABLE POWER SCOPE

This Fullfield, Hi-Lume Burris scope is a good bet for the western big game hunter or the eastern chuck hunter. The field of view ranges from 19 feet to 50 feet (at 100 yards) depending upon the power used. It's fog and dust proofed, plus it's adjustable for windage and elevation.

Price: Plex or Crosshair reticle $152.95; Post and Crosshair $157.95, 1- or 3-inch Dot $162.95.

From The Burris Company.

BURRIS 3X TO 9X VARIABLE POWER SCOPE

This Hi-Lume, Fullfield Burris scope is perfectly suited for big game or varmint hunting. It has a field of view that ranges from 15 to 40 feet (at 100 yards) depending upon the power selected. Fully fog and dust proofed. Adjustable for windage and elevation.

Price: Plex or Crosshair reticle $159.95; Post and Crosshair $164.95; 1- or 3-inch Dot $169.95.

From the Burris Company.

BURRIS "MINI" 3X TO 9X VARIABLE POWER SCOPE

This is the scope that got a lot of shooters—and gun writers—excited when it was announced a few months back. It's the smallest variable power scope money can buy; however, it's big on quality. The provided fields of view are comparable to scopes twice the size of Burris' new Mini 3X-9X. It has a 4-inch eye relief, has fully coated optics and provides fog-free performance.

Price: Plex reticle model $129.95; Post and Crosshair model $134.95; 1-inch or 3-inch Dot $139.95.

From the Burris Company.

BURRIS 4X TO 12X VARIABLE POWER SCOPE

This Fullfield, Hi-Lume Burris scope is well suited for the widest variety of game or varmint shooting. The objective lens is fully adjustable for ranges running from 50 yards to infinity. It's fog and dust proofed, and it's fully adjustable for both windage and elevation. Field of view runs from 20 feet to 10½ feet at 100 yards, depending upon the power selected.

Price: Plex or Fine Crosshair $195.95; 7-inch or 2.0-inch Dot $205.95.

From the Burris Company.

BURRIS 2-3/4X FULLFIELD SCOPE

All Burris Fullfield scopes now have Hi-Lume optics which provide excellent light gathering qualities at dawn and dusk. The 2¾X model offers a generous 53-foot field of view at 100 yards. It's suited for brush country hunting. This scope is fully adjustable for windage and elevation and is nitrogen filled for fog-free service.

Price: Plex reticle $102.95; Crosshair $102.95; Post and Crosshair $107.95; 3-inch Dot $112.95.

From the Burris Company.

See the Directory for complete company addresses.

BURRIS 2X AND 3X LONG EYE RELIEF SCOPES

Both of these scopes are well suited for handgun use; and, Burris has bases available for many Ruger, Interarms, Dan Wesson, T/C and Smith & Wesson handguns. (A mount is available for the Model 94 Winchester as well.) Eye relief runs from 10 to 20 inches. These scopes are well made, fog-free and fully adjustable. Good field of view. Specify gun when buying bases.

Price: 2X with Plex or Crosshair reticle $84.50; 3X with Plex or Crosshair reticle $88.95. Bases $10.95 each.

From the Burris Company.

BURRIS 6X FULLFIELD SCOPE

This 6X scope features Hi-Lume optics and a 24-foot field of view at 100 yards. It's well suited for long range big game hunting. Not a bad choice for varmints either. Fog and dust proofed for reliable field use. Fully adjustable for windage and elevation.

Price: Plex or crosshair reticle $114.95; Post and Crosshair $119.95; 2-inch Dot $124.95.

From the Burris Company.

BURRIS MINI 4X, 6X AND 8X SCOPES

These well made compact scopes feature both short overall length and reduced weight when compared to other 1-inch tubed scopes. The range of powers—4X, 6X and 8X—allows the shooter to select the scope or scopes that best suit his hunting needs. The lenses are fully coated; the tube is nitrogen filled and the bodies nicely finished. They are fully adjustable for windage and elevation.

Price: See below.

Mini 4X	
With Plex Reticle	$84.50
With Post & Crosshair Reticle	$89.50
With 3-inch Dot	$94.50
Mini 6X	
With Plex Reticle	$89.95
With Post & Crosshair Reticle	$94.95
With 2-inch Dot	$99.95
Mini 8X	
With Plex Reticle	$94.50
With Post & Crosshair Reticle	$99.50
With 1½-inch Dot	$109.95

From the Burris Company.

BURRIS 4X FULLFIELD SCOPE

Featuring Hi-Lume optics, this 4X Burris scope offers 25 percent more field of view than conventional models. It's a good choice for general game hunting. It's also fully fog and dust proofed for reliable service. Fully adjustable for windage and elevation.

Price: Plex or Crosshair reticle $108.95; Post and Crosshair $113.95; 3-inch Dot $118.95.

From the Burris Company.

BURRIS 10X FULLFIELD SCOPE

This 10X Burris scope is well suited for serious target or varmint shooting. It features Burris' Hi-Lume optics and a generous 12½-foot field of view at 100 yards. The objective lens is adjustable from 50 yards to infinity. Fully fog and dust proofed, it's also fully adjustable for windage and elevation.

Price: Plex or Fine Crosshair Reticle $157.75; ½-minute Dot $167.75.

From the Burris Company.

BURRIS 12X FULLFIELD SCOPE

This Burris scope is a perfect choice for the long-range rifleman. It has an 11-foot field of view at 100 yards and features an adjustable objective lens that lets the shooter focus on anything ranging from 50 yards to infinity. It's fully adjustable for windage and elevation, and it's fog and dust proofed for reliable field use.

Price: Plex or Fine Crosshair $163.95; ½-minute Dot $173.95.

From The Burris Company

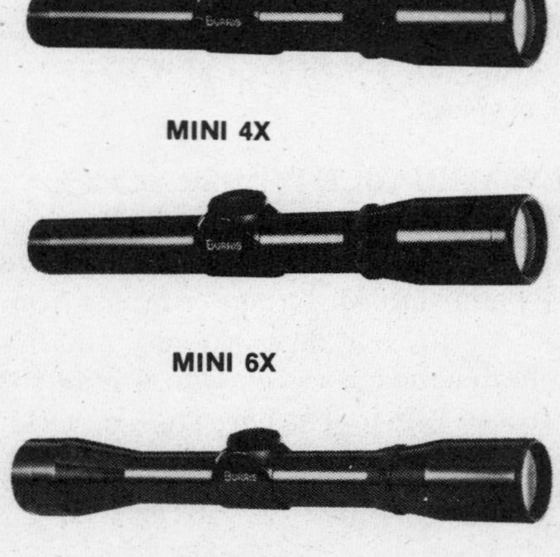

MINI 4X

MINI 6X

MINI 8X

Prices shown are subject to change.

BURRIS 1-INCH SCOPE RING

These steel rings are beautifully blued and come in low, medium and high styles. Extension-type rings are also offered in the above heights. (Below prices are per pair).

Prices: Low $18.95; Medium $18.95; High $18.95. All extension rings are priced at $22.95 in Low, Medium or High configuration.

From The Burris Company.

BURRIS 1-INCH "22" RINGS

These 1-inch rings are made for those shooters who want to mount a 1-inch scope on their favorite rimfires. They go on or come off in seconds. Made of hard anodized aluminum.

Price: $8.98

From The Burris Company.

BURRIS 1 INCH "SEE-THRU" SCOPE MOUNT

These 2-piece ring mounts are made of hard anodized aluminum. Available for most rifles. They allow the shooter to use his iron sights, or scope as desired.

Price: $15.95 per pair.

From the Burris Company.

BURRIS ¾-INCH SCOPE RINGS

These well made rings are designed for .22 rimfire scopes. They quickly go on, or come off any standard grooved rimfire receiver. They are made of tough aluminum and hard anodized.

Price: $8.98 per pair.

From the Burris Company.

BURRIS MOUNT FOR BROWNING STANDARD .22 AUTO

This one-piece mount is grooved and attaches to the Browning Standard Auto's barrel, not receiver. Insures the best accuracy from that popular rimfire. Made of tough anodized aluminum.

Price: $8.95

From the Burris Company.

BURRIS UNIVERSAL SCOPE BASE

These solid blued steel bases are offered in 1- or 2-piece styling. They are available for a wide selection of rifles. Specify rifle when purchasing.

Price: 2-piece $10.95; 1-piece $12.50.

From The Burris Company.

BUSHNELL "SCOPE CHIEF" RIFLE SCOPES

All of the Scope Chief line of Bushnell scopes feature long eye relief, coated optics and fog-free operation. Optional features include Bushnell's patented Bullet Drop Compensator. Shown nearby, from top to bottom are the 3X-9X variable; 2.5X-8X variable; 1.5X-4.5X variable and the 4X fixed power Scope Chief. Also available is Bushnell's new Prismatic Rangefinder. This item allows you to bracket your game between stadia and cross wire and directly read the distance.

Prices: See Below.

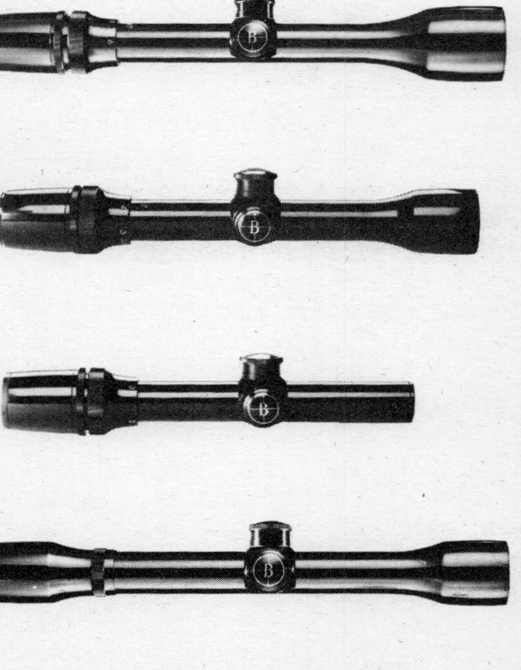

Description	Model no.	Suggested list price
3x-9x40mm with BDC and Prismatic Rangefinder	70-5002	$199.95
3x-9x40mm with BDC	70-3002	$169.95
3x-9x40mm	70-2002	$164.95
2.5x-8x32mm with BDC	70-3580	$144.95
2.5x-8x32mm	70-2580	$139.95
1.5x-4.5x20mm with BDC	70-3545	$139.95
1.5x-4.5x20mm	70-2545	$134.95
4x32mm with BDC	70-3001	$104.95
4x32mm	70-2001	$ 99.95

From Bushnell Optical Company.

BUSHNELL "BANNER" VARIABLE POWER RIFLE SCOPES

Shown nearby is a complete lineup of Bushnell Banner Variable Power rifle scopes. These reasonably priced variables come with Bushnell's "MX" reticle; and they are also offered with the Bullet Drop Compensator feature as an option. The big 3X-9X is also offered with the new Prismatic Rangefinder that allows you to direct read the distance of the game you're shooting at. These scopes feature long eye relief for use on magnums as well as fully coated optics and fog-free service.
Prices: See below.

Description	Model no.	Suggested list price
4x-12x40mm	71-1423	$144.95
4x-12x40mm with BDC	71-3423	$149.95
3x-9x40mm	71-1398	$134.95
3x-9x40mm with BDC	71-3398	$139.95
3x-9x40mm with BDC and Prismatic Rangefinder	71-5398	$169.95
3x-9x38mm	71-2102	$149.95
3x-9x39mm with BDC	71-3102	$154.95
3x-9x32mm	71-1393	$122.95
3x-9x32mm with BDC	71-3393	$127.95
1.75x-4.5x21mm	71-2104	$127.95
1.75x-4.5x21mm with BDC	71-3104	$132.95
1.5x-4x21mm	71-1543	$112.95
1.5x-4x21mm with BDC	71-3543	$117.95

From Bushnell Optical Company.

BUSHNELL "BANNER" FIXED POWER RIFLE SCOPES

These Bushnell scopes are reasonably priced and feature fully-coated optics along with the optional Bullet Drop Compensator. All Bushnell scopes are nitrogen filled to provide fog-free service. Available powers: 2.5x, 4x, 6x and 10x.
Price: See below.

Description	Model no.	Suggested list price
10x40mm	71-1143	$124.95
10x40mm with BDC	71-3143	$129.95
6x32mm	71-1603	$ 94.95
6x32mm with BDC	71-3603	$ 99.95
4x40mm (Wide Angle)	71-2103	$114.95
4x40mm (Wide Angle) with BDC	71-3103	$119.95
4x32mm	71-1403	$ 84.95
4x32mm with BDC	71-3403	$ 89.95
2.5x20mm	71-1203	$ 74.95

From Bushnell Optical Company.

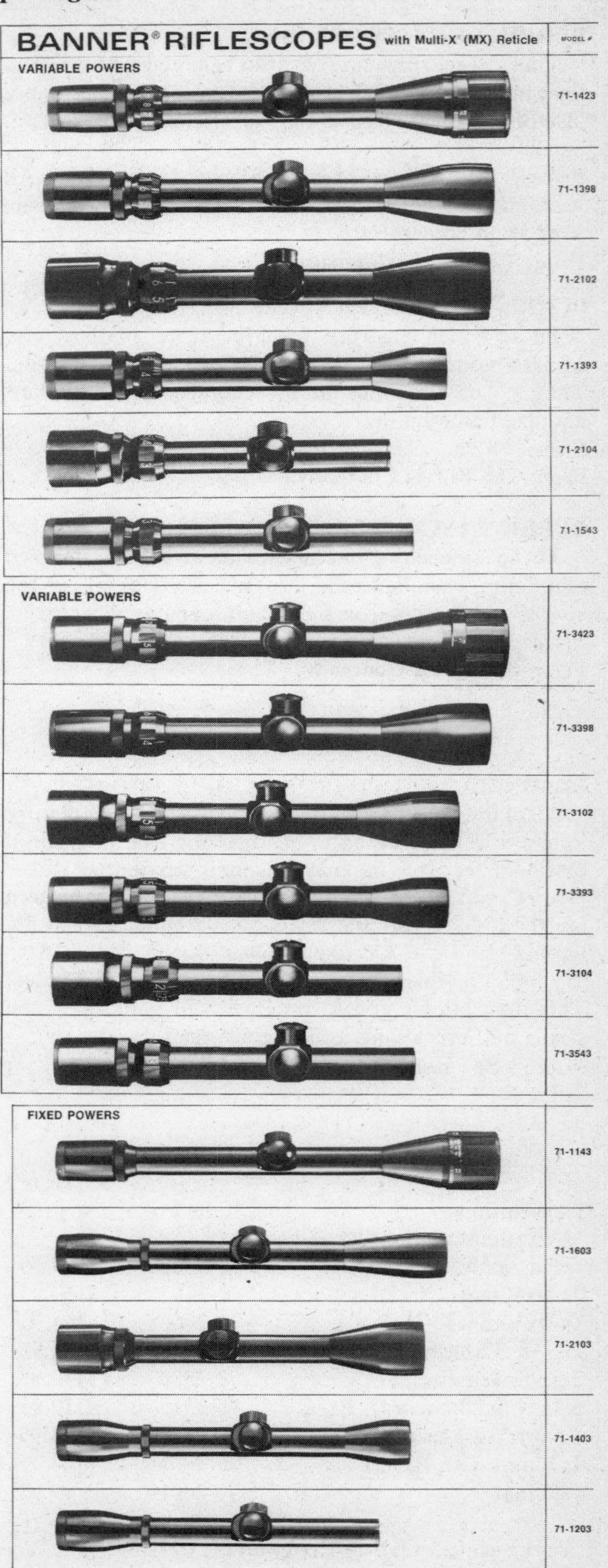

Prices shown are subject to change.

BUSHNELL "MAGNUM PHANTOM" 1.3X PISTOL SCOPE

This pistol scope is identical to the nearby Magnum Phantom 2.5X scope except for the power. It's fully adjustable and well suited for close to medium range pistol shooting.

Price: $63.50

From Bushnell Optical Company.

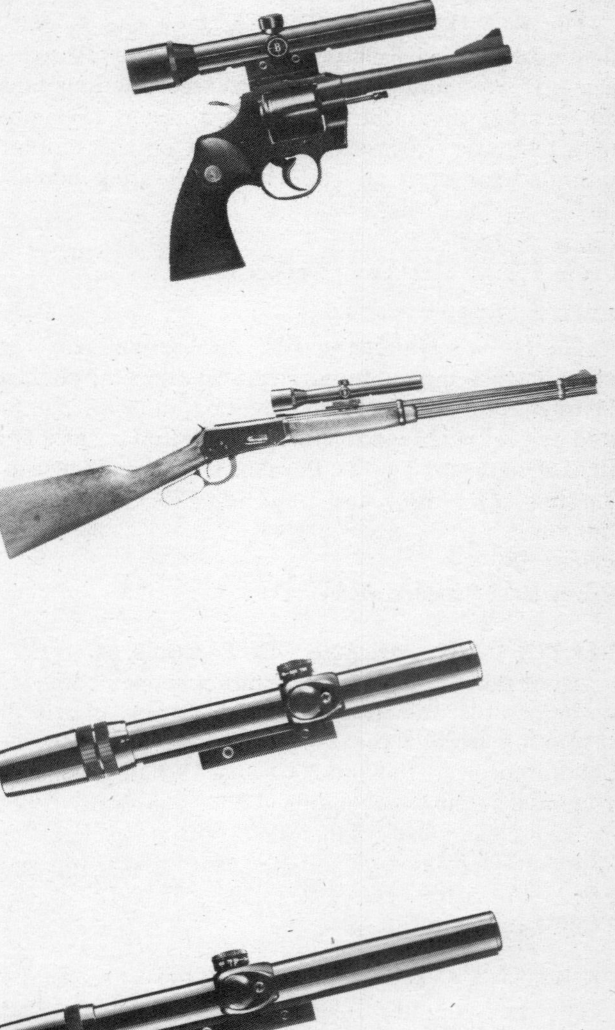

BUSHNELL "MAGNUM PHANTOM" 2.5X PISTOL/RIFLE SCOPE

This fully adjustable scope features ultra-long eye relief; and, while primarily designed for pistol use, it may be mounted on Winchester Model 94-type rifles as well. Comes complete with mount—easy to install. Well suited for close- to medium-range shooting.

Price: $67.50

From Bushnell Optical Company.

BUSHNELL 3X TO 7X VARIABLE RIMFIRE SCOPE

This well made rimfire scope features fully coated optics and comes with integral mount. May be mounted to any grooved receiver in seconds. Bullet Drop Compensator available as an option.

Price: $41.95; with BDC option $43.95.

From Bushnell Optical Company.

BUSHNELL 4X RIMFIRE RIFLE SCOPE

Available in variable or fixed-power models, these scopes come with integral mounts and are ready to be mounted on any grooved receiver. Bullet Drop Compensator available as an option. Features fully coated optics.

Price: $33.95; with BDC option $35.95.

From Bushnell Optical Company.

BUSHNELL "TRUSCOPE" BORE SIGHTER

This pocket sized bore sighter instantly collimates your favorite hunting target scope. An adjustable arbor (.243 to .308) comes with each unit. Other arbors are available as optional purchase items. Comes with complete instructions. Easy to use.

Price: With above arbor $24.95; spare arbor in .22 to 7mm (.284) $9.95; spare arbor in .308 to .45 $9.95.

From Bushnell Optical Company.

H & R 4X SCOPE

H&R's Model 432 rifle scope has fully coated optics and a permanently centered reticle. Features ¼-minute click adjustments for both windage and elevation. Field of view at 100 yards is 28 feet.

Price: See your local dealer.

From Harrington & Richardson.

H&R 4X RIMFIRE SCOPE

Comes complete with mount and rings—ready to install on most rimfire rifles. Eye relief 1¾ inches. Field of view at 100 yards: 20 feet. Fully adjustable ½-minute clicks. (Model 415.)

Price: See your local dealer.

From Harrington & Richardson.

See the Directory for complete company addresses.

OPTICAL SIGHTING DEVICE

The R.A.D. sight is 9 inches long and 1 inch in diameter—it's easily mounted on all manually sighted arms. It's fog and water resistant and functions under all weather conditions. Utilizes ambient (available) light or battery to present a red dot on the shooter's intended target. Fully adjustable—1 click equals 3 inches at 100 yards.
Price: $84.95
From F.T.L. Marketing Corporation.

PISTOL SCOPE

The Hutson Handgunner II pistol scope measures a compact 5½ inches long. Features internal click adjustments for windage and elevation along with unlimited eye relief. Magnification is 1.7X and it has a good field of view at 100 yards. Parallax is adjusted for zero at 75 feet (25 yards) and beyond. Fits standard rail mounts.
Price: $89
From JPM Sales (Hutson).

LEUPOLD 16X, 20X AND 24X TARGET SCOPES

All of these superbly made target scopes come with an adjustable objective lens. The power, clarity and resolution are such that you will be able to clearly see a bullet imprint at 100 and 200 yards. When purchasing, you have an option of standard crosshair or dot reticle. A 2½-inch sunshade is included. Nitrogen filled. Fully adjustable for windage and elevation. Precision made.
Price: 16X, 20X or 24X $263.50.
From Leupold & Stevens, Inc.

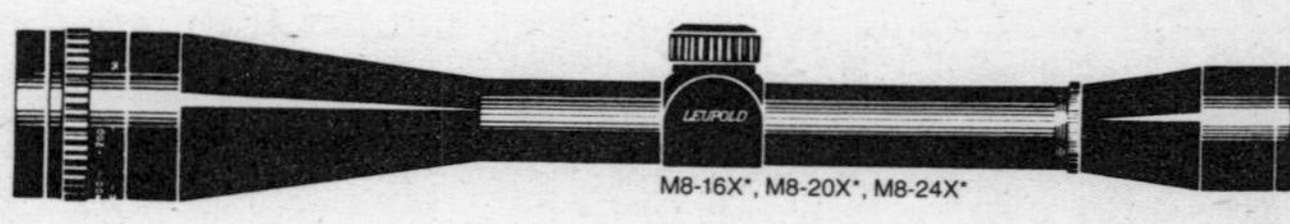

LEUPOLD VARI-X III VARIABLE POWER SCOPES

This is Leupold's newest series of scopes. Three models of the Vari-X III series are available: 1.5x5; 2.5x8 and 3.5x10 (with adjustable objective lens). All three models are precision made and cover the range of hunting needs—from brush country bucks to long range varmints. All are fog-free and come with fully adjustable elevation and windage turrets. Available with Duplex, CPC or Dot reticle.
Price: 1.5x5 $191.50; 2.5x8 $216.50; 3.5x10 $225.50, 3.5x10 with adjustable objective lens $248.50.
From Leupold & Stevens, Inc.

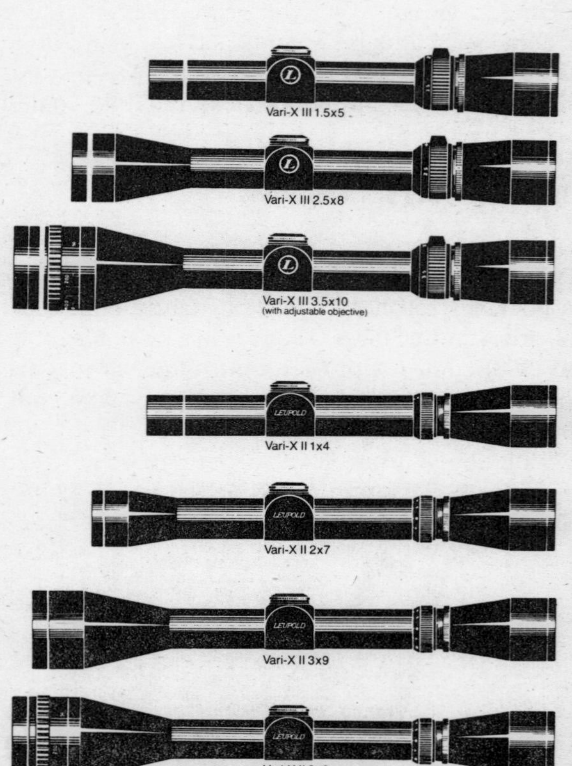

LEUPOLD VARI-X II VARIABLE POWER SCOPES

These Leupold variables come in the following models: 1x4; 2x7; 3x9 and 3x9 with adjustable objective lens. All are precision made and provide the shooter with a fog-free view of his game. Fully adjustable eye pieces. Fully adjustable for windage and elevation. Available with Duplex, CPC or Dot reticle.
Price: 1x4 $160.50; 2x7 $176.50; 3x9 $189.50; 3x9 with adjustable objective lens $212.50.
From Leupold & Stevens, Inc.

Prices shown are subject to change.

LEUPOLD 12X RIFLE SCOPE

The superb optical qualities of this scope make it suitable for serious target shooting and long range varminting. Comes with adjustable objective lens that can be focused from 50 yards to infinity. Nitrogen filled tube. Fully adjustable for windage and elevation.
Price: $190.50
From Leupold & Stevens, Inc.

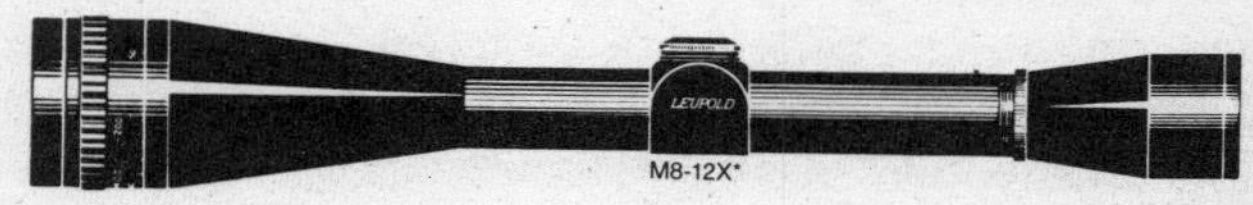

LEUPOLD 10X RIFLE SCOPES

This particular Leupold comes in two models. The standard model features a fully adjustable objective lens for any range beyond 50 yards. The "Silhouette Model" has the same features plus target-style windage and elevation adjustments. Comes nitrogen filled and has fully coated optics.
Price: Standard $186.50; Silhouette Model $217.50.
From Leupold & Stevens, Inc.

LEUPOLD 8X RIFLE SCOPE

This Leupold scope has plenty of power for most varmint hunting; and, even some varieties of long range big game and target shooting. Comes with fully coated optics and is adjustable for windage and elevation. Tube is nitrogen filled to eliminate fogging.
Price: $186.50
From Leupold & Stevens, Inc.

LEUPOLD 6X RIFLE SCOPE

The 6X Leupold is a good scope for moderate to long range big game and varmint hunting. It's precision made, comes with fully coated optics and is nitrogen filled for fog-free viewing. Fully adjustable for windage and elevation.
Price: $139.50
From Leupold & Stevens, Inc.

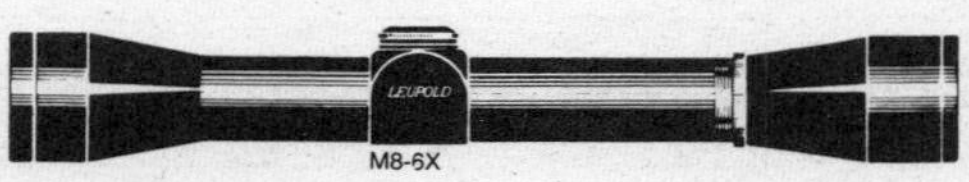

LEUPOLD 4X RIFLE SCOPE

The 4X Leupold is a highly popular scope—it's a good choice for general hunting. The scope is fully adjustable for windage and elevation. It's also nitrogen filled for fog-free service.
Price: $130.50
From Leupold & Stevens, Inc.

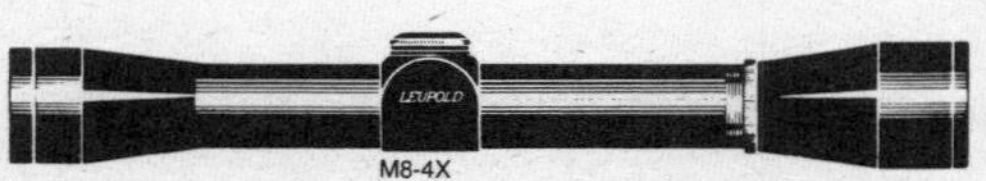

LEUPOLD 3X RIFLE SCOPE

This Leupold scope is a good choice for the larger calibers, moderate distances and light to heavy cover. Fully adjustable for windage and elevation; precision made; fog-free.
Price: $122.50
From Leupold & Stevens, Inc.

See the Directory for complete company addresses.

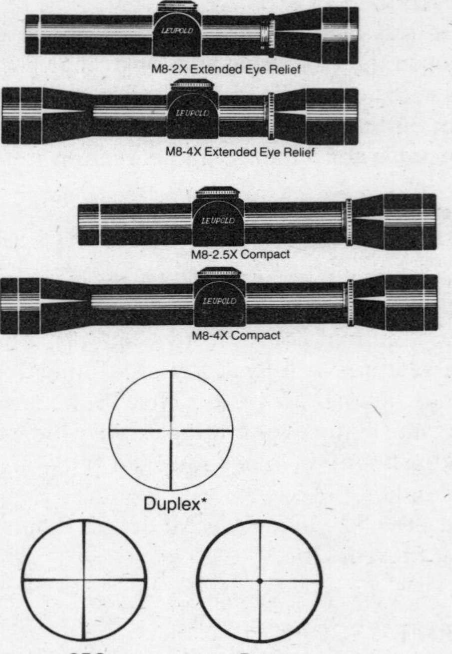

LEUPOLD EXTENDED EYE RELIEF SCOPES

Available in 2X or 4X, these scopes are perfect for mounting on handguns or rifles where necessary. These scopes are precision made, fully adjustable for windage and elevation and are highly compact.
Price: 2X $108.50; 4X $122.50.
From Leupold & Stevens, Inc.

LEUPOLD 2.5X and 4X "COMPACT" SCOPES

These scopes feature a lightweight, compact design that's important to the big game hunter who totes a lot of heavy gear. They are precision made, fog free and rugged. A *very popular* scope.
Price: 2.5X $108.50; 4X $122.50.
From Leupold & Stevens, Inc.

LEUPOLD RETICLES AND SCOPE SPECS

Shown nearby is Leupold's spec chart for scopes along with a guide as to what reticles are available with what scope. Consult this chart to determine what scope and reticle combo is available.
Price: Dot reticle is $17 additional, others standard.
From Leupold & Stevens, Inc.

Leupold Scope Specifications

Scope		M8														Vari-X II						Vari-X III					
		2X[2]	4X[2]	2.5X[3]	4X[3]	3X	4X	6X	8X[4]	10X[4]/10X[5]		12X[4]	16X[4]	20X[4]	24X[4]	1x4		2x7		3x9/3x9[4]		1.5x5		2.5x8		3.5x10/3.5x10[4]	
																1X	4X	2X	7X	3X	9X	1.5X	5X	2.5X	8X	3.5X	10X
Actual Magnification		1.8	3.5	2.3	3.6	2.7	4.1	5.9	7.8	10.1		12.2	16.3	19.6	23.6	1.6	4.2	2.5	6.6	3.5	9.0	1.5	4.6	2.7	7.9	3.4	9.9
Field	Feet[1]	22.0	9.5	42.0	26.5	43.0	30.0	18.0	14.5	10.3		9.0	6.6	5.4	4.5	70.5	28.5	42.0	18.0	30.5	13.0	64.0	23.0	36.0	12.7	29.5	10.5
	Meter[1]	7.3	3.2	14.0	8.83	14.3	10.0	6.0	4.8	3.3		3.0	2.2	1.8	1.5	24.3	9.5	14.0	6.0	10.2	4.3	21.3	7.7	12.0	4.2	9.8	3.5
Optimum Eye Relief	inch	10-24		4.3	4.1	3.9	3.9	3.9	3.6	3.5		3.5	3.5	3.5	3.5	4.3	3.4	4.1	3.7	4.1	3.5	4.7	3.5	4.2	3.4	3.9	3.4
	mm	254-610		109	104	99	99	99	91	89		89	89	89	89	109	86	104	94	104	89	119	89	107	86	99	86
Length	inch	8.1	8.4	8.5	10.3	10.3	11.9	11.7	12.9	12.9		14.3	15.2	15.2	15.2	9.5		10.9		12.6		9.7		11.6		12.8	
	mm	206	213	216	262	262	302	297	328	328		363	386	386	386	241		277		320		246		295		325	
Weight	oz.	6.8	7.6	7.4	8.5	8.7	9.3	10.4	13.5	14.0	15.0	14.4	16.0	16.0	16.0	9.5		10.9		13.6	15.0	9.8		11.5		13.5	14.9
	gram	193	215	210	241	247	264	295	383	397	425	408	454	454	454	269		309		386	425	278		326		383	422
Adj. Scale Div. Equal	mins. angle	1	1	1	1	1	1	1	1	½	1[6]	½	1[7]	1[7]	1[7]	1		½		½		1		1		½	
Max. Adj. Elev. & Wind	inch[1]	100	75	100	100	100	80	70	68	60		60	60	60	60	50		36		26		80		60		44	
	cm[1]	278	208	278	278	278	222	194	189	167		167	167	167	167	139		100		72		222		167		122	
Available with these reticles.																											
Duplex		✓	✓	✓	✓	✓	✓	✓	✓	✓		✓	—	—	—	✓		✓		✓		✓		✓		✓	
CPC		—	—	—	—	✓	✓	✓	✓	✓		✓	—	—	—	✓		✓		✓		✓		✓		✓	
Crosshair		—	—	—	—	—	—	—	—	—		—	✓	✓	✓	—		—		—		—		—		—	
Dot		—	—	—	—	✓	✓	✓	✓	✓		✓	8	9	10	✓		✓		✓		✓		✓		✓	

(1) @ 100 Yards/Meters
(2) Extended-eye-relief model
(3) Compact model
(4) With adjustable objective
(5) Silhouette model, with adjustable objective
(6) Silhouette model has 1-Min. divisions, with 1/2-Min. "clicks"
(7) Target models have 1-Min. divisions, with 1/4-Min. "clicks"
(8) 3/16-Min.-0.19" (5.3mm); 3/8-Min.-0.38" (10.6mm)
(9) 5/32-Min.-0.16" (4.4mm); 5/16-Min.-0.31" (8.6mm)
(10) 1/8-Min.-0.13" (3.6mm); 1/4-Min.-0.25" (6.9mm)

SUNSHADE FOR LEUPOLD SCOPES

This 2½-inch long sunshade also acts as support for an improved "mirage tube." For scopes with adjustable objective lenses only. You can install it yourself—it just screws in.
Price: $8
From Leupold & Stevens, Inc.

50-FOOT FOCUS ADAPTER FOR LEUPOLD SCOPES

This adapter is for those Leupold scopes that come with an adjustable objective lens. Allows sharp focusing for 50-foot gallery target shooting. Easy to install—you just screw it in.
Price: $33.50
From Leupold & Stevens, Inc.

Prices shown are subject to change.

LEUPOLD BASES

Leupold STD bases are available for a good selection of sporting firearms. Shown nearby is a chart showing what's available.
Price: $14.50 per base.
From Leupold & Stevens, Inc.

Leupold "STD" Mount Bases fit these popular models:

Model	Firearm Model
STD BA	Browning Automatic Rifle, all calibers
STD BLA	Browning Lever Action
STD FN	FN Mauser and other rifles using this basic long action
STD HC	Husqvarna Crown Grade, J.C. Higgins (after 1955), Smith & Wesson and HVA-Carl Gustaf
STD 336R	Marlin 36 and 336 Models and Western Field M/740
STD M	Mauser 95 and 98*
STD 700RH-LA	Remington 700, 721, 725 (long actions); Ruger M/77 (round receiver); and Weatherby Mark V
STD 700LH-LA	Remington 700 (left hand, long action)
STD 700RH-SA	Remington 700, 722, 725 and 40X (short actions)
STD 700SA-Spec	Long base for Remington Short Action 700
STD 760	Remington 740, 742, 760
STD 788	Remington 788 (long and extra long actions)
STD RBH	Ruger Black Hawk and other Ruger revolvers having adjustable rear sight*
STD R77	Ruger Model 77 (short or long action) w/Dovetail receiver*
STD R1022	Ruger 1022 Rimfire
STD 99R	Savage 99 Lever Action
STD 110RL	Savage 110, 110C, 111 (long action)
STD S&W-K	Smith & Wesson K & N-frame Revolver*
STD S	Springfield 1903*
STD S-Spec	Springfield 1903A3*
STD T/C-C	Thompson/Center Contender
STD T/C-H	Thompson/Center Hawken Rifle
STD 70A	All Winchester Model 70s above #66,350, not including .300 H&H and .375 H&H Magnums
STD W94	Winchester Model 94 Carbine*

*Drilling and tapping required.

LEUPOLD RINGS FOR 1-INCH SCOPES

Leupold's 1-inch rings come in three heights, low, medium and high, as can be seen nearby. They are designed to fit any Leupold STD base.
Price: $21.50, any size.
From Leupold & Stevens, Inc.

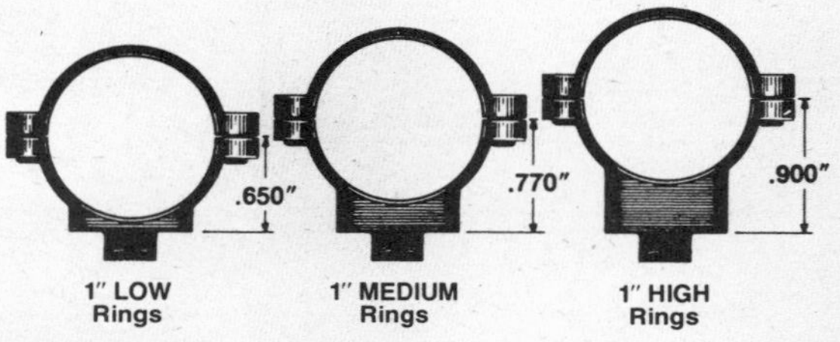

LYMAN 20X AND 25X "L.W.B.R." SCOPES

These ultra high power scopes are designed for the serious rifleman or varmint hunter. Each scope is hand assembled and repeatedly inspected prior to shipping. Both scopes feature ⅛-minute of angle click adjustment. Field of view for the 20X is 5½ feet at 100 yards; 4 feet, 8 inches for the 25X. A good selection of reticles is available for these scopes.
Price: 20X $259.95; 25X $289.95.
From Lyman Products Corporation.

Standard reticles available:

	#7 Standard Fine Crosswire	#8 Extra Fine Crosswire	1 Minute Dot	½ Minute Dot	¼ Minute Dot	⅛ Minute Dot
	(.0007) Center Covers	(.0005) Center Covers	Dot Covers	Dot Covers	Dot Covers	Dot Covers
20X	.175 inch at 100 yds.	.125 inch at 100 yds.	1 inch at 100 yds.	½ inch at 100 yds.	¼ inch at 100 yds.	⅛ inch at 100 yds.
Item No.	42400400	42400450	42400460	42400470	42400480	42400490
25X	.125 inch at 100 yds.	.062 inch at 100 yds.	1 inch at 100 yds.	½ inch at 100 yds.	¼ inch at 100 yds.	⅛ inch at 100 yds.
Item No.	42400500	42400550	42400560	42400570	42400580	42400590

RETICLES FOR LYMAN "L.W.B.R." SCOPES

Shown nearby is a chart showing the standard reticles for Lyman "L.W.B.R." You may select one of these reticles when ordering a "L.W.B.R." scope.
From Lyman Products Corporation.

LYMAN 10X SILHOUETTE SCOPE

This is Lyman's highest power silhouette scope. It features ⅓-minute of angle click adjustment and provides the shooter with a 12-foot field of view at 100 yards. A wide selection of reticles is available for this scope.
Price: $189.95
From Lyman Products Corporation.

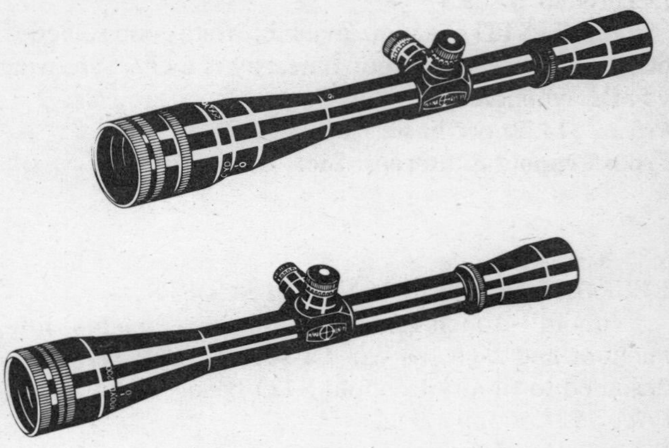

LYMAN 8X SILHOUETTE SCOPE

This scope is identical to the 6X Silhouette scope with the exception it offers the shooter a bit more power. The field of view at 100 yards is 14 feet. This scope features ⅓-minute of angle click adjustments. Designed for the silhouette shooter; also a good bet for the varmint hunter.

Price: $179.95

From Lyman Products Corporation.

LYMAN 6X SILHOUETTE SCOPE

This Lyman scope is designed for silhouette competition; however, it's not a bad choice for varmints either. Comes with ½-minute of angle click adjustment and provides the shooter with a 20-foot field of view at 100 yards. A wide selection of reticles is available.

Price: $169.95

From Lyman Products Corporation.

RETICLES FOR LYMAN SILHOUETTE SCOPES

The nearby chart shows 9 separate reticles that are available as standard when a Lyman Silhouette scope is purchased.

From Lyman Products Corporation.

Standard reticles available:

	#7 Standard Crosswire	#4 Center Range	#3 Center Range	#5 Tapered Post and Crosswire	#6 Tapered Post	2 Minute Dot	1 Minute Dot	½ Minute Dot	¼ Minute Dot
	Center Covers	Center Wire Covers	Post top Covers	Post top Covers	Post top Covers	Dot Covers	Dot Covers	Dot Covers	Dot Covers
6X-SL	1.1" at 200 m.	1.8" at 200 m.	3.27" at 200 m.	3.27" at 200 m.	3.27" at 200 m.	4.37" at 200 m.	2.2" at 200 m.	1.1" at 200 m.	NA
8X-SL	.65" at 200 m.	.54" at 200 m.	1.6" at 200 m.	2.7" at 200 m.	2.7" at 200 m.	4.37" at 200 m.	2.2" at 200 m.	1.1" at 200 m.	NA
10X-SL	.54" at 200 m.	.54" at 200 m.	1.6" at 200 m.	2.2" at 200 m.	2.2" at 200 m.	4.37" at 200 m.	2.2" at 200 m.	1.1" at 200 m.	.55" at 200 m.
Item No. 6X-SL	42400100	42400110	42400120	42400130	42400140	42400150	42400160	42400170	NA
8X-SL	42400200	42400210	42400220	42400230	42400240	42400250	42400260	42400270	NA
10X-SL	42400300	42400310	42400320	42400330	42400340	42400350	42400360	42400370	42400380

LYMAN 3X TO 9X VARIABLE SCOPE

This Lyman scope is a good choice for varmint shooting or long range big game hunting. It features ½-minute of angle click adjustments. Field of view runs from 39 feet to 13 feet, at 100 yards, depending upon the power selected. Lyman's No. 7 crosshair or No. 4 "Center-Range" reticles are standard.

Price: $149.95

From Lyman Products Corporation.

LYMAN 1.75X TO 5X VARIABLE SCOPE

Well suited for general hunting purposes, this Lyman 1-inch tubed scope features ½-minute of angle click adjustments. Field of view at 100 yards ranges from 48 feet to 18 feet depending upon the power selected. Lyman's No. 7 crosshair or No. 4 "Center-Range" reticles are standard.

Price: $129.95

From Lyman Products Corporation.

LYMAN 2X TO 7X VARIABLE SCOPE

This 1-inch tubed scope is well suited for long range big game hunting or varmint shooting. It features ½-minute of angle click adjustments. Field of view runs from 49 feet to 19 feet at 100 yards depending upon the power selected. Lyman's No. 7 crosshair or No. 4 "Center-Range" reticles are standard.

Price: $139.95

From Lyman Products Corporation.

LYMAN 8X AND 10X SCOPES

These Lyman scopes are well suited for the bench or varmints. Tube diameter is 1 inch and the field of view is 14 feet (for the 8X) and 12 feet (for the 10X) at 100 yards. Both scopes feature ⅓-minute of angle click adjustments. A wide choice of reticles is available.

Price: 8X $169.95; 10X $179.95.

From Lyman Products Corporation.

Prices shown are subject to change.

LYMAN 6X SCOPE

This 1-inch tubed scope is a good intermediate bet for the eastern chuck hunter or the western coyote shooter. It features ½-minute of angle click adjustments and provides the shooter with a 24-foot field of view at 100 yards. Lyman's No. 7 crosshair or No. 4 "Center-Range" reticles are standard.
Price: $129.95
From Lyman Products Corporation.

LYMAN 4X SCOPE

This 1-inch tubed Lyman scope is a good all-around choice for the hunter. The field of view at 100 yards is a generous 36 feet. Features ½-minute of angle adjustment clicks. Lyman's No. 7 crosshair or No. 4 "Center-Range" reticles are standard.
Price: $124.95
From Lyman Products Corporation.

LYMAN 2½X SCOPE

This 1-inch tubed Lyman scope is perfect for brush-country hunting. Features minute of angle click adjustments, and a 43-foot field of view at 100 yards. No. 7 Crosshair or Lyman's No. 4 "Center-Range" reticles are standard.
Price: $99.95
From Lyman Products Corporation.

OPTICAL HANDGUN SIGHT

The Precision Reflex Pistol sight is a unique optical pistol sight. There's no magnification involved. As ambient light enters the front of the sight it activates a colored crosshair which is then placed over the intended target. It's fully adjustable and, again, the unit works on available light, not batteries. It's parallax free at a distance of 50 yards. Bases are available for S&W K or N Frames; Ruger revolvers with adjustable sights; Colt and Dan Wesson revolvers with adjustable sights. Specify base when purchasing.
Price: $73; base $7.50 each.
From Precision Reflex, Inc.

REDFIELD 12X SILHOUETTE SCOPE

This precision scope features micrometer adjustment for windage and elevation. It also features an adjustable objective lens, and is fog-proofed. It's designed to take the heavy use a competitor will give it. Comes with Plex reticle.
Price: $221.35
From Redfield.

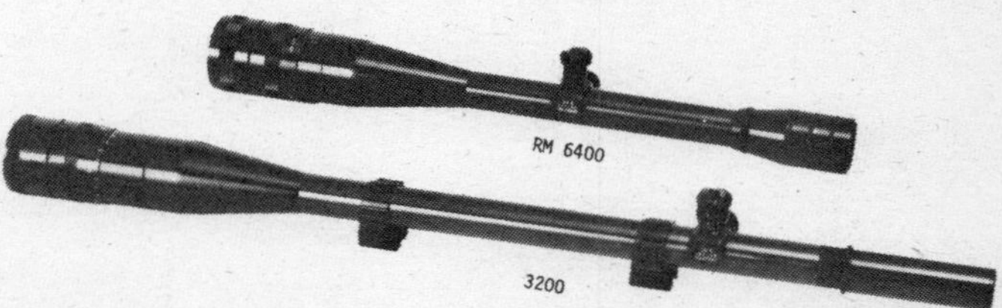

REDFIELD RM 6400 AND 3200 TARGET SCOPES

These scopes are made for the serious rifleman and target shooter. The 3200 comes in 16X, 20X and 24X. The RM 6400 is available in the same powers, only the buyer gets his choice of ⅛- or ¼-minute click adjustments. Both models are offered with Redfield's Fine Crosshair reticle.
Price: 3200 in 16X, 20X or 24X $296.50; RM 6400 in 16X, 20X or 24X (⅛- or ¼-minute click adjustments) $265.20, $274.15 and $283.10 respectively.
From Redfield.

See the Directory for complete company addresses.

REDFIELD METALLIC SILHOUETTE SCOPES IN 6X, 3X-9X, 8X AND 10X

These Redfield silhouette scopes are designed for competition shooting or varmint hunting. They all feature superior optics and round eye piece design. (Only the 3X-9X variable is offered with a Wide Field ocular lens.) All feature precise windage and elevation adjustments and all are fog proof. The 8X and 10X scopes also come with an adjustable objective lens to eliminate parallax.

Price: 6X (see your dealer); 3X-9X (see your dealer); 8X $191; 10X $205.30.

From Redfield.

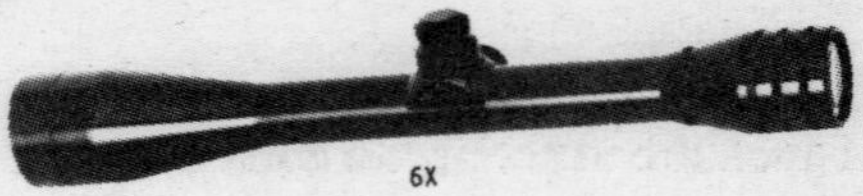

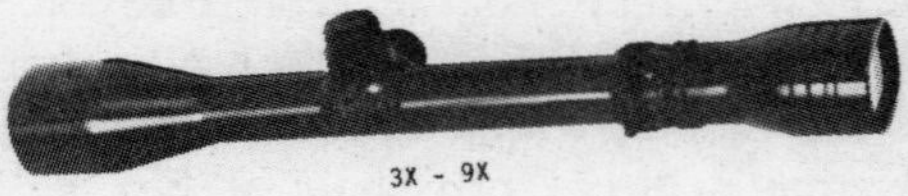

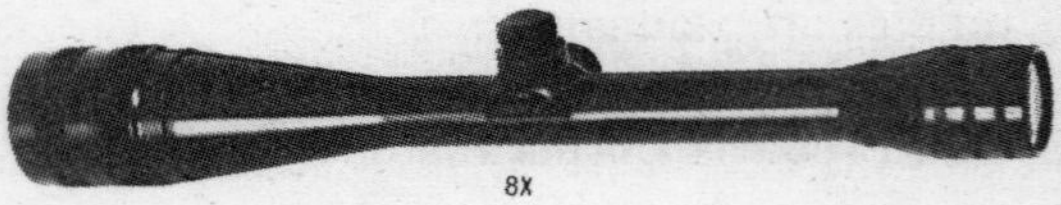

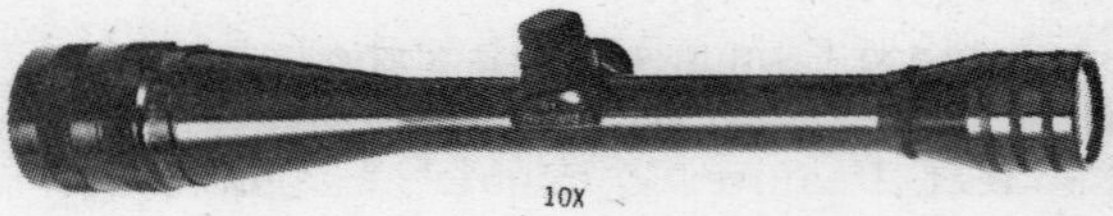

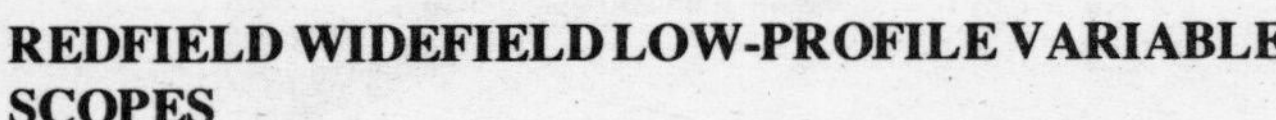

6X

3X - 9X

8X

10X

REDFIELD WIDEFIELD LOW-PROFILE VARIABLE SCOPES

These scopes are designed for low mounting and feature excellent fields of view. Within their power ranges they pretty well fill the shooting needs of any sportsman. All feature full adjustment of windage and elevation. Fog proofed. All are offered with either Plex or Post and Crosshair reticle.

Price: 1¾X-5X$160.65; 2X-7X $178.50; 3X-9X $214.35.

From Redfield

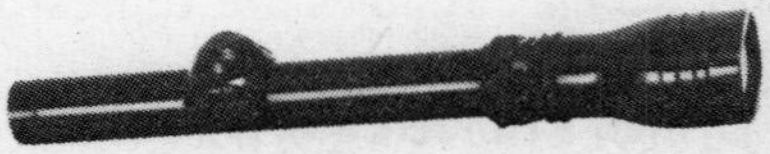

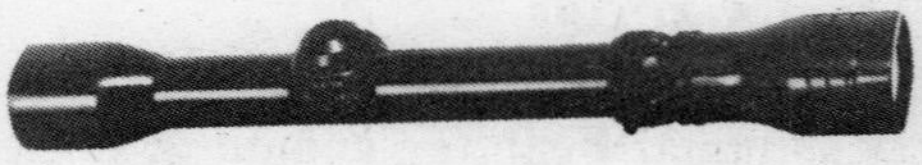

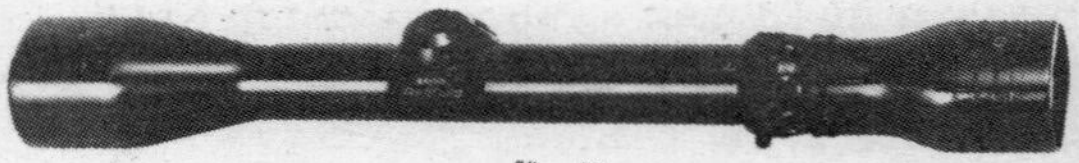

1-3/4X - 5X

2X - 7X

3X - 9X

REDFIELD WIDEFIELD LOW-PROFILE FIXED POWER SCOPES

Designed for low-mounting, these scopes come in 2¾X, 4X and 6X powers. All feature precision optics and fog-free service. They are fully adjustable for windage and elevation. The 2¾X is a good brush scope while the 4X and 6X are well suited for general and longer-ranged shooting and hunting. Post and Crosshair or Plex reticle available.

Price: 2¾X $124.95; 4X $142.80; 6X (Plex reticle only) $157.10.

From Redfield.

2-3/4X

4X

6X

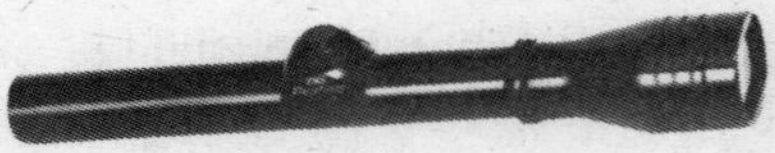

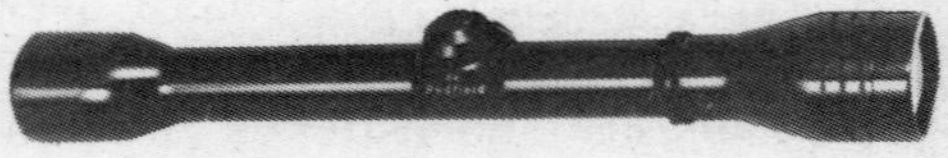

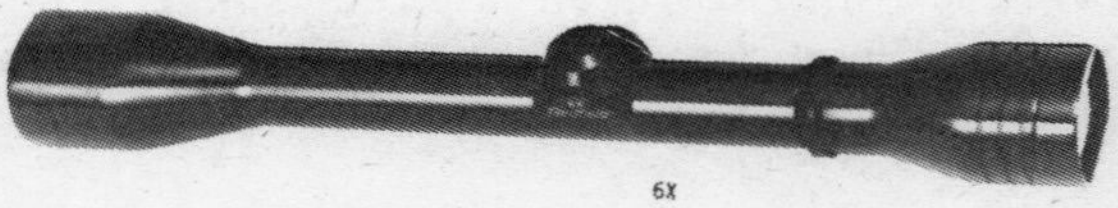

REDFIELD TRADITIONAL ROUND EYE PIECE VARIABLE POWER SCOPES

These scopes are available in 2X-7X, 3X-9X, 4X-12X and 6X-18X. All are fully adjustable for windage and elevation while the 4X-12X and 6X-18X models also come with an adjustable objective lens. All are precision made and are fog-free. Plex reticle is standard on all while the crosshair reticle also is available for the 4X-12X and 6X-18X models.

Price: 2X-7X $147.35; 3X-9X $177.70; 4X-12X $249.95; 6X-18X $276.75.

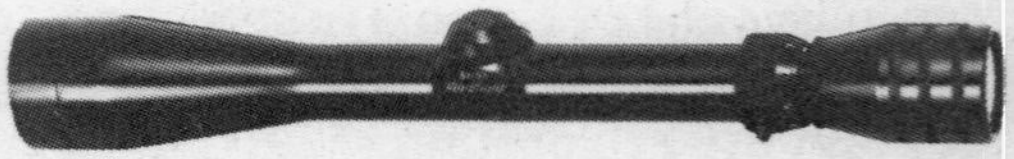

From Redfield.

2X - 7X

3X - 9X

4X - 12X

6X - 18X

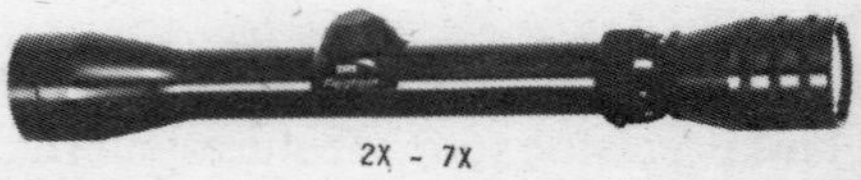

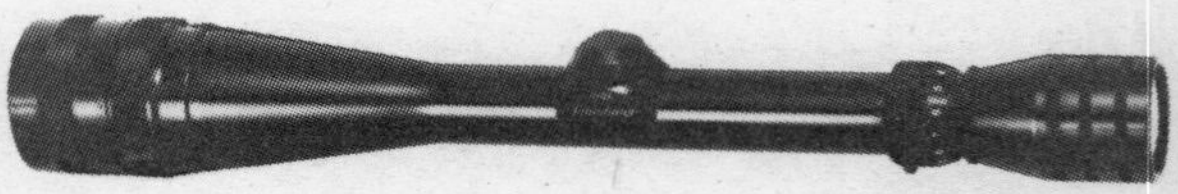

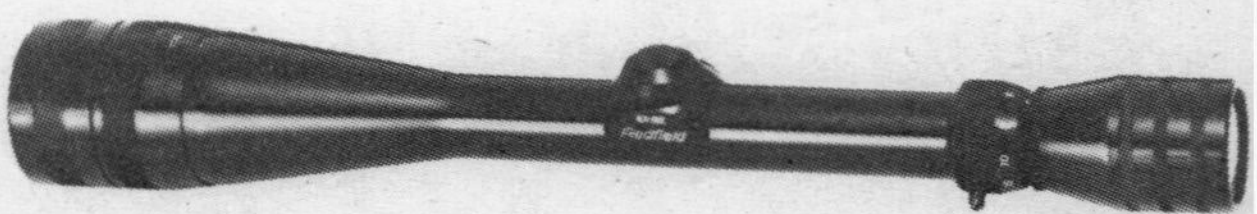

Prices shown are subject to change.

REDFIELD TRADITIONAL ROUND EYE PIECE SCOPES

These Redfields are available in 2½X, 4X, 6X, 8X and 10X powers. They all feature full adjustment for windage and elevation, while the 8X and 10X models come with an adjustable objective lens as well. All feature superb optics and are fog free. Post and Crosshair and Plex reticles are standard for most of these scopes.

Price: 2½X 93.75; 4X $109.40; 6X $124.95; 8X and 10X (see your local dealer.)

From Redfield.

REDFIELD "MP" PISTOL SCOPES

These new Redfields come in either 2½X or 1½X and feature long eye relief. Bases are available for most popular handguns. Scope is fully fog proofed and adjustable for both windage and elevation. Field of view at 100 yards is 9 feet for the 2½X, 14½ feet for the 1½X.

Price: 1½X $108.95; $114.30; Bases $40—specify gun.

From Redfield.

REDFIELD SCOPE COLLIMATOR

This handy, precision-made unit enables the user to optically bore sight his favorite scoped rifle. Spuds are sold separately in all popular calibers ranging from .17 to .45.

Price: $49.85; Spuds $8.40 each; Collimator and all available (14) spuds $156.20.

From Redfield.

JR Bases

REDFIELD JR 1-PIECE SCOPE BASES

These blued-steel bases are made for just about any popular rifle. They accept JR Low, Medium, or High rings. Specify rifle when purchasing.

Price: $14.50 per base.

From Redfield.

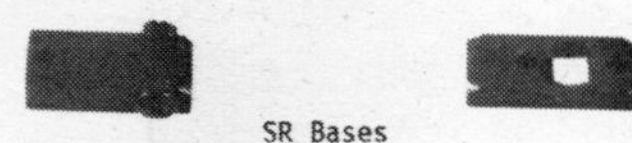

SR Bases

REDFIELD 2-PIECE SR BASES

These blued bases are available for a wide selection of sporting rifles.

Price: Ranges from $14.50 to $25.50 depending on the gun you wish to mount these bases on.

From Redfield.

REDFIELD 2-PIECE SR BASES FOR COLT SAUER RIFLES

These 2-piece bases are specifically made for the Colt Sauer rifles.

Price: $25.50

From Redfield.

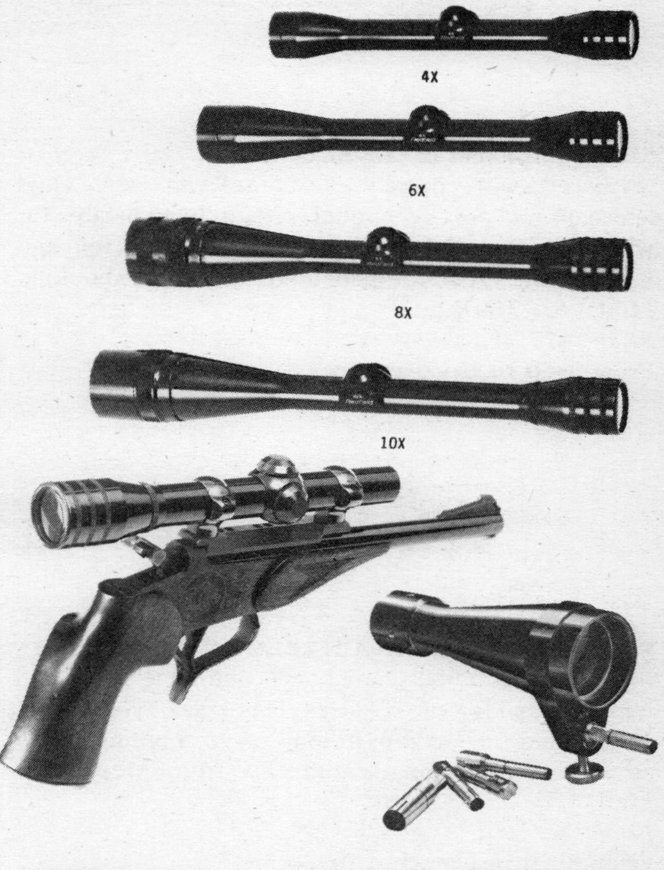

2½X

4X

6X

8X

10X

REDFIELD ¾-INCH RING MOUNT FOR .22 RIFLES

These blued-steel mounts quickly attach to any grooved rimfire receiver—easy on, easy off.

Price: $13.20 per pair.

From Redfield.

REDFIELD MODEL 94 SIDE MOUNT

This rugged mount is made specifically for the 94 Winchester. No drilling or tapping.

Price: $23.80

From Redfield.

REDFIELD 1-INCH RING MOUNT FOR .22 RIFLES

These mounts allow you to use a regular 1-inch rifle scope on a standard grooved rimfire receiver—easy on, easy off.

Price: $15.80 per pair.

From Redfield.

REDFIELD JR 1-INCH SPLIT RINGS

These rings are available with either top or bottom access ring screws in High, Low or Medium configuration. Come in plain or engraved styles—engraved available only in Low or Medium styles.

Price: Ranges from $21.50 to $40.70 depending upon style purchased.

From Redfield.

SWIFT 6X 40mm RIFLE SCOPE

Like all Swift scopes, the 6X comes with a set of vinyl lens caps and plex-type reticle. It's fully adjustable for windage and elevation. The 40 mm 6X is both fog- and water-proof. Good for medium to long range shooting. Model 657 Mark I.
Price: $72.50
From Swift Instruments, Inc.

SWIFT 3X-9X, 32mm VARIABLE RIFLE SCOPE

This 1-inch tubed scope comes complete with vinyl lens caps and fog-proof lenses. Has a plex-type reticle. Well suited for medium to long range shooting. Fully adjustable for windage and elevation. Model 654 Mark 1.
Price: $81.25
From Swift Instruments, Inc.

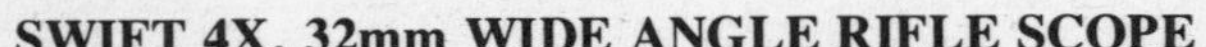

SWIFT 4X, 32mm WIDE ANGLE RIFLE SCOPE

This scope comes fully fog- and water-proofed and offers the shooter a field of view of 37.3 feet at 100 yards. Features a plex-type reticle and is fully adjustable for both windage and elevation. Model 651 Mark I.
Price: $70
From Swift Instruments, Inc.

SWIFT 3X-9X 40mm WIDE ANGLE VARIABLE POWER RIFLE SCOPE

This scope is a good bet for all around hunting use—it handles brush and distance with equal ease. This is a wide-angle scope that provides the shooter with a 42½- to 13½-foot field of view at 100 yards, depending upon the power selected. Fully fog proofed and adjustable for windage and elevation, it's also water-proof. Model 656 Mark I.
Price: $94
From Swift Instruments, Inc.

SWIFT 4X, 40mm WIDE-ANGLE RIFLE SCOPE

This Swift scope comes with vinyl lens caps and is fully fog- and water-proof. It's suited for medium to close range shooting. Field of view at 100 yards is 35.4 feet. Comes with a plex-type reticle and is fully adjustable for both windage and elevation. Model 653 Mark I.
Price: $80
From Swift Instruments, Inc.

SWIFT 1.5X-5X, 32mm VARIABLE RIFLE SCOPE

This 1-inch tubed scope is designed for both brush and medium range shooting. Comes with a plex-type reticle and is fog-proofed. Fully adjustable for both windage and elevation. Also comes with vinyl lens caps. Model 658 Mark I.
Price: $87.50
From Swift Instruments, Inc.

SWIFT 4X, 15mm RIMFIRE SCOPE

This Swift scope is made especially for .22s. Comes complete with mount that's designed to be quickly attached to any grooved receiver.
Price: $20
From Swift Instruments, Inc.

Prices shown are subject to change.

TASCO 4X-12X 40mm VARIABLE POWER SILHOUETTE SCOPE

Tasco's new Model 619S features fully coated optics and haze filler caps. It was specifically designed for the silhouette competitor. It's fog and shock proof and is fully adjustable for windage and elevation. Has an adjustable objective lens.
Price: $159.95
From Tasco Sales, Inc.

TASCO 3X TO 9X VARIABLE POWER SCOPE

Tasco's Model 624V variable power scope features a 43½-foot to 16½-foot field of view at 100 yards, depending upon the power used. It's fully waterproof, shockproof and fog proof. Features fully adjustable windage and elevation knobs. Comes with haze filter caps.
Price: $129.95
From Tasco Sales, Inc.

TASCO 10X 40mm SILHOUETTE SCOPE

This scope features an adjustable objective lens, fully coated optics and haze filter caps. It also sports precise windage and elevation adjustments. It's fog and shock proof. Especially made for the silhouette shooter. Model 703S.
Price: $149.95
From Tasco Sales, Inc.

TASCO 4X SCOPE

Features a fully coated 11-lens optical system and ¼-minute click adjustments for windage and elevation. Also features a rubber eye piece and haze filter caps. Model 648B.
Price: $109.95
From Tasco Sales, Inc.

TASCO 4X 32mm SCOPE

This wide-view type scope has a field of view of 36 feet at 100 yards. It comes with a set of haze filter caps and features ¼-minute click stop adjustments. Has an 11-lens optical system. Model 662V.
Price: $99.95
From Tasco Sales, Inc.

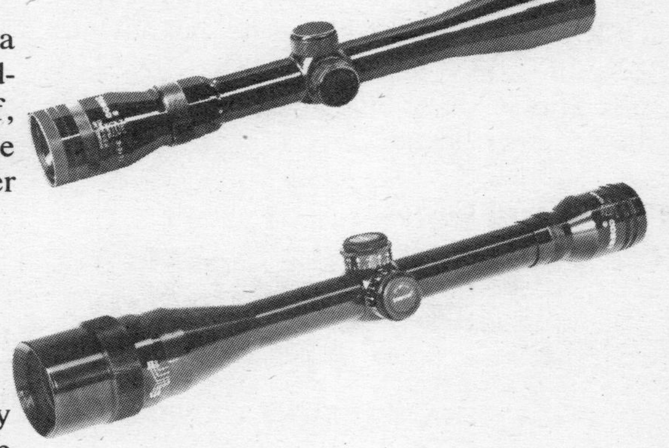

TASCO OPTICAL SIGHTING DEVICE

The "Tasco Rama No.755" fits all standard shotguns. It electronically superimposes a red dot in the center of your sighting picture. This unit is fully adjustable and works on batteries (included).
Price: $99.95
From Tasco Sales, Inc.

TASCO OPTICAL SIGHTING DEVICE

The "Tasco Rama No.756" is specifically made to fit Remington 870 and 1100 shotguns. A red dot is electronically superimposed in the center of your sighting picture. This unit is fully adjustable and works on batteries (included).
Price: $99.95
From Tasco Sales, Inc.

TASCO OPTICAL SIGHTING DEVICE

The "Tasco Rama No. 757" superimposes a red dot in the center of your sighting picture. This unit is fully adjustable and functions on batteries (which are included). Fits standard scope bases.
Price: $99.95
From Tasco Sales, Inc.

TASCO OPTICAL SIGHTING DEVICE

Tasco's "Tasco Rama No.758" superimposes a red dot in the center of your sighting picture. This unit functions on batteries (which are included). The No.758 is designed to fit most grooved .22 caliber receivers. Fully adjustable.
Price: $99.95
From Tasco Sales, Inc.

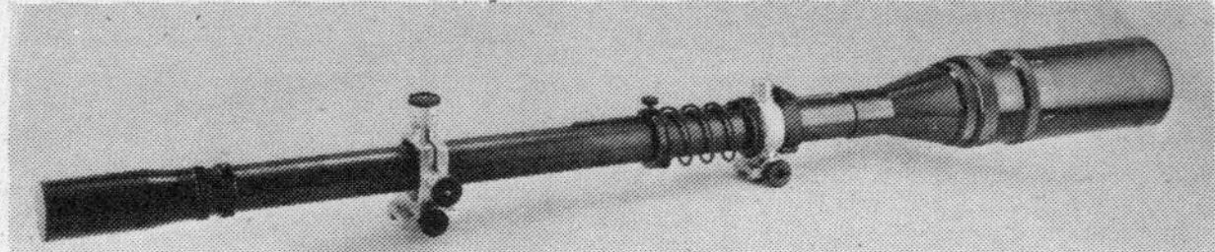

UNERTL PROGRAMMER-200 TARGET SCOPE

This Unertl target scope represents that firm's top-of-the-line item. Focusing ring runs from 50 feet to infinity. Comes with a set of Unertl's ¼-minute click "Posa" mounts, Magnum tube clamp, recoil spring, bases, screw-in dust caps. The power of this scope is pretty much left up to the shooter as he can have his choice of 8X, 10X, 12X, 14X, 16X, 18X, 20X, 24X, 32X and 36X. This scope is, indeed, a precision instrument for the serious rifleman.

Price: $317

From the John Unertl Company.

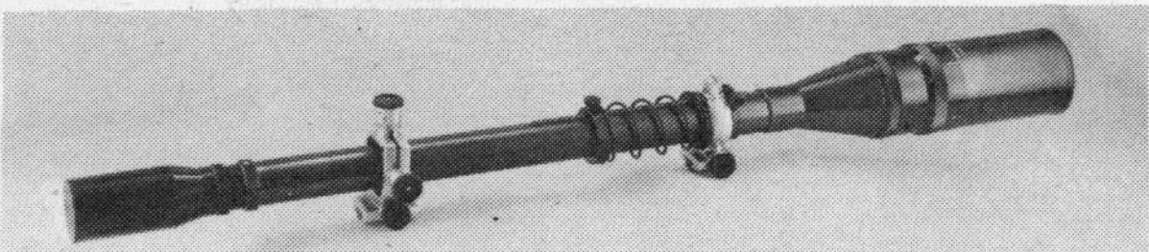

UNERTL 2-INCH ULTRA VARMINT/CALIBRATED HEAD SCOPE

Features a larger ocular lens than the standard 2-inch Target Scope. (Also somewhat shorter.) Comes with standard ¼-minute click target or dehorned mounts, recoil spring, clamp, screw lens caps and choice of any listed power and standard reticle. Fully adjustable for parallax from 50 feet to infinity. Comes in 8X, 10X, 12X and 15X. Good choice for varmints or bench work. Beautifully blued.

Price: $239

From the John Unertl Optical Company.

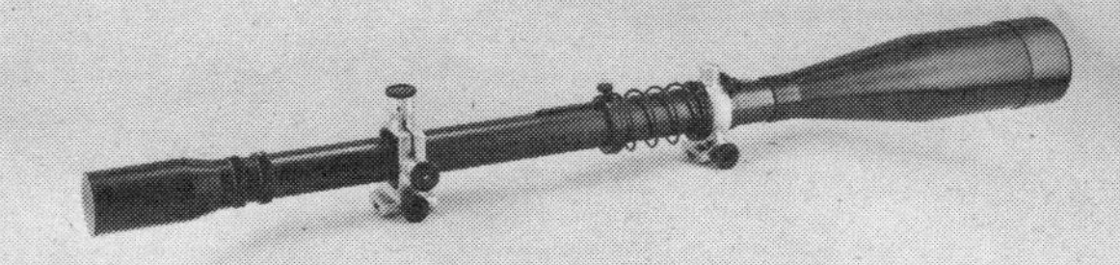

UNERTL 2-INCH ULTRA VARMINT PLAIN SCOPE

In terms of quality, this scope is identical to the nearby 2-inch Ultra Varmint with calibrated head. The only difference is that this scope has no calibrated head and comes pre-set for parallax; and, it can be focused from 50 feet to infinity. However, it must be focused by trial and test. It's somewhat lighter than the calibrated-head version; and, is recommended for field work.

Price: $213

From the John Unertl Optical Company.

UNERTL 1¼-INCH VARMINT SCOPE

This scope is equal in optical quality and precision to Unertl's 2-inch Ultra series scopes. It features a slightly smaller objective aperture and physical size. Excellent for use on light sporting rifles. Objective head is graduated. Comes beautifully blued and features ¼-minute click dehorned mounts, recoil spring, clamp, screw dust caps, choice of 6X, 8X, 10X or 12X powers and standard reticle.

Price: $167; with target mounts, same price.

From the John Unertl Optical Company.

UNERTL 1¼-INCH TARGET SCOPE

This intermediate size scope comes in 8X, 10X, 12X, or 14X powers. Included are ¼-minute click target mounts, clamp, screw dust caps, recoil spring and choice of any of the above powers and standard reticle. Features focusing ring that's graduated from 50 feet to 200 yards. Objective head may be changed to 1½-inch size at a later date if the shooter decides he wants to upgrade his equipment. Beautifully blued. Perfect for target shooting.

Price: $166

From the John Unertl Optical Company.

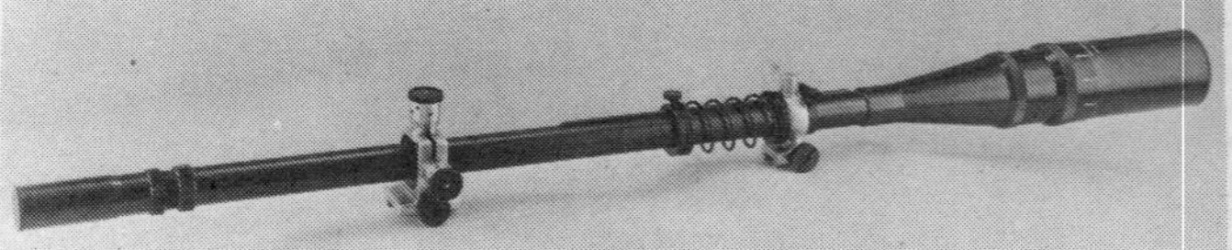

UNERTL 1½-INCH TARGET SCOPE

This Unertl scope is fully adjustable for focus. It has excellent clarity and resolution. Comes in 8X, 10X, 12X, 14X, 16X, 18X, and 20X powers. The steel body is beautifully blued. Standard on this scope are ¼-minute click mounts, recoil spring, clamp, screw dust caps, choice of any of the above powers and a standard reticle.

Price: $189

From the John Unertl Optical Company.

UNERTL 2-INCH TARGET SCOPE

This Unertl scope comes in 8X, 10X, 12X, 14X, 16X, 18X, 20X, 24X, 30X, or 36X; it's made for the bench shooter. Beautifully blued steel tube which comes with screw-in objective and ocular lens caps. Comes with standard ¼-minute click target-type mounts, recoil spring, clamp ring and choice of any listed power and standard reticle. Excellent resolution. This is a precision instrument for the serious rifleman.

Price: $225

From the John Unertl Optical Company.

Prices shown are subject to change.

UNERTL'S BV-20 SUPER GRADE SCOPE

This scope is identical to the nearby BV-20 standard with the exception that it has split "Posa" mounts, recoil spring and magnum recoil ring.

Price: $220

From the John Unertl Optical Company.

UNERTL BV-20 STANDARD GRADE SCOPE

Comes in 20X only and is more than suitable for bench and varmint purposes. The standard model comes as shown with standard mounts (¼-minute adjustments) and range-adjustment ring. All steel construction.

Price: $210

From the John Unertl Optical Company.

UNERTL "VULTURE" 8X or 10X SCOPES

Unertl's Vulture hunting scope comes with either internal or external (shown) adjustments for windage and elevation. At 100 yards the Vulture provides the shooter with a shade over 11 feet of field of view. The entire Unertl line has a reputation for quality; and, the Vulture lives up to that reputation. This scope has proven popular with varmint hunters.

Price: Internal W/E adjustments $152; external W/E adjustment $191.

From The John Unertl Optical Company.

UNERTL 6X "CONDOR" SCOPE

The Unertl Condor has a 1-inch steel tube and black anodized aluminum ocular and objective lens cells. Features internal adjustments and provides the shooter with a 17-foot field of view at 100 yards. A good selection of reticles is offered at no extra cost.

Price: $118

From the John Unertl Optical Company.

UNERTL 4X "HAWK" SCOPE

This Unertl scope features internal adjustments, a 1-inch steel tube and anodized aluminum objective and ocular lens cells. Field of view at 100 yards is 34 feet. The Hawk is a good all-around choice for hunting. A good selection of reticles is offered at no extra cost.

Price: $94

From the John Unertl Optical Company.

UNERTL 2¾X "FALCON" SCOPE

This quality Unertl scope features internal adjustments, a 1-inch steel tube and black anodized aluminum lens cells. Perfect for the bush country deer hunter. The shooter gets a generous 40-foot field of view at 100 yards. A good selection of reticles is offered at no extra cost.

Price: $87

From the John Unertl Optical Company.

UNERTL SMALL GAME SCOPE

Well suited for small game hunting, this Unertl scope is offered in 3X, 4X or 6X configuration. Has an overall length of 18 inches and comes with ¼-minute click adjustment mounts. Will withstand the recoil of any rifle, even though it's specially intended for small game use.

Price: $95

From the John Unertl Optical Company.

UNERTL 1-INCH TARGET SCOPE

This intermediate sized target scope is well suited to indoor gallery target work. It has excellent clarity and comes with an adjustment ring for focusing. Also comes with clamp and ¼-minute click-type mounts. Available in 6X, 8X, or 10X powers with your choice of standard reticle. Beautifully blued.

Price: $126

From the John Unertl Optical Company.

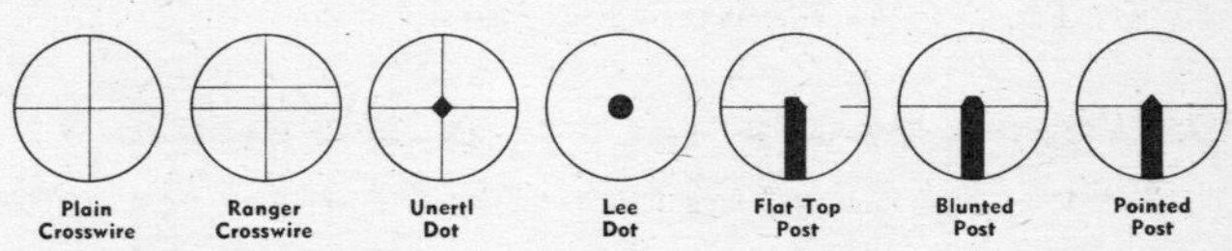

RETICLES FOR UNERTL SCOPES

The Unertl reticles shown nearby are all standard for that firm's line of scopes. With the exception of the Lee Dot and Ranger Crosswire, those reticles can be ordered with Unertl scopes without extra charge.

Price: Lee Dot $20; Ranger Crosswire $42; other reticles no charge when ordering a Unertl scope.

From the John Unertl Optical Company.

WEATHERBY PREMIER 3X to 9X VARIABLE SCOPE

Features excellent light gathering qualities. Instantly adjustable from 3X to 9X and comes with plain crosshair, "Lumi-Plex" or Tapered Post and Crosshair reticles. Also features precise ¼-minute click adjustments. Wide angle models available.

Price: Crosshair or Tapered Post and Crosshair $142.95; with "Lumi-Plex" $153.95; Wide angle with Crosshair or Tapered Post and Crosshair $169.95; with "Lumi-Plex" $179.95.

From Weatherby's Inc.

WEATHERBY 2¾X SCOPE

This lightweight scope features a 45-foot field of view at 100 yards. It also features ¼-minute click adjustments and is available with plain cross-hair reticle or "Lumi-Plex" reticle. The scope is nitrogen filled and sealed. It's also submersed in water to test for all-weather performance.

Price: Crosshair $126.95; "Lumi-Plex" reticle or dot $131.95; Wide Angle with "Lumi-Plex" $164.95; Tapered Post and Crosshair $159.95.

From Weatherby's, Inc.

WEATHERBY MARK XXII RIMFIRE SCOPE

Weatherby's Mark XXII 4X rifle scope comes complete with an integral set of dovetail mounts. This scope may be used on any rimfire rifle that is grooved or has a grooved base attached to it. The field of view at 100

yards is 25 feet and the scope features ¼-minute click adjustment for both windage and elevation.

Price: 4X with crosshair $57.95; 4X with "Lumi-Plex" reticle $65.95.

From Weatherby's Inc.

WEAVER'S T-MODEL SCOPES

These Weaver scopes are available in 6X, 10X, 16X, 20X or 25X configurations. They are made specifically for varmint hunting and competition silhouette shooting. They feature ¼-minute of angle adjustment and are made to take the rugged use a varmint shooter, or competitor, can dish out.

Price: T-6 $175; T-10 $185; T-16 $195; T-20 $220; T-25 $232; Dot or fine crosshair reticle $13.30 extra.

From The W.R. Weaver Company.

WEAVER'S V12 VARIABLE POWER SCOPE

This Weaver scope comes with ¼ minute adjustments for both windage and elevation. It's available in standard (round eye piece) model only. Field of view at 100 yards is 23 to 9 feet, depending on power selected. Crosshair or Dual-X reticles are standard.

Price: Standard V12 $139; dot reticle $13.30 extra.

From The W.R. Weaver Company.

WEAVER'S V9 VARIABLE POWER SCOPE

This 1-inch tubed Weaver scope features ¼-minute of angle adjustments for both windage and elevation. Has an adjustable power range that runs from 3.3X to 8.8X. Field of view at 100 yards ranges from 31 to 12 feet depending on power selected (Wider-View model has a field of view that ranges from 35 to 13 feet). Crosshair of Dual-X reticle is standard.

Price: Standard V9 $127.50; Wider View Model V9W $153.50. With fine crosshair, the V9F sells for $139; the V9WF for $165. Dot reticle $13.30.

From The W.R. Weaver Company.

WEAVER'S V7 VARIABLE POWER SCOPE

This 1-inch tubed Weaver scope features ¼-minute of angle adjustments for both windage and elevation. Adjustable power range runs from 2.5X to 6.7. Field of view at 100 yards ranges from 40 to 15 feet depending on power selected. (Wider View models: 43 to 17 feet.) Traditional round eye piece (ocular lens) or Wider-View configuration (shown) available. Crosshair or Dual-X reticle is standard.

Price: Standard V7 $116; Wider-View model V7W $142; Dot reticle $13.30 extra.

From The W.R. Weaver Company.

Prices shown are subject to change.

WEAVER'S V4.5 VARIABLE POWER SCOPE

This Weaver scope has an adjustable power range of 1.6X to 4.3X. It's a 1-inch tubed scope that provides a field of view (at 100 yards) of 63 to 24 feet, depending on the power selected. (Wider View models: 74 to 27 feet). Features ½-minute of angle clicks—fully adjustable for windage or elevation. A wide variety of reticles is available—crosshair is standard.

Price: $105; Dot reticle $13.30 extra.

From The W.R. Weaver Company.

WEAVER'S K12 SCOPE

Weaver's K12 is a proven favorite with accuracy minded shooters and varmint hunters. It has a field of view of 10 feet at 100 yards; has a parallax adjustment ring that's graduated from 50 to 1000 yards and has ¼-minute of angle click adjustments. Crosshair, Dual-X or Range-Finder reticles are standard.

Price: $130

From The W.R. Weaver Company.

WEAVER'S K10 SCOPE

This big Weaver is another favorite with varmint hunters; benchresters too. Features full parallax adjustment from 50 to 1000 yards and has ¼-minute click adjustments for both windage and elevation. Comes with crosshair or Dual-X reticle as standard. If you are a varmint shooter, we suggest you consider Weaver's Range-Finder reticle at no extra charge.

Price: $118.50; dot reticle $13.30 extra.

From The W.R. Weaver Company.

WEAVER'S K8 SCOPE

This 1-inch tubed Weaver scope is a favorite with varmint shooters. It has a field of view of 15 feet at 100 yards and features ¼-minute of angle windage and elevation adjustments. Comes with crosshair or Dual-X reticle or Range-Finder reticle as standard. Parallax adjustment from 50 to 1000 yards.

Price: $113.50; dot reticle $13.30 extra.

From The W.R. Weaver Company.

WEAVER'S K6 SCOPE

Weaver's K6, 1-inch tubed scope has a field of view of 19 feet at 100 yards (24 feet with the Wider View model). It's a favorite with medium range varmint shooters. It features ¼-minute of angle adjustments for both windage and elevation. Crosshair or Dual-X reticle is standard. Wider View (shown) or round eye piece models are available.

Price: Standard $99; Wider View model $124.50; dot reticle $13.30 extra.

From The W.R. Weaver Company.

WEAVER'S K4 SCOPE

This Weaver scope is a traditional favorite. It features a 27-foot field of view at 100 yards (38 feet for the Wider View Model) and comes with ¼-minute of angle click adjustments for both windage elevation. Available in standard (round eye piece) or Wider View models. Dual-X or crosshair reticles are standard.

Price: Standard $88; Wider View model $113.50; dot reticle $13.30 extra.

From The W.R. Weaver Company.

WEAVER'S K3 SCOPE

Weaver's 1-inch tubed K3 comes in standard (round eye piece) or Wider View models. Features ½-minute of angle windage and elevation adjustments. Crosshair or Dual-X reticle standard. Field of view at 100 yards is 34 feet; 48 feet with Wider View model.

Price: Standard $76; Wider View model $102; dot reticle $13.30 extra.

From The W.R. Weaver Company.

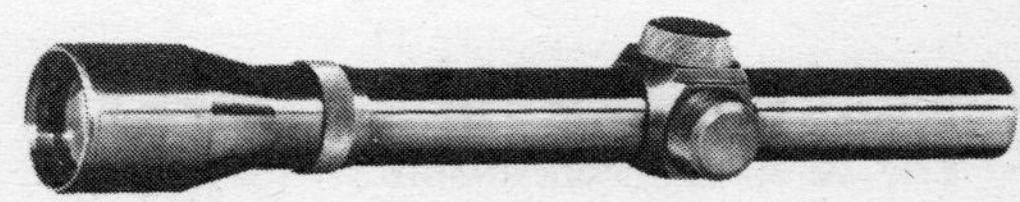

WEAVER'S K2.5 SCOPE

This 1-inch tubed Weaver scope is another sure bet for brush country deer hunters. It has a field of view that measures 38 feet at 100 yards. Features ½-minute of angle click adjustments for both windage and elevation. Crosshair or Dual-X reticle standard.

Price: $71; dot reticle $13.30 extra.

From The W.R. Weaver Company.

See the Directory for complete company addresses.

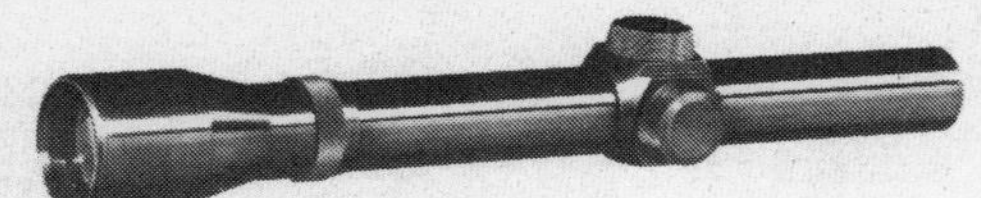

WEAVER'S K1.5 SCOPE

This 1-inch tubed Weaver scope has a generous field of view—55 feet at 100 yards. It's a good bet for close range big game in brush country hunting situations. Features ½-minute of angle adjustments, for windage and elevation. Comes with crosshair or Dual-X reticle as standard.

Price: $59; dot reticle $13.30 extra.

From The W.R. Weaver Company.

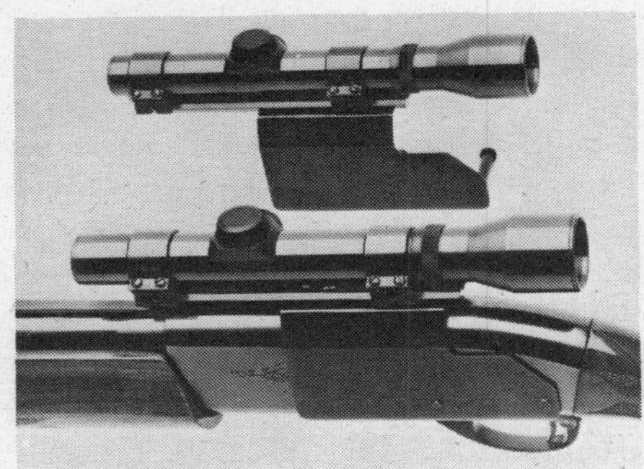

SCOPE/MOUNT COMBO FOR REM. 1100/870 SHOTGUNS

This scope/mount combo goes on in seconds—a screwdriver is the only tool you'll need. Mount comes with either K-1.5 or K-2.5 Weaver 1-inch scope. Mounts require no drilling or tapping of your 1100 or 870 receiver—they utilize the existing drift-pin holes in your gun's receiver. (Scope has Dual-X reticle.)

Price: Mount with K-1.5 $86; with K-2.5 $98.

From The W.R. Weaver Company.

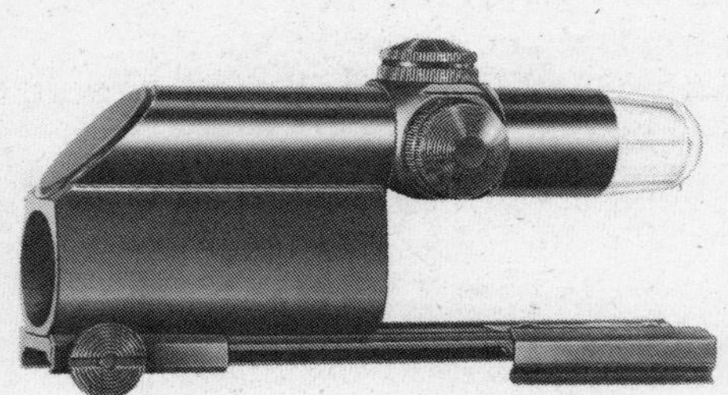

QWIK-POINT AND TIP-OFF MOUNT

The Weaver Qwik-Point scope is designed for close range game shooting. When the shooter looks through the scope a bright fluorescent blaze-orange dot appears in the center of your shooting picture. Place the dot—which is fully adjustable—on the desired point of aim and fire. It's a simple system that provides the shooter with a wide field of view. Available for centerfire rifles, rimfire rifles and most shotguns.

Price: All models $56.50.

From The W.R. Weaver Company.

QWIK-POINT/MOUNT COMBO FOR REM. 1100/870 SHOTGUNS

This Weaver scope/mount combo installs on a Remington 870 or 1100 shotgun in seconds. A screwdriver is the only tool needed—no drilling or tapping is required.

Price: $56.50

From The W.R. Weaver Company.

WEAVER'S D-SERIES RIMFIRE SCOPES

These scopes come with an N-type or tip-off mount at no extra charge. The D-Series ¾-inch scopes are available in 4X or 6X and come with a standard crosshair reticle. (Dual-X reticle available at extra cost.) These scopes have earned a good reputation with .22 shooters.

Price: 4X $18.50, with Dual-X reticle $20.50; 6X $20.50, with Dual-X reticle $22.50.

From The W.R. Weaver Company.

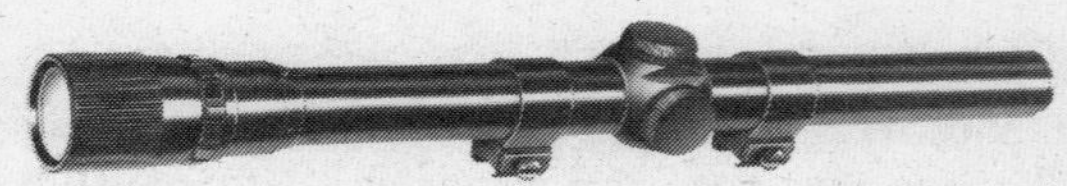

WEAVER'S "V22" VARIABLE POWER RIMFIRE SCOPE

Called the "V22," this Weaver scope comes with N-type or tip-off mount at no extra charge. The power range runs from 3X to 5.8X; and, you can easily select the power you want to use with a turn of the wrist.

Price: $24.50; with Dual-X reticle $27.

From The W.R. Weaver Company.

WEAVER LENS CAPS

These handy lens caps help keep dust, moisture and other foreign matter off of the lenses of your Weaver scope. When purchasing, specify what type of Weaver scope you will use them on.

Price: $4

From The W.R. Weaver Company.

Prices shown are subject to change.

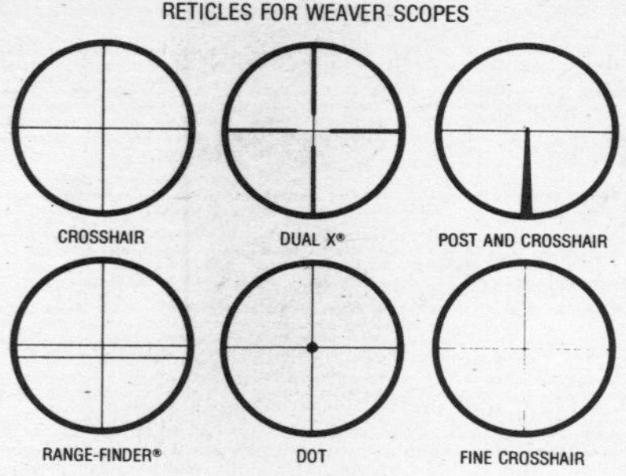

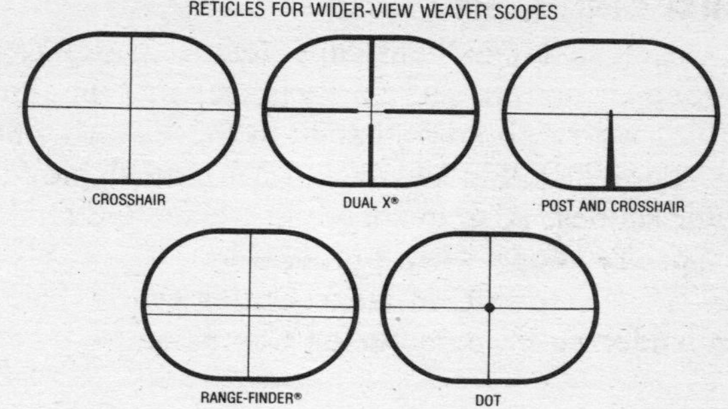

RETICLES FOR STANDARD WEAVER SCOPES

Weaver offers the nearby reticles as standard, or extra-cost equipment on all K model scopes. All of the reticles shown, with the exception of the fine crosshair and dot, are available at no extra cost when purchasing most K-type scopes.

Prices: Dot $13.30; Fine crosshair $13.30; the remainder of the shown reticles are for the asking when purchasing most Weaver K-type scopes.

From The W.R. Weaver Company.

WILLIAMS 3X-9X VARIABLE TWILIGHT SCOPE

Each Williams 3X to 9X scope has a field of view that ranges from 36½ to 12¾ feet at 100 yards, depending upon the power selected. It comes fully fog-proofed and it is fully adjustable for both windage and elevation.

Price: $99 (crosshair reticle is standard).

From Williams Gun Sight Co.

WILLIAMS 2X TO 6X VARIABLE POWER TWILIGHT SCOPE

This Williams scope is a good all-around hunting scope for the game and varmint hunter. Each scope is fully fog-proofed and is adjustable for windage and elevation.

Price: $94 (crosshair reticle is standard).

From Williams Gun Sight Co.

WILLIAMS TWILIGHT 4X SCOPE

This 4X Williams scope's a good short to medium range hunting choice. It's fully fog-proofed and adjustable for windage and elevation. At 100 yards the scope offers the shooter a 29-foot field of view.

Price: $68 (crosshair reticle is standard).

From Williams Gun Sight Co.

WILLIAMS STREAMLINE SCOPE MOUNTS

These mounts are made of hardened, black anodized aluminum. Available to fit all popular rifles.

Price: $15 per pair.

From Williams Gun Sight Co.

RETICLES FOR WEAVER WIDER-VIEW SCOPES

Shown nearby are the available reticles for the Weaver Wider-View scopes. All of the reticles—crosshair, Dual-X, Post and Crosshair, Range-Finder—are available as standard equipment on most Wider-View scopes; the Dot reticle costs extra.

Price: Dot reticle $13.30; all others are standard.

From The W.R. Weaver Company.

WILLIAMS TWILIGHT 2½X SCOPE

This Williams scope is ideally suited for deep woods or heavy brush hunting purposes. The scope is fully adjustable for windage and elevation. At 100 yards, this scope offers the shooter a 32-foot field of view. Fully fog-proofed.

Price: $62 (crosshair reticle is standard).

From Williams Gun Sight Co.

WILLIAMS QC MOUNT & RINGS

This Williams mount allows the shooter to quickly remove or install his favorite scope sight. The rings and bridge can be purchased as a single unit. Specify your rifle when buying.

Price:

Rings and Base	$26.20
New AR-15 Base & Rings Combo	33.90

From Williams Gun Sight Co.

WILLIAMS "SIGHT-THRU" SCOPE MOUNT

These mounts allow the shooter to use either his telescope or iron sights as he chooses. Excellent choice of mounts for brush country hunting. Made of hardened, black anodized aluminum.

Price: $15.70 per pair.

From Williams Gun Sight Co.

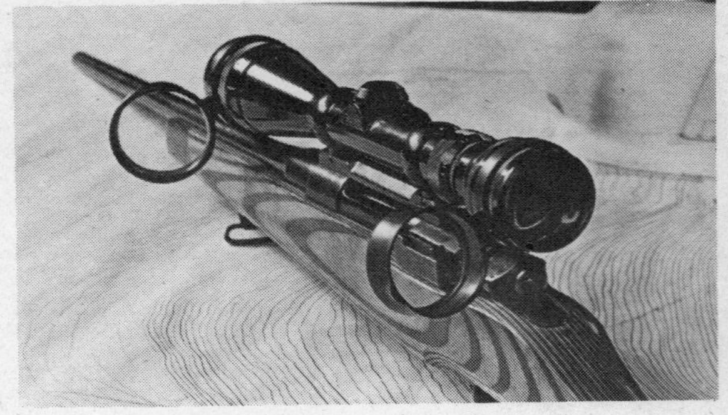

STORM KING LENS COVERS

These clear, hinged lens caps, feature watch crystal acrylic construction. The clarity is such that the shooter need not worry about a change in the bullet's impact point. They install in seconds and are available for all popular scopes. Also available in "Haze Cutter" yellow. Specify scope when purchasing.
Price: $5.45 per pair, in Haze Cutter yellow $6.55.
From Anderson Manufacturing Company.

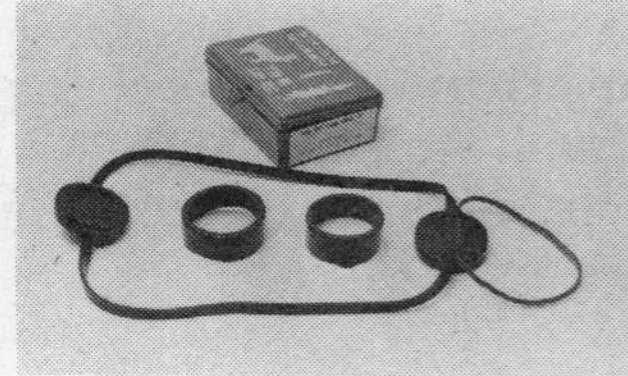

STORM QUEEN LENS COVERS

These covers snap on to the ocular and objective lenses; and, the objective cover has an extra flexible band that attaches to your gun's sling swivel. The effect of this set up is such that when you flip off the ocular cap, the front cap pops off as well. It's handy. Available for all popular scopes. Specify when purchasing.
Price: $4.95
From the Anderson Manufacturing Company.

MINI-14 MOUNT

This B-Square mount is specifically made for Ruger's Mini-14 auto rifle. May be mounted over the bore or offset for iron sight use. (Uses same mounting holes for either position.) Drill jig available for earlier, undrilled models. Made of durable alloy; features Allen-head screws.
Price: $24.95
From B-Square.

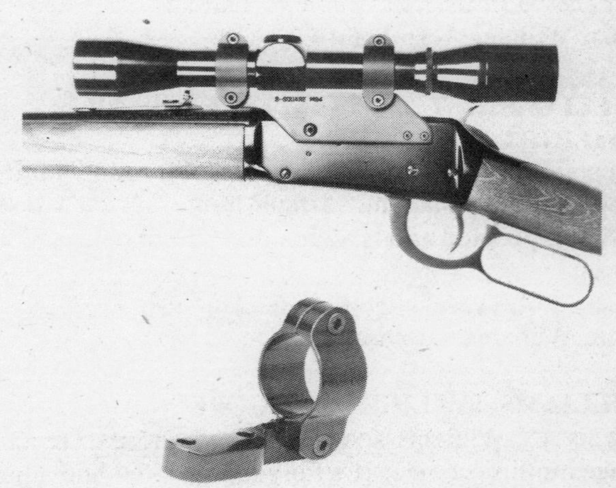

MODEL 94 SIDE MOUNT

B-Square Model 94 side mount fits on the side of the receiver and allows the use of iron sights. This is the lowest and least offset mount for the Winchester 94. (Drill jig available for pre-1964 models.) Made of durable alloy; features Allen-head screws.
Price: $19.95
From B-Square.

BENCHREST/SILHOUETTE 2-PIECE MOUNTS

These mounts have been especially designed for lightweight benchrest and silhouette rifles. The mounts permit stress-free mounting. Made of lightweight alloy; features Allen-head screws.
Price: $19.95
From B-Square.

COLT AR-15 MOUNTS

This mount requires *no* drilling or tapping. It quickly screws onto the AR-15's carrying handle. Can be removed without affecting zero. Made of durable alloy; features Allen-head screws.
Price: AR-15/16 $14.95; AR-15 $14.95.
From B-Square.

Prices shown are subject to change.

RUGER BLACKHAWK MOUNT

This is the newest addition to their line of scope mounts. Fully bolts to the frame of any Ruger Blackhawk revolver. Comes with Allen-head screws. Mount is made of durable aluminum alloy.
Price: $21.95
From B-Square

EMERGENCY SCOPE MOUNT IRON SIGHTS

These Buehler iron sights are designed for scope mount use *only*. In the event your scope should become damaged in transit or during a hunt, these sights can be quickly installed. They come in peep or open configuration. (Specify when purchasing.) They fit all Buehler mounts.
Price: $3.35
From Maynard P. Buehler.

EXTERNALLY ADJUSTABLE MOUNT

This Buehler mount is specifically made for those scopes that come without any provision for windage or elevation adjustment. Features ¼-minute click adjustment. No tools are required to adjust scope. Comes without rings. Blued steel.
Price: $27.50
From Maynard P. Buehler, Inc.

SHORT 1-PIECE TOP MOUNT BASES

This Buehler base locates the front ring over the top of the receiver ring about 1 inch aft of the long 1-piece base. The rear ring is in about the same location; thus, ring spacing averages 4 inches. Recommended for shorter scopes, scopes with turrets near the center of the tube and for "non-stock crawlers."
Price: $17.95, less rings.
From Maynard P. Buehler, Inc.

DOVETAIL RINGS

B-Square's basic dovetail rings require no base. They fit directly on any standard grooved receiver. Come with Allen-head screws. Rings are made of durable alloy.
Price: $11.95
From B-Square.

LONG, 1-PIECE BASE

Made to fit most rifles in common use. In most models it has the rings spaced about 5 inches apart, with the front ring located ahead of the receiver on all bolt-action rifles. The long base gives the greatest possible support to the scope and the longest amount of eye relief. It is recommended for long scopes, scopes with adjustment turrets located ahead of center and for "stock crawlers."
Price: $17.75 less rings.
From Maynard P. Buehler.

BUILT-IN ¼ inch CLICK ELEVATION.
INSTANTLY ADJUSTABLE WITHOUT TOOLS.

PISTOL BASES

These sturdy blued steel bases are easy to install. They are made to fit the Micro Sight slot or screw holes where provided. Bases are made for the following guns.

Code	To Fit
TC	Thompson Contender
K	S&W revolvers (Micro rear sights)
52	S&W Mod. 52 Auto
41	S&W Mod. 41 and 46
C	Colt Python, Trooper MK.III
45	Colt .45 Gov't. Model
WM	Colt Woodsman
RB	Ruger, all Blackhawks
RA	Ruger .22 Auto
XP	Rem. XP100
CT	Hi-Standard Citation - Trophy
VH	Hi-Standard Victor
DW	Dan Wesson Revolver
AM	Auto-Mag .44 Cal.
SV	Weatherby Silhouette

Price: $17.75 less rings.
From Maynard P. Buehler, Inc.

See the Directory for complete company addresses.

STREAMLINED SOLID RINGS

These Buehler rings are sleek, smooth and make for the lowest of all mount/ring combinations. They put the scope about ¼-inch above the receiver. Comes in one height, only, .040-inch. For ¾-inch tubes.

Price: $15

From Maynard P. Buehler.

BUEHLER DOUBLE SPLIT RINGS

DOUBLE-SPLIT RINGS

These Buehler rings feature a smoothly rounded ball turret top. While the steel spacer at the top of each ring serves to fill up space, it is also made up of 16 laminations; you can peel off one or more at a time, thus accurately fit all scopes up to .010 smaller in size than the normal dimension of the ring.

Price: Codes 6, 7, 8 $23.25 per set; Codes 10 through 16 $30 per set. (See codes below).

Code		Scope Diam.	Height, in.
6	1″ Low	(1.004 to .995)	.075
7	1″Med	(1.004 to .995)	.136
8	1″High	(1.004 to .995)	.212
10	26mmStd.	(1.023 to 1.013)	.125
11	26mm High	(1.023 to 1.013)	.200
16	28mm	(1.103 to 1.093)	.181

From Maynard P. Buehler, Inc.

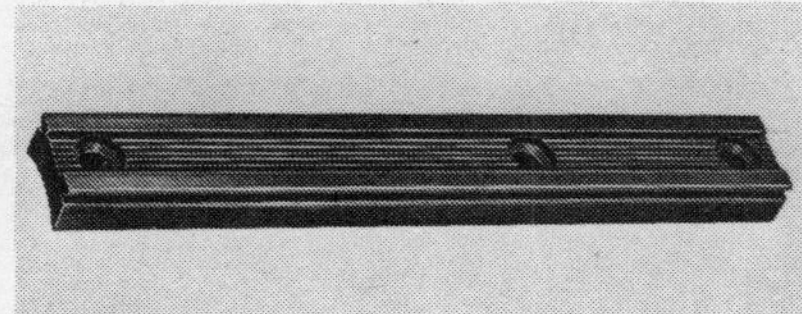

DOVETAIL SCOPE BASE

This adapter permits use of scopes with standard tip-off rings with earlier .22 rifles not grooved for such mounts. It's 3⅞ inches long, with a screw hole at each end which is offset from the center to provide flexibility in mounting to a variety of both long and short action rifles. Two styles are available: No. 840 for .840-inch diameter receivers and the No. 100 for 1-inch diameter receivers.

Price: $1.98 (specify style).

From Brownells.

CUSTOM SCOPE RINGS AND BASES

Lenard Brownell hand makes these custom scope rings and bases for any gun/scope combination you have; they are beautifully made. Rings come with screws or levers (shown). Bases are available for most popular sporting rifles; left-hand Remington, Weatherby and Wichita actions as well.

Price: Rings $75; Bases $20 ($30 for unaltered 98 Mausers).

From Lenard M. Brownell Custom Rifles.

BUTLER CREEK SCOPE COVERS

These flip-up lens covers are available for most popular rifle scopes. A simple flip of the thumb (as shown) makes the scope instantly ready for use. When closed they help protect the lenses from foul weather and dust.

Price: $8.95 per set.

From Butler Creek Corporation.

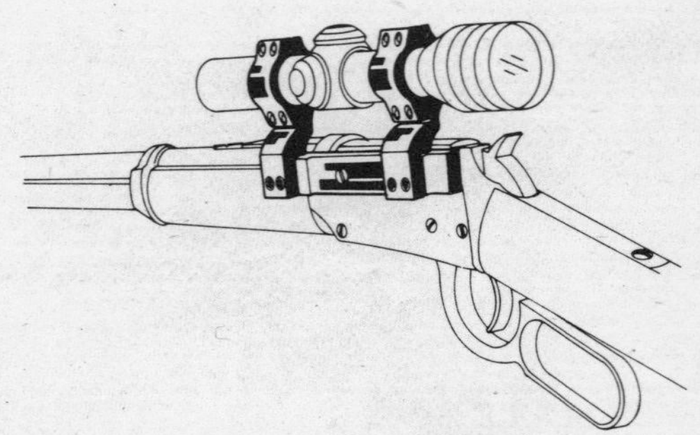

CLEARVIEW MODEL 94 MOUNT

These side mounts readily install on most Winchester Model 94 receivers. They require no drilling or tapping and come with a lifetime guarantee. Offset to avoid interference with ejected brass.

Price: $19.95

From Clearview Manufacturing Co., Inc.

Prices shown are subject to change.

CLEARVIEW STANDARD "SEE-THRU" MOUNT

These 1-inch mounts come with a lifetime guarantee and are made to handle 1-inch scopes. Allows the shooter to use either scope or iron sights.

Price: $14.95

From Clearview Manufacturing Co., Inc.

CLEARVIEW RIMFIRE SCOPE MOUNTS

These mounts may be used with either 1-inch, ⅞-inch or ¾-inch scopes. A set of inserts comes with each set of mounts. They enable the user to mount his own choice of rimfire scope. Has a lifetime guarantee.

Price: $7.95 per set.

From Clearview Manufacturing Co., Inc.

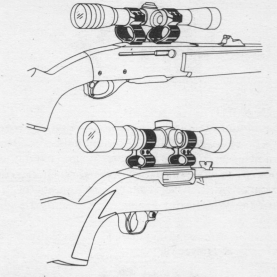

CONETROL 1-PIECE AND 2-PIECE SCOPE BASES:

These bases are made of beautifully blued steel. They come in 1-piece (bridge) or 2-piece styles and are made to fit just about all popular rifles—specify rifle when purchasing. Well made.

Price:

1- or 2-Piece Scope Bases	
Huntur	$12.50
Gunnur	17.00
Custum	19.95

From Conetrol Scope Mounts.

CONETROL PROJECTIONLESS SCOPE RINGS

These rings are beautifully made of high-polish blued steel. They come in high low and medium sizes and are offered in three grades—*Huntur, Gunnur* and *Custum.*

Price:

Solid Rings	
Huntur	$ 5.00
Gunnur	7.25
Custum	9.00
Split Rings	
Huntur	$ 7.75
Gunnur	10.00
Custum	12.50

From Conetrol Scope Mounts.

D&H SUPER SCOPE COVER

This one-piece scope cover is made to be removed with a flick of the fingers. The cover is easily attached to the rifle proper to avoid field loss. It comes in two basic sizes that are designed to fit all scopes. Even at sub-zero temperatures this pliable rubber cover provides good elasticity.

Price: $3.45 each.

From D&H Products.

SCOPE MOUNT

Davidson's "Bridgemount" is made for the Remington 700, 721, 722, 40-X, 788, 600, 660, and XP-100; also Winchester Models 70 and 670; Wichita Mini and Shilen DGA rifles. Made to take Unertl "Posa" and Redfield 3200 external adjustment rings with 7.2 inches between spacing notches. Made of 7075-T6 alloy; hard anodized black.

Price: $16

From Davidson.

GRIFFIN & HOWE TOP MOUNT

Each ring has an independent locking lever system allowing for fast attachment or removal. These mounts are completely hand crafted—one set at a time. They are offered on an installed basis only.

Price: $200

From Griffin & Howe, Inc.

See the Directory for complete company addresses.

GRIFFIN & HOWE SCOPE MOUNTS

These mounts feature locking levers that allow for fast attachment or removal. The mount holds the scope immovable in its split ring brackets. It can be mounted high enough to enable the use of iron sights. Offered for most popular rifles. Also available are mounts (of this style) for the Winchester Model 94, Garand M-1 and the M-14.

Price: Mount only $85; installed $155.

From Griffin & Howe, Inc.

J.B. HOLDEN "IRONSIGHTER" MOUNTS

These see-through mounts allow the user to select the sight *he* wants to use. While these mounts rigidly hold the scope in place, they also have a tunnel through which you can see, and use, your rifle's iron sights. Ironsighter mounts are available for all centerfire rifles and for rimfires with grooved receivers. Made of high strength alloy. Specify gun when purchasing.

Price: Centerfire mounts $14.95; rimfire mounts $7.95.

From the J.B. Holden Company.

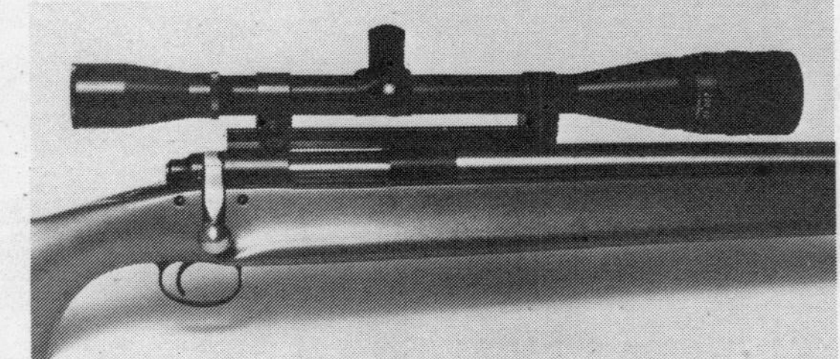

BRIDGE MOUNT

This bridge mount is intended for the longer scopes such as the Lyman LWBR and Leupold 24X when mounted on Remington 40X, 700, 722 actions using Weaver rings. Mount has ample cross section to insure a sturdy installation. It's 8 inches long. Weight 3½ ounces, black anodized aluminum.

Price: $20.50

From K.W. Kleinendorst, Gunsmith.

KRIS 2-PIECE MOUNTS FOR RIFLES

These see-through mounts accommodate most 1-inch rings. They are available for a *wide* selection of popular rifles. (Specify rifle when purchasing).

Price: $7.98 per pair.

From Kris Mounts.

KRIS 1-PIECE MOUNT FOR WINCHESTER 94

This 1-piece mount attaches to most 94 receivers without any drilling or tapping. Easily installed in minutes. Mount positions scope to the left of the bore line so as to not interfere with ejected spent brass.

Price: $10.98

From Kris Mounts.

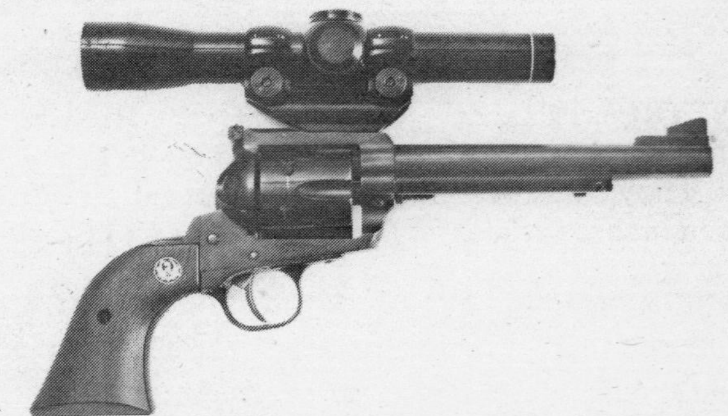

KRIS 1-PIECE ALL-WEATHER MOUNTS FOR RUGER HANDGUNS

This one-piece handgun scope mount is specifically designed for Ruger revolvers. Accommodates most 1-inch rings. Features see-through design so iron sights can be used.

Price: $10.98

From Kris Mounts.

SEE-THROUGH SCOPE MOUNT

Kwik-Site's "Wider View" scope mount installs in minutes to any drilled and tapped receiver. The extra-wide viewing tunnel helps make the shooter's target more distinct, more "hitable." Specify gun when purchasing.

Price: $14.75 per pair.

From Kwik-Site.

Prices shown are subject to change.

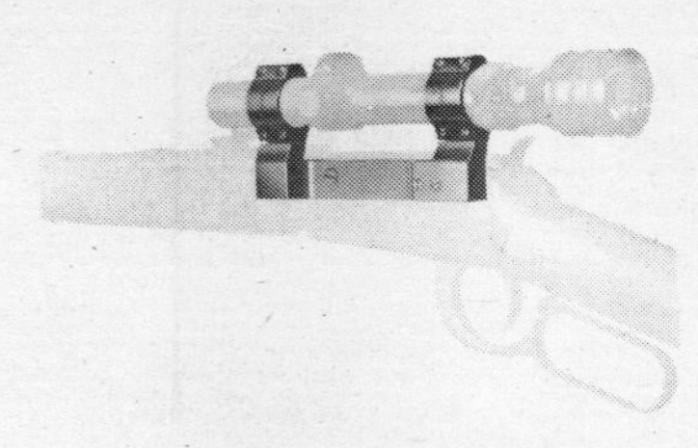

SIDE MOUNT FOR THE WINCHESTER 94

This mount attaches to the receiver via existing receiver screw holes—no drilling or tapping is required. Patented adjustable windage bushing screw assures precise scope alignment.
Price: $19.95
From Kwik-Site.

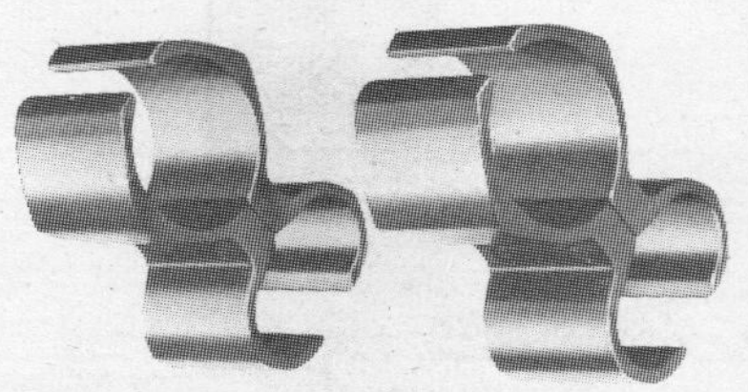

SEE-THROUGH SCOPE MOUNT

Kwik-Site's .22 rimfire mount quickly attaches to any standard grooved receiver. Available to handle 1-inch or ⅞-inch scopes.
Price: $7.90 per pair.
From Kwik-Site.

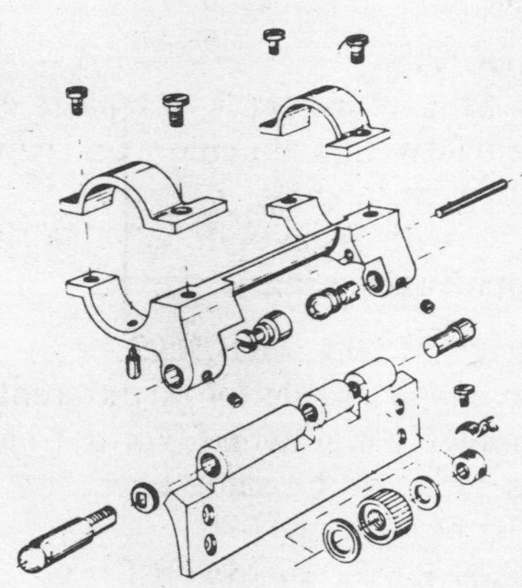

LO-SWING SIDE MOUNT

Shown nearby is an exploded view of Pachmayr's Lo-Swing side mount. It's beautifully made and is designed for the hunter who knows what it's all about. There are moments in the field when you need iron sights; and, the Lo-Swing is perfect for that purpose. You simply swing the mount and scope off to one side and use your iron sights. This mount has received praise from some of the best known hunters.
Price: $30 (see chart below).

Gun Maker	Model	Mount
Winchester	54,70	W-70
	64, 94, Rem. 121, 241	W-94
	Model 12 shotgun	W-12
	88,100	W-88
Remington	Enfield 30S, R720	Enf
	8, 81	R-81
	141,14	R-14
	721, 722, 725 and 700 series	R-721
	740, 760, 742	R-740
	Shotgun 1100	R-1100
	870	R-1100
Savage	40, 45	S-40
	20	S-20
	99	S-99
	340, 342	S-340
	24DL	S-24DL
	340, 342,Sako .222	S-340
	24 DL	S-24 DL
Springfield	1903, A3, 1922, Sedgley-Newton	Spr.
Marlin	36A, 336	M-36
	39A	M-39
Mauser	93	S-40
	98	MR
	All FN Bolt Actions	Mr
	98	MR
	All FN Bolt Actions	Mr
Foreign	Arisaka, Husqvarna Cr	
	Swedish Mauser	S-40
	Japanese 25	S-20
	Sako 222	S-340
	FN 1949 Auto	FN49A
Rem.11	Shotguns	B-R
Military	*Carbine 30Ml	M-1 Carbine
Lee Enfield	SMLE No.1, MK.1,2,3	L-Enf A
	SMLE No.4, MK.1	L-Enf B
Ithaca	37	W-12
Ruger	Mini 14 S/N Prefix 180 or 181	RU-14-180-190
	Mini 14 S/N Prefix 181 or 191	RU-14-181-191

*Due to near vertical shell ejection, it is recommended that these bases be used with a left-hand loop and a crosshair reticle scope.

From Pachmayr Gun Works.

S&K "INSTA-MOUNT" FOR M-1 GARANDS

The base installs into the rear-sight pocket without any alteration to the rifle. Scope sits to the left of the bore allowing for proper ejection of spent brass. Base only.

Price: $42

From S&K Mfg. Co.

S&K "INSTA-MOUNT" FOR M-1 CARBINES

This mount can be installed in minutes without any alteration to the gun. Mount itself deflects spent brass away from scope. Hex key is provided for installation. Base only.

Price: $24

From S&K Mfg. Co.

S&K "INSTA-MOUNT" FOR 1949 F.N. AUTO

The entire mount replaces the F.N. 49's receiver housing covering. Well thought out. No alteration to the gun is necessary. Base only.

Price: $42 (uses S&K rings only).

From S&K Mfg. Co.

S&K "INSTA-MOUNT" for 94/64 WINCHESTERS

This 2-piece mount readily attaches to most 94's or 64's with drilling or tapping. Base only.

Price: $22

From S&K Mfg. Co.

S&K "INSTA-MOUNT" FOR NO. 4 OR 5 LEE ENFIELD.

This mounting system replaces a No. 4 or No. 5 Lee Enfield's rear sight. No alteration of the gun is required and the mount can be installed in minutes. Available to accept Weaver or S&K rings. Base only.

Price: $24.00

From S&K Mfg. Co.

S&K "INSTA-MOUNT" FOR P-14/P-17 ENFIELDS

This S&K mount replaces rear sight on the above rifles. Installs in minutes without any alteration to the rifle. Available to accept Weaver; or, available to accept S&K mounts. Base only.

Price: $23

From S&K Mfg. Co.

MINI-14 MOUNT

Wichita's Mini-14 mount is of 1-piece construction. It's made of lightweight aluminum and can be installed without drilling or tapping.

Price: $17.50; with Weaver detachable rings $29.95.

From Wichita Engineering.

"WIDEVIEW" SCOPE MOUNTS

These mounts are made for 40 different guns. They allow the shooter to mount his favorite 1-inch scope and use the iron sights at the same time.

Price: $14.95 per set.

From the Wideview Scope Mount Corp.

WIDEVIEW MODEL 94 SCOPE MOUNT

This mount utilizes existing receiver holes for attachment—no drilling or tapping required. All aluminum construction. Offset to avoid interference with shell ejection.

Price: See your local dealer.

From the Wideview Scope Mount Corp.

Gunsmithing Tools; Finishing & Refinishing Supplies

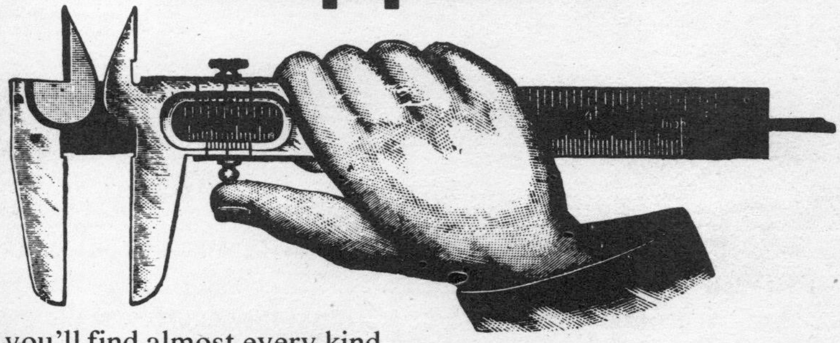

In this section of the book you'll find almost every kind of tool you'll need to dissemble, repair and reassemble practically any kind of firearm, modern or antique. A great many of the tools described and pictured are unique to gunsmithing, practical necessities for successfully accomplishing a specific gunsmithing task but with little other application, while much of the remainder are simply high quality versions of familiar everyday tools particularly suited to gunsmithing.

Top quality, *proper* tools are the cornerstone to successful gunsmithing, even of the simplest kinds. It is probably accurate to say that every serious gun enthusiast has encountered more than one fine sporting or collector's firearm whose value and sometimes even utility has been impaired by the attentions of some well-meaning but poorly equipped and/or careless would-be "gunsmith." Chewed up screw heads from ill-fitting or cheap screwdrivers are the most common evidence of such misdirected efforts, followed by scratched frames or tangs (when the same cheap screwdriver slipped or bent), vise or plier marked barrels or receivers, and a host of other atrocities committed in the name of "home gunsmithing!"

Though you'll find some everyday tools such as screwdrivers described here, the versions we include are those specifically designed for gunsmith work. The key point here is quality, and that's what separates them from the typical household tool that came out of the 99¢ bin at the local discount house. On the other hand, some other general purpose tools necessary for home gunsmithing won't be found in these pages. That's because they're the kinds of tools that should be a part of every man's tool kit, equally usable for general household repairs and work on guns. The only restriction is again quality: buy the product of a first-class maker from a professional hardware store, and the added investment will be repaid many fold, even if the tool is used more for repairing the lawn mower than it is for maintaining your top money making trap gun!

Finishing and refinishing is a very important part of complete gun maintenance, and the necessities for that very important field are also included here. You'll find a very adequate cross-section of finishes for the various metals used in guns, as well as for stock finisihing. When finishing a gun, every first-rate professional refinisher will tell you, the key is *preparation*. The polish of the metal determines the appearance of the finished job, so don't shortcut that part of the job.

You'll find the contents of the first part of this section, tools, arranged roughly by function, starting with basic hand tools. The second part of the section is devoted to finishing and refinishing materials. Many of the latter items are carried by local gun shops; they may also carry a modest selection of gunsmithing tools. For the other items you'll have to go direct to the maker or one of the large gunsmith specialty houses, like Brownells or Herter's.

See the Directory for complete company addresses.

BASIC GUNSMITHING TOOL KIT

Set of 24 tools plus six additional screwdriver bits cover the basic needs for almost any home gunsmith. Included is a gunsmith toolbox of impact-resistant plastic; individual retail price total for the kit is $80.97.

Price: $61.75

From Brownells.

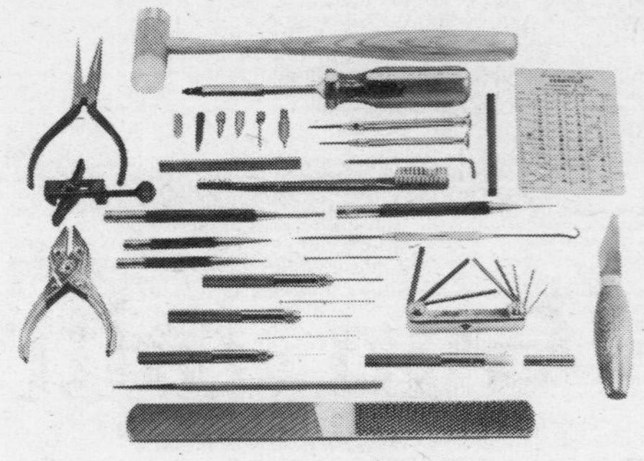

GUN ASSEMBLY/DISASSEMBLY TOOL KIT

Similar to basic gunsmithing kit, except four specialized tools for takedown have been substituted. Individual retail value $79.87.

Price: $58.45

From Brownells.

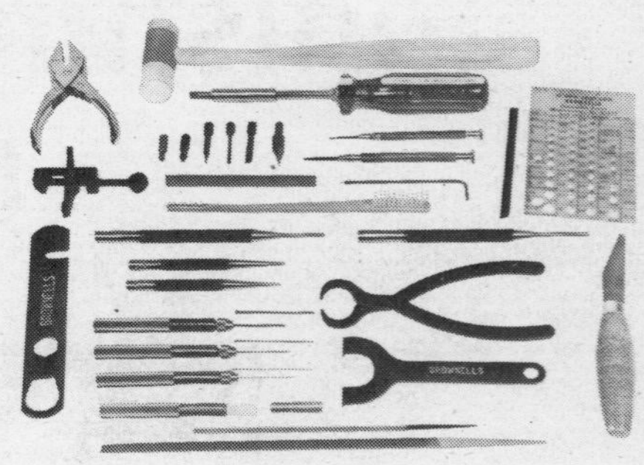

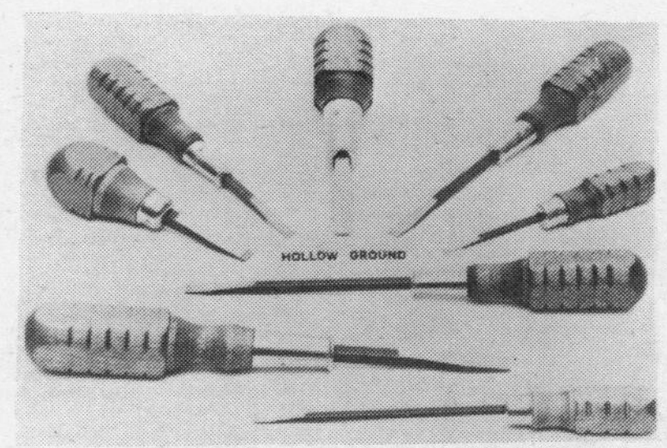

GUNSMITH'S SCREWDRIVERS

Set of eight spring steel, hollow ground screwdrivers, hand forged and guaranteed not to twist or chip. Wood handles.

Price: $26.00

Deluxe set as above, with Pyrolyn handles, plated bits and leatherette roll.

Price: $32.00

From Grace Metal Products.

GUNSMITH PUNCH SET

Set includes five pin punches, one starter punch and one center punch, in a convenient compartmented pouch.

Price: $18.00

From Grace Metal Products.

BRASS GUNSMITH'S HAMMERS

8-oz. and 16-oz. brass hammers won't mar gun steel, feature machine turned white hickory handles.

Price: $7.20 (8 oz.); $8.00 (16 oz.).

From Grace Metal Products.

GUNSMITH'S SCREWDRIVER SET

"Magna-Tip" screwdriver shank holds hollow ground bit securely while permitting instant change to any of 24 bits in set. Included are 11 screwdriver, three Phillips, and 10 hex bits. Handle is shock-proof plastic either solid or hollow with storage space for four bits (specify), shank chrome plated, in fitted carrying/storage case.

Price: $18.45 ($16.95 without case).

Same as above except no Phillips or hex bits.

Price: $9.95

Magna-Tip screwdriver only with one screwdriver blade.

Price: $3.70 (solid); $4.75 (hollow).

From Brownells.

SCREWDRIVER BLADE SHARPENER

Clamps to bench grinder or drill press to hold screwdriver blade for precision hollow grinding, assuring parallel blade faces and square blade tips.

Price: $17.95 plus 85¢ for shipping. Diamond grinding wheel dresser: $9.95 plus 85¢ shipping; Blade sharpener with dresser: $26.95.

From B-Square.

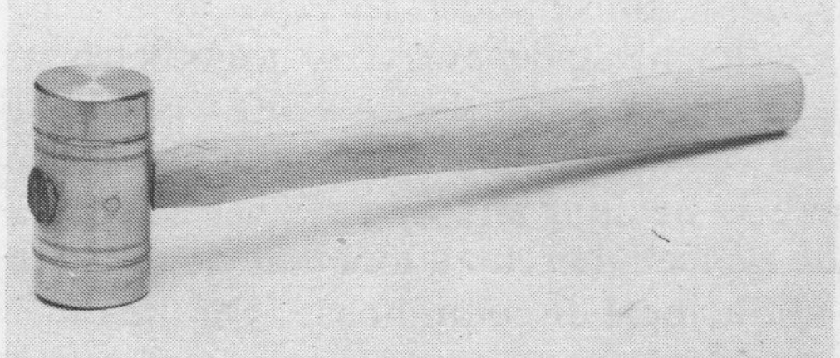

Prices shown are subject to change.

CHECKERING FILES

These specially cut Swiss files are designed for checkering or knurling steel butt plates, sight ramps, triggers, pistol straps and so on. 6 inches long, ½-inch wide, 11/16-inch thick; available in 20, 30, 40, or 50 lines per inch.
Price: $8.49 (specify lines per inch).
From Herter's.

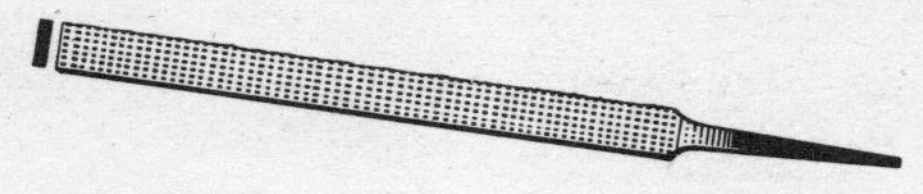

MICRO FILES

Extra-fine files permit working in slots and screw holes where even Swiss files won't go. Round file is 2½-3″ long, about .040″ in diameter; square is 3″ long, .050″ maximum on a side.
Price: $2.50 (round); $2.95 (square).
From Brookstone.

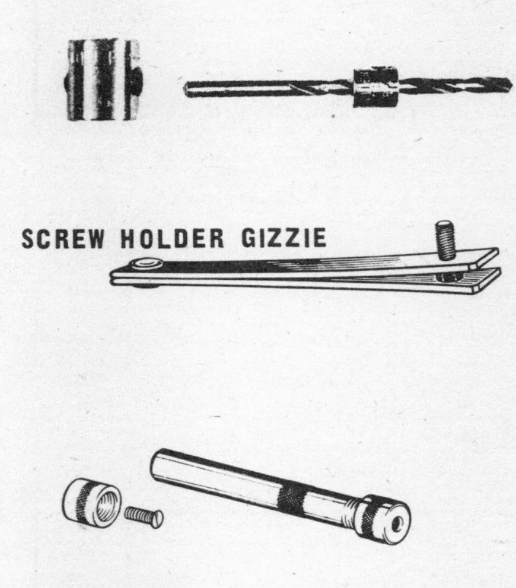

FROZEN SCREW REMOVER

Clamping jack clamps a screwdriver blade firmly into a screw slot, permitting removal of frozen screws without chance of slippage. Includes ratchet wrench and four blades.
Price: $29.95 plus $1 for shipping.
From B-Square.

FLEXIBLE RULER

Ideal for duplicating shapes, matching stock dimensions. Smooth vinyl cover over flexible core, with ledge on one edge for use with ruling pen.
Price: $2.95 (12″); $4.35 (24″).
From Brookstone.

ADJUSTABLE DRILL STOPS

Precision bored high-quality tool steel collars are locked into position with two hex socket set screws, prevent drilling through barrels or other work.
Price: 95¢ (1/16 to ⅛); $1.05 (3/16); $1.15 (¼); $1.35 (5/16); $1.75 (⅜); $2.10 (½).
From Brownells.

SCREW HOLDER

Simple device holds screws firmly while grinding off, filing or shaping the point.
Price: $1.25
From Brownells.

SCREW HOLDER

Screw shortening or point shaping is made easy when a #6 or #8 screw is firmly clamped in this simple device. Eliminates burned fingers, lost or damaged screws.
Price: $6.95 plus 50¢ shipping.
From B-Square.

SPRING WIRE ASSORTMENT

High quality drawn music wire, 100 pieces, each 12″ long, in nine diameters from .020 to .0625″ diameter, for above winder.
Price: $4.95
From Brookstone.

COIL SPRING WINDER

Wind those hard to find extension or compression coil springs. Handles up to about 1/16″ round, flat or square spring wire.
Price: $9.95
From Brookstone.

UNIVERSAL DRILLING FIXTURE

Self-Centering rapid clamping fixture for cylindrical surfaces such as barrels and actions assures precisely centered and drilled holes for sight bases, ribs, etc. Also useful for angled drilling, milling, accommodates bits to 9/16″; clamping capacity ⅛″ to 2″.
Price: $267.00; add $58.00 for set of 16 drill bushings.
From Moderntools.

STOCK INSIDE-THE-BUTT SCREW WRENCH

Unscrew stock screw without damage to screw slots or stock with this special tool. Longer tool is for most stocks, the shorter is a special wrench for the Remington Model 1100 action spring tube nut.

Price: $19.95 each (specify length), plus $1.50 shipping.

From B-Square.

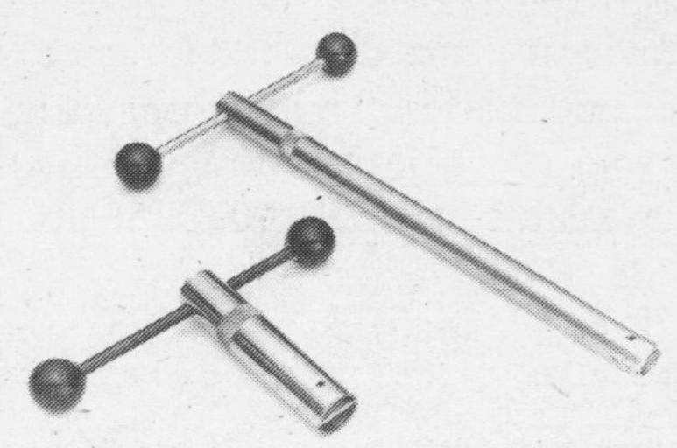

HEADSPACE GAUGES

Go, No-Go and Field headspace gauges are available for most rifle and pistol calibers; Go and No-Go only are offered for shotguns.

Price:

Rifle and pistol, $8.00 (each); $22.50 (set of three).

Shotgun, $17.00 (each).

From Clymer Mfg.

FIRING PIN PROTRUSION GAUGE

Precision device permits accurate measurement of bolt action rifle firing pin protrusion, a must for safe, reliable primer ignition.

Price: $9.25

From Brownells.

GO/NO-GO GAUGES

Gauges are available singly or in sets of two for rimmed and rimless calibers, shotgun gauges.

Price: $13.00 each ($20.00 set) for rimmed and belted cartridges; $16.00 each ($32.00 set) for rimless or shotgun.

From Keith Francis.

STAMPING GUIDE

Permits stamping lettering or numbers evenly aligned and correctly spaced on either round or flat surfaces. Accommodates up to 20 1/16" or 13 3/32" characters.

Price: $19.95 plus 75¢ shipping (includes spacers).

Letters and numbers for above guide, in either 1/16" or 3/32" characters (specify).

Price: $27.25 plus $1.50 shipping (26 characters); $9.19 plus $1 shipping (nine numbers).

From B-Square.

STAMP GUIDE SET

Stamping guide as above, complete with letters and numbers set with 1/16" or 3/32" characters (specify).

Price: $49.95 plus $2 shipping.

From B-Square.

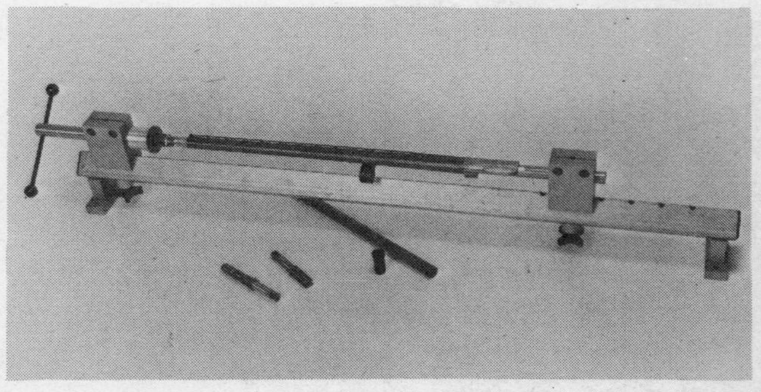

CHOKE INSTALLING TOOL

Special tool bores and threads inside of shotgun barrel to accommodate Winchester Winchokes or Mossberg Accu-Choke. Complete, ready to use, with cutters for 12 gauge.

Price: $299.50; Extra chamber arbor, cutter and top for 20 gauge, $89.95.

From B-Square.

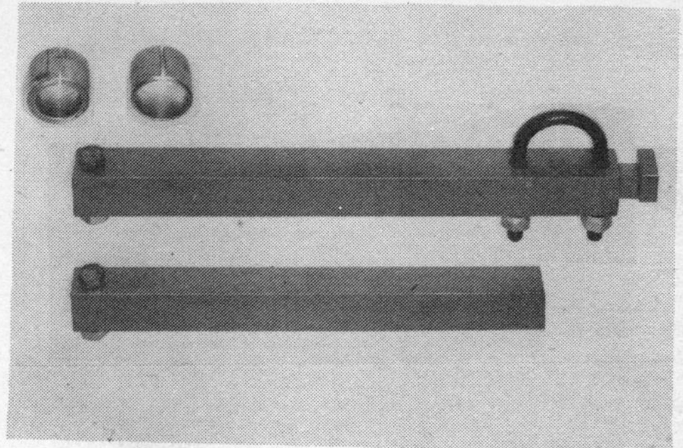

IMPACT ACTION WRENCH

Heavy steel bar wrench will fit both round and flat-bottomed receivers, will often loosen an action that won't respond to usual methods.

Price: $24.95

From Brownells.

REMINGTON ACTION WRENCH

Fits all Remington actions except Model 788.

Price: $20.00

From Davidson.

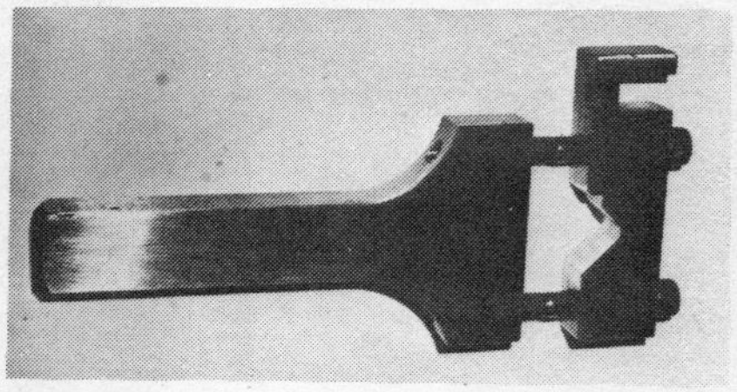

RIFLE ACTION WRENCH

Three-V action wrench will remove virtually any rifle action, is usable with many pistols and muzzle loaders.

Price: $64.95

From Brownells.

LOADING PORT WRENCH

12″ long wrench of 7075-T6 aluminum fits loading ports of Remington, Shilen DGA and most Mauser actions.

Price: $20.00

From Davidson.

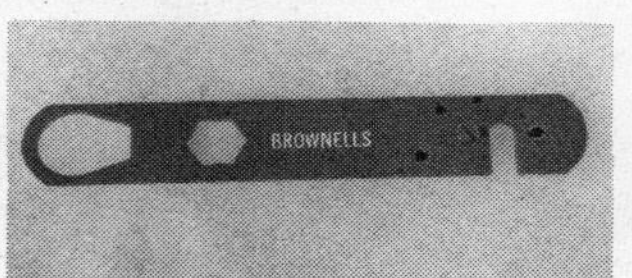

COLT DISASSEMBLY WRENCH

Specially designed wrench fits 1911 auto barrel bushing plus ejector/extractor ratchet from large and small frame Colt revolvers.

Price: $3.95

From Brownells.

COLT CRANE BUSHING TOOL

Makes removal of crane bushing easy and damage-free.

Price: $8.95

From Brownells.

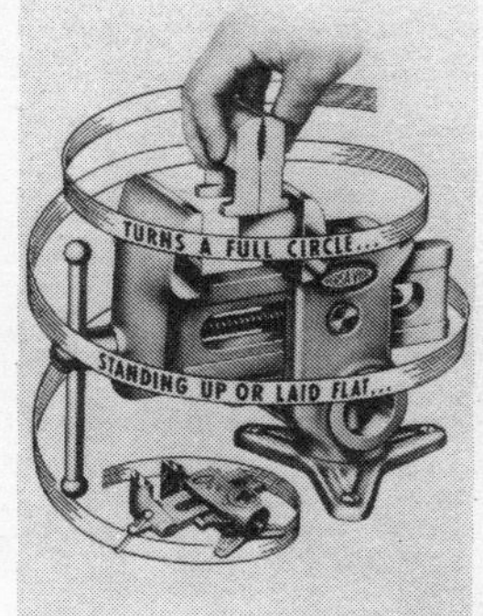

GUNSMITH'S VISE

The "Versa-Vise" is particularly useful for gunsmithing because of its flexibility. 3½″ wide by 2½″ high jaws open to 5″, includes removable serrated jaws for round stock up to 1½″.

Price: $34.50

From Will-Burt Co.

VISE JAW FACING MATERIALS

Protects fine finishes from damage from vise jaws, helps keep work from slipping.

Price: 5/32″ thick leather, $2.40 (pair 4″ x 6½″).

Price: 3/64″ thick lead, $1.29 (4 - 2 x 4″ sheets); $1.90 (4 - 3″ x 4″ sheets).

From Brownells.

VISE JAW FACING

"Accu-Grip" vise pads are made of unique elastomeric materials that hold work securely without excessive clamping pressure. Two types, one for soft materials such as wood (red colored) and the other for metals (green colored) are available, either as vise jaw facing with backing or in 7″ x 7″ sheets.

Price: $12.50 (specify type, color, and configuration).

From H. S. Precision.

See the Directory for complete company addresses.

BARREL VISE

Machined from heavy steel bar, but small enough to swing in lathe. Specify bushings.

Price: $31.95 (vise, less bushings); Bushings are $3.50 each—specify for Enfield, Mauser, Springfield, Sporter (1.125″), Winchester M-70, or undrilled. Shipping $1.50 additional.

From B-Square.

BARREL VISE

Three-V barrel vise is solid steel to provide extreme clamping force to any barrel. Supplied with bushings for tapered (Springfield, Enfield, etc.), stepped (Mauser 98), Douglas and straight barrels.

Price: $86.95

From Brownells.

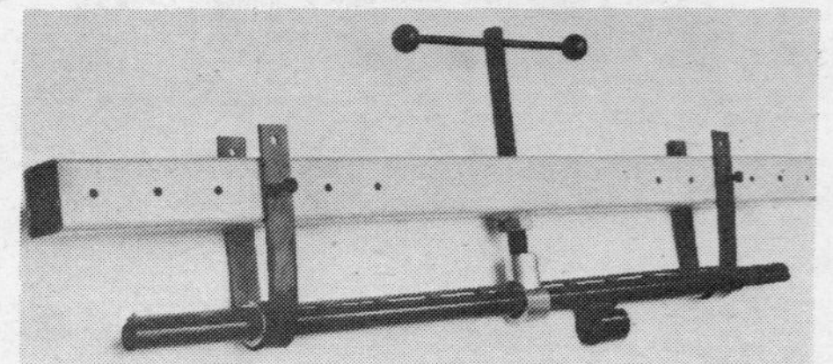

BARREL PRESS

Portable press permits accurate, controlled straightening of both plain and vent rib shotgun barrels without harming finish.

Price: $59.95 plus $3.00 shipping.

From B-Square.

RIFLE VISE

Permits firmly, but safely mounting rifle or shotgun for cleaning, bore sighting, inletting, scope base mounting and many other operations. Available in left- or right-hand models (specify).

Price: $29.95

From Decker Shooting Products.

BARREL VISE

Vee Vise is 7″ long, made from 2024-T3 aluminum, fits barrels up to 1.5″ diameter.

Price: $25.00

From Davidson.

MAINSPRING VISE

Convenient tool compresses "V" type mainsprings for easy removal and installation.

Price: $3.50

From Brownells.

REMINGTON MAINSPRING TOOL

Controls mainspring while removing or installing crosspin through the firing pin and firing pin head of a Remington bolt.

Price: $7.50

From Davidson.

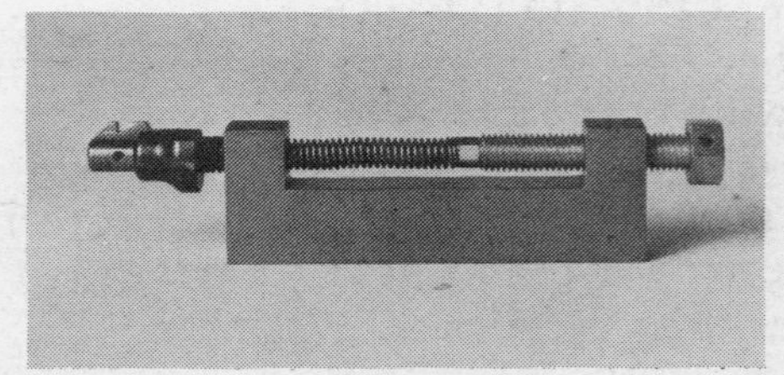

REMINGTON FIRING PIN TOOL

Special tool permits compression of mainspring for disassembly or reassembly when replacing spring or firing pin. For Remington Model 40X, XP100 or 700 series.

Price: $9.50

From K. W. Kleindorst.

CHAMBER REAMERS

An extensive line of chamber reamers for most rimmed, rimless and belted cartridges, current and obsolete. Wildcats are also available on special order. Request catalog and price list.

From Clymer Mfg.

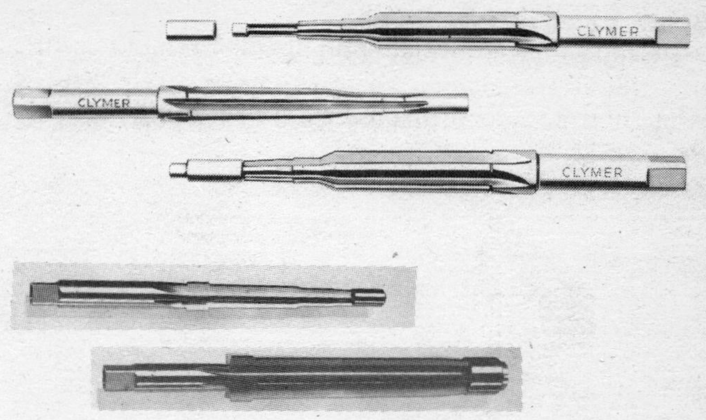

CHAMBERING REAMERS

Furnished in both finish and resize dimensions for calibers from .22 Long Rifle to .50 Government, plus shotguns from .410 to 12 gauge.

Price: $36.00 up (request detailed price list).

From Keith Francis.

CHAMBER REAMERS

Rifle and pistol chamber reamers from .22 Long Rifle through .460 Weatherby Magnum. Roughing reamers are high-speed steel; finishing reamers are finishing or high-speed steel. Shotgun dies, for 10 through 28 gauge and .410, are high carbon steel.

Price: $17.50-36.00 (roughing dies); $20.00-48.00 (finishing dies).

From F. K. Elliott.

CHAMBERING REAMERS

Finish and resize chamber reamers from .22 Long Rifle through Nitro Express calibers range from $28.00 through $65.00 each. Shotgun reamers from .410 through 20 ga. are $55.00; 16 and 12 ga. are $60.00 each. A wide range of other reamers, gauges are also offered.

Price: Request detailed price list.

From Henriksen Tool Co.

ADJUSTABLE SPANNER FOR FIRING PIN BUSHINGS

Specially designed wrench has a fully adjustable head that can be set to fit all 2- or 3-hole firing pin bushings from 3/16″ to 7/16″ spacing. A must for easy, damage-free servicing of quality European, Japanese and American double barrel and over-under shotguns.

Price: $34.95 plus $1 shipping.

From B-Square.

REMINGTON BOLT TOOL

Permits quick, easy removal of striker assembly from Remington Model 40X and 700 series bolts.

Price: $15.50

From K. W. Kleindorst.

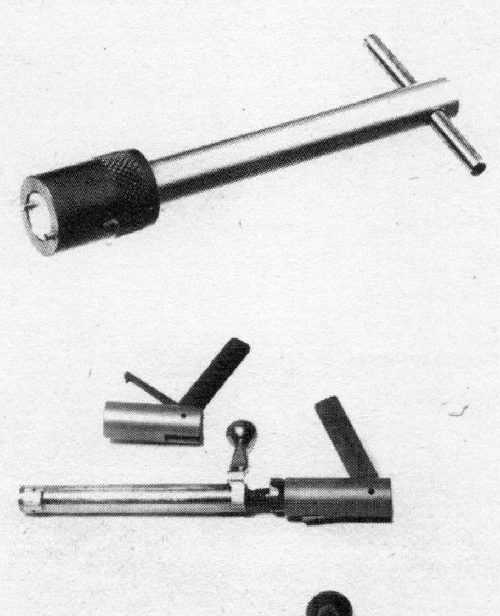

WINCHESTER BOLT TOOL

Winchester Model 52 bolts can be disassembled and reassembled quickly with this easy-to-use tool, which screws into rear of bolt.

Price: $12.50

From K. W. Kleindorst.

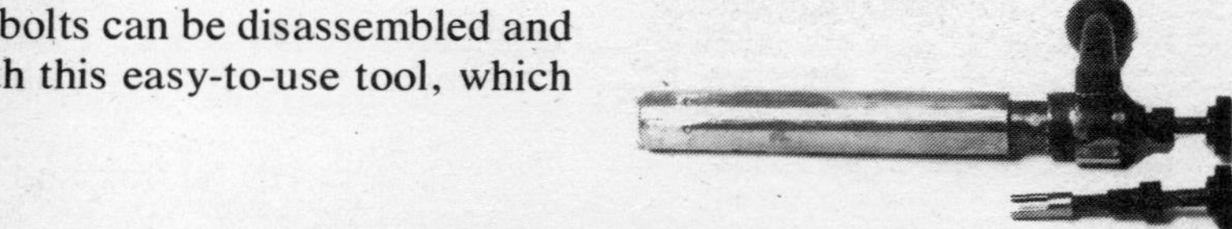

BOLT FACING LATHE BIT

Specially ground carbide tipped steel cutter permits opening bolt faces to magnum dimension.

Price: $5.45 (1/4″ shank); $6.00 (5/16″ shank).

From Brownells.

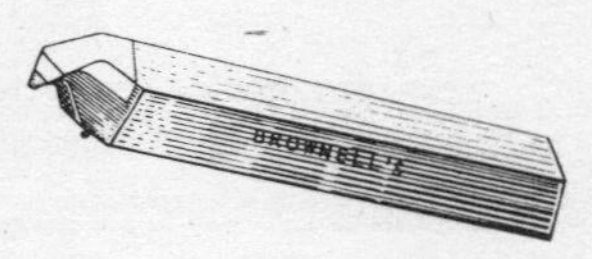

ENFIELD BOLT STRIPPING TOOL

Tool steel bolt-stripping tool facilitates takedown of British SMLE rifle bolts. Supplied with detailed instructions.

Price: $4.95

From The Sight Shop.

See the Directory for complete company addresses.

BOLT BENDING BLOCKS

Permits altering straight bolt handles without cutting or welding. Heat handle shaft with oxy-acetylene torch while bolt body is protected from heat by the block.

Price: $22.75

From Buehler.

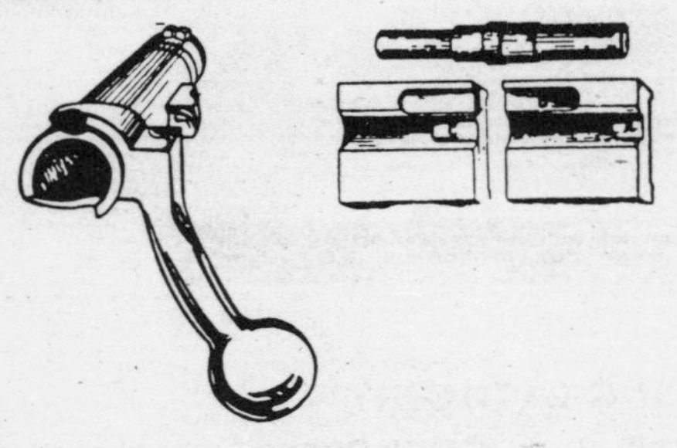

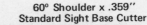

60° Shoulder x .359″
Standard Sight Base Cutter

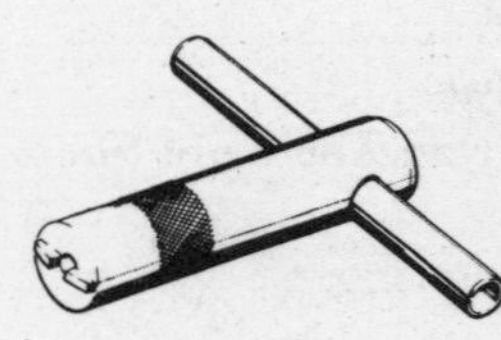

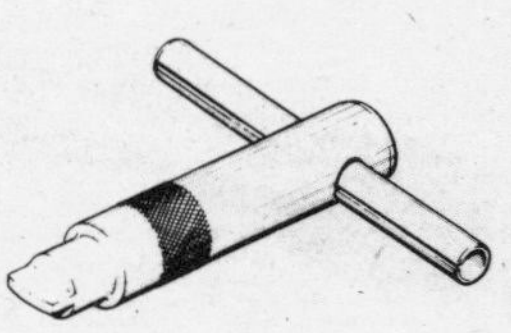

ENGINE TURNING HEAD

This engine turning tool can be chucked in any hand tool, drill press or lathe that will accommodate a 3/16″ shank. Includes two rubber tips to do the engine turning, two felt tips for final polishing.

Price: $1.49; extra rubber tips, 10 for $.89; felt tips, 20 for $.79.

From Herters.

BARREL CROWNING LATHE BIT

Double-ended cutters permit a smooth radius crown to be cut on any barrel.

Price: $5.60 (¼″ shank); $6.70 (⅜″ shank).

From Brownells.

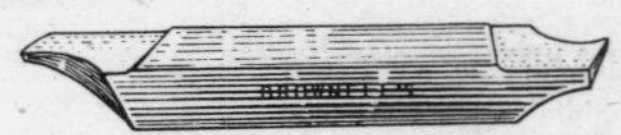

SIGHT SLOT CUTTERS

Cutter for 60° shoulder x ⅜″ standard front and rear sights is slightly undersize to permit compensating for variation in factory sight bases.

Price: $8.95

Same, except 65° x ⅜″ for Colt 1911 rear sight.

Price: $8.95

Same, except 65° x ½″ for low profile Colt 1911 rear sight.

Price: $10.95

From Brownells.

SCOPE MOUNT WRENCH

The blade on this specially made wrench makes tightening the large ring clamp nut on Weaver or similar scope rings a cinch.

Price: $7.95 plus 50¢ shipping.

From B-Square.

SCREWDRIVER BLADE SCOPE MOUNT WRENCH

Special wrench enables Redfield and Ruger scope rings to be properly tightened without burring or marring screw slots.

Price: $7.95 plus 50¢ shipping.

From B-Square.

FRONT SIGHT PUSHER

Avoid damage to sight, ramp or barrel finish by installing and adjusting from sights with this easy to use tool instead of a hammer.

Price: $23.85

From Williams Gun Sight.

QUICK-CHANGE GRINDER MOUNTS

Snap-in work arbors mount instantly to the "Roto-Lock" chuck, permit easy use of a single bench motor for grinder, wire brush, polishing, etc. Maximum speed 5,000 rpm.

Price: $34.95 (Roto-Lok and three arbors).

From MarshAl's.

Prices shown are subject to change.

VARIABLE SPEED GRINDER

Speed adjustable from 5,000 to 30,000 rpm, with electronic motor regulation that holds speed constant with changes in load. Supplied with both 3/32″ and 1/8″ collets. Available separately or cased with a variety of accessories.

Price: $63.00 (Grinder only, Model 6000 PMS).

Same as above but single speed (30,000 rpm) only.

Price: $44.00 (Grinder only, Model 6000 PM).

From Chicago Wheel & Mfg.

GRINDER ACCESSORIES

Grinder wheels, brushes, polishing wheels, steel rotary cutters, saws and many other accessories are available for use with Chicago Wheel and other grinders, both in sets and as individual items.

Price: 75¢ up individually; sets also available.

From Chicago Wheel & Mfg.

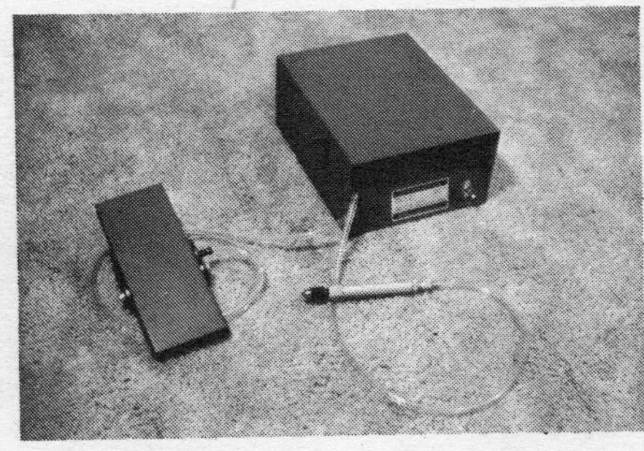

POWER ENGRAVING SYSTEM

Controlled impact power delivered by a compact, maneuverable handpiece at a rate variable from 800 to 1200 strokes per minute makes the "Gravermeister" a necessity for beginning as well as experienced engravers. Ideal for matting and other background forms as well as figures and deep carving.

Price: $598 (Gravermeister II, complete with three engraving tools).

From Glendo Corp.

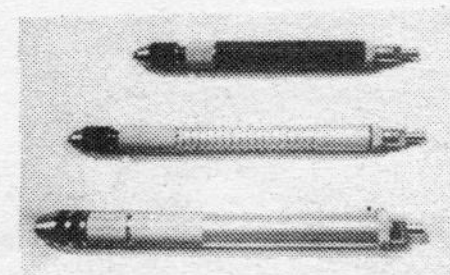

ENGRAVING BLOCK

This massive (28½ lb.) engraving block is fully adjustable yet locks and remains locked in the position required. Has one fixed, one pivot attachment plates.

Price: $288

From Glendo Corp.

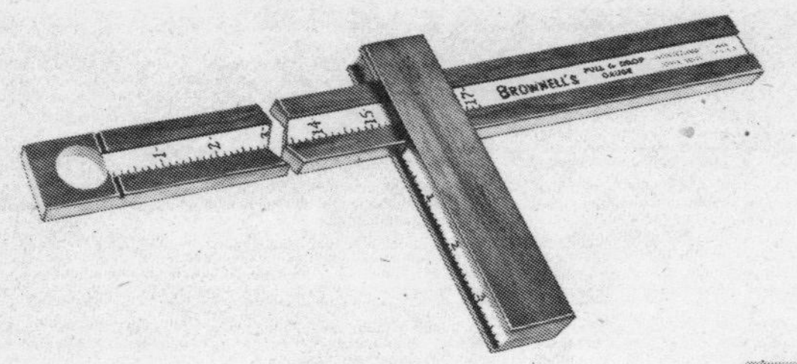

STOCK PULL AND DROP GAUGE

This gauge quickly, easily and accurately measures the pull and drop of any rifle or shotgun stock, plus the pull of a shooter's forearm-trigger finger. Of oil-finished solid cherry wood.
Price: $7.35
From Brownells.

STOCK INLETTING BLACK

Non-drying, non-greasy inletting black that facilitates inletting yet cleans easily from metal parts with a wipe of a rag. Sufficient for four to five stocks.
Price: $1.95 (½-oz.).
From Jarrow's.

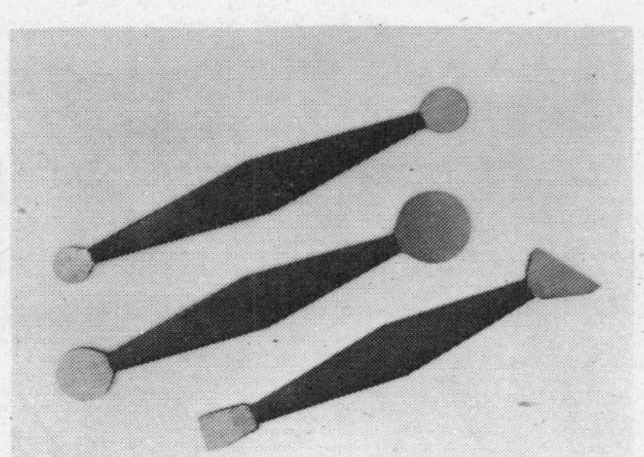

STOCK INLETTING SCRAPERS

Double-ended inletting scrapers, one with circular ends and the other flat cut, are offered. The flat cut scraper is ground at angles designed for inletting octagon barrels and for straight-sided mortises. The circular scraper is offered in 1″x¾″ and ⅝″x½″ combinations (specify); all are heat-treated alloy steel, easily sharpened on an ordinary bench grinder.
Price: $6.50 each (specify style and size).
From Jerry A. Fisher.

INLETTING SCRAPERS

Set of two wood-handled inletting scrapers, one with rounded blade and one straight-edged, can be reground to fit specific stockmaking needs.
Price: $12.00 (set of two).
From Grace Metal Products.

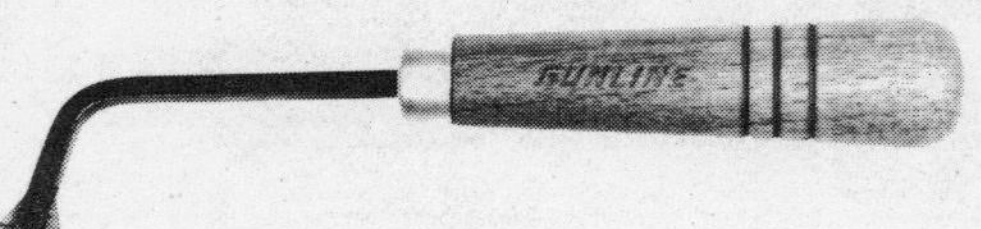

BOTTOMING AND SHAPING TOOLS

Tool set includes handle, three cutters of assorted shapes to take care of almost any stock inletting problem.
Price: $13.15 (Bottoming Set); $13.50 (Shaper File Set).
From Gunline Tools.

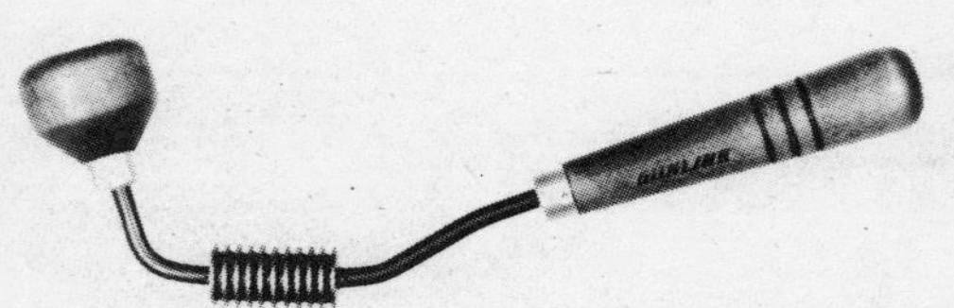

BARREL BEDDING TOOL

Hardened, cushioned multi-cutters cut barrel grooves with a smooth, chatterless finish. Specify 5/8″, 11/16″ or 3/4″ diameter cutters.
Price: $5.60; $3.20 (extra set of separators and cutters).
From Gunline Tools.

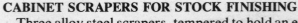

CABINET SCRAPERS FOR STOCK FINISHING

Three alloy steel scrapers, tempered to hold an edge, provide almost every shape needed for fine stock or other wood work. Rectangular blades are about 2¼x6″; curved, about 3x4½″.
Price: $6.50 (set of three).
From Brookstone.

Prices shown are subject to change.

POWER CHECKERING TOOL

Fast, easy checkering of 16 to 24 lines can be done with Miniature Machine Co.'s M/2 power checkering tool. The M/2 is designed to be used with a Foredom Flexade Model B8D or Series CC or EE flexible shaft handtool, on which it replaces the hand guard. Cutters should remain sharp through at least five stocks; cutter sharpening service is $5.30 (return to factory).
Price: $277.50 (with carbide cutter).
From Brownells.

CHECKERING AND CARVING TEMPLATES

Decals provide an easy-to-use guide for stock checkering and carving. 34 different patterns including borders, animals and many checkering variations are offered.
Price: $2.50 (per pattern).
From Stan deTreville

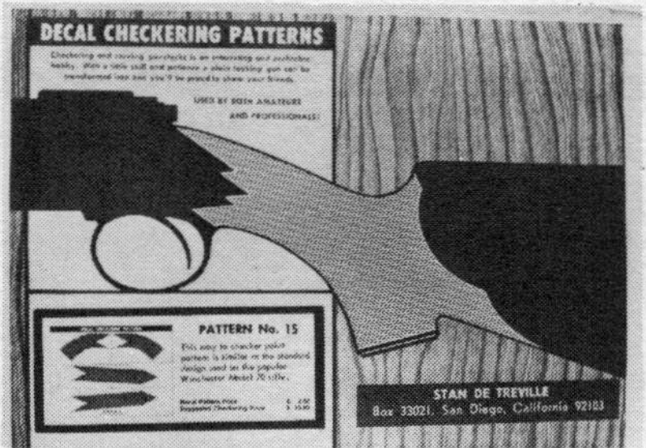

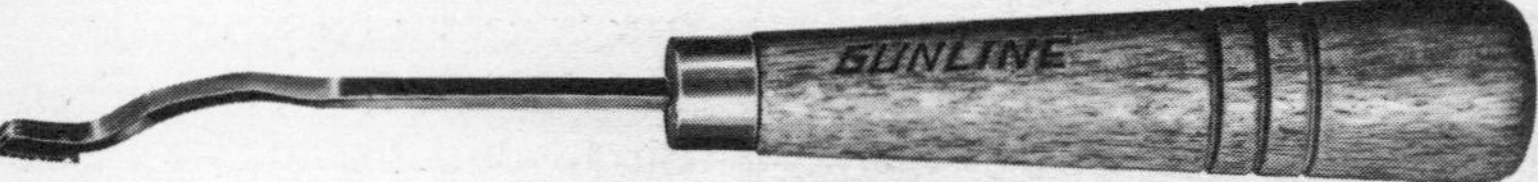

CHECKERING TOOLS

Checkering cutters are available in sets with gauge and instructions. "Leader" set includes 2-edge spacer, Border-Vex, V-Edger, Pointer-Long; "Camp Perry" set also includes 3-Edge spacer, Veiner.
Price: $16.75 ("Leader"); $25.00 ("Camp Perry").

"E-Z Checkit" tool is equipped with 4 spring-activated guides for maximum flexibility; extra coarse or fine cutting heads are also available.
Price: $15.70 (tool, complete); $2.30 (extra heads, specify coarse or fine).
From Gunline Tools.

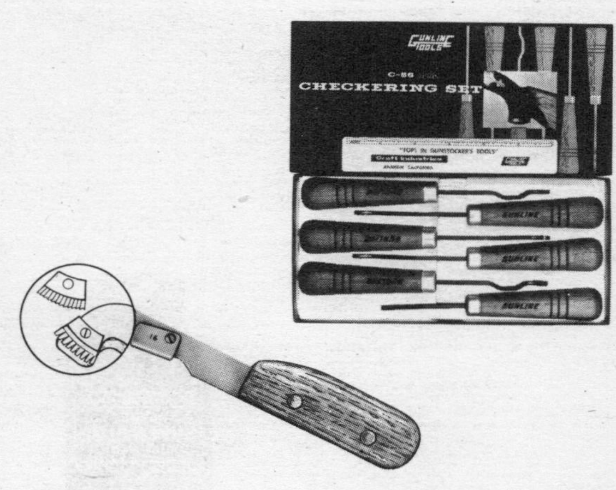

CHECKERING TOOL SHARPENING STONE

Configured specially for sharpening checkering tools, this 4-inch long by ¼-inch thick stone has 60° angled sides and is available in either fine or medium grit.
Price: $2.19 (specify fine or medium).
From Herter's.

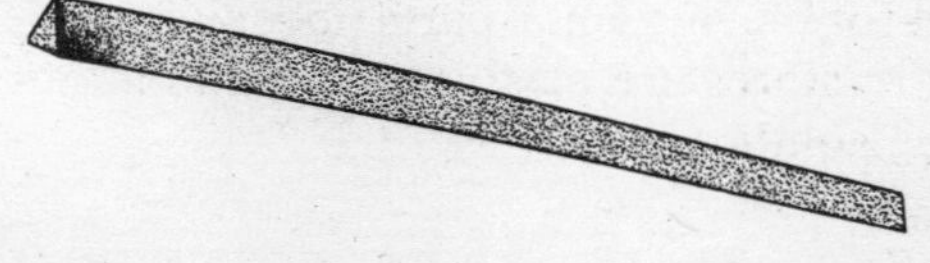

CHECKERING TOOLS

Double action high-carbon chromium steel cutters cut backward as well as forward; patented holder allows unobstructed view of the work. Available separately or as a kit with a holder and five cutters; specify 16, 18, 20, 22, 24, 26, 28 or 32 lines per inch.
Price: $15.50 (kit); $4.35 (holder only); $2.20 to $5.05 each (cutters).
From W. E. Brownell.

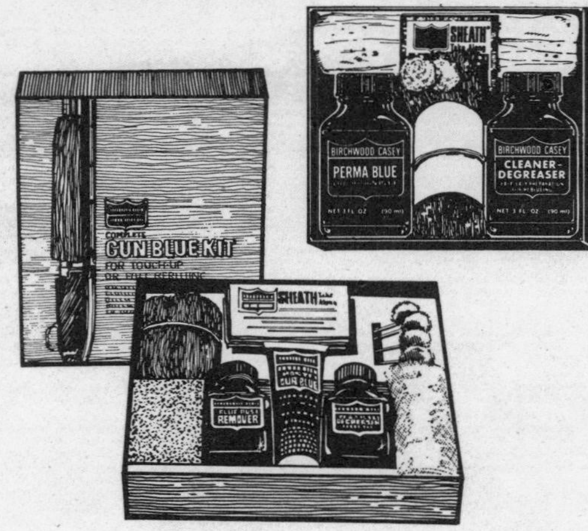

GUN BLUE KITS

Custom "Perma Blue" Kit contains cleaner, "Perma Blue," steel wool, gun wipes and applicator swabs for touch up or simple reblueing. More complete kit also includes blue and rust remover, paste gun blue. Deluxe kit has the same blueing materials as the complete kit, plus everything needed for a professional like stock finishing job.

Price: Custom Perma-Blue Kit, $3.50; Complete Perma-Blue Kit, $5.95; Deluxe Perma-Blue Kit, $9.95.

From Birchwood Casey.

BARREL BLUEING KITS

Immersion blueing provides a more even blue for rifle and shotgun barrels, other large gun parts. Includes 36″ plastic tank, cleaner, blue concentrate, steel wool, applicators and wiping cloths.

Price: $26.95

From Birchwood Casey.

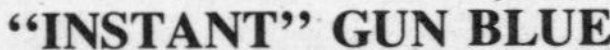

"INSTANT" GUN BLUE

Designed for touch-up or complete gun reblueing, Birchwood Casey's "Perma Blue" penetrates and blues steel with a durable, rust-resistant finish.

Price: $1.75 (3-oz. bottle).

From Birchwood Casey.

PASTE GUN BLUE

Easily applied paste-type touch up blue provides a durable, attractive blue-black finish.

Price: $1.75

From Birchwood Casey.

"SUPER" TOUCH-UP BLUE

Extra strong formula "Super Blue" works through grease and oil, requires no prior preparation to touch up nicks or scratches.

Price: $2.50 (3 oz. bottle)

From Birchwood Casey.

TOUCH-UP BLUE

"Dicropan T-4" is a professional type touch up blue that blends well with existing finish, yet is easy to apply and durable.

Price: $3.75 (4-oz.); $6.75 (pint).

From Brownells.

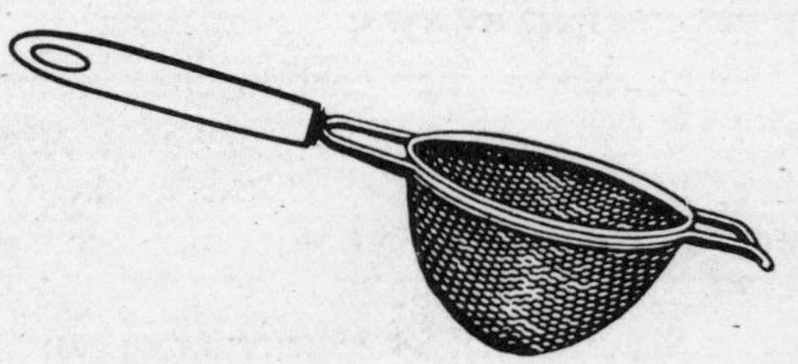

BLUEING PARTS BASKET

Iron wire mesh vegetable strainer makes an ideal basket for blueing small parts (most vegetable strainers found in stores are plastic or aluminum, not usable in blueing solutions).

Price: $1.19

From Brownells.

Prices shown are subject to change.

GENERAL PURPOSE BLUE

"Oxpho-Blue" penetrates old rust, under oil, grease and surface dirt to provide a deep, durable blue-black finish with minimum preparation. Ideal for touch up or quick reblueing of actions.

Price: $2.98 (4-oz.); $5.45 (pint).

From Brownells.

BLUEING TANKS

Professional-type blueing tanks come in three (two-heated) and six (four-heated) styles; the three tank unit is for blue and rinse only, while cleaning and oiling operations can also be carried out with the six-tank style.

Price: Three-tank, $394.00; six-tank, $708.00

From Heatbath Corp.

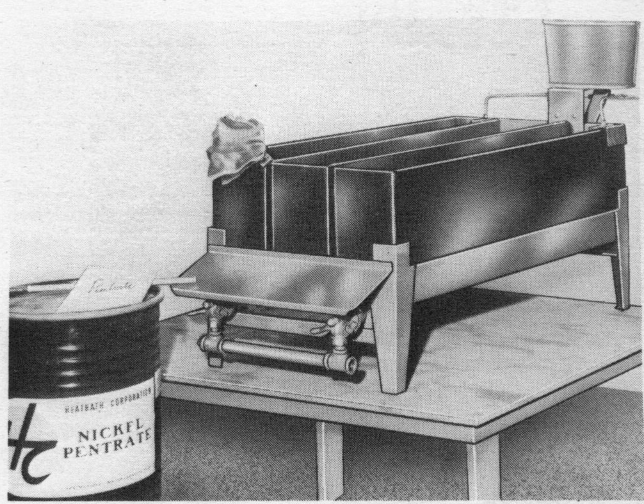

BLUEING CHEMICALS

"Pentrate" cleaner and blueing salts assure well cleaned metal surfaces for even deep blue, the blueing salts provide a deep, lustrous blue-black finish. "Sol-U-Dip" oil is specifically designed to complement the action of the blueing salts and stabilize the blue after rinse.

Price: Cleaner, 40¢/lb; Blueing salts, 60¢/lb; Oil, $5.18/gallon.

From Heatbath Corp.

RAPID GUN BLUE

"Minute Man" gun-blue is ideal for touch up of scratches or worn spots.

Price: $2.59 (2-oz. plastic bottle).

From New Method.

TOUCH-UP GUN BLUE

"44-40" provides easy to use room temperature touch up of scratched and worn blued steel surfaces. Available in 2-oz. plastic bottles for gun hobbyists; larger quantities for industrial users.

Price: $3.00 (2-oz.).

From Numrich Arms.

RUST BLUE SOLUTION

Rust blueing provides the same finish used on fine quality arms of the last century. Successive applications provide a deeper, darker finish.

Price: $3.10 (2 oz. bottle).

From Dixie Gun Works.

COLD BLUE KIT

Quick acting cold blue (2-oz. bottle) for touch up, blueing scopes or soldered shotgun barrels that cannot be hot blued. Complete with metal cleaning liquid (2-oz.), steel wool and polishing cloth.

Price: $2.79

From Herters.

BELGIAN GUN BLUE

Easy to use non caustic blue for touch up or complete gun blueing. Parts to be blued are first boiled for cleaning, then blueing solution swabbed on. Successive coats may be applied for deeper, heavier blue. Will not attack solder.

Price: $1.39 (3-oz.); $2.49 (8-oz.); $4.49 (pint).

From Herter's.

BLUE REMOVER

Removes rust or old blue prior to polishing for reblue.

Price: $1.25 (2-oz.); $3.19 (pint).

From Herter's.

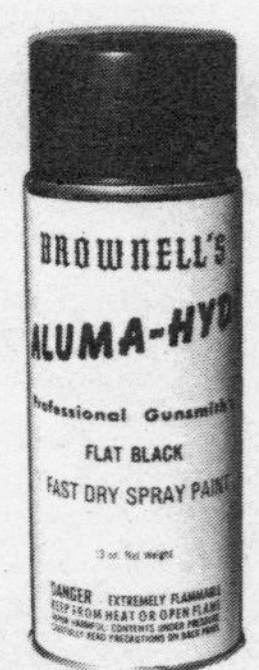

SURFACE-HARDENING COMPOUND

Harden surfaces of steel or iron gun parts for maximum durability. Non-Poisonous Kasenit No. 1 compound is applied by heating parts to red heat, dipping them in Kasenit, reheating and quenching in cold water.

Price: $4.65 (one-lb can).

From Kasenit.

"PLUM BROWN" ANTIQUE BARREL FINISH

Cold chemical provides iron and steel with the traditional brown finish found on antiques of the muzzle-loading era.

Price: $3.00 (3-oz. bottle).

From Birchwood Casey.

ALUMINUM BLACK METAL FINISH

Imparts a dark-grey to deep black finish to aluminum gun parts.

Price: $3.00 (3-oz. bottle).

From Birchwood Casey.

BRASS BLACK METAL FINISH

Easy to use touch up liquid gives brass or copper parts a dark finish, hides scratches and nicks.

Price: $3.00 (3-oz. bottle).

From Birchwood Casey.

ALUMINUM SPRAY BLACK FINISH

A special nitrocellulose lacquer, "Aluma-Hyde" provides a tough, durable coating to aluminum gun parts whose original anodized finish has been worn bright. Kit includes zinc chromate primer.

Price: $5.39 (13 oz. each of primer, black "Aluma-Hyde").

From Brownells.

GOLD OR SILVER "FILLER"

Highlight engraving, markings and serial numbers with gold or silver with these easy-to-use kits.

Price: $3.00 (specify gold or silver).

From Bonanza Sports.

BROWNING FINISH

Imparts a deep reddish brown finish to iron and steel similar to that found on early muzzle loaders.

Price: $1.95 (2 oz. bottle).

From Dixie Gun Works.

GOLD SHEET

10 Karat, 22 gauge gold sheet for nameplates and inlays.

Price: $25.75 (square inch).

From Dixie Gun Works.

STERLING SILVER SHEET

22 gauge Sterling silver sheet for nameplates, decoration.

Price: $3.05 (square inch).

From Dixie Gun Works.

SILVER WIRE
Sterling silver 22 gauge wire for inlays, decorative nails and rivets.
Price: $1.15 (foot).
From Dixie Gun Works.

BLUE AND RUST REMOVER
Quickly and thoroughly removes old blue and rust, a must before reblueing.
Price: $1.60 (3-oz. bottle); $3.95 (8-oz. bottle).
From Birchwood Casey.

CLEANER-DEGREASER
Thoroughly removes grease, oil, wax from metal preparatory to blueing.
Price: $1.60 (3-oz. bottle); $5.50 (quart).
From Birchwood Casey.

METAL POLISHING PASTE
Cleans, polishes and protects brass, silver and gold from tarnish. Won't scratch.
Price: $1.98 (4 fl. oz.).
From Birchwood Casey.

GUN CLEANING SOLUTION
Soak cleaner removes caked-on dirt, dried grease, lacquer from guns and gun parts preparatory to refinishing. To be mixed with water, strength dependent on job.
Price: $5.75 (gallon).
From Brownells.

RUST AND BLUE REMOVER
Removes rust and old blue from guns too fragile or complicated to permit thorough polishing before reblueing.
Price: $4.95 (quart); $11.15 (gallon).
From Brownells.

DEGREASER/CLEANER
Specially formulated "Minute Man" Degreaser & Cleaner removes dirt, grease, oil, wax and powder residue from metal surfaces preparatory to blueing or browning.
Price: $1.50 (2-oz. bottle).
From New Method.

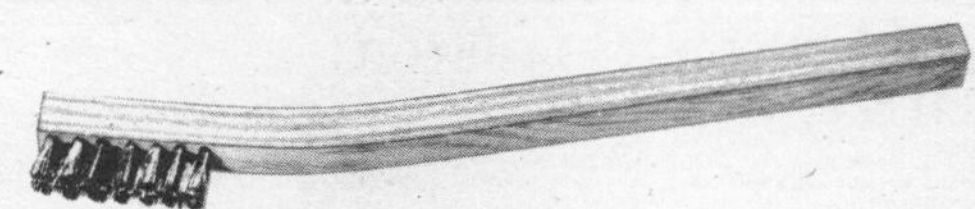

STAINLESS STEEL BRUSH
Has .005" stainless steel wire bristles, with heavy seven-ply laminated handle. Ideal for cleaning hard to reach corners in actions, threads.
Price: $1.80
From Brownells.

SHEET BRASS, GERMAN SILVER
Sheet metal in thicknesses from 1/32" to ¼" is used for gunsmithing or Kentucky-rifle style decoration.
Price: (Brass, 6"x8") $1.25 (1/32"); $2.65 (1/16"); $3.00 (3/32"); $4.50 (⅛"); $9.50 (¼").
(German Silver, 6"x8") $1.95 (1/32"); $2.75 (1/16"); $3.75 (3/32").
From Dixie Gun Works.

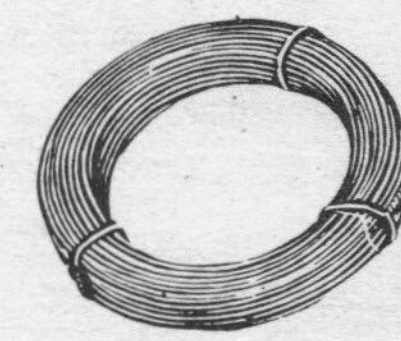

IRON WIRE
Soft annealed black 18-gauge iron wire is ideal for hanging parts in wash or blueing tank, jigging up parts for welding, brazing or soldering.
Price: $.69 (50-foot roll).
From Brownells.

PARTS CLEANING BRUSH
Dual head brush has a notched "toothbrush" at one end, a single row of short stiff bristles at the other. Bristles are solvent-proof polypropylene.
Price: $1.39
From Brownells.

See the Directory for complete company addresses.

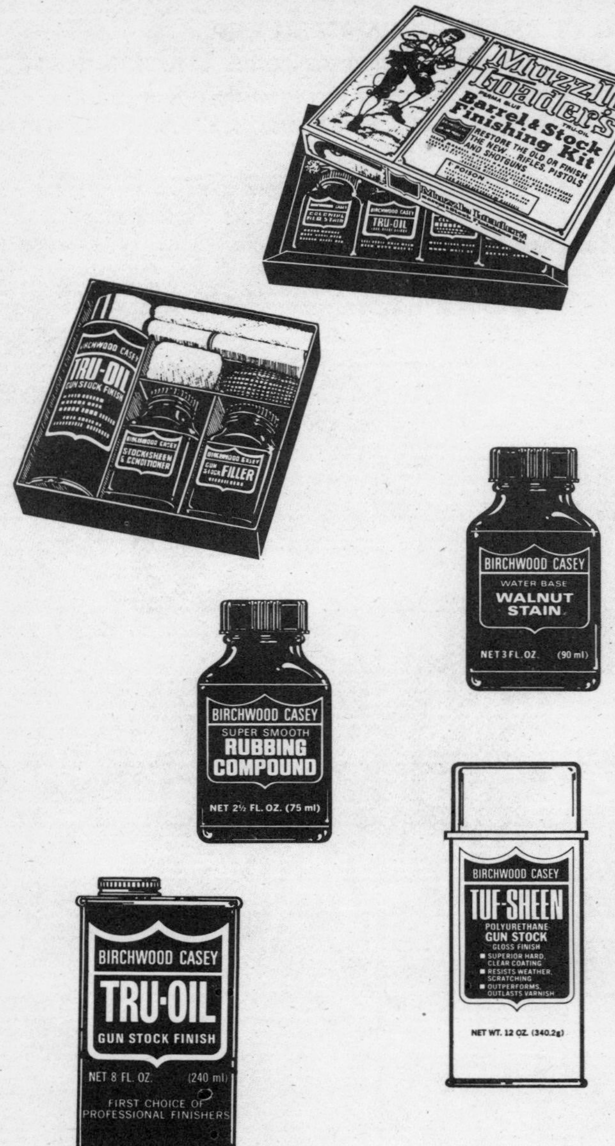

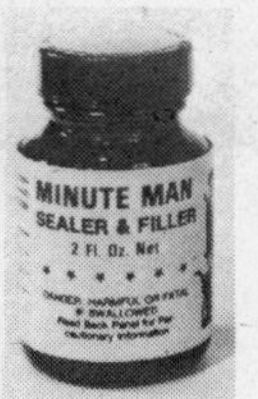

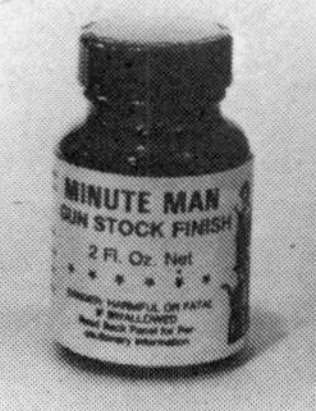

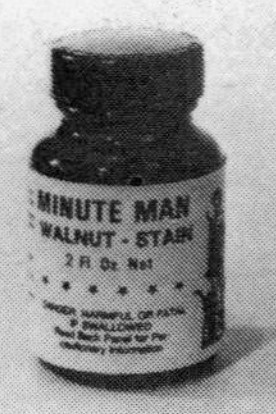

STOCK SEALER/FILLER

"Minute Man" Sealer & Filler seals out moisture, fills pores of stock wood prior to final finishing.
Price: $1.50 (2 oz. bottle).
From New Method.

MUZZLE LOADER'S BARREL AND STOCK FINISHING KIT

Includes cleaner-degreaser, Plum Brown Barrel Finish, Tru-Oil Stock Finish, and Colonial Red Maple stain plus sandpapers, steel wool, applicators and cloths for complete muzzle loader refinishing.
Price: $8.50
From Birchwood Casey.

STOCK FINISHING KIT

Includes "Tru-Oil," filler and conditioner plus assorted grades of sandpaper, steel wool pads, applicator and polishing cloths.
Price: $6.50
From Birchwood Casey.

WATER-BASE WOOD STAINS

Provide gun stocks, other wood with clear, rich, sunproof colors, available in walnut, cherry, or "Colonial Red" (maple).
Price: $1.50 (3 oz.—specify color).
From Birchwood Casey.

STOCK RUBBING COMPOUND

Removes high gloss from an oil finished stock, leaving wood with a low, rich satin sheen.
Price: $1.60 (2½ oz.).
From Birchwood Casey.

POLYURETHANE GUN STOCK FINISH

"Tuf-Sheen" provides a clear, hard finish that protects stocks from water, oil and chemicals.
Price: $3.75 (12 oz. aerosol can).
From Birchwood Casey.

OIL GUN STOCK FINISH

"Tru-Oil" is a quick-drying blend of linseed and natural oils that dries fast enough to permit application of several coats in one day. Available in liquid or aerosol form; dries to a high lustre but may be rubbed to a dull, stain finish.
Price: Liquid $1.75 (2½ oz.); $3.50 (8 oz.); $6.00 (pint);
Aerosol: $2.39 (8 oz.); $3.50 (16 oz.).
From Birchwood Casey.

WALNUT STAIN

Alcohol based "Minute Man" walnut stain enhances wood grain, minimizes feathering.
Price: $1.50 (2-oz. bottle).
From New Method

GUN STOCK FINISH

"Minute Man" stock finish is easily applied, provides a hard, durable high gloss finish that can be rubbed down for a softer appearance if desired.
Price: $1.50 (2-oz. bottle).
From New Method.

 Prices shown are subject to change.

Gun Cleaning Accessories & Supplies

Certainly one of the gun owner's top responsibilities to the arms he owns and uses is for their proper care. Whether those guns are "working" guns in daily use, with or without being fired, or collector's items stored under lock and key, proper maintenance is the key element to maintaining their value. Fortunately *most* shooters no longer need be concerned with the effects of the corrosive ammunition that was universal earlier in this century. However, some of that older stuff is still around (and shootable), and corrosive primed military surplus ammo is all that's available for shooters of some military arms, so thorough bore cleaning is not only desirable, but sometimes necessary.

Despite the improvement in ammunition, rust is still the arch enemy of the gun owner. Perspiration, or blood drops from fresh-killed game, can spot bluing in a matter of minutes; climatic damage to an improperly protected gun will take longer, but can effectively destroy its value or usefulness in a surprisingly short time.

In this section we're going to present cleaning equipment—rods, brushes, cleaning kits and the like—first, then the various solvents, lubricants and preservatives. The other important aspect of gun maintenance is protection, of course, and for that take a look at the many fine items in Section 9, *Gun Cases, Storage & Security*. There's a lot more to keeping a gun in good shape than running a brush through the bore and wiping the outside down with an oily rag!

Almost every gun shop has a good selection of equipment and materials for gun maintenance—it's a basic need!

UNIVERSAL CLEANING KIT

Made for rifle, pistol or shotgun. Comes with aluminum rod, oil, patches, loop tips and jags. Handles everything from .22 to 12 gauge.
Price: $5.95
From Marble Arms.

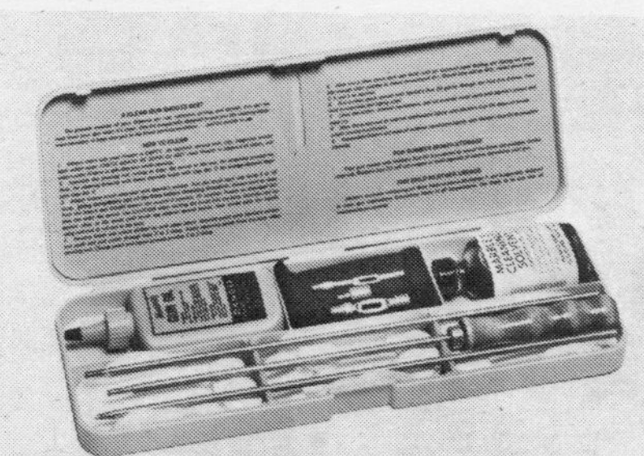

DELUXE UNIVERSAL CLEANING KIT

Made for rifle, pistol or shotgun. Features a 3-piece brass rod that will handle everything from .22 to 12 gauge. Comes with patches, solvent, gun oil, looped tips and jags. All packaged in a tough polypropylene box.
Price: $8.95; $7.95 for the same kit, but with an aluminum rod.
From Marble Arms.

CLEANING KIT

Hoppe's Cleaning Kits come with solvent, rod, brush, jag, patches—all contained in a durable polypropylene box. Available for rifle, pistol or shotgun.
Price: About $7.25 per kit.
From Penguin Industries

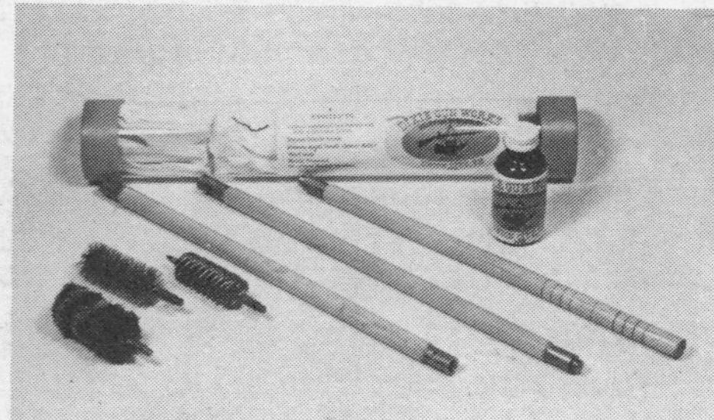

SHOTGUN CLEANING KIT

Dixie Gun Works is now offering a traditional English style shotgun cleaning kit. This 32½ inch rod will handle 12- and 16-gauge guns. It's made of varnished beechwood and comes with solid brass points. Each kit contains the above three-piece rod, solvent, wool mop, two bronze brushes, a heavy-duty spiral brush and 50 cotton flannel patches.
Price: $12.95
From Dixie Gun Works.

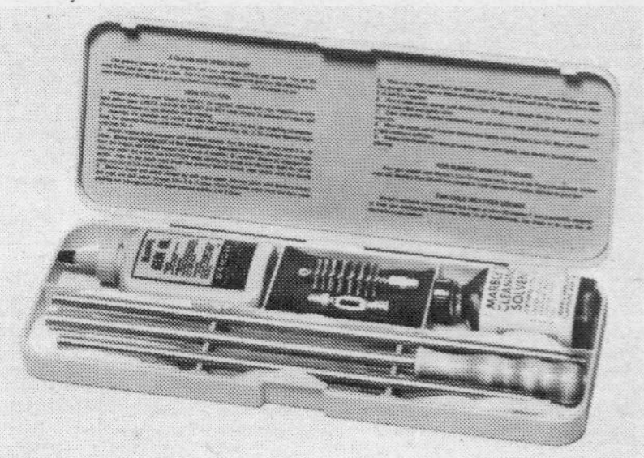

SHOTGUN CLEANING KIT

Comes with 3-piece aluminum rod, patches, oil, solvent, brush and combination loop/jag. All packaged in a tough polypropylene box. Available in 12, 16, 20 and .410.
Price: $7.95
From Marble Arms.

SHOTGUN CLEANING KIT

Available for all gauges. Each kit contains rod, oil, patches, solvent, brush, slotted tips and solvent pans.
Price: $7.84
From Outer's Labs.

SHOTGUN CHAMBER CLEANING KIT

Consists of sturdy rod and phosphor bronze brush—available in all gauges.
Price: $4.96
From Outer's Labs.

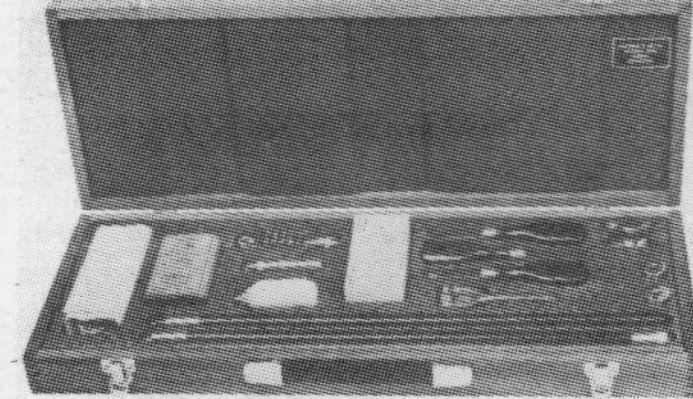

CASED CLEANING KIT

Best quality English style cleaning kit comes with solvent/lube, oiler, snap caps, rod, stuck-shell remover, screwdriver, brush, jag and mop, all cased in mahogany presentation box. For shotguns, of course.
Price: $150, complete.
From Wm. Larkin Moore.

SHOTGUN CLEANING SET

Consists of 2-piece rod, split brass jag, brush, mop, patches, "Nevarust" oil and polishing cloth, all in a partitioned box. In 12, 16, 20, 28 and .410.
Price: $17.50.
From Wm. Larkin Moore.

CLEANING PACK

This Hoppe's product contains patches, oil, solvent and grease—everything needed for proper gun cleaning, except for rod.
Price: $3.25
From Penguin Industries.

RIFLE CLEANING KIT

Available for all rifle calibers. Each kit contains patches, brush, jag, slotted tip, rod, solvent and oil.

Price: $10.11.

From Outer's Labs.

PISTOL CLEANING KIT

Available for all popular handgun calibers. Each kit contains patches, brush, jag, slotted tip, rod, solvent and oil.

Price: $7.36.

From Outer's Labs.

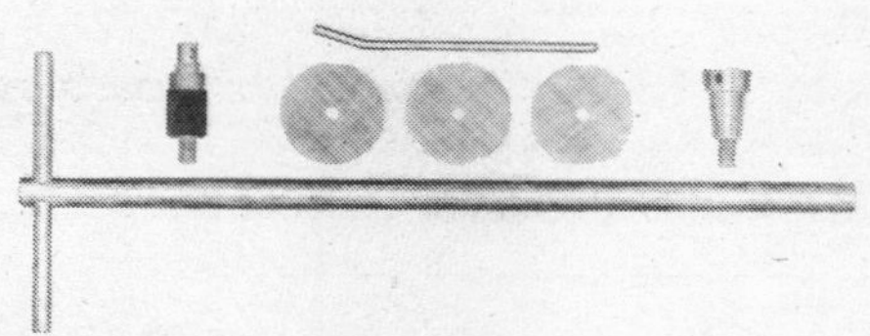

LEWIS LEAD REMOVER

Special cleaning rod utilizes brass cloth patches, unique patch tips, to thoroughly scrub bore, cylinder and forcing cone of accuracy-destroying lead build up in high performance revolvers and auto pistols. Available in .38, .41, .44, and .45 calibers only.

Price: $7.95; adaptor kit (second caliber); $5.75; Extra brass patches: $1.50 (package of 10).

From L.E.M.

BLACK POWDER CLEANING KIT

This kit is specifically made for black powder firearms. Each kit contains Hoppes No. 9 Plus solvent, rod, patches and oil.

Price: $9.20, rifle; $8.35, pistol.

From Penguin Industries.

BLACK POWDER CLEANING KIT

Available for rifles from .45 thru .58 caliber. Each kit comes with sectioned rod, bottle/tube nipple cleaning attachment, black powder solvent, oil, jag and tip, plus one roll of cleaning patch material (6′ x 2¼″).

Price: $9.62

From Outer's Labs.

.17 CALIBER CLEANING ROD KIT

Consists of a one-piece steel rod, oil, Hoppes No. 9 solvent and patches. For .17 firearms.

Price: $7.85

From Penguin Industries.

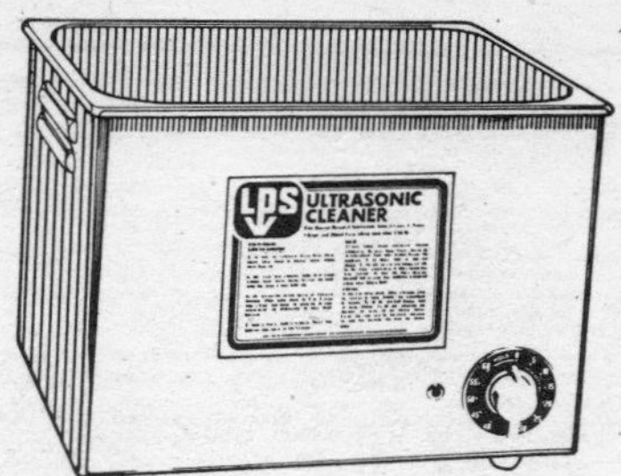

ULTRASONIC CLEANING UNIT

Designed for use with cleaning solvents, the LPS Ultrasonic cleaner's tank measures 12⅝″ x 10⅜″ x 8½″ and is made of stainless steel. Solvent capacity: 8 quarts. Excellent for gunsmiths, collectors or advanced shooters who must thoroughly clean firearms.

Price: $395.

From LPS Research Laboratories.

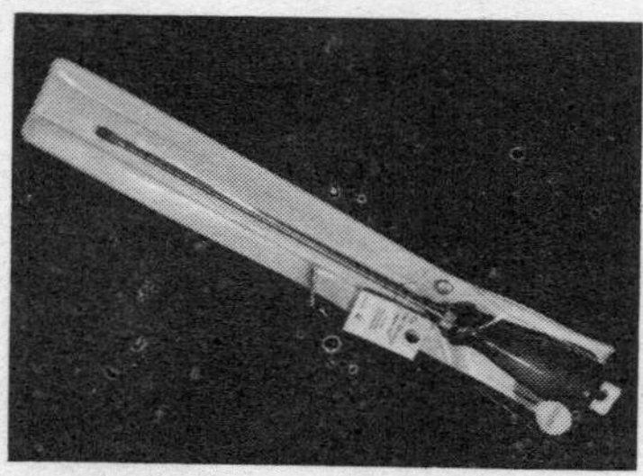

CLEANING ROD

Durango offers 10 models of their cleaning rod in calibers ranging from .22 through .62. All rods feature nylon grommets and ball bearing handles. Rod shown is the Laramie pistol cleaning rod—it's available in calibers ranging from .22 through .45.

Price: For the Laramie rod, $13.95.

From Durango U.S.A.

CLEANING ROD

A one-piece stainless steel cleaning rod with Mull-jag tip (double slotted tip optional) and brush. Overall length, 36″. Available in two sizes. Small size fits everything from .22 through .257; large size fits everything from .270 through .458.

Price: $6.65 each.

From Belding & Mull, Inc.

FLEXIBLE CLEANING ROD

Ideal for field use. From .22 to .270; or .270 up.

Price: $10.40

From Lenard M. Brownell.

CLEANING ROD & GUIDE

An elastomeric guide and stainless steel rod, the Accu-Guide helps prevent bore and chamber damage.

Price:

AG-400 "Accu-Guide" Cleaning rod guide and rod	$14.95
AG-450 "Accu-Guide" Cleaning rod guide only	7.95
Extra Tips	2.25
Extra Brushes	.75
Rod extensions, 12"	2.00

From H-S Precision.

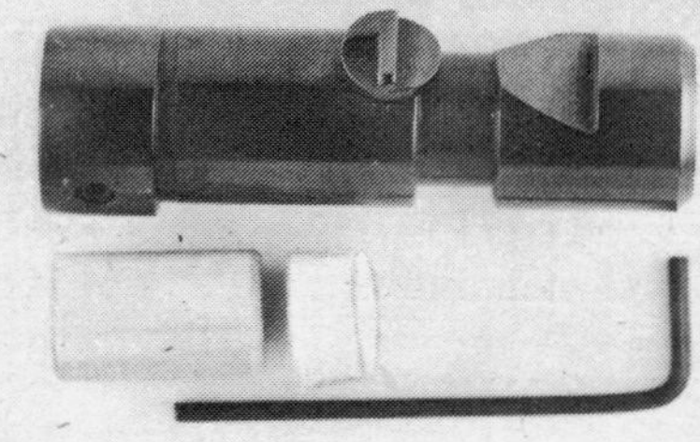

CLEANING ROD GUIDE

Described as a "Throat and Bore Saver" by the manufacturer, this cleaning accessory is designed to fit into the rear bolt bearing areas of a rifle, once the bolt's been removed. Available to fit most popular bolt action rifles.

Price: Ranges from $10.95 to $12.95 depending on model of bolt action rifle.

From Taylor & Robbins.

PORTABLE CLEANING CABLE

Available in calibers ranging from .17 to .30. Sturdy nylon covered steel cable will not damage bore. Comes with handy pocket size pouch. Available in four styles.

Price: Ranging from $4.25 up to $6.

From K. W. Kleindorst Company.

CLEANING ROD GUIDE

Helps keep the rod in perfect alignment and avoid wear in the chamber throat area. Prevents solvents and oil from entering magazine well or trigger mechanism. See below for your needs:

BGR-L .25 to .375 cals. Fits Rem. 700, 788, & 40X; Ruger short, etc.

BGW-S .222 to 6 x 47 cals. Fits Win. and Ruger short actions.

BGW-L .25 to .375 cals. Fits Win. Models 54 and 70; Rem. 700 long and 788; Mauser 300, Wthby, Van-

BGW-L .25 to .375 cals. Fits Win Models 54 and 70; Rem 700 long and 788; Mauser 300, Wthby Vanguard, Ruger 77 long, Savage 110, Mossberg 3500, etc. *Price:* $3.89, all styles.

From MTM Molded Products Company.

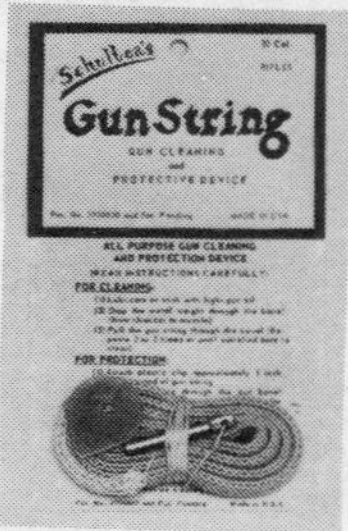

PORTABLE CLEANING ROD/STRING

The Schultea Gun String is a portable, pocketsized, full-length bore cleaner and lubricator. It's available in bore sizes running from .17 to .33 caliber. A shotgun version is also available for .410 through 12 gauge.

Price: $2.95 for the rifle string; $4.95 for the shotshell version.

From Schultea's Gun String.

COMBO BORE BRUSH/MOP

Available in 12, 16 or 20 gauge. Hard manmade bristles are backed by mop made of nylon.

Price: Brush/mop, $3.10; complete with rod in 12 or 16 gauge, $6.99.

From Penguin Industries.

SHOTGUN CLEANING BRUSH

Available in phosphor bronze for best possible cleaning. Comes in all gauges.

Price: 87¢

From Outer's Labs.

GUN CLEANING BRUSHES

Made with Dupont's Tynex® bristles, these brushes are available for all rifle and pistol calibers, and all gauges of shotguns.

Price: Rifle or pistol brush, 67¢; shotgun brush, 78¢.

From Penguin Industries.

GUNSMITH'S BORE BRUSHES

Called the "Tornado," this brush has specially designed spirals of stainless steel that are stiff enough to remove all powder fouling, yet won't damage the barrel. Available in .22, .30 and .35 calibers; 12, 16, 20 and .410 gauges. (Removes plastic residue from shotgun bore).

Price: $1.89.

From Penguin Industries.

PISTOL CLEANING BRUSHES

Come in nylon, bronze or bristle; in all calibers.

Price: 67¢

From Outer's Labs.

CLEANING PATCHES

Made of Dupont "Reemay," these patches come 50, 75 and 100 to a pack and may be used for any number of gun cleaning chores. Sizes cover everything from .22 up through 12 gauge.

Price: 78¢

From Penguin Industries.

BORE CLEANER

Minute Man Bore Cleaner comes in a 4-ounce bottle and has sufficient penetrating power to remove powder residue, lead and metal fouling. Also has a special moisture remover and rust inhibitors.

Price: $1.98

From New Method Manufacturing Co.

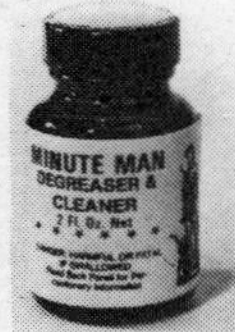

CLEANER/DEGREASER

Minute Man Degreaser and Cleaner is designed to remove dirt, oil, wax, grease and powder residue. Comes in a 2-ounce bottle.

Price: $1.50

From New Method Manufacturing Co.

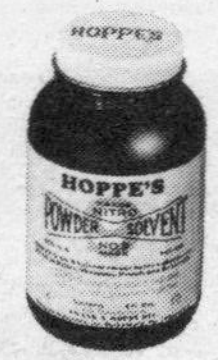

GUN SOLVENT

Hoppe's No. 9 is an old, trusted product when it comes to cleaning jacket fouling and lead out of pistol, rifle and shotgun bores.

Price: 2-ounce bottle, $1.19; 4-ounce, $2.20; pint, $4.75; quart, $7.95.

From Penguin Industries.

BORE SOLVENT

Gunslick gun cleaning solvent removes bore fouling and powder residue.

Price: 89¢ (2 oz.).

From Outer's Labs.

RIFLE-SHOTGUN BORE CLEANER

Dissolves plastic residue in shotgun bores and removes metal fouling in rifle bores.

Price: $1.98

From Blue & Gray Products, Inc.

HANDGUN BORE CLEANER

Blue & Gray's magnum pistol bore cleaner removes heavy lead and fouling deposits. Won't harm metal, blueing or wood.

Price: $1.98

From Blue & Gray Products, Inc.

BLACK POWDER SOLVENT

Hoppe's No. 9 Plus solvent may also be used as a patch lube. Cleans fouling from bore and helps prevent rust and corrosion.

Price: 9½-ounce squeeze bottle, $2.65; pint, $4.75.

From Penguin Industries.

AEROSOL SOLVENT/LUBE

Helps remove moisture and surface rust; helps to protect metal under all weather conditions, salt spray included.

Price: 4-ounce aerosol can, $1.50.

From Sportsmen's Laboratories.

CLEANER/DEGREASER/LUBE

TSI-300 contains no petroleum distillates, it's a pure synthetic. It won't freeze at −95°F. and won't burn at +450°F. TSI-300 is also a rust preventative.

Price: $2.98 in a 4-ounce aerosol can; $6.98 for the 20-ounce can.

From American Gas & Chemical.

See the Directory for complete company addresses.

CLEANER/LUBRICANT/PRESERVATIVE

Break-Free CLP removes firing residue in a gun bore and leaves a protective coating that inhibits rust and reduces future powder build-up.

Price: $5.95 for a 1-pint aerosol can.

From The San/Bar Corporation.

LUBRICANT/PENETRANT

Dri-Slide is a "reaction" lube whose solid (dry film) boundry lubrication penetrates into inaccessible areas. It is also for use on mating metal parts where friction is present.

Price: 8-ounce aerosol, $2.98; 8-ounce spout can, $2.56; needle applicator, 79¢ (3½"); 85¢ (5½").

From Dri-Slide Inc.

SOLVENT LUBRICANT/DEMOISTURIZER

Kel H_2O-D is a penetrant-lubricant that can also dry out ignition switches and relays. It protects against salt water, body acids and terminal corrosives.

Price: About $2.89 per 10-ounce aerosol can.

From Kellogs Professional Products.

SOLVENT/LUBRICANT AND RUST PREVENTATIVE

Clenzoil helps remove lead and powder fouling, plus provides a rust-preventative coating for exposed metal surfaces. Clenzoil also dissolves rust. In a 4-ounce pump-spray container.

Price: About $2, 4-ounce; $3.30, 16-ounce, both available direct for additional $1 postage/handling fee.

From the Clenzoil Corporation.

GUN CLEANING LUBES & SOLVENT

The following may be purchased directly as a kit or individually from your dealer: XF-10 (4 oz.) super gun solvent, $5; XF-15 (11 oz.) aerosol bore coating, $9; XF-20 (4 oz.) can of liquid gun lube, $4; six special compression bore swabs (70¢ each), $4.20.

Price: Total kit cost, postage and packing included, $27.20.

From Rice Gun Products.

GUN OIL

Comes in a 4-ounce bottle with nozzle applicator. Called Minute Man Gun Oil, this product is a light, low temperature oil with water displacing properties.

Price: $1.50

From New Method Manufacturing Co.

GUN OIL

Hoppe's Lubricating Oil is made for firearms and other precision mechanisms. Does not harden, gum up or become rancid.

Price: $1.10 (3 oz.).

From Penguin Industries

GUN OIL

Helps prevent rust and keep internal working parts operating smoothly.

Price: 82¢ (2.5 oz.).

From Outer's Labs.

LOW TEMPERATURE GUN OIL

"−60" is a lubricant/rust preventative that's designed for use up to −60°F. It displaces moisture.

Price: $1.80 per 8-ounce can.

From Sportsmen's Laboratories.

CUSTOM OIL BOTTLES

These oil bottles are made of nickel plated brass. They come in square or round configuration—your choice. This is a nice addition to your cleaning gear. Beautifully made.

Price: $20 each.

From Bill McGuire & Associates.

SILICONE LUBRICANT

Kel-Sport is designed for use with guns, other sports equipment. Functional from +700°F. down to −70°F.

Price: About $2 for a 5-ounce aerosol can.

From Kellogs Professional Products.

"GREASELESS" LUBRICANT

Displaces moisture and sets up non-dust-attracting bond with metal due to its "greaseless" properties. Suitable for both guns and leather.

Price: 6-ounce can, $1.99; 11-ounce can, $2.60.

From LPS Research Labs.

Prices shown are subject to change.

RIG GUN GREASE

This product has a reputation with shooters that goes back almost a half century. The job it performs is simple — it stops rust. Perfect for gun storage or use in foul weather. Goes on smoothly. Talk to someone who has used Rig — it works. Available in 1-ounce jar, 4-ounce jar and 15-ounce can (shown).

Price: 1-ounce jar — $1; 4-ounce — $2; 15-ounce can $4.45.

From Rig Products, Div. of Mitann, Inc.

RIG IMPREGNATED SHEEPSKINS

Called the "Rig-Rag," these pure wool sheepskins are impregnated with Rig Universal gun grease. They are perfect for applying Rig to your firearms.

Price: $3 each.

From Rig Products, Div. of Mitann, Inc.

GUN GREASE

Gunslick helps smooth out rough actions and triggers.

Price: 49¢ (2 oz.).

From Outer's Labs.

GREASE

A synthetic fluid grease packed in a hypo-needle bottle.

Price: $1.98 (½-oz.).

From Penguin Industries.

WIPE-DOWN CLOTH

Hoppe's Treated Gun Cloth is designed for the exterior cleaning of all firearms.

Price: $1.49

From Penguin Industries.

GUN STOCK WAX

Combines protective properties of carnauba, beeswax and silicone to give a hard finish that won't wear off.

Price: $1.50 per 2-ounce bottle.

From New Method Manufacturing Co.

AEROSOL STOCK SPRAY

Hoppe's Gunstock Polish protects and enhances stock finish.

Price: 6-ounce spray, $2.10.

From Penguin Industries.

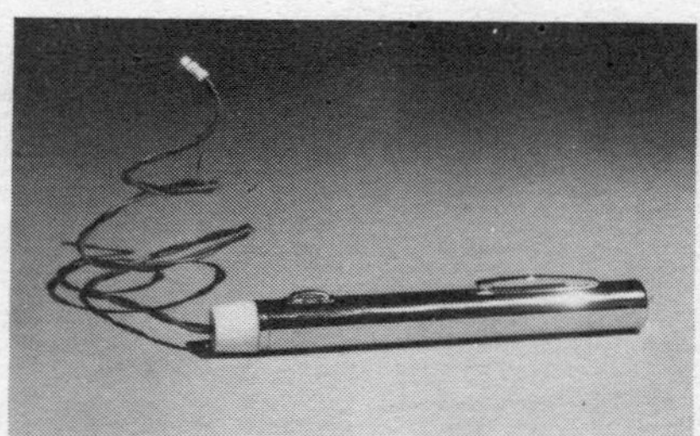

BORE INSPECTION LIGHT

This pen-type bore inspection lamp features a "grain-of-wheat" bulb on a flexible cord. Designed for bore inspection and the examination of other hard-to-get-at internal areas of most sporting firearms. With batteries and plastic storage box.

Price: About $5; without batteries and box, $4.

From AC/DC Electronics.

MOISTURE CONTROL

Available in a number of sizes, these self-contained metal units are packed with the highest quality silica gel—used to absorb moisture in gun cabinets, cases,

Price: "Compact Unit", $4.95; "Lifetime Naval Unit", $60; 2,000-gram cannister, $35.

From Hydrosorbent Company.

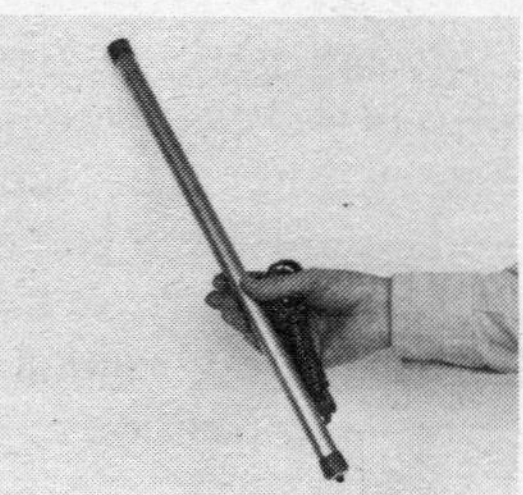

ELECTRONIC DEHUMIDIFIER

The "Golden-Rod" is designed for fast installation in gun cabinets, gun safes and closets—any area where guns are to be stored. Removes moisture from the air.

Price: 8-watt, $13.25; 12-watt, $14; 18-watt, $17.75; 25-watt, $18.95.

From Buenger Enterprises.

See the Directory for complete company addresses.

Gun Parts: Replacement & Obsolete

Finding replacement or custom parts for a no-longer-made or even uncommon current model rifle, pistol or shotgun can be one of the gun enthusiast's most difficult challenges. Fortunately, there are people and companies who have recognized this need and are filling it, some in a very broad sense and others within a very narrow area of specialization.

In the following pages we've assembled a broad cross-section of unusual parts sources. Some direct their efforts to only one make or even one model of arm, while others inventory original (or reproduction) parts for literally hundreds of different guns from all corners of the world. For the most part their offerings are replacements for lost or broken original parts; most *custom* parts will be found in Sections 1 and 2.

Because of the diversity of this section, we've made no attempt to organize it into categories. Instead, the suppliers are simply listed alphabetically. For those whose offerings are very limited, specific items are listed and priced. For the larger firms you must refer to their own lists or catalogs, some of which run to 100 pages or more.

When in need of replacement parts don't overlook your nearby gun shops. Almost all have at least a modest junk box of old parts, and those that do a lot of gunsmithing often have an extensive inventory. You might just be lucky! If your local search is unsuccessful, try some of the sources we have listed, preferably with a self-addressed, stamped envelope. At least one of them will surely have what you need!

CURRENT FOREIGN PISTOL PARTS

Replacement parts for more than 100 different current foreign-made pistols, including some replica cap and ball models, are stocked by Bob's Gun Shop. Some foreign rifle and shotgun parts are also stocked. Write with specific needs or send for their detailed Parts Catalog No. 7.

Price (catalog): $2 postpaid.

From Bob's Gun Shop.

AUTO PISTOL AND RIFLE MAGAZINES

Current manufacture replacement magazines for a great many both modern and obsolete pistols and rifles are available from D & E. At press time the complete list was eight pages long; a new list is printed quarterly to reflect additions to the line. Prices vary widely, so write regarding specific needs.

Some representative prices are:

Colt Woodsman, High Standard .22s: $11.95
Most 25 autos: $8.95.
Most 32 autos: $9.95 - $10.95.
Astra, Beretta 1934, Colt .380s: $9.95.
Astra 400, Llama, S&W 39, Star, P. 38, Radom 9mm: $12.95.

Extra capacity extended magazines are also available for a number of pistols, some rifles.

From D & E Magazine Mfg.

U. S. MILITARY PARTS

Original replacement parts for U. S. issue military arms back to the Civil War period are the specialty of J. DeChristopher. His stock includes the Spencer rifle and carbine, percussion, .50-70 and .45-70 Trapdoor Springfield, Krag and Model 1892 Colt revolver as well as the more current Garand and M-1 carbine. Write with specific needs, or see his detailed catalog.

Price (catalog): $3.

From J. DeChristopher.

WINCHESTER BUTT PLATES

Accurate reproductions of both crescent and carbine type steel butt plates for older Winchester rifles. Available with or without trapdoor in blue or color case hardened finish (specify).

Price:

	Plain	With Trap Door
Crescent (2½″ Tang)	$20.00	$22.50
Carbine	20.00	22.50

From Den-Rus Parts.

ANTIQUE GUN PARTS

Parts for many older U.S. made pistols, rifles, and shotguns are available from Dixie Gun Works. Much of their stock is original manufacture a century or more old, supplemented by well-made reproductions of often-needed parts no longer available. Springfield "Trap-Doors," Remington and Whitney rolling blocks, Sharps, Spencer, Stevens rifles and pistols, L. C. Smith shotguns, and Winchesters from 1866 on are just a sampling of the many collector's (and shooter's) guns for which Dixie can supply parts. Much of their stock is listed and pictured in their big $2 catalog; a limited stock of parts for less popular guns is also maintained.

From Dixie Gun Works.

RIFLE AND SHOTGUN STOCKS

One-piece and two-piece rifle and shotgun stocks for literally hundreds of obsolete American and foreign made arms are available in both semi-finished and finished form. Semi-finished stocks are machined to size and inletted, require some fitting and finishing by owner. Completely finished stocks have been fitted to shop sample gun and finished with oil filler type finish.

Prices:	One-Piece (rifle or shotgun)	Double Barrel Buttstock	Double Barrel Forend	Lever/Pump/Auto Buttstock	Lever/Pump/Auto Forend
Finished	$42.95	$42.00	$26.50	$40.50	$26.50
Semi-Finished	22.95	25.50	15.50	25.00	17.00

From Reinhart Fajen.

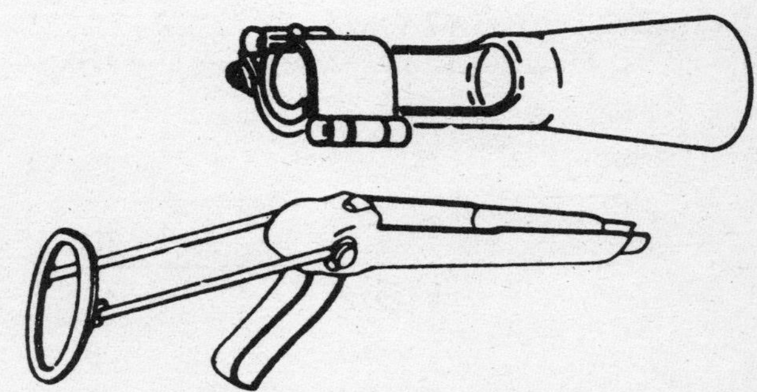

RUGER AND M-1 CARBINE ACCESSORIES

Federal Ordnance manufactures its own line of military and sporting accessories for Ruger's Mini-14, 10/22, and both military and newly manufactured M-1 carbines. Some of the more popular items are:

	Mini-14	10/22	M-1 Carbine
Folding Stock	N/A	$49.95	$49.95
Flash Hider	$15.95	N/A	11.99
30-Round Magazines	9.95	N/A	4.99
20-Round Magazines	8.95	N/A	2.99 (15-rd.)

From Federal Ordnance.

See the Directory for complete company addresses.

WINCHESTER LEVER ACTION PARTS

A good selection of parts for Winchester 92 and 94 lever action rifles is maintained. Send a self-addressed stamped envelope with your request for a price quote and current availability.

From Greg's Winchester Parts.

OBSOLETE RIFLE AND PISTOL PARTS

Owners of discontinued, military surplus or foreign guns are often hard put to find replacement parts. Jack First Distributors attempts to meet this need by buying such guns for parts and offering the parts on an "as available" basis. At present, they have quantities of parts for 66 different guns, from 1900 Browning through more than two-dozen different Winchesters and including BSA, Colt, Dreyse, Martini, Mauser, Nambu and Webley. Prices vary widely, depending on availability, popularity and condition. Write for a quotation for a specific need. New manufacture parts for many more popular pistols are also offered.

From Jack First Distributors.

LOW SAFETY FOR BOLT ACTION RIFLES

Mauser and Springfield sporter standard safeties often will not clear a scope. The Mark II safety is an easy-to-install replacement that is usable with a low-mounted scope and looks good as well. It has a non-glare blued finish and a nylon friction piece for smooth, rattle-free operation.

Price: $7.50

From Walter H. Lodewick.

OBSOLETE WINCHESTER PARTS

Probably the best source of factory original obsolete Winchester parts in the world is Walter Lodewick. In his extensive inventory are parts for the Models 06, 12, 52, 61, 62/62A, 63, 67/67A, 69A, 70, 72/72A, 75, 77, 90, 94, and 97. Magazines, magazine tubes and sights for those and a number of other models are also available. He also has a few parts for Remington Models 11, 12, 31, 81 and 121 in stock. Send a self-addressed stamped envelope for a detailed, illustrated stock/price list.

From Walter H. Lodewick.

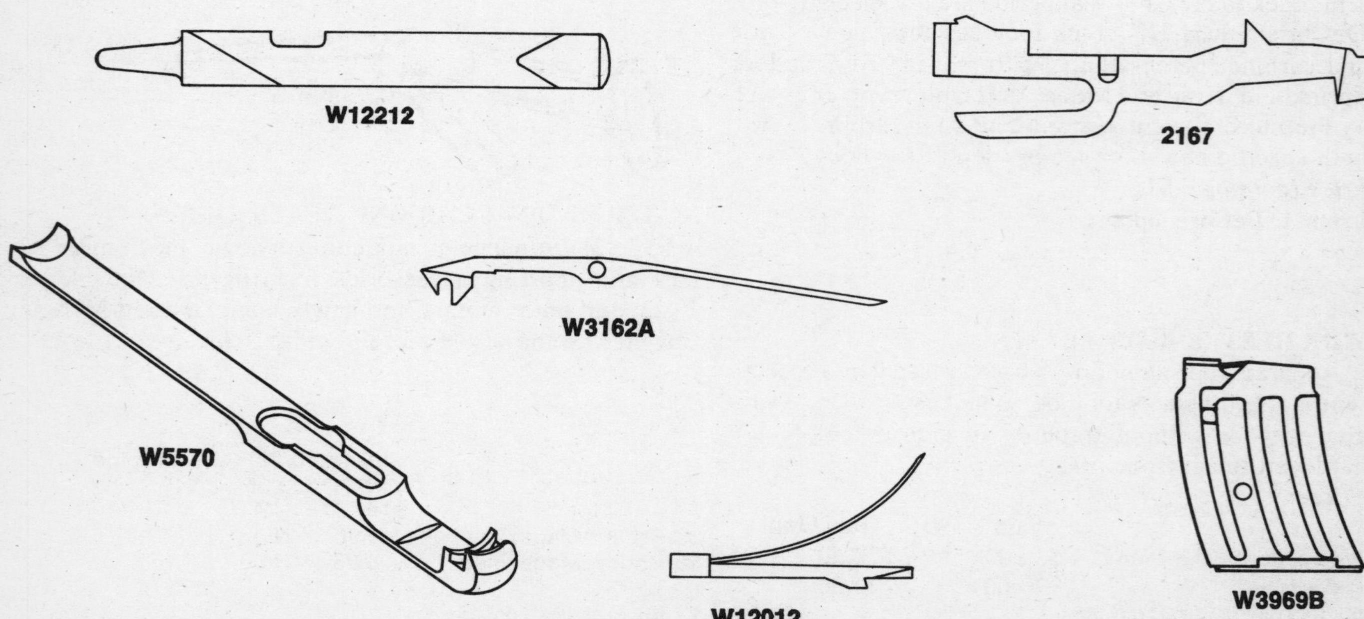

Prices shown are subject to change.

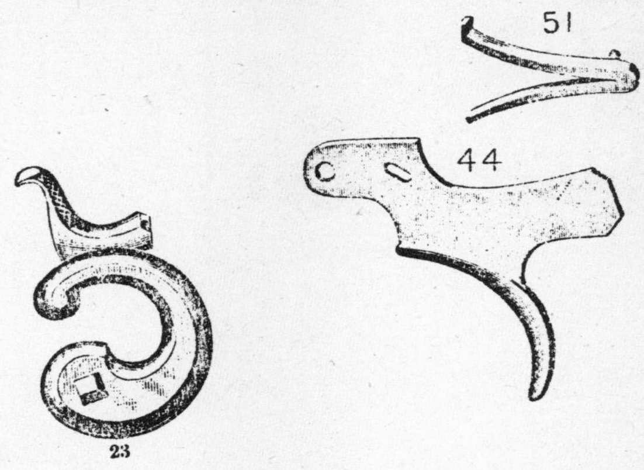

OBSOLETE REMINGTON PARTS

Remington double barrel shotgun parts for both hammer and hammerless models, plus parts for the Model 24 and 241 .22 caliber auto rifles, are available from Arthur McKee. Most parts, including wood, are usually available. Send a self-addressed stamped envelope for a current illustrated price list of the model Remington for which parts are needed.
From Arthur McKee.

ANTIQUE WINCHESTER PARTS

Many parts for earlier Winchester lever and pump actions, High Wall single shots are available from Tommy Munsch. His detailed price list includes Henry, 1866, 1873, 1876, 1886, 1890, 1892, 1894, 1895, 1897, High Wall and Model 71.
From Tommy Munsch.

A
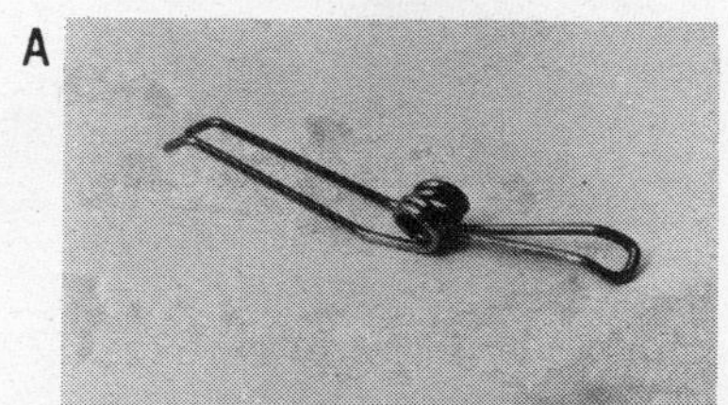

GUN PARTS

Numrich bills themselves as the world's largest supplier of gun parts, and it doesn't take much browsing through their 195-page parts catalog ($2.95, postpaid) to believe they may be right. Included are most domestic guns, both modern and antique, and military surplus arms from around the world. Numrich also stocks newly-made replacement parts and a wide range of accessories for both collector and shooter. Write with specific needs, or buy their detailed Parts Catalog No. 8.
Price (catalog): $2.95 postpaid.
From Numrich Arms.

A **RUGER TRIGGER SPRING**

Owners of Ruger's New Model Single Action revolver can reduce the trigger pull by installing one of these replacement springs.
Price: $6.95
From Omega Sales.

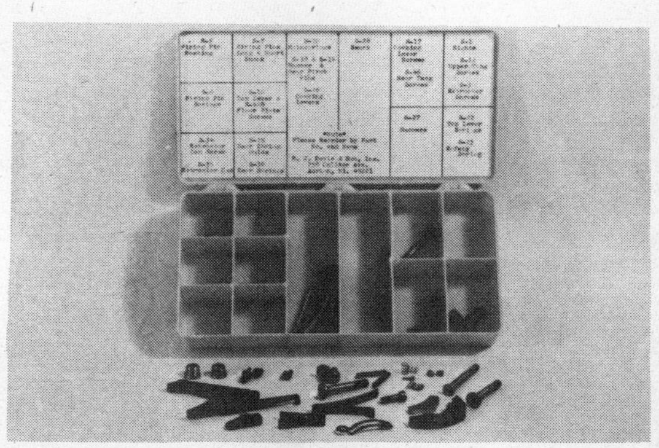

SPANISH SHOTGUN PARTS

An almost complete stock of Zabala Hermanos double barrel shotgun parts, along with many parts for a number of other European over-under and side-by-side shotguns, is maintained by R. J. Davis & Son. An illustrated price list is available for the Zabala Hermanos; many of its parts may be used on other current Spanish doubles but fitting is often required. For active shooters and gunsmiths Davis offers a parts kit for Spanish doubles.
Price: $31.75
From R. J. Davis & Son.

See the Directory for complete company addresses.

SURPLUS AND OBSOLETE PARTS

Sarco maintains an extremely large stock of parts for both foreign and domestic firearms, particularly military and police models. As the stock changes continually, you'll have to write or call regarding specific needs.

From Sarco.

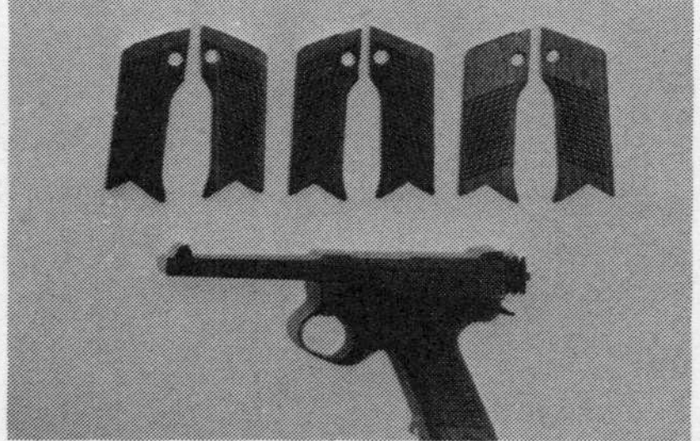

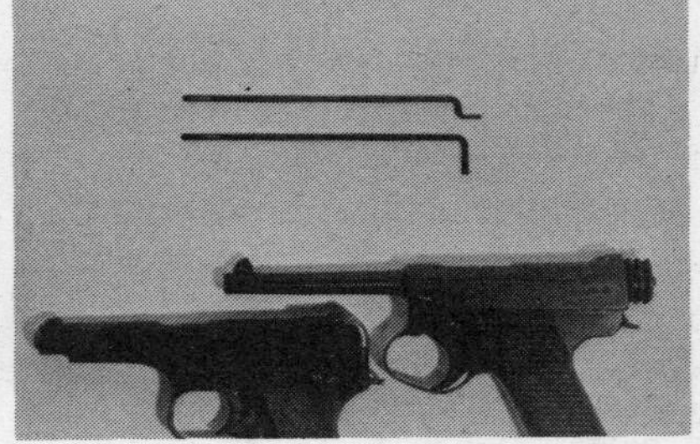

REPLICA NAMBU GRIPS, CLEANING RODS

Nambu pistol collectors can replace damaged or missing grips with accurately inletted and finished replacements of mahogony, as were the originals. Three styles, for the three different manufacturing variations, are offered (specify). Early style (blued) and later (nickel plated) Nambu, Model 94 cleaning rods are also available.

Prices: $25 (grips); $18 (cleaning rods).

From the Sight Shop.

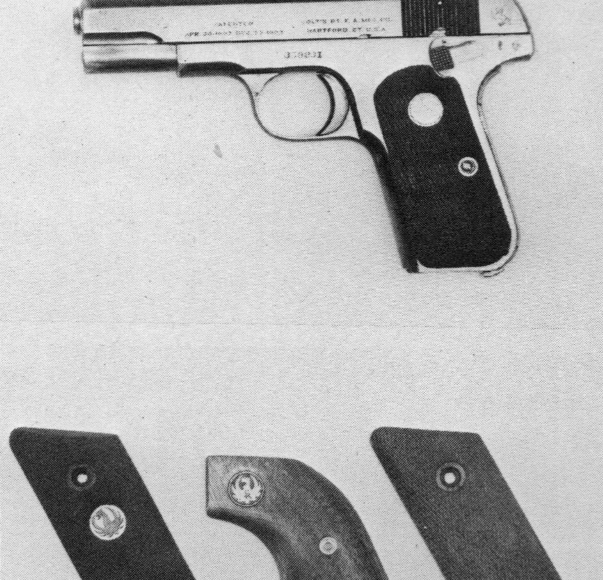

AUTO PISTOL GRIPS

Walnut replacement grips made to original patterns enable owners to put older Colt, Ruger, S&W and other handguns back into original configuration.

Representative prices include:

Colt Pocket Auto: $9.85.
Ruger SA Revolver: $25.85.
Ruger 22 Auto: $13.55.
Luger: $13.55.
"K" Frame S&W: $8.50.

From Sile Distributors.

AUTO PISTOL MAGAZINES

Replacement magazines closely duplicate the original factory-made product.

Prices: $14.95 (Browning High Power, Luger); $12.95 (Walther PP or PPK/S, PPK, in .380 only).

From Sile Distributors.

PISTOL AND RIFLE PARTS

A very extensive stock of parts for many obsolete military and commercial rifles, pistols and shotguns is maintained by Sherwood. Among the many guns whose parts are listed in their price list are Mauser, Carcano, Enfield, Martini, Garand, FN and Springfield rifles; Winchester, Stevens, Remington, Ithaca and Savage shotguns; Colt, Walther, Browning, Mauser, High Standard and Lahti auto pistols; and Colt, Smith & Wesson and Webley revolvers.
From Sherwood Distributors.

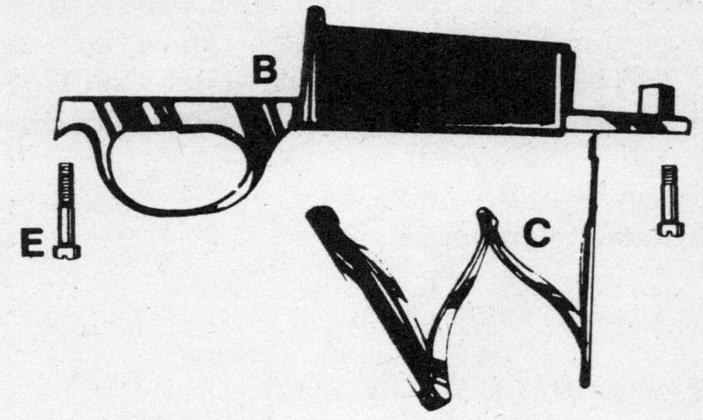

SURPLUS PARTS

Parts for a large number of surplus military pistols are offered. Included are various models of Astra, Browning, Colt, Enfield, Luger, Lahti, Mauser, Nambu, Star and Webley. Write with specific needs.
From Springfield Sporters.

REPLACEMENT RIFLE AND PISTOL PARTS

Firing pins, pistol grips and magazines are a specialty with Tom Forrest, but he also maintains an extensive stock of other parts for 1911 Colts, 1903 Springfields, various Winchesters and Mauser 98s. Write with specific needs.
From Tom Forrest, Inc.

A

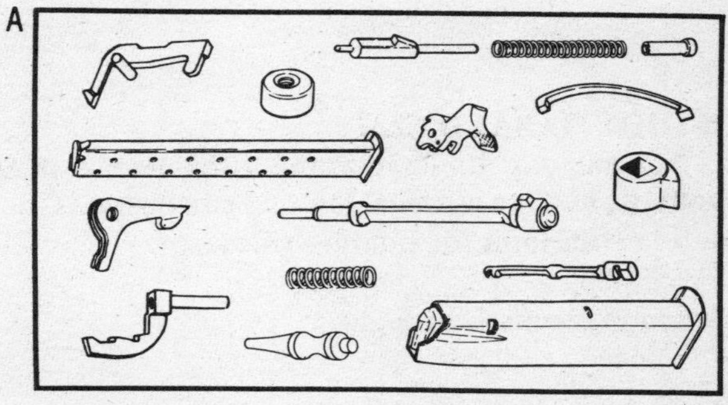

A PISTOL GRIPS, PARTS

Triple K has supplemented its magazine line with grips, firing pins and other often requested parts for a number of popular obsolete pistols. See Triple K's $2 catalog for a complete listing with prices.

Prices: Grips — $10-$14 (pair).
Firing Pins — $10-$15.
Extractors — $10-$15.

From Triple K.

FRONT SIGHTS

A full line of ramp type front sights for both revolvers and auto pistols, with options such as colored inserts, are offered. Some types require a milling operation to install; others can be mounted with just the aid of a file. Write for a detailed listing of prices and installation instructions ($1).
Price: From $6.50.
From The Sight Shop.

See the Directory for complete company addresses.

AMBIDEXTROUS SAFETY FOR COLT, BROWNING

An easy-to-install safety lever that can be operated equally well by southpaws is available for Colt Government Model series pistols and the Browning High Power.

Prices: Colt, $40; Browning, $45.

From Armand Swenson.

PISTOL AND RIFLE MAGAZINES

Established in 1963 to help fill the need for replacement magazines for obsolete pistols, Triple K now has expanded to become probably the world's largest supplier of these necessary accessories. Hundreds of magazines, for collector's items such as the Austrian "Little Tom" and blow-forward-action Schwarzlose as well as for Colt, Savage, Mauser, Nambu and other more common pistols, are available. Extra capacity magazines for some popular current model pistols are also available. All are pictured and priced in Triple K's 104-page catalog ($2).

Prices: $10 - $15 (most standard capacity pistol magazines); $18 - $20 (most oversize, 15- or 20-round, pistol magazines); $15 - $18 (most rifle magazines).

From Triple K.

5-SHOT GARAND CLIP

Special clip limits Garand rifle magazine to five rounds, making it a legal hunting gun in states that have a five shot limit for hunting rifles.

Price: $6

From Williams Gun Sight.

GUN SPRINGS

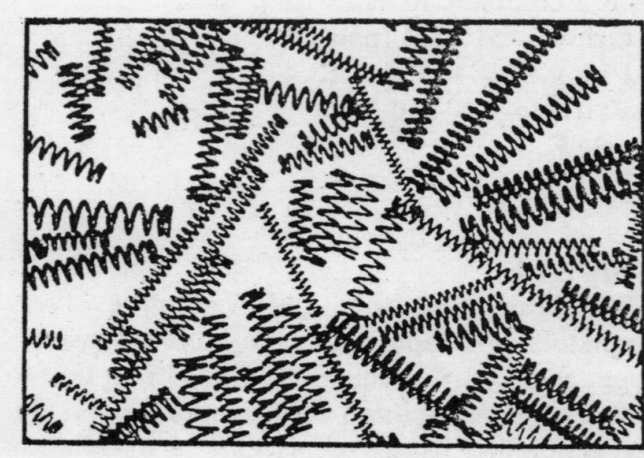

A tremendous variety of coil springs to fit many current and obsolete auto pistols, bolt action rifles, and tubular feed rifles and shotguns is offered by W. C. Wolff. Springs are available singly or in various combination packs (see detailed price list, available on request). Extra length recoil springs for long slide 1911 Colts, extra or reduced power recoil springs for Colt and Browning pistols, are also offered. Some leaf and V-type springs are also available. Custom springs can also be made to specification.

Representative Prices: Auto Pistol Recoil Springs: $3.75; Firing Pin Springs: $2.25; Tubular Magazine Springs: $3.75 (.22 through shotgun); Military Bolt Rifle Striker Springs: $5.25 (kit of two); Luger old style (leaf) Recoil Spring: $21.75. Add 50¢ packing/shipping to orders under $10; $1 over $10.

From W. C. Wolff Co.

Custom Guns & Gunsmithing Services

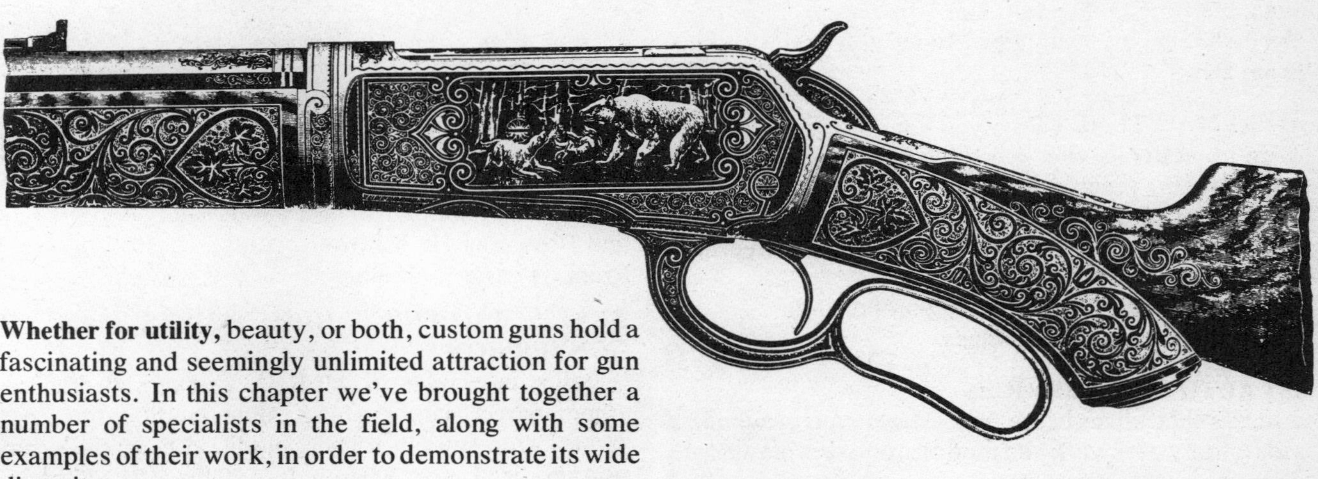

Whether for utility, beauty, or both, custom guns hold a fascinating and seemingly unlimited attraction for gun enthusiasts. In this chapter we've brought together a number of specialists in the field, along with some examples of their work, in order to demonstrate its wide diversity.

Included are combat and target conversions of popular pistols and rifles, custom-made hunting rifles and shotguns, restoration work, and highly specialized custom alterations. You'll find that custom pistols lead off the section, followed by rifles and shotguns, rebarrelers, restoration specialists and refinishers.

In addition to the various types and degrees of custom gun work you'll find in this section, there are a number of custom gun accessories to be found in other parts of the book. The greater part of these are in the first two sections, but some will also be found in Section 7, *Gun Parts: Replacement and Obsolete,* and Section 10, *Target & Bench Shooting Accessories.*

The talents represented in the following pages are highly specialized and uncommon. As a result, many of these craftsmen have backlogs of months and, sometimes, years. However, as the illustrations amply demonstrate, the results can be well worth waiting for!

See the Directory for complete company addresses.

DEVEL MODEL 39 COMBAT CONVERSION

Smith & Wesson Model 39 is shortened, lightened and extensively reworked to make a compact, reliable combat weapon. Conversion price includes holster, spare magazine, magazine holder and belt. Specify if for right- or left-handed shooter (ambidextrous safety available for $23.50 additional.)
Price: $357 (buyer supplies Model 39 for conversion).
From Devel.

AUTO MAG TUNE UP

Entire action is checked, polished and honed to assure smooth, reliable function. All worn or damaged parts replaced. Rear sight is blued and excess play removed. At least 100 rounds are fired to confirm proper operation. Barrel is Mag-na-ported.
Price: $195; ($175 without Mag-na-porting).
From Lomont Precision Bullets.

BBI AUTO MAG SERVICES

Beal's specializes in the Auto Mag pistol, providing a wide variety of rework and modification services. Some of the more popular include:

Custom Performance/Reliability Tuning ...$235.00
Convert Safety to one-hand operation $27.50
Adjust to Proper Headspace ....$25.00-$40.00
Action Deburring and Smooth up ... approx. $90.00
Install Special Scope Mount & Leupold M8-2X on 6½" barrel$215.00; on 8½" barrel ... $375.00
Smooth and Polish Frame $375.00

Contact Beal's for a detailed list of additional Auto Mag services they can provide.

Auto Mag Accessories

Rosewood Laminated Grips $65.00
Hardwood Laminated Grips $65.00
Ivory Micarta Grips $86.00
BBI Custom Heavy Barrel Assemblies (must be fitted to individual pistol). .357, .41, .44, .45 BBI, .308x1.5", or 7MM BBI in various lengths from $425.00

From Beal's Bullets, Inc.

CUSTOM AUTO PISTOLS

Armond Swenson does accurizing and customizing work on .45 autos. In addition to action and trigger work and restyling, Swenson also offers ventilated ribs and his own patented ambidextrous safety for both Colt and Browning High Power pistols.

From Swenson's .45 Shop.

BEAL'S BROWNING HIGH POWER 10mm BBI CONVERSION

Ballistics similar to .40 BBI. Conversion includes 10mm barrel with bushing, slide modification, new sights, wide smooth trigger, modified magazines, custom anodized case, 200 rounds of 10mm BBI 170-grain.
Price: $800 (approximately).
From Beal's Bullets, Inc.

WALTERS COLT CONVERSIONS

Government Model combat conversions include trigger job, ejection port relief, barrel throat and feed ramp polish, speed safety, blocking grip safety (IPSC Combat Job); complete conversion also includes magazine well funneling, checkered mainspring housing, speed slide stop, fitted barrel bushing, fitting barrel lugs, and refinish (blue).
Price: $100 (IPSC); $150 (Complete).

Target Conversions

.45 Hard Ball	$175
.45 Standard with rib	$195
.45 Standard with extension rib	$205
.45 Long Slide with 6" rib	$260
.45 Long heavy slide	$270

From Walters Industries.

Prices shown are subject to change.

GOVERNMENT MODEL .45 CUSTOMIZING

Crown City's extensive line of Model 1911 auto pistols is well known, but what is less common knowledge is the tune up and modification work done by the Crown Custom Shop on both Crown City and other Government Model guns.

Price:

Trigger and Action Job: $22.50
Throat Barrel, Polish Ramp: $12.50
Install Long, Adjustable Trigger: $7 (plus trigger: $5.95 steel; $7.95 stainless).
Bevel Magazine Well: $15.

From Crown City Arms.

MAG-NA-PORT

Mag-na-port is a barrel muzzle venting process that reduces recoil and muzzle jump by altering the barrel itself rather than attaching an accessory device to it. The actual machining is by electrical discharge, which permits precise control of the cutting process and produces a clean, burr-less cut of the desired shape. It can be used with similar benefits on handguns, rifles and shotguns.

Price:

Handguns .... $39.95 (two ports)
Rifles .... $55.00 (four ports)
Single Barrel Shotguns $60.00
Over/Under Shotguns ..... $105.00 (both barrels)
Over/Under Shotguns .... $75.00 (bottom barrel only)
Side-By-Side Shotguns $75.00

For bull barrels add $5.00 to above prices; return shipping, handling and insurance are not included.

From Mag-na-port.

DiSTEFANO CUSTOM COLT .45 AUTO

Compact conversions of Colt 1911 made to customer's specifications. Example shown is shortened to 4″ barrel, frame cut to 6-round magazine capacity, "K" sights, Gold Cup trigger, checkering and long safety.

Price: Open, based on individual requirements.

From Dominic DiStefano.

PISTOL SERVICES

Walters also provides a variety of services for the Colt Government Model, including all conversion steps listed above, sight installation, ambidextrous safety etc. Write for detailed price list.

From Walters Industries.

SEECAMP 1911 COLT D/A CONVERSION, MODIFICATIONS

Converts Colt 1911 or Combat Commander to double action lock without alteration to sear or safety linkage. Replacement wide trigger and short double-action pull make it unnecessary to shift trigger finger from double action to single action hold. Larger combat style trigger guard facilitates two-handed hold. For all calibers of Model 1911, Mark IV and Commanders except aluminum framed Commander.

Price: $144.50 (blue); $149.50 (nickel).

Combat Sights

Top of slide is milled flat and serrated like Gold Cup, Seecamp low-profile combat sight installed. Fully adjustable for windage, elevation.

Price: $80; with plastic, orange insert front sight add $20; with loaded cartridge indicator, add $25.

Shortened Slide

Slide is shortened 1-1/16″ in 1911, 11/16″ in Combat Commander. Uses Seecamp's unique "Spring Extender System."

Price: $110.00

Shortened Butt

Removes 7/16″ (approximately) from butt of Model 1911, decreasing magazine capacity by one round. One customer-supplied magazine is also altered, though full size Colt magazine will work as back up.

Price: $110; additional customer supplied magazine can be altered at $12 each.

From Seecamp.

See the Directory for complete company addresses.

CLARK TARGET CONVERSIONS

Ruger .22
Replaces factory barrel with 6¼″ Douglas premium barrel with muzzle brake. Includes deluxe Bo-Mar rear sight and ramp front, complete trigger job with steel trigger.
Price: $178
Same as above except 5½″ Douglas barrel with full-length Bo-Mar rib and sights.
Price: $188

Long Heavy Slide 38 Special Colt
Colt Super .38 slide is lengthened 1″, 6″ Douglas barrel is fitted and gun completely accurized. Includes full length Bo-Mar rib with accuracy tuner.
Price: $310
Same as above except uses a shorter, lighter Bo-Mar Mini-Rib with accuracy tuner.
Price: $320

Standard Length .38 Special
Same as above except standard length slide with 5″ Colt .38 Special barrel.
Price: $248
Same as above except extension front sight that provides 8½″ sight radius.
Price: $253

Long Heavy Slide Custom .45
Same as long heavy slide .38 Special, except in .45 ACP.
Price: $307

Heavy Slide Custom .45
Same as above except standard length, standard front sight.
Price: $222
Same as above except extension front sight that provides 8½″ sight radius.
Price: $229

Custom .45 Long Slide
Similar to long heavy model, except uses a shorter, lighter Bo-Mar rib.
Price: $307

Custom .45
Same as above, except standard length slide and 5″ Colt barrel.
Price: $222

Extended Sight Custom .45
Same as above except extended front sight provides 8½″ sight radius.
Price: $229

.45 Hard Ball
Same as .45 Custom except uses a Bo-Mar Deluxe sight without Mini-Rib.
Price: $197
From Clark.

PISTOL AND REVOLVER WORK
A variety of services for 1911 pattern Colts and revolvers is available. These include:
1911 accurizing: $100
Adjust trigger pull to given weight: $15.
Mill for adjustable sights: $15 (1911); $20 (revolvers).
Drill and tap for Bo-Mar sights or scope mounts: $3 per hole.
Send 50¢ for detailed price list.
From J. Korzinek.

CLARK CUSTOM COMBAT REVOLVERS
Heavy Douglas barrel has full length Bo-Mar rib and sight protectors, complete action and trigger job. For Ruger Security-Six (regular or stainless), S & W Model 10, some Colts.
Price: $245.90
From Clark.

CLARK COLT COMBAT CONVERSIONS
Includes accuracy job, reworked trigger, low mounted Bo-Mar or S&W sights, stippled front strap, altered feed ramp, lower ejection port, and beveled magazine well.
Price: $224.50
From Clark.

REVOLVER ACTION JOBS
Tune and polish action of Ruger Single Action, Colt (Python-type actions only), Ruger and Smith & Wesson double action revolvers.
Price:
Ruger Single Action: $35.00
Double Action Revolvers: $50.00
Mag-na-port also provides a number of other custom gunsmithing services. Contact them to discuss specific needs.
From Mag-na-port.

BEAL'S COLT PYTHON .40 BBI CONVERSION
.40 BBI ballistics, 1340 fps muzzle velocity with 170 gr. bullet. Conversion includes 6″ barrel, custom cylinder, Pachmayr Signature grips, tuned action, wide smooth trigger, hard chrome finish, custom aluminum case plus 200 rounds of .40 BBI 170 gr.
Price: $1200 (approximately).
From Beal's Bullets, Inc.

Prices shown are subject to change.

LARGE CALIBER REVOLVER CONVERSIONS

Large-frame Smith & Wessons, Colts, single actions from Colt, Ruger and various foreign makers can be converted to larger calibers such as .38-40, .44-40, .41 and .44 Magnum, .44 Special, .45 Long Colt, .45 ACP and .45 Auto Rim.

Price: $60 (add $5 for yellow, orange or red front sight insert installed at time of conversion).

Cylinder only: $30 (reaming and polishing cylinder only to chamber a different cartridge).

From David Woodruff.

RUGER SINGLE ACTION CONVERSIONS

Includes Mag-na-port and crowning barrel, remounting front sight, and deluxe blue job.

Price: $140

Same as above but also includes satin nickel finish for trigger guard, backstrap, ejector rod housing and cylinder pin.

Price: $160

Same as above but with S.S. Metalife, a hard chrome finish that looks like stainless steel (cannot be used on alloy backstrap and ejector rod housings.)

Price: $155

From Mag-na-port.

CUSTOM RUGER BLACKHAWKS

Custom cylinders for practically any cartridge with an overall loaded length of 1.8 inches or less are offered by Snapp's Gunshop, but must be fitted to the individual revolver. Barrels for non-standard calibers can, when required, also be supplied. Cylinder installation includes head-spacing and test firing.

Price: $110

From Snapp's Gunshop.

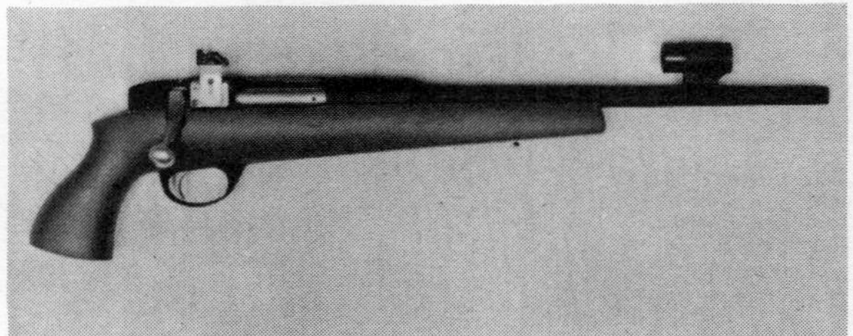

DEVER SILHOUETTE PISTOLS

Custom made silhouette pistols use Wichita or Shilen actions, set up to meet individual shooter's needs. Fiberglass stocks.

Price: Wichita action: $595 (forward or rear trigger).
Shilen action: $650 (rear trigger).

From Jack B. Dever.

XP-100 CONVERSIONS

A number of XP-100 conversions are offered, including a lightweight version of IHMSA and hunting models.

Price: From $229.50.

Threaded, chambered XP-100 barrels: $99.50
Fiberglass XP-100 stock blanks: $65.00
Fully inletted, ready for outside finish: $120.00
Completely finished and inletted: $150.00

From Jack B. Dever.

MARSHAL'S XP-100 CONVERSIONS

MarshAl's builds silhouette and hunting versions of the XP-100 and offers a number of services and accessories for those pistols.

Standard Target Grade Barrel $39.00
Stainless Steel Barrel $62.00
Barrel Installation on XP-100 Action $69.50
Open Bolt Face, Install Claw Extractor ....$35.00 (less parts)
Open Bolt Face, Install Remington Type Extractor ....$25.00 (less parts)
Inletting Wood Stock ....$50.00 up
Fiberglass Stock $69.95
Electric Trigger System ....$100.00 (plus installation)

From MarshAl's.

MARSHAL'S CONTENDER CONVERSIONS

MarshAl's specializes in options and accessories for the Thompson Center Contender. Included are:

15″ Custom Barrels, from .22 LR to .45 Magnum $119.95
16″ and 20″ (Rifle Length) barrels, bull or standard weight $119.95
Rifle Conversion Butt and Fore End, inletted to individual contender action, unfinished 64.95
Butt & Fore End with Rifle Barrel (complete conversion) 179.95
23″ .410 Shotgun Barrel (legal as long "pistol" or shotgun 109.95
23″ .410 Shotgun Barrel with rib 129.95
Contender Accurizing Job (per barrel) 45.20
Modified Barrel Release 69.95
Heavy Recoil Pistol Stocks 19.95
Custom Fore End 13.95
Contra-Jet (Muzzle Brake Installed) 55.00
Custom Chambering 20.00

Write for a detailed listing of all their Contender Services and Accessories.

From MarshAl's.

CUSTOM RIFLES, SILHOUETTE PISTOLS

Dave Cook offers a complete repair and restoration facility as well as custom gun building of all kinds.
From Dave Cook.

CUSTOM RIFLES

Custom sporting rifles built on surplus military or commercial actions to customer's specifications. The example pictured uses an Argentine Mauser action and a .270 Shilen barrel.
From Don Allen.

CUSTOM MINI-14

Mini-14 conversion includes Mannlicher style stock, with or without checkering, cut-down gas block, barrel step removed, ramp front sight, low profile steel handguard, polished and blued.

Price: $350 (Series 180 with stock checkering, but less cost of stock).
Price: $250 (Series 180 without stock checkering, but less cost of stock).
Stocks priced from $68 up, depending on wood. For new Model Mini-14 (Series 181) add $50.
From Bain & Davis.

CUSTOM RIFLES, RIFLE ACCESSORIES

Restocking, rebarreling and complete custom rifle building are all done by Lenard Brownell. He also manufactures a custom bolt handle and bolt stop for Mauser actions and a grip cap for sporter stocks. Custom rifle work is quoted on an individual basis.
From Lenard Brownell.

De HAAS MILLER RIFLES

Single shot sporting rifles using the De Haas Miller single shot action, built only to order on a custom basis only. Delivery 2-3 years.
Price: $1,500 (approximately).
From C-D Miller Guns.

CUSTOM RIFLES

Sporting Rifles built on commercial actions. Pictured is an FN action with .25-06 Douglas barrel.
From Custom Guns West.

RIFLE MAKING SERVICES

A wide variety of rifle services, from bolt handle alteration to complete custom match and long range rifle building, is offered. Cloward also does hot bath bluing, rebarrels using Douglas or Hart barrels, and custom stocking. Write for his detailed price list.
From Jim Cloward.

Prices shown are subject to change.

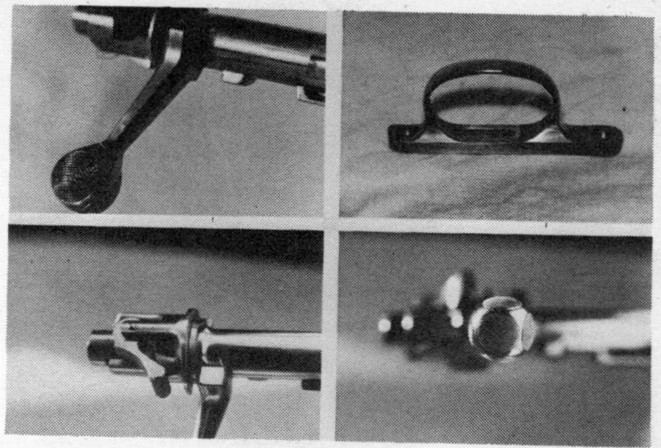

HERMAN WALDRON, CUSTOM GUNSMITHING
Shown nearby are some excellent examples of this gunsmith's work. He makes custom bolt handles, safeties, trigger guards, sights and other items including complete rifles. He will modify your rifle to order. However, this work must be done on a scheduled (not mail order) basis. The prices are, of course, dependent upon the work to be done; we suggest you contact this gunsmith for more information.
Price: Write gunsmith direct.
From Herman Waldron, Gunsmith.

CUSTOM RIFLES
Hunting rifles are built using Winchester, Sako, Remington or Mauser actions, Douglas or Hart barrels. A full range of wood is offered, with customer choice of combination and decoration. Delivery 6-14 months.
Price: $600 to $2,500.

Varmint and bench rest rifles are built on Remington 40X, Shilen, Sako and HVA receivers, with stainless steel barrels only. Stocks are laminated wood or fiber glass. Delivery averages eight months.
Price: $800 to $1,200

Stocking services for all modern rifles and shotguns using fancy and extra fancy, high grade wood, design, checking and finish to customer's specifications. Average delivery eight months.
Price: $400 (approximate).
From The Custom Gunsmith.

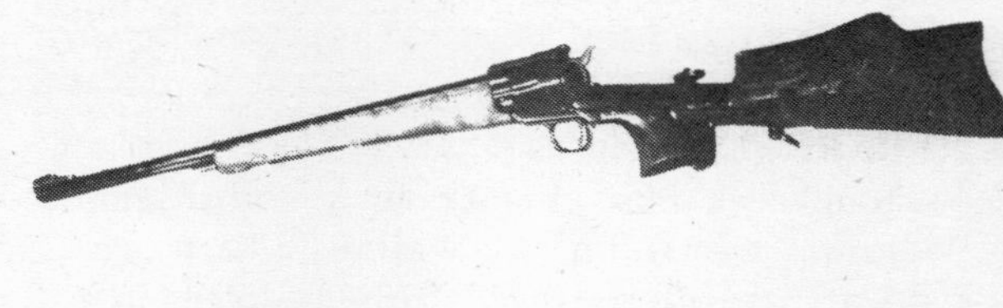

CUSTOM RIFLES
DiStefano builds custom rifles in both conventional sporter style and unique one-of-a-kind customer designs. The carbine-pistol is built on a Ruger Blackhawk revolver, with both .357 Magnum and 9mm cylinders. Price and delivery are quoted to individual needs.
From Dominic DiStefano.

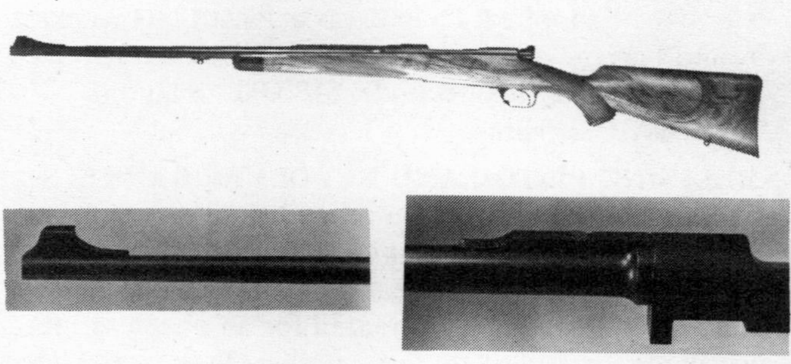

CUSTOM RIFLES
Custom rifles in classic style, custom modifications to standard guns are available as offered by Jay Frazier. Pictured is a custom pre-war Model 70 in .375, with low quarter rib mounted express sights. Quarter ribs with rear sights and matching front sights are also available separately.
Price (Quarter Rib Sight, Multiple Leaves): From $250;
Matching Machined Front Sight: From $50.
From Jay Frazier.

CUSTOM RIFLES
Mauser and Springfield bolt actions are rebuilt into sporters with Model 70 style safety, push button bolt stop, custom polish and blue, restocking. Price depends on individual requirements.
From H. L. "Pete" Grisel.

See the Directory for complete company addresses.

CUSTOM TAPERED OCTAGON BARRELS

Top quality barrel blanks are cut to tapered octagon form with or without quarter- or full-length rib, draw filed and polished ready for bluing. Combinations other than those listed are also available; prices do not include barrel blank.

Price: $96.50 (no rib); $146.50 (quarter rib); $176.50 (full rib).

Integral front sight ramp with dovetail, add $25; integral sling swivel lug or fore-end lug, $15 each.

From Ralph L. Carter.

TAPERED OCTAGON BARRELS

Existing barrel can be removed from action, cut to octagon shape and then reinstalled. New tapered octagon barrels are made from Douglas blanks.

Price: $45 (pull, cut to octagon and reinstall customer's barrel); $85 (machined from Douglas blank); $115 (same, but half-octagon, half-round). Add $15 for polishing, $40 for blue.

From Kogot.

BARREL OCTAGONING SERVICE

Round barrels are made octagon without removing them from the action by Larry Forster. If desired the contour can also be changed at the same time.

Price: $35 (sporter weight); $50 (target weight).

From Larry Forster.

REBARRELING, REBORING

P. O. Ackley barrels are made from specially heat treated 4140 chrome Moly steel and are button rifled for proper bore dimensions.

Price: $90 (.22-.45 caliber); $95 (.17-.20 caliber).

For: Duplication of old barrel ....add $10.00
Bluing 10.00
Recoil Lugs 20.00
Single Shot 20.00

Reboring: $50 (add $10 if rechambering is required).

From P. O. Ackley Barrels.

RIFLE BARREL REBORING

Shot-out rifles can be restored to service by reboring to a larger caliber, for example .22 Hi-Power to .25-35 or .30-30 to .32 Special. Twists from 8 through 20 available.

Price: $65 up.

1892 Winchester can be converted to .357 Magnum by reboring and rechambering.

Price: $130 (.32-20); $140 (.25-20).

J. W. Van Patten offers a range of custom services for both bolt action and single shot rifles. Write for detailed price list.

From J. W. Van Patten.

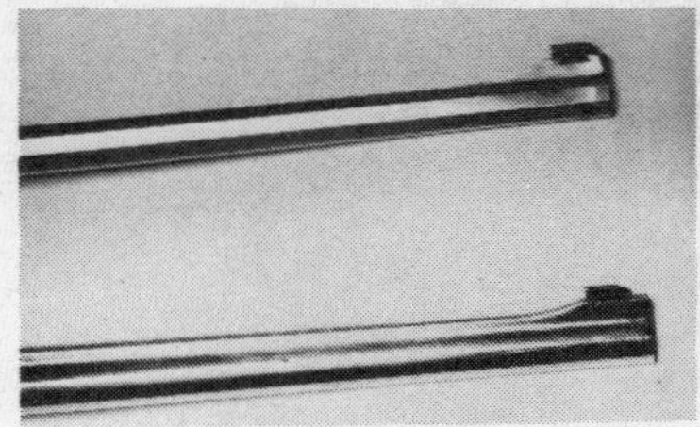

RIFLE BARREL REBORING, RELINING

Restore shot-out rifle barrels to service by reboring to a larger caliber. .22 through .50 caliber bores in 8, 9, 10-24 (even numbers) inch twists, six grooves, are available.

Price: $75

Convert 92 Winchester to .357 Magnum, including reboring.

Price: $125 (from .32-20); $160 (from .25-20).

Low pressure barrels can be relined to the original caliber when preferred.

Price: $55 (.22 LR); $75 (.22-.32); $90 (.32 up).

From Robert G. West.

REBARRELING

Douglas blanks, chambered for most standard and Magnum cartridges as well as the more popular wildcats, are offered in .17 through .460 caliber. Barrels and barreled actions, carefully finished and blued or in the white, are available in feather-weight through heavy bench rest styles. A classic tapered octagon contour can also be supplied. Delivery is at least 12-14 weeks on round barrels, six months on tapered octagons.

Price: From $75.00 (round); $180.00 (octagon).

From W. C. Strutz.

RELINING PISTOL AND REVOLVER BARRELS

Handgun barrels can be relined to like-new firing condition without disturbing original outside finish or otherwise disturbing appearance. Relining also permits changing a gun chambered for an obsolete, unavailable cartridge to fire another that is readily available.

Price: $19.50 for P.38, Nambu, Radom, Steyr, etc. to 9mm or 7.65mm Parabellum.

Mauser 1896 to 7.63mm or 9mm Mauser, 7.65mm or 9mm Parabellum, .38 Super: $24.50.

.25 ACP auto pistols: $8.50 (small); $11.50 (large)

.32 ACP auto pistol converted to .380: $19.50 (barrel only; be sure magazine will hold and feed .380 before sending barrel in for relining)

.22 Rimfire rifle barrels: $22.50

All prices plus postage.

From David Woodruff.

REBARRELING, ACTION AND CUSTOM STOCK WORK

A Douglas premium barrel blank is turned to any standard weight and length, fitted to user-supplied action, chambered, lapped, throated, marked and test fired. Completed action and barrel assembly is then hand polished and deluxe blued, with mirror or matte finish as desired.
Price: $205 (add $33 for benchrest length and weight). Barrels can be rechambered to any practical caliber ($60) or turned to a new contour ($55 up). Shotgun barrels can be altered to a more open choke ($28), chambers lengthened ($28), and bores lapped ($28). Competition choking, which includes test firing, is $66 for single barrel guns; $120 for doubles.
Write for Heritage's detailed price list.
From Heritage Gunsmiths.

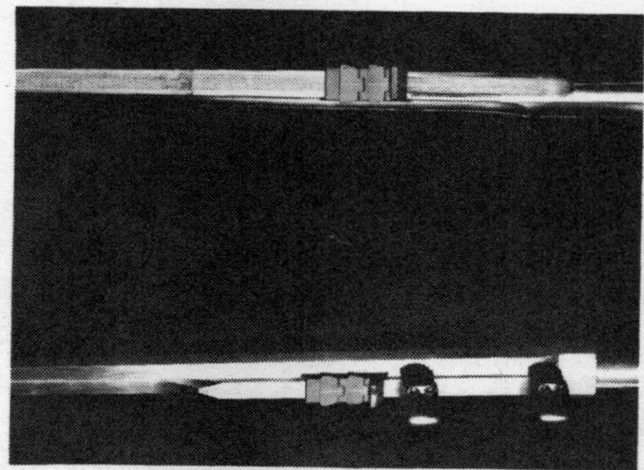

CUSTOM RIFLE RIBS, EXPRESS SIGHTS, QUARTER RIBS AND RIBS MACHINED FOR SCOPE RINGS

All of these (and other) items and services are done by Ralph Carter. In the nearby photo you can see (top) a full-length rib with three-leaf express-type sight. The barrel on the bottom sports a quarter rib complete with three-leaf express-type sight—this rib has also been cut to accept Lenard Brownell custom rings or standard Ruger rings.
Prices: Write gunsmith direct.
From Ralph L. Carter.

BARREL RESTORATION

Reboring and rerifling or relining a worn bore are a must if a shot-out but otherwise useful arm is to provide good accuracy. All rifling by Bruce Jones is six-groove, right-hand twist.
Price:
Rebore and rifle: $45
Chambering: $5 to $10
Reline and rifle: $90 (larger calibers); $50 (.22, including chambering for any .22 rimfire)
Add $5 for shipping and handling.
From Bruce Jones.

REPAIR AND RESTORATION

Restoration of a valuable firearm requires repair of broken or badly worn parts and careful duplication of original polishing and blueing methods. J.J. Jenkins has long been a specialist in this kind of work, with emphasis on fine shotguns and rifles as well as the rarer variations of Luger, Mauser and other collectable automatic pistols. Restoration or duplication of original wood and custom stocks for sporting arms are also offered; a stock of replacement parts for all Merkel shotguns, other sporting arms is also maintained. Prices depend on individual job—call or write for quote.
From J.J. Jenkins.

RESTORATION SERVICE

As the supply of fine rare and older firearms dwindles, collectors are turning to examples that have been badly used or are no longer complete. Rather than including such a less-than-adequate item in their collections, many collectors are turning to knowledgeable restorers like John Kaufield of Small Arms Engineering to put them back in factory-new condition. Old-time techniques provide a finish close to the original, while cut-off barrels can be restored to proper length, deep pits filled by welding, and original markings restamped or engraved.
Price on an individual job basis.
From Small Arms Engineering.

REPAIR, RESTORATION, CUSTOM RIFLE MAKING

Lester Womac also does repair and restoration work, specializing in commercial Mauser sporting rifles, including hand polish and reblue by original factory techniques. Classic style custom stocks are also offered. Write for detailed price list.
From Lester Womac.

CUSTOM STOCKMAKING, RESTORATION

David Trevallion is an Englishman who learned his trade as an apprentice with England's top gunmakers. His specialty is custom stocks for fine shotguns and double rifles; he also does complete metal and wood restoration of antique as well as modern arms. All work is priced on an individual job basis.
From Trevallion Gunstocks.

RESTORATION, REFINISHING AND CUSTOM WORK

Complete refinishing services, with original type polishing and hot or rust blue as appropriate. Color case hardening. Prices vary depending on amount of preparation and type of blue, starting at $33 for a handgun. A wide range of gunsmithing services is also included. Write for detailed price list.
From Vic's Gun Refinishing.

RIFLE AND SHOTGUN FINISHING; SERVICES

Blue and cold rust brown (for black powder arms), color case hardening, anodizing (for aluminum) and gold plating for triggers are all offered.

Price:

Standard blue: $35 (polish or matte)
Deluxe Blue: $45
Cold rust blue (doubles): $50
Color case harden receivers: $35 up
Cold rust brown: $35 up
Stock refinishing: $45 (oil); $50 (high gloss or satin).

Stock making in both wood and fiberglass is also available, along with a wide range of trigger, action and barrel work for both rifle and shotgun. A custom Remington Model 600, fitted with a Model 700 bolt handle and one of Korzinek's bolt sleeves (inset) and glued into a McMillen stock blank, is shown.
Write for detailed price list (50¢).
From J. Korzinek

STAINLESS STEEL BLUING

Korzinek applies a true blue finish to rifle barrels made of 400 family stainless. Price shown is for barrels only; receivers or other stainless parts can be quoted on an individual basis.
Price: $35
From J. Korzinek

TEFLON FIREARMS FINISH

Teflon-S offers an alternative finish that is especially appropriate for guns that will see hard service. Its non-reflective surface offers excellent resistance to corrosion and has self lubricating properties. Available in black or olive drab.
Price: $42.50 (long guns); $33 (handguns). (A $4 discount is allowed for disassembled guns.)
From West Coast SECOA.

COLOR CASE HARDENING

Disassembled and polished actions and associated parts can be color case hardened in two to four weeks from receipt. Action heat treating, with emphasis on toughness rather than color, is also offered (specify).
Price: $15 (plus $2.50 return shipping).
From Twin City Steel Treating.

PLATING AND FINISHING

Plating in nickel, chrome, gold, silver, rust and hot blue, and browning is offered.
Price: $50 up.
From Ken's Metal Finishing.

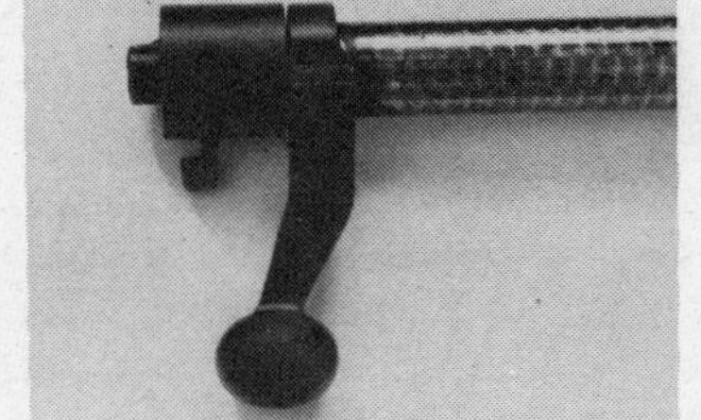

BOLT ACTION SERVICES

Mauser 98 bolt sleeve can be altered to utilize a Model 70 type safety and equipped with a custom bolt handle, with or without checkering. Checkered bolt stop tab, action restyled, on Model 98. Various other services are also offered; send for detailed price list.
Price:
Standard Safety: $29.95 (installed on your bolt sleeve).
Custom Safety: $39.95 (same, except original safety hole filled in and sleeve refinished).
Bolt Handle: $30 (welded to your bolt; for checkering, add $50 for each panel).
Checkered Bolt Stop Tab: $15 (installed on your housing).
From Ken Jantz.

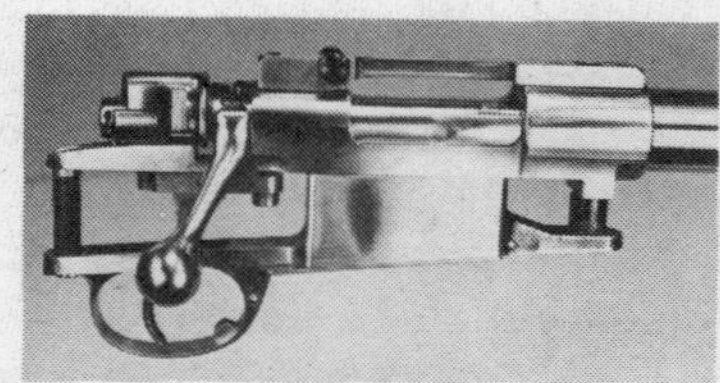

LIGHTWEIGHT SHORTENED MAUSER ACTION

Commercial or Military Mauser bolt actions are extensively reworked to remove all possible excess weight and/or shortened appropriately for short-case commercial or wildcat cartridges. Work is done on a custom basis, with various options available per customer's wishes. The scope bases and rings shown on a light-weight Mauser action are machined from solid bar stock, permanently mounted and line bored on the bore axis.
Price (Lightweight Action): $1,650.
Price (Scope Mounts, Rings): $500.
From Ron Lampert.

REBARRELING, ACTION MODIFICATIONS

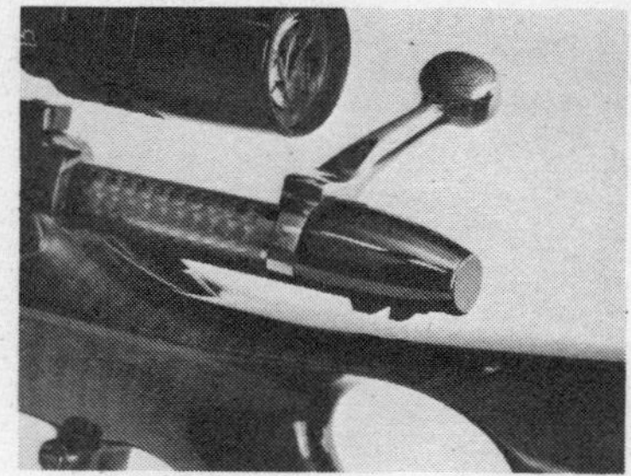

Actions are rebarreled with Shilen custom grade chrome-moly barrels, cut to desired length, and crowned, blued and installed. Bolts are altered by forging, high-polished or engine turned. Lawson Safety Shroud can be installed on most bolts, Lawson button safety installed in trigger, and Lawson muzzle brake installed.

Price:
- Rebarreling: $135
- Bolt Handle Alteration: $16.50 (add $10.50 for high polish bolt and extractor; $16 for engine turning).
- Lawson Safety Shroud: $16 (installed on Remington, Enfield, Sako; $18 on Model 70; $20 on Mauser, Springfield).
- Lawson Button Safety: $30 (installed in customer's guard).
- Lawson Muzzle Brake: $42.50 (installed).

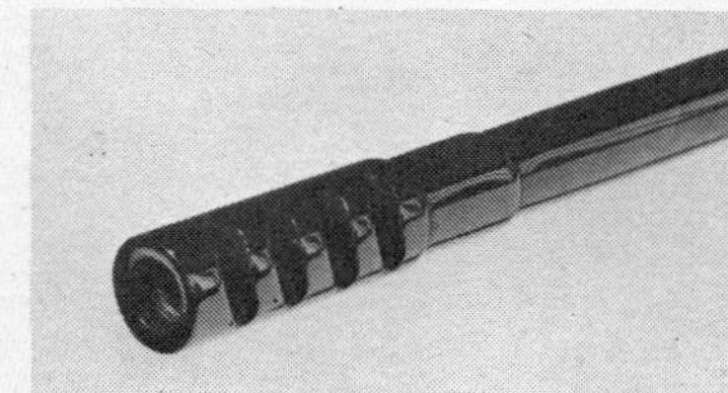

From Harry Lawson.

CUSTOM RIFLE ACTIONS

Bolt handle alteration, bolt knob checkering, Mauser action rework, and custom trigger guards for Model 70 Winchester, Remington 700, and Weatherby are offered.

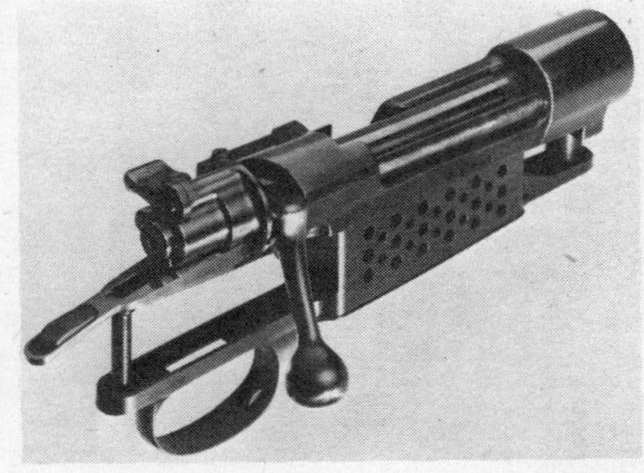

Price:
- Bolt Handle Restyle and Polish $40
- Hand Checker Bolt Knob ....$20-$45
- Remove Mauser Charger Bridge and Polish Entire Action $35
- Polish and Checker Bolt Stop $15

From Dick Willis.

BOLT HANDLE FORGING

Altering a Mauser or Springfield bolt handle to clear low-mounted scopes is often done by cutting and rewelding the handle; but reshaping the handle by heating and forging into shape can result in a safer, more reliable conversion. Special blocks draw heat from the bolt itself, preventing annealing and scale formation.

Price: $25

From Lester Womac.

CUSTOM RIFLE STOCKS

Complete stockmaking service using highest quality woods, individually fitted to the customer. Prices vary with individual requirements.

From Bill Dowtin.

CLASSIC SPORTER STOCKS

Sporter stocks of simple, classic lines are David Dunlop's specialty. He prefers to work with European, French or Circassian walnut. Current delivery time is 12-18 months.

Price: $550 (basic stock, including checkering).

From David R. Dunlop.

See the Directory for complete company addresses.

CUSTOM STOCKS

Custom fitted stocks, made to customer specifications, oil finished with full coverage checkering. A number of options are available at extra cost.

Price:
Rifle Stock: $1,000 (including checkering).
Boxlock Shotgun or Two-piece Rifle: $1,100.
Sidelock Shotgun: $1,500 up.

From Maurice Ottmar.

CUSTOM STOCKING

In addition to making stock blanks and stocks to fit practically every domestic and foreign rifle and shotgun, Reinhart Fajen will also fit a specified grade of wood to a customer's action and semi-finish or finish, with or without checkering, to his specifications. Prices vary considerably with grade of wood and the type of finishing required. Price for a shaped but unfinished stock of standard pattern, hand fitted to customer's action, is from $97 to $205 (depending on grade of wood); including hand checkering and finishing increases the price to $160 to $280. The "Aristocrat" style stock illustrated runs $15 to $20 more. Special finishes, other custom features are also available.

From Reinhart Fajen.

CUSTOM STOCKS

Custom rifle and shotgun stocks, and refinishing and recheckering of original stocks, are offered by Edward Hefti. Each job is quoted on an individual basis, so write him with your specific request.

From Edward O. Hefti.

CUSTOM STOCKS, RIFLES

Hand-made sporter stocks of French, California, English or Claro walnut, complete with fleur de lis or point pattern checkering. Various grip caps, butt plates, and fore-end types are also available at additional cost; action work and rust or hot bluing are also offered.

Price: $950 (stock work only; add $50 to $500 for blank. Other options quoted on request.)

From Dale W. Goens.

CUSTOM GUNSTOCKS, INLETTING SERVICE

Customer supplied blanks are precision machine inletted and shaped to customer's requirements, fully finished with recoil pad, grip cap and sling swivels. Checkering, Biesen butt plates and grip caps can also be supplied at additional cost.

Price:
One Piece Bolt Action Rifle $625
Two Piece Rifle or Shotgun $675
Sidelock Shotguns or Rifles $825

From Al Lind.

CUSTOM STOCKING

Custom stocks in the classic pattern are inletted to the individual action, shaped, finished and fitted with recoil pad, grip cap and swivels. Various special accessories such as ebony fore-end tips, Biesen butt plates and grip caps are also available at additional cost.

Stock Prices: $450 (bolt action rifle); $500 (two-piece rifle or shotgun); $700 (sidelock guns).
Checkering: from $100.

From Philip Letiecq.

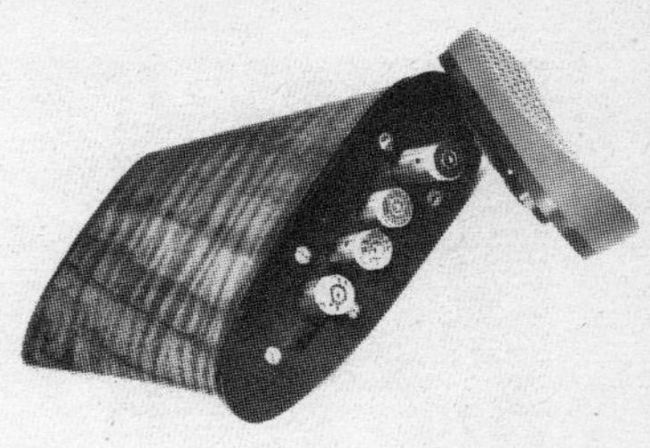

CUSTOM TRAP-TYPE BUTT PLATE

The pad is of the stylish thin-rubber variety backed by black anodized aluminum, or ⅛″ steel—customer's choice. The outside will be shaped to small, medium or large recoil pad sizes and white finished with brass screws furnished. Installed by maker.

Price: Write maker direct.

From Hubert J. Hecht.

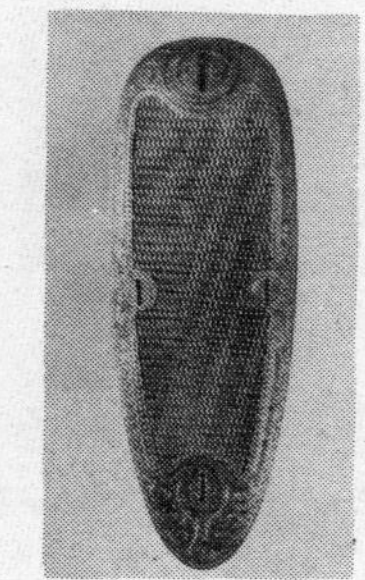

SKELETON BUTT PLATES

Each plate is made-to-order and custom-fitted to the owner's favorite rifle. The work is all hand done and expertly executed. We sincerely suggest you write the gunsmith direct for more information on this and other available services.

Price: Write gunsmith direct.

From Bill McGuire, Gunsmith.

GUN ENGRAVING

Traditional styles of engraving with a distinctly southwestern Indian motif is offered by Bryan Bridges. Though each job is quoted on an individual basis, some representative prices are:

Medium sized revolvers, fully engraved: $5000.
Grip Cap (illustrated): $400.

From Bryan Bridges.

GUN ENGRAVING

A very wide range of stock patterns as well as custom design based on owner's suggestion are available from J. R. French. Prices depend on grade of engraving, area to be covered, and the percentage of coverage. Some examples are:

Handgun, Grade I engraving, 50% coverage: $200
Handgun; Grade II engraving, full coverage: $450.
Long Arms, Grade III, two-thirds coverage: $550.
Add 20% for stainless; gold or silver inlays are also available. A well-illustrated brochure and detailed price list are offered for $3 (refundable).

From J. R. French.

GUN ENGRAVING

Ben Shostle engraves both pistols and long guns in classic style, pricing his work by the amount of gun surface the engraving covers.

Representative prices are:

Class "A" (25%): $125 - $265
Class "B" (50%): $200 - $325
Class "C" (75%): $300 - $400
Class "D" (full): $325 - $625

From The Gun Room.

See the Directory for complete company addresses.

GUN AND KNIFE ENGRAVING

Engraving and precious metal inlaying in a variety of styles is offered by Master Engraver Ralph W. Ingle, who offers a photo-illustrated catalog of his work on both guns and knives for $2.

From Ralph W. Ingle.

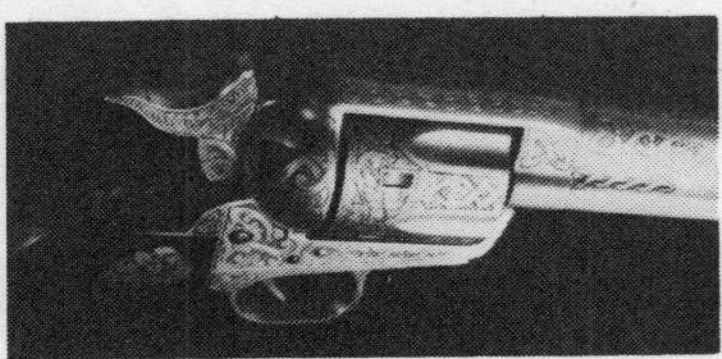

GUN ENGRAVING, INLAYS

Classic style gun engraving with a specialty in pearl grip inlays and custom ivory grips are offered by Jim Kelso of Iron Age Craftworks. Work is quoted on an individual basis.

From Iron Age Craftworks.

GUN ENGRAVING

Antique, modern and custom styles of engraving, with or without gold or silver inlays, are offered. Bill Johns also does relief carving of ivory grips. Work is quoted on an individual basis.

From Bill Johns.

GUN ENGRAVING

Scroll engraving, with or without figures or gold or silver inlay, is offered by Ken Eyster on both long guns or pistols. Although each job must be quoted on an individual basis, some representative prices are:

Rifle or Shotgun: $1,450 - $1,600 (full coverage); from $500 up (partial coverage).

Pistols and Revolvers: $450 - $1,200 (full coverage, depending on size of gun); from $400 up (partial coverage).

From Heritage Gunsmiths.

GUN ENGRAVING

Engraving in all traditional patterns, inlays of game scenes or monograms, special patterns to customer's request, are all available from E.C. Prudhomme's Shop. Prices vary widely so must be quoted on a job-by-job basis.

From E. C. Prudhomme.

Prices shown are subject to change.

GUN AND KNIFE ENGRAVING

Beth Lane does scroll engraving only at this time, on knives as well as rifles and pistols. Work is quoted on an individual basis, but the examples pictured cost their owners:

Colt Gold Cup: $375.

Knife: $125.

From Beth Lane.

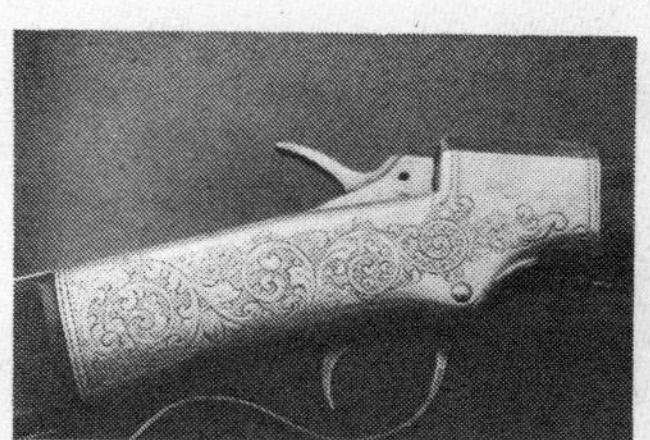

GUN ENGRAVING

George Sherwood specializes in floor plate and trigger guard, lever action rifle, shotgun and knife engraving, both line and relief. A profusely illustrated brochure showing examples and detailing prices is available for $1. Prices for the work illustrated are:

Ballard Rifle Receiver (both sides): $200.

Savage 99 (high relief, three different scenes): $875.

Floor Plate (line cut, including trigger guard): $85.

From George Sherwood.

ENGRAVING, STOCK MAKING

Traditional engraving and precious metal inlaying as well as custom classic-style stock making are services provided by John Vest. All work is quoted on a job-by-job basis.

From John Vest.

GUN ENGRAVING

Scroll engraving of rifles, shotguns and pistols, with or without gold or silver inlays, is offered by Vernon Wagoner. Representative prices for scroll engraving over the action and part of the barrel (rifles and shotguns), the entire gun (pistols and revolvers) are:

Bolt Action Rifle: $525.

Pump or Auto Shotgun: $630.

Double or O/U Shotgun: $630 - $700.

Pistol or Revolvers: $210 - $475 (depending on size).

For Inlays, add $150 (silver); $175 (gold).

From Vernon G. Wagoner.

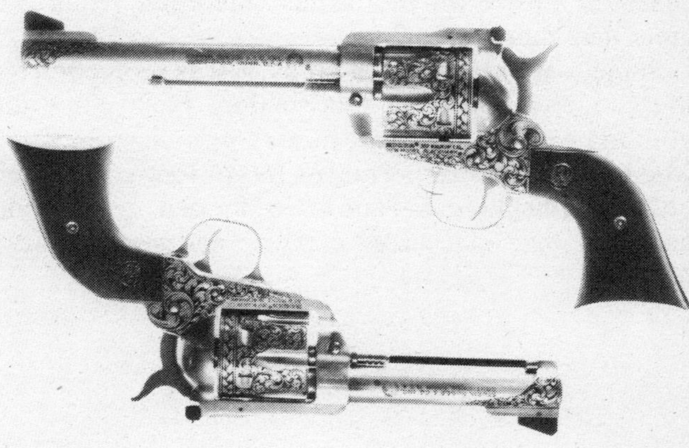

GUN ENGRAVING

Traditional style engraving to customer's instruction is Mel Wood's forte. Prices of the work on the examples pictured are:

Stainless Rugers: $300 each.

From Mel Wood.

See the Directory for complete company addresses.

Section 9

Gun Cases, Storage & Security

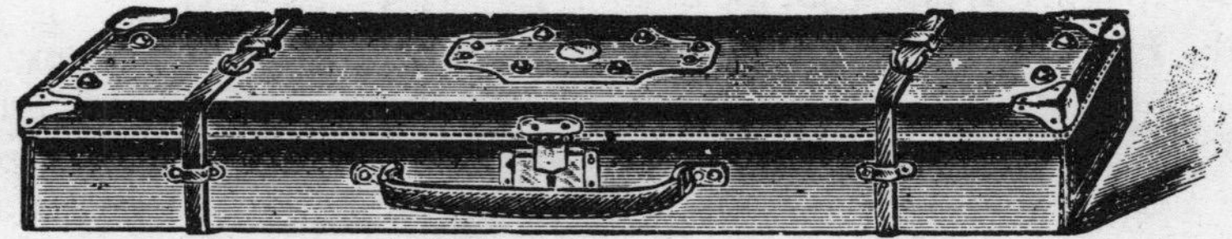

Gun protection can mean anything from keeping rain and dust away from action and finish to keeping the gun away from a burglar or sneak thief. Soft or hard cases generally suffice for the former; the latter requires a great deal more.

Some cases are works of art as well as protection for the gun; those lead off this section. Next come the utilitarian cases, soft and hard, for basic protection when storing or transporting pistols or long guns. Then you'll find display cases and racks, for den or gun room, and after that specialized carrying and storage racks and lockers for autos, campers and light trucks. Safety items conclude this important section, with heavy duty gun "safes" and action locking devices.

Soft and hard gun cases are almost always available from local gun shops, which also carry action locks or other safety devices and may also stock racks and display cabinets. For the custom fitted English-type cases you'll have to go direct to the makers; because of shipping costs, most of the heavy steel gun cabinets are also sold direct by the makers.

CUSTOM GUN CASE

Each case is hand made of the best materials by Norbert Ertel. Shown is the Ertel oak and leather gun case. All sides of the lid and body are fully dovetailed for maximum strength. Only the finest oak and top grain hides are used in the construction of this case. Comes with the finest brass hinges, locks, buckles and corners. Mr. Ertel makes these cases one-at-a-time; and, he also offers a number of accessories you might wish to order with your fully fitted case. (He also offers a complete restoration service for quality gun cases.) We urge you to write the craftsman direct for more information.

Price: As shown $430; two set of barrels case $480; "Pair-of-guns" case $580.

From Norbert Ertel.

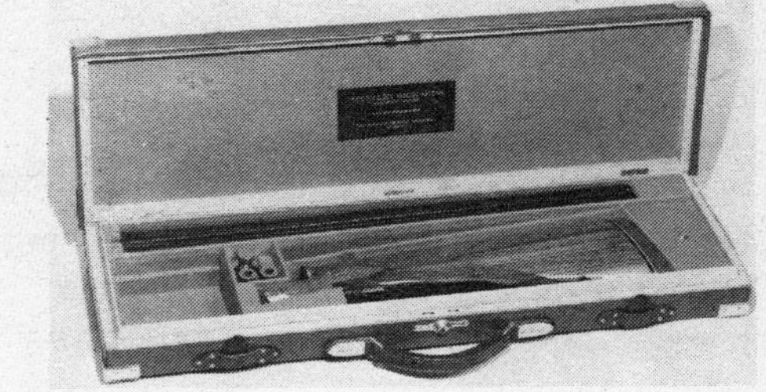

BEST QUALITY LEATHER TRUNK GUN CASES

These cases are beautifully made. In fact they are totally hand made. Built by Marion Huey, they are constructed of selected ash, best grade cowhide, choice wool and suede cloth linings. All bolsters, covers and pads are hand stitched. Comes with lidded compartments for loose parts and built-in brass lid stops and supports. *Many* options are available on request. Five different rifle, pistol shotgun or ammo cases are available. Shown nearby is a classic "Hunting Case" for take-down shotguns.

Prices for Marion Huey's work are listed below; however, we must again mention the wide array of available options and suggest you write the maker direct for more information.

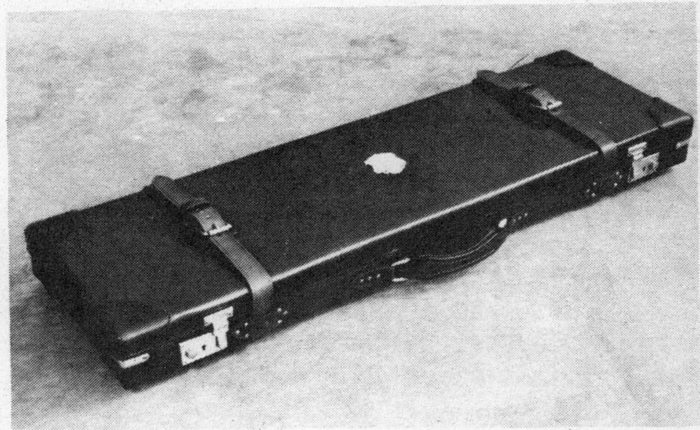

Prices:

Pistol case	$285.00
Cartridge box	285.00
Trunk case (single gun)	425.00
Trunk case (pair of guns)	510.00
Motorcase	435.00
Full-length flat carbine case	450.00
Bolt action rifle chest (open sights)	460.00
Bolt action rifle chest (telescopic sights)	475.00

From Huey Gun Cases.

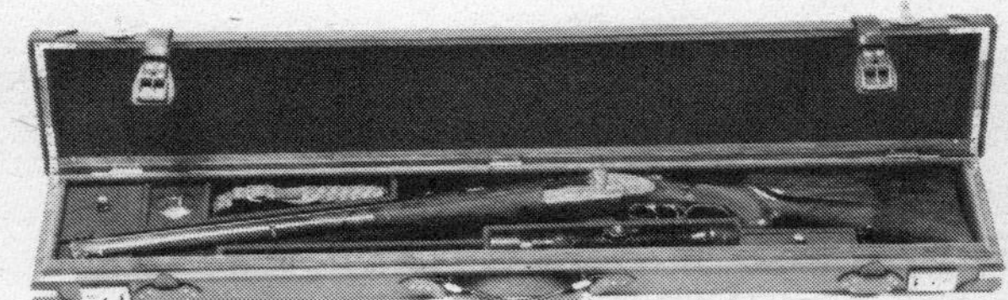

CUSTOM GUN CASE

Bill McGuire's hand-made custom gun cases represent the epitome of the case-maker's art. Feature leather, brass and hardwood construction. Simply put, this maker will produce whatever you want for your favorite rifles, shotguns or handguns. We suggest you write to the maker direct for more information on prices and delivery schedule.

Price: From $385.

From Bill McGuire & Associates.

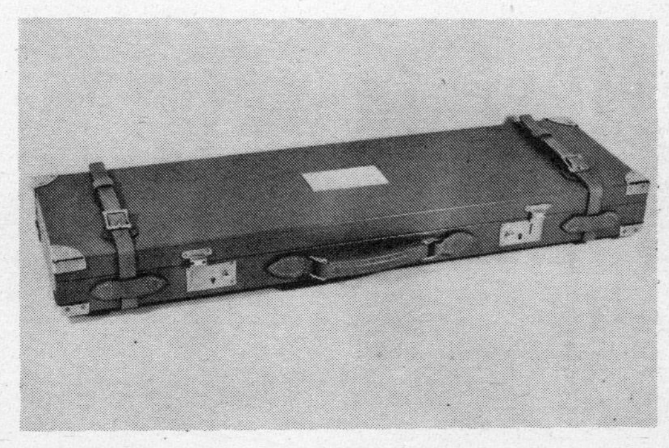

See the Directory for complete company addresses.

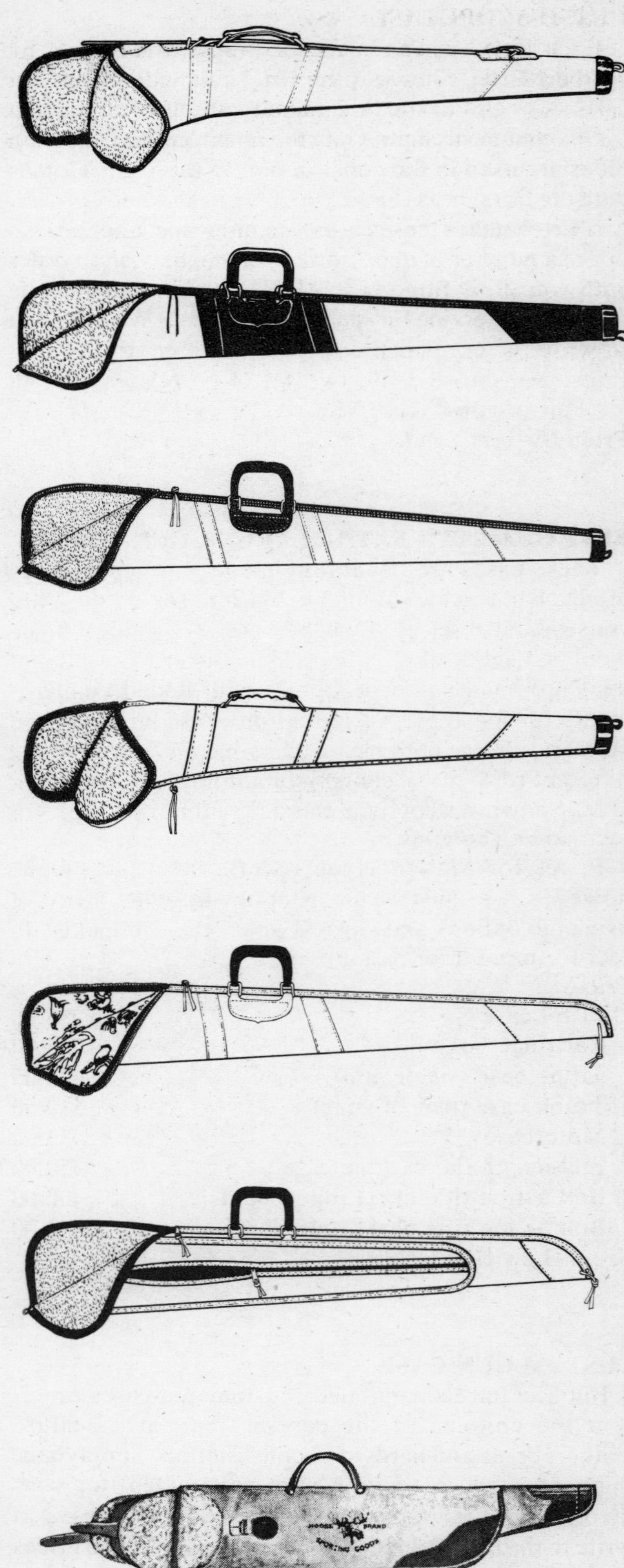

RIFLE/SHOTGUN CASE

This is Bucheimer's Model 52 gun case. It's available in all popular lengths and is made of split cowhide and orlon fleece. Features a full zipper, carrying sling and protective tip. *Well made.* Available for scoped rifles.
Price: See your local dealer.
From J. M. Bucheimer.

RIFLE/SHOTGUN CASE

Comes in lengths ranging from 40 to 52 inches. It's made of split cowhide and has orlon fleece lining. Has a full nylon coil zipper. Color: brown and sand. Comes with a luggage-type handle.
Price: About $45.
From J. M. Bucheimer.

RIFLE/SHOTGUN CASE

Bucheimer's Model 30 gun case comes in lengths ranging from 40 to 50 inches. Split cowhide construction. Acrylic pile lining. Features a full length nylon zipper and luggage-type carrying handles. Available for scoped rifle.
Price: About $45.
From J. M. Bucheimer.

RIFLE/SHOTGUN CASE

Comes in lengths ranging from 40 to 52 inches. Features a full aluminum zipper. Bucheimer's Model 50 gun case is made of split cowhide and has flannel lining. Comes with luggage-type carrying handles and protective rubber tip. Natural leather color.
Price: Under $30.
From J. M. Bucheimer.

RIFLE/SHOTGUN CASE

This is Bucheimer's Model 522 gun case. It's available in lengths ranging from 40 to 52 inches. Features split cowhide construction and flannel lining. Also has a full aluminum zipper and luggage type carrying handles. Natural color.
Price: About $25.
From J. M. Bucheimer.

EXTRA BARREL SHOTGUN CASE

Bucheimer's Model 302XB shotgun case features an outside-mounted spare barrel case. Overall lengths range from 46 to 54 inches. Spare barrel compartment handles any length shotgun barrel. Outer material light brown expanded vinyl; acrylic pile lining. Full zippers.
Price: $29
From J. M. Bucheimer.

SHOTGUN CASE

Comes in several styles. Made from genuine bark tanned shearling and reinforced with top-grain cowhide. Fits most shotguns with barrel lengths up to 32 inches. *Well made.* Specify gun and barrel length when ordering. Model 27 series.
Price: About $70; with extra barrel pouch, about $85.
From Brauer Bros.

Prices shown are subject to change.

HIGH-SCOPE GUN CASE

This one's made for rifles with large and/or extra high scopes. Body is light brown vinyl with black trim. Heavily padded with 2 inches of self-aerating foam. Chamois fleece lining with full nylon zipper. Comes in a wide variety of lengths.

Price: Model 007SS $28.10.

From Weather Shield Sports Equipment Co.

LEATHER GUN CASE

Weather Shield's Model B010, solid black leather gun case is well made. The lining is siliconized acrylic shearling and the padding is extra thick and self-aerating. It comes with a full length brass zipper and molded rubber tip. Available in a wide variety of lengths.

Price: Regular $68.10; scope size $79.65.

From Weather Shield Sports Equipment Co.

SUEDE LEATHER GUN CASE

This Kolpin case has two-tone brown suede construction. Inside, the lining is siliconized pile and humidity-proof padding. Comes with a full length zipper and rubber sight-protector tip. Available in 48-, 50- and 52-inch lengths.

Price: No. 54 $43.50, No. 540 (accommodates scope-sighted rifles) $47.50.

From Kolpin Manufacturing, Inc.

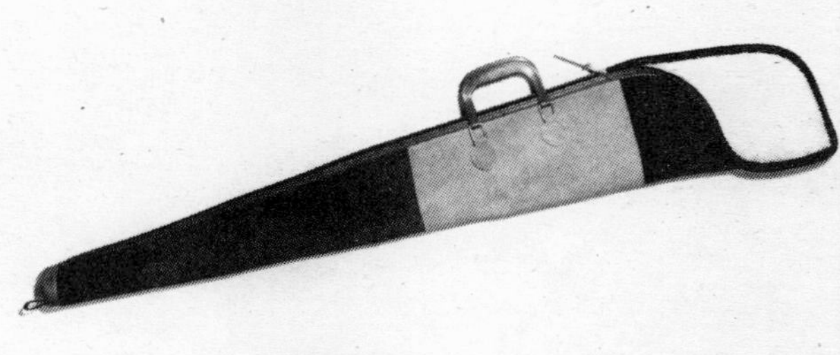

LEATHER GUN CASE

Made of genuine split cowhide, this Allen Model 570 gun case has a lot of quality features. It comes with luggage-style handles, plush acrylic pile, ½-inch of Tufflex padding. Colors are brown and dark tan. Comes in 40-, 44-, 48- and 52-inch lengths. Has a full-length nylon zipper.

Price: $41.07

From The Allen Co.

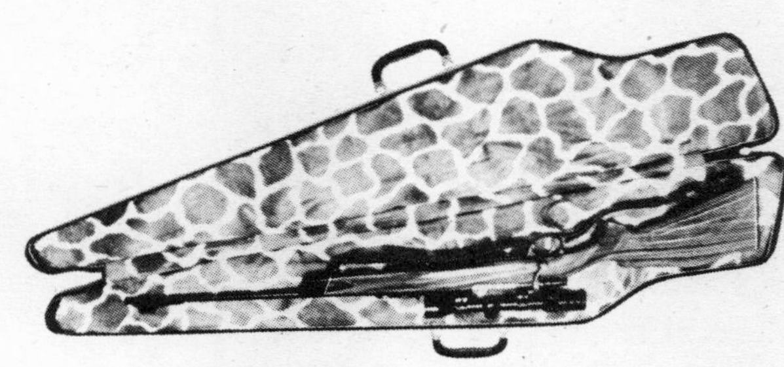

SCOPED-RIFLE CASE

This is Matchpoint's Model 103 gun case. It's designed to hold any rifle or shotgun that's scope-equipped. Features include luggage-type handles, a full zipper, deep-pile foam and cotton back. Comes in either black or brown.

Price: $53.10

From Matchpoint Industries, Inc.

GUN CASE

This particular case is Kolpin's No. 301 "Gun Cover." It's made of lightweight black vinyl over fabric. Folds up easily. Protects from dust, rain, etc.

Price: $3.60

From Kolpin Manufacturing, Inc.

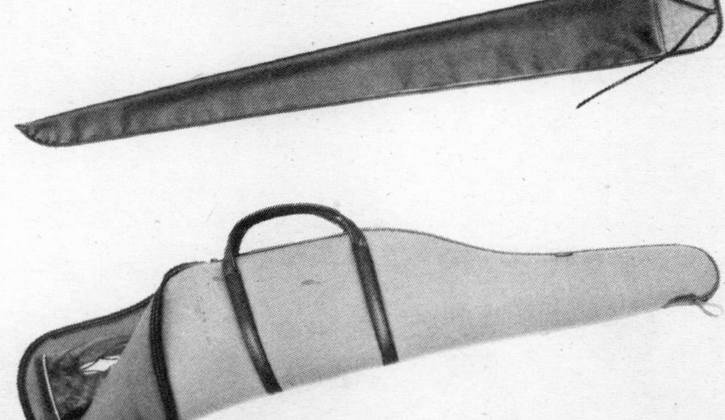

FOAM-PADDED GUN CASE

Kolpin's No. 620 gun case is foam padded for extra protection. Its shape is designed to accommodate scope-equipped rifles. Available in 42- and 46-inch lengths. Features a polyester coil zipper and locking ring. Medium-weight canvas construction.

Price: $30.50

From Kolpin Manufacturing, Inc.

See the Directory for complete company addresses.

GUN CASE

Kolpin's No. SP40 "Patchwork" case features an attractive dark brown vinyl outer pattern and an inner lining of ¼-inch padding covered in yellow cotton. Features sturdy zipper and luggage-type handles. Comes in 40-, 44-, 48- and 52-inch lengths.

Price: $16.75

From Kolpin Manufacturing, Inc.

EXTRA BARREL GUN CASE

Kolpin's No. 79XB gun case has an extra compartment for a spare shotgun barrel. It's fully padded. The spare-barrel compartment holds the longest barrel you might want to store in it. The whole case is water repellent and is made from extra fine hose duck canvas. Features a fully adjustable sling and sturdy handle for carrying. Comes in 50-, 52-, 54- and 56-inch lengths.

Price: $37

From Kolpin Manufacturing, Inc.

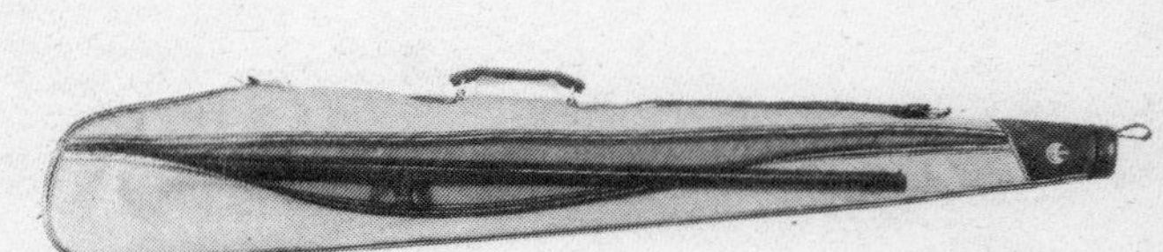

GUN CASE

Kolpin's No. 79 gun case is made from fine, hose duck canvas and has a water repellent lining. Features a leather-anchored plastic handle, black cowhide sling and full zipper. Comes in lengths ranging from 40- to 56-inches.

Price: $24

From Kolpin Manufacturing, Inc.

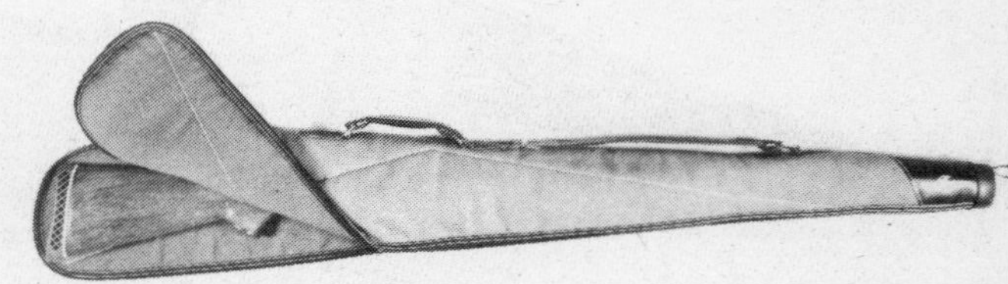

CAMOUFLAGE GUN CASE

This Kolpin case (Model No. 89) sports green, brown, black and tan camouflage patterns. Case fabric is rubberized nylon. Lining is water repellent corduroy. Padding is humidity proof. Features a full zipper, hang-up loop and rubber tip. Perfect for waterfowlers. Comes in 42-, 50- and 52-inch lengths.

Price: $19.50

From Kolpin Manufacturing, Inc.

TAKEDOWN GUN CASE

Perfect for doubles, over/unders—any shotgun (or rifle) that can be broken down into space-saving length. Case is constructed of rugged black vinyl and has two compartments that are fully padded and lined with siliconized pile. Takes up to 34-inch barrel(s).

Price: (No. 529) $23.50.

From Kolpin Manufacturing, Inc.

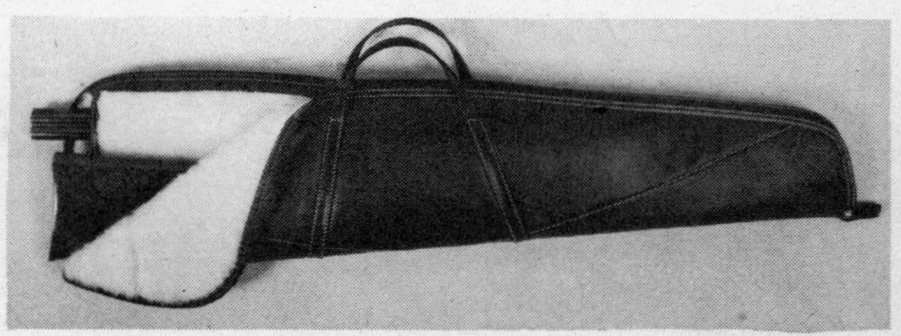

Prices shown are subject to change.

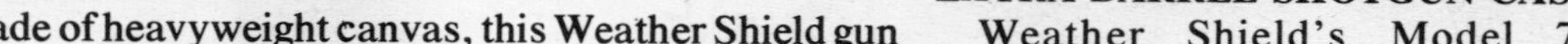

TAKEDOWN GUN CASE
Made of heavyweight canvas, this Weather Shield gun case is well suited for double barreled shotguns (or other firearms) that can be broken down for transport or storage. Comes with a full length zipper and luggage type handles. Length: 34-inches.
Price: $22.45
From Weather Shield Sports Equipment Co.

EXTRA BARREL SHOTGUN CASE
Weather Shield's Model 70XB comes in "gunsmoke" saddle expanded, cloth-backed vinyl. The side-mounted barrel compartment—and the case itself—feature full length zippers. It also comes with luggage-type handles and molded rubber tip. Available in a variety of lengths. (Case also available with canvas construction.)
Price: Vinyl or canvas $34.45.
From Weather Shield Sports Equipment Co.

EXTRA BARREL SHOTGUN CASE
This Boyt gun case comes with an extra barrel pouch sewn to the side of the case. The case features a full zipper while the pouch features a buckled flap. Comes with a leather carrying strap and leather trim. Made of top quality canvas—case is well padded.
Price: $40, model GC021XBF.
From Boyt (Div. of Welsh Sporting Goods Corp.)

GUN CASES
These Gun-Ho cases (Model AFS, top; Model VTM, bottom) are available in a wide range of lengths to accommodate most popular rifles or shotguns—with or without scopes. The AFS is black with pile lining, tan trim, a full 2 inches of foam, padding and "breathes," thereby preventing condensation. The VTM is of fabric construction with vinyl trim, pile lined and 2 inches of padding. Also has 2 accessory pockets and heavy-duty zipper.
Price: VTM $40.50; AFS $37.
From Gun-Ho Sport Cases & Equipment Mfrs.

GUN CASES
The Model LHS Gun-Ho gun case (top) comes in a wide variety of lengths, is constructed of tan leather-like material and comes with 2 inches of padding and pile lining. It also has a heavy duty zipper and is mildew proof. The Model MWF (bottom) also comes in a variety of lengths. It's identical to the LHS case with the exception it has fabric construction. Comes in Green.
Prices: Model LHS $32; Model MWF $30.
From Gun-Ho Sport Cases & Equipment Mfrs.

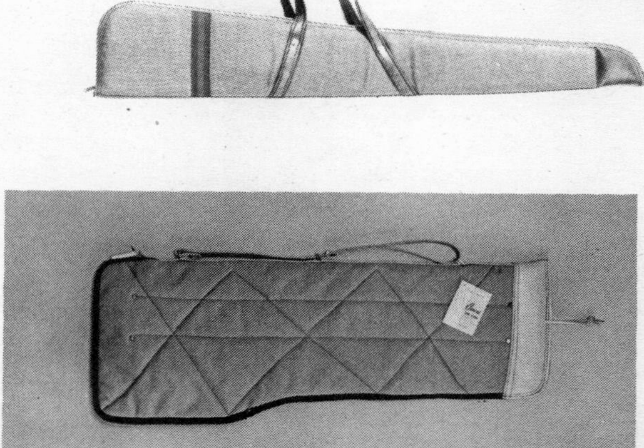

TAKE-DOWN SHOTGUN CASE
This is Boyt's Model GC 2214, 2-barrel gun case. Holds one break-down shotgun and a spare barrel. Made of the best canvas available and comes well padded. Features leather carrying strap, trim, and, full zipper.
Price: $59.70
From Boyt (Div. of Welsh Sporting Goods Corp.).

RIFLE/SHOTGUN CASE

This case looks and feels like leather but it's actually constructed of a man-made material. It's the Boyt Model GC031. It comes with a full zipper, black leather trim and carrying strap; plus, tuflex padding and the best made pile. Comes in lengths from 38 to 52 inches.
Price: GC031 $41.35, GC036 (for scoped guns) $48.60.
From Boyt (Div. of Welsh Sporting Goods).

RIFLE/SHOTGUN CASE

This is Boyt's regular pattern gun case that's been popular for years. It's the Model GC 021-F. This case is made of the best, most durable canvas obtainable. Comes with a full brass zipper, leather trim and leather carrying strap. Features full felt lining. Also available for scope-equipped rifles. Comes in sizes ranging from 38 to 52 inches.
Price: $31.35; for scope-equipped rifles $35.70.
From Boyt (Div. of Welsh Sporting Goods Corp.).

RIFLE & SHOTGUN CASE

Eutaw's Model CH-1000 is a handy sleeve-type gun case. It's flannel lined; and, is 54 inches long.
Price: $3.75
From the Eutaw Co.

SLEEVE-TYPE GUN CASE

Made of dark brown, water resistant, rubberized suede cloth. Has strap tie closure. Length is 52 inches.
Price: Regular $3.65; scope size $4.35.
From Weather Shield Sports Equipment Co.

SUEDE LEATHER PISTOL CASE

Kolpin's No. 28 pistol case features full brown suede leather construction, ¼-inch of padding and water repellent brown corduroy lining. Also has a full zipper and comes in 4½-, 7-, 10-, 13- and 15-inch lengths.
Price: From $10.50 to $11.95 depending on length.
From Kolpin Manufacturing, Inc.

PISTOL CASE

Kolpin's No. 21 pistol case is lined with water-repellent corduroy and is made from sturdy, tan, water repellent canvas. Comes with a full zipper and is available in 4½-, 7-, 10-, 13- and 15-inch sizes.
Price: From $6.50 to $7 depending on length.
From Kolpin Manufacturing, Inc.

PISTOL CASE

Kolpin No. 20 pistol case has brown vinyl construction, ¼-inch of padding, yellow napped cotton lining and a full zipper. Comes in 4½-, 7-, 10-, 13- and 15-inch lengths.
Price: From $4.25 to $5.25 depending on length.
From Kolpin Manufacturing, Inc.

CANVAS GUN CASE

Comes with leather trim, ½-inch of Tufflex padding and flannel lining. Comes in 40-, 44-, 48- and 52-inch lengths. Scope-type case comes in 40-, 43- and 46-inch lengths. Has a full-length zipper.
Price: Regular (Model 490) $16.66; scope-type (Model 491) $18.33.
From The Allen Co.

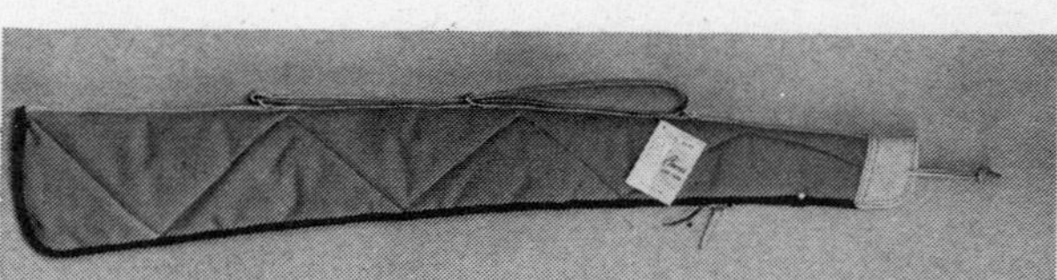

LEATHER PISTOL CASES

Weather Shield's "Pistol Blankets" are made of real split leather and natural (siliconized) acrylic shearling. Feature a full zipper and available in a good variety of sizes.
Prices: From $7.45 to $15.65 depending on length.
From Weather Shield Sports Equipment Co.

PISTOL CASE

The cases shown are Kolpin's No. 175 (corduroy lined) and No. 185 (pile lined) cases. Both feature ¼-inch of padding and full zipper as well as black vinyl construction—13-inches long.
Price: No. 175 $10.50; No. 185 $11.50.
From Kolpin Manufacturing, Inc.

PISTOL CASE

Kolpin's No. 24 pistol case comes with siliconized pile lining, full zipper, black vinyl construction and ¼-inch padding. Available in 4½-, 7-, 10-, 13-, 15- and 20-inch lengths.
Price: From $5.75 to $7 depending on length.
From Kolpin Manufacturing, Inc.

PISTOL CASES

Browning's pistol cases come in sizes ranging from 7 to 11 inches in overall length. Outer material is available in green canvas or black vinyl. Comes with siliconized pile lining and full zipper.
Price: $8.95, your choice of length.
From Browning Arms.

PISTOL CASE

Comes fully lined and is designed to hold the larger handguns. Features vinyl carrying handles and a full zipper.
Price: Model RCR-10 $12.95.
From the Eutaw Company.

PISTOL CASE

Boyt's Model PP60 series pistol case features a full zipper and lock loop; plus, tuflex padding, vinyl construction and deep pile lining.
Prices: See below.

PP 60 — 4½-inches long	$17.25
PP 61 — 7-inches long	$20.30
PP 62 — 9½-inches long	$20.70
PP 63 — 11-inches long	$20.95

From Boyt (Div. of Welsh Sporting Goods Corp.).

PISTOL CASE

This is the Eutaw Company's pistol case that's designed to hold pistols with up to 12-inch barrels. Comes with carrying handles, full zipper and plush pile lining.
Price: Model RCR-8 $11.95.
From the Eutaw Co.

PISTOL CASE

Boyt's Model PP-66 pistol case measures a generous 16 inches wide by 9 inches high (closed). It comes with a sturdy set of handles, tough vinyl outer material and rich, deep pile lining and a full brass zipper with locking ring. Holds just about any handgun.
Price: $28.75
From Boyt (Div. of Welsh Sporting Goods Corp.).

See the Directory for complete company addresses.

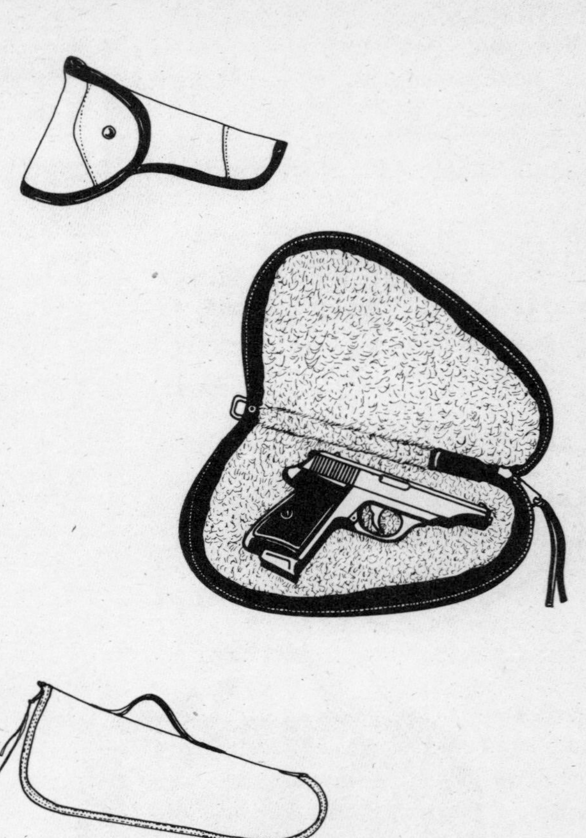

HOLSTER-TYPE HANDGUN CASE

Features snap closure. Made of canvas with split cowhide trim; flannel lined. Also has belt loop. Available for barrel lengths up to 7 inches.
Price: $8
From J. M. Bucheimer.

HANDGUN CASES

Bucheimer has a wide selection of pistol cases fashioned of vinyl, canvas or suede leather. All are beautifully lined with man-made fleece or flannel and come fully padded. They feature a full zipper and lock ring. Available for all handguns, all lengths—including an extra long case for TC single shots.
Prices: From about $4 to about $15, depending on size and style.
From J. M. Bucheimer.

EXTRA LONG HANDGUN CASE

While this Bucheimer case has been made especially for single shot handguns, it will easily accommodate any revolver or auto with a long barrel. Comes in black expanded vinyl with heavy orlon fleece lining. Has extra pocket for spare barrel.
Price: $13.50
From J. M. Bucheimer.

HANDGUN CASE

Fully padded and comes with full zipper. Vinyl construction. Model 151.
Price: $6.70
From Brauer Bros.

LEG-O-MUTTON CASE FOR ALL SHOTGUNS

Brauer's Model 41 and 141 cases are beautifully made of the best top-grain leather molded over a fiber base. Available with spare barrel compartment on special order. Model 41 fits all pumps, over unders and double barrel shotguns. Model 141 is specifically made for automatic shotguns.
Price: $133.35 for either model.
From Brauer Bros.

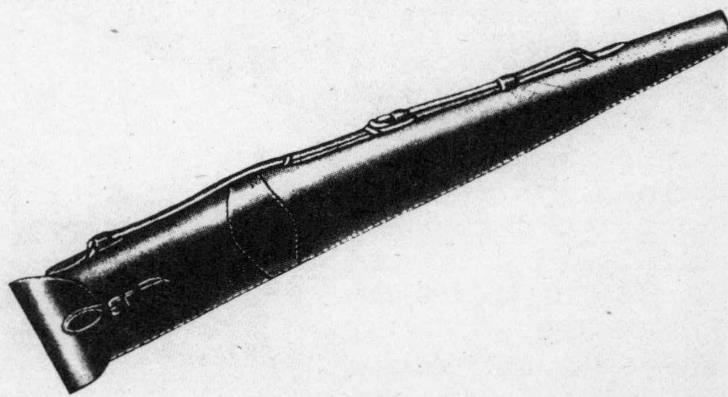

SOLID LEATHER RIFLE/SHOTGUN CASE

It's made of dark brown, oil treated 8- to 9-ounce leather. Comes with adjustable sling and brass hardware. Fully lined with shearling. Model 23W. *Well made.*
Price: $111.10; with plain padded lining $77.75 (Model 22)
From Brauer Bros.

Prices shown are subject to change.

PISTOL CASE

This one's made specifically for small autos and snub-nosed revolvers. It comes with foam padding and plush pile lining.
Price: Model RCR-1 $4.95.
From the Eutaw Co.

PISTOL CASE

Eutaw's Model RCR-3 is that firm's "medium-size" case that holds any revolver or auto with a barrel length of up to 4 inches. Features a full zipper, padding and plush pile lining.
Price: Model RCR-3 $6.25.
From the Eutaw Co.

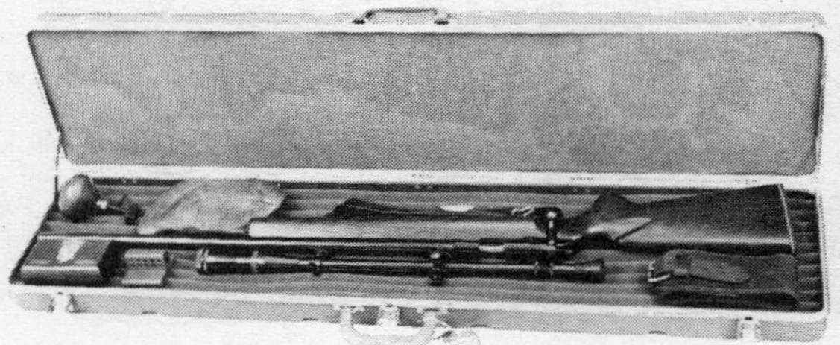

TARGET SHOOTER GUN CASE

This Protecto gun case measures 11 inches by 51 inches by 4½ inches deep. It's fully lined to protect and firmly hold your favorite target rifle. (There's room for accessories in this case). Comes in green and has rugged plastic/aluminum construction. Comes with built-in lock.
Price: $60.25 (Model RC011).
From Protecto Plastics, Div. of Penguin Ind.

COMPACT SHOTGUN CASE

This case features short overall measurements which allow you to carry your favorite shotguns fully broken down. It's a good space-saver in a cramped car or truck. Features rugged aluminum/plastic construction and comes fully lined to prevent damage to, or shifting of, your shotguns barrel/action assemblies. (Overall length 36-inches.) Has built-in lock.
Price: $57.50 (Model SC004).
From Protecto Plastics, Div. of Penguin Ind.

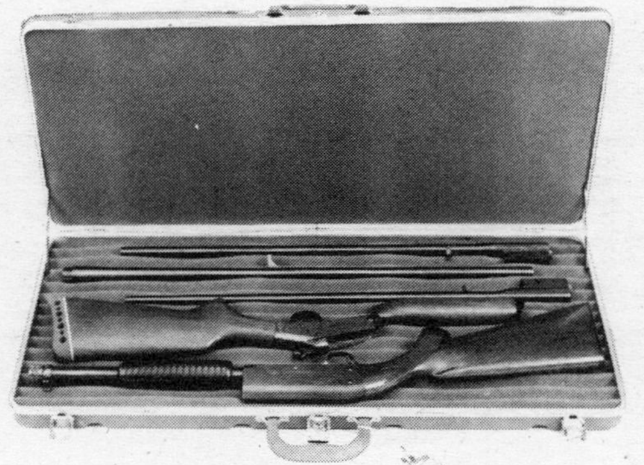

COMPACT GUN CASE

Protecto Plastic's "Traveler" gun case is extra wide to accommodate one or two guns and spare barrels. This is ideal for the man who wants all his barrels in the field—not at home. Comes in either green or teakwood colors. Features full lining and rugged aluminum/plastic construction. Has built-in lock.
Price: $65.75 (Model SC024).
From Protecto Plastics, Div. of Penguin Ind.

TAKE DOWN SHOTGUN CASE

Matchpoint Model 100 "take-down" shotgun case measures 36 inches overall and is a real space saver. It features full foam lining, luggage-type handles and comes in either black or brown with harmonizing interior. Has a full-length zipper.
Price: $37.80
From Matchpoint Industries, Inc.

See the Directory for complete company addresses.

HARD SHELL GUN CASE

Gun-Ho's "BHS" series of hard shell gun cases feature tough Royalite construction. They are available in a variety of lengths and shapes for rifles, pistols or shotguns; and, come fully padded with foam. The case shown is Gun-Ho's BHS-5310. It measures 53 inches by 10 inches by 4 inches thick.

Price: $66

From Gun-Ho Sport Cases & Equipment Mfrs.

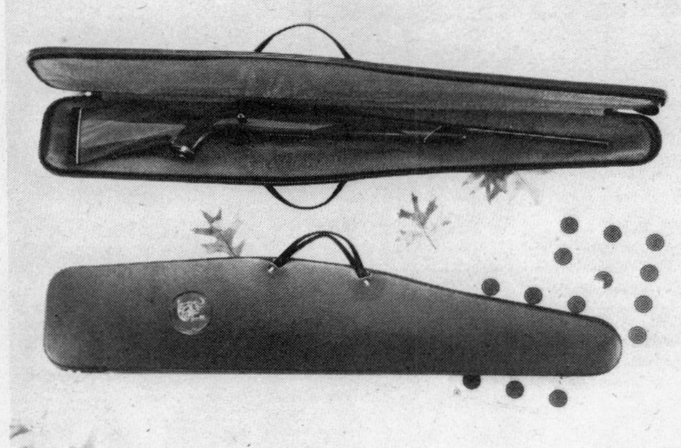

HARD SHELL GUN CASE

This is Gun-Ho's "Turtle-Tuff" hard shell case. The outer shells are made of tough, buffalo-grained Royalite. It's fully padded inside with foam and pile. The exterior withstands bumps, water and severe knocks. If you drop this one into the water, and it's fully zipped, it will *float*. Comes in 45-, 47-, 48-, 50- and 53-inch lengths for scoped or unscoped rifles and shotguns.

Price: Model "MTG"—all lengths and configurations $45.

From Gun-Ho Sport Cases & Equipment Mfrs.

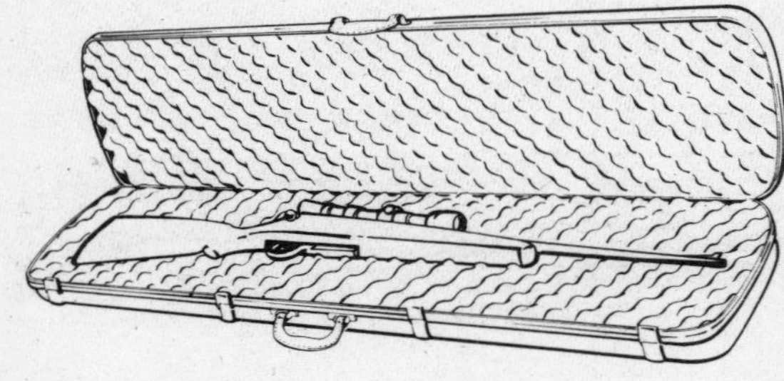

GUN CASE

Doskocil's Model 101 single rifle/shotgun case measures 48⅜ inches long by 9 inches high by 4 inches deep. Features hard-shell construction, full foam padding and luggage-type handles. Holds one scoped rifle or one shotgun and a spare barrel.

Price: $39

From Doskocil Manufacturing Co., Inc.

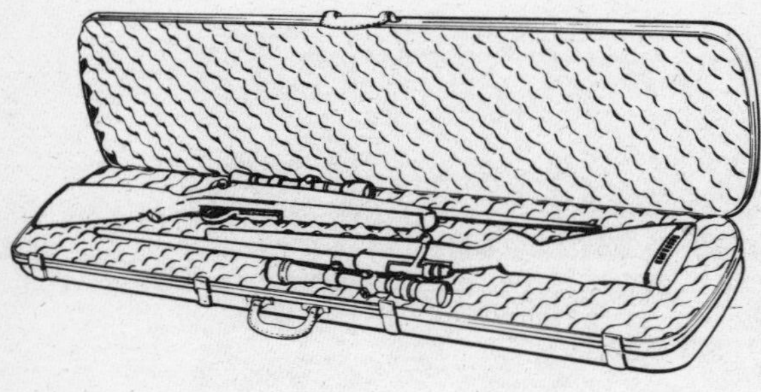

GUN CASE

Doskocil's Model 202 is large enough to hold two scoped rifles or a pair of full-size shotguns. Measures 52½ inches long by 11½ inches wide by 4 inches deep. Comes with luggage-type handles, full foam lining and has hard-shell construction.

Price: $45

From Doskocil Manufacturing Co., Inc.

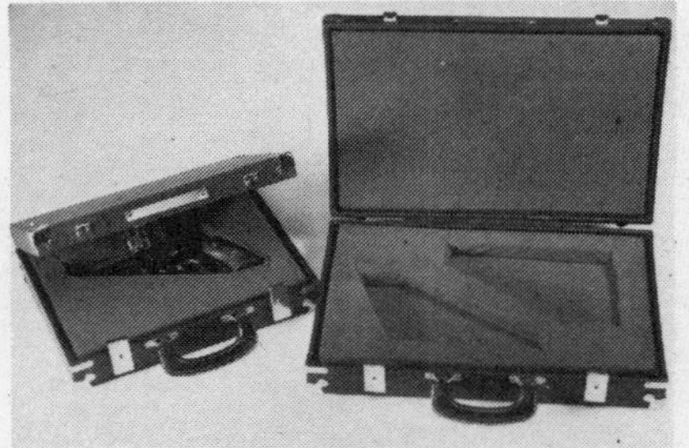

PISTOL CASE

This lockable case features an attractive vinyl covering, brass corners and an engraved nameplate attached above the handle. Your gun is surrounded on all sides by no less than 1 inch of soft foam rubber. Case interior is lined with quality upholstery fabric. Comes in 1- or 2-gun sizes.

Price: 1-gun $59.95; 2-gun $74.95.

From Lino Custom Case Mfg. Co.

Prices shown are subject to change.

ALUMINUM GUN CASES

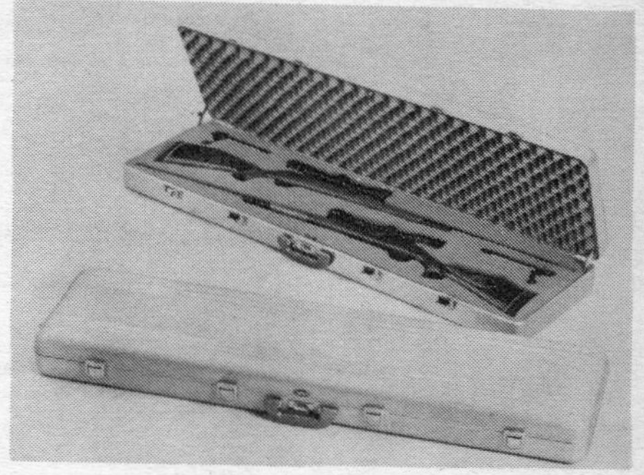

Weatherby's series of top quality gun cases are made of sturdy aluminum, come fully foam lined and are lockable for maximum security. They come available in single and double rifle (shown) configurations along with one case specifically made for shotguns.

Price: Double rifle case $229.50, single rifle case $199.50; shotgun case $169.50.

From Weatherby, Inc.

OVER/UNDER SHOTGUN CASE

Browning's hard gun cases are well known by sportsmen everywhere. The outer material is Naugahyde while, internally, the case is fully sectioned, padded and lined with the best shag pile. It's designed to hold any Browning over-under along with cleaning gear, ammo or other accessories. The case features luggage-type handles and comes with locks.

Price: From $76.50 to $84.50 (spare barrel case available).

From Browning Arms.

RIM FIRE RIFLE CASE

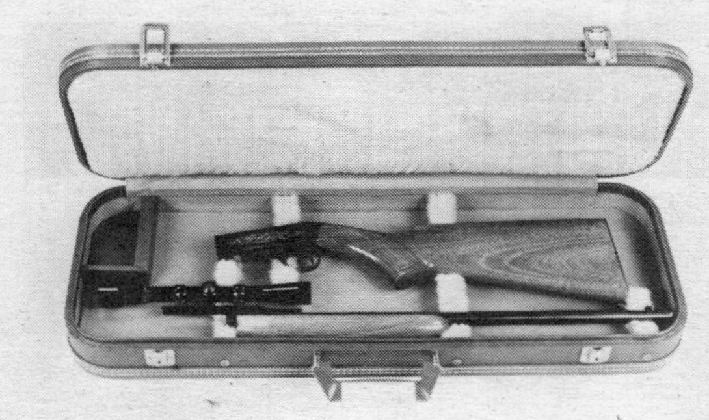

This Browning case is fully sectioned, padded and lined with the best shag pile. Comes with locks and luggage-type handles. Designed to hold a Browning Standard .22 Auto Rifle with or without scope. Features a handy compartment for ammo or accessories.

Price: $62.50

From Browning Arms.

BROWNING A-5 SHOTGUN CASE

This Browning case is specifically designed to hold their A-5 automatic shotgun and one spare barrel. (Also accommodates Browning Model 2000 automatic shotgun.) It comes with luggage-style handles and has locks. Internally the case is padded and pile lined. Outer construction features Naugahyde.

Price: $76.50

From Browning Arms.

GUN CASES

Complete line of gun cases feature high-impact styrene exteriors with full length piano hinge, locking draw-bolt latches; interiors are of extra thick convuluted foam specially treated with long-life rust- and corrosion-preventing vapor barrier, 13 models, for pistols, rifles, or shotguns, are offered.

Price: From $25.31 (two-pistol utility, 14x9x4") to $79.64 (two-rifle/shotgun, 53x13x4½").

From Outers.

RIFLE/SHOTGUN CASE

Matchpoint's Model 102 gun case holds two rifles or shotguns and measures 52 inches long. It comes with a full zipper, foam lining and luggage-type handles. Available colors are black with charcoal foam or brown with tan foam.

Price: $53.10

From Matchpoint Industries, Inc.

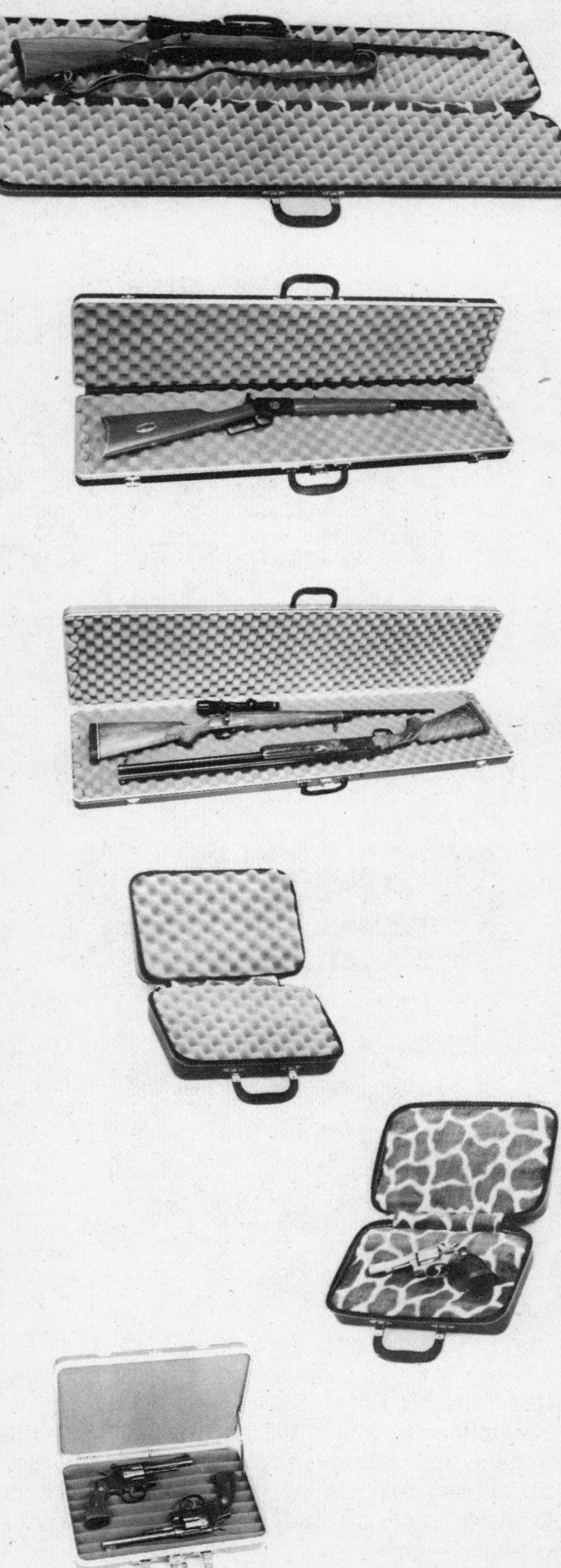

RIFLE/SHOTGUN CASE

This is Matchpoint's Model 106 "single-gun" case. It comes with full foam lining, luggage-type handles, and measures 48 inches long. It holds one rifle or take-down shotgun. Comes black or brown with charcoal and tan lining, respectively. Has a full-length zipper.
Price: $44.44
From Matchpoint Industries, Inc.

GUN CASE

Outers Defender gun case is of hard-shell construction and comes fully foam lined. It has a black leather-grain finish, aluminum interlocking frame, luggage type carrying handles and is lockable. It also features a full piano-type hinge. Overall length 41 inches.
Price: $41.22
From Outers Laboratories, Inc.

TWO-GUN CASE

Featuring hard-shell, aluminum construction, Outers Model 525AX gun case is indeed a sturdy item. It comes with full foam padding, locks, aluminized finish and 6 bumper feet. It measures 53x13x4½ inches. Weighs 16½ pounds. Sturdy.
Price: $79.64
From Outers Laboratories.

PISTOL CASE

Matchpoint's Model 109 gun case has a full nylon zipper, foam lining and comes in black or brown. Holds your handgun securely during storage or transport. Holds most popular handguns.
Price: $26.66
From Matchpoint Industries, Inc.

PISTOL CASE

Matchpoint's Model 111 holds most popular handguns. It comes with a full zipper, luggage-type handles and high-density foam lining. Color schemes include black with zebra-pattern lining or brown with giraffe-pattern lining.
Price: $33.10
From Matchpoint Industries, Inc.

PISTOL CASE

Measures 9 inches by 14 inches by 3¼ inches deep, comes with built-in locks and features rugged aluminum/plastic construction. Fully lined to protect your favorite handguns. Holds two standard size autos or revolvers.
Price: $34.25 (Model PC 005).
From Protecto Plastics, Div. of Penguin Ind.

Prices shown are subject to change.

PISTOL CASE

Multi-handgun case holds four or more autos or revolvers, depending upon size. Measures 12 inches by 18 inches by 3½ inches deep. Has lock, handle and full lining. Comes in green or teakwood colors.
Price: $42.50 (Model PA007).
From Protecto Plastics, Div. of Penguin Ind.

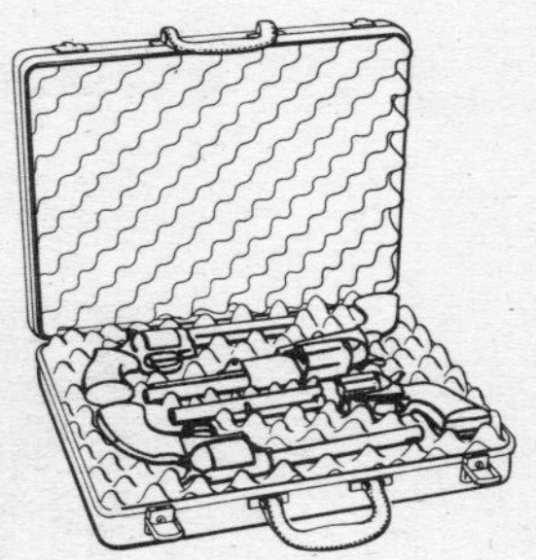

HANDGUN CASE

The Doskocil Model 404 handgun case holds up to four handguns and measures 18 inches long by 14 inches high by 4 inches deep. It's fully foam lined, has luggage-type handles and is lockable. Features hard-shell construction.
Price: $28
From Doskocil Manufacturing Co., Inc.

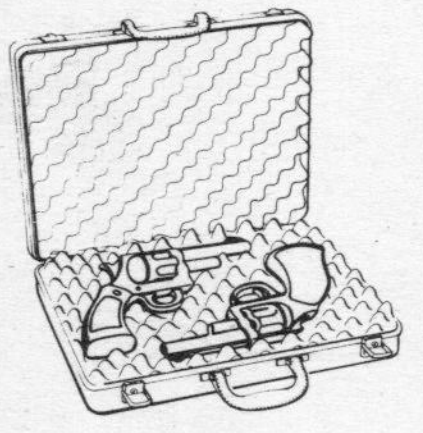

HANDGUN CASE

This is Doskocil's two-hanger carrying case, Model 402. It's lockable, has full foam lining and hard-shell construction. This case also has luggage-type handles and measures 14 inches long by 9 inches high by 4 inches deep. Holds two handguns.
Price: $21
From Doskocil Manufacturing Co., Inc.

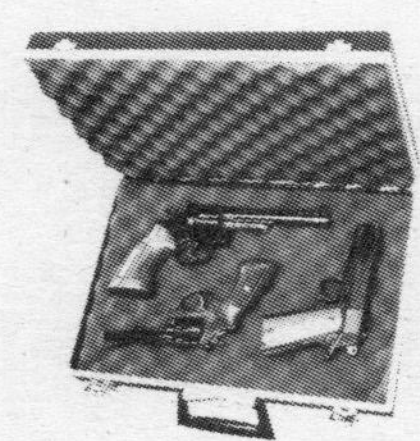

PISTOL/REVOLVER CASE

This is Outers' Defender three-gun case made especially for handguns. It measures 17x12x4 inches. Features all aluminum construction, locks, full piano-type hinge and foam lining.
Price: $25.47
From Outers Laboratories, Inc.

PISTOL/REVOLVER CASE

Holds four or more handguns depending on size. Comes in three sizes: 8¼x12½x4 inches; 18¼x12½x5½ inches or 20¾x15x6½ inches — Models 180 AX, 188AX and 189AX, respectively. All have full blue foam lining, an aluminum frame, full piano hinge and four bumper feet.
Price: Model 180AX - $37.13; Model 188AX - 41.22; Model 189AX - 45.18.
From Outers Laboratories, Inc.

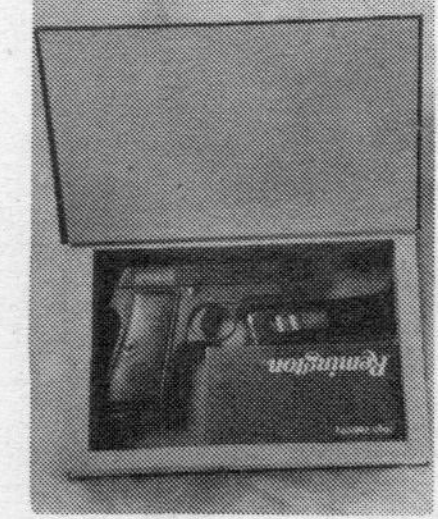

BOOK-TYPE GUN CASE

This security oriented item is simply a hollowed-out book that holds small frame autos and revolvers. Keeps the gun out of sight, but not out of reach.
Price: $8.95 each.
From Rogchild, Inc.

CUSTOM PISTOL CABINET

This custom cabinet holds eight handguns, is made of solid cherry, features a clear lacquer finish and comes with plate glass doors. It also has a security lock. Measuring 35 inches wide by 31 inches high and 8 inches deep this cabinet is hand crafted and the maker guarantees full satisfaction.

Price: $245

From C & T Cabinetry, Inc.

CUSTOM RIFLE/SHOTGUN CABINET

This custom cabinet is made of solid natural oak and comes with a hand-rubbed lacquer finish. It has six brackets that hold two guns each in a horizontal position—optional vertical placement available; holds 13 guns. Features plate glass door; security lock and white lacquer back and brackets. Comes with levelers on all four corners of the base.

Price: $625

From C & T Cabinetry.

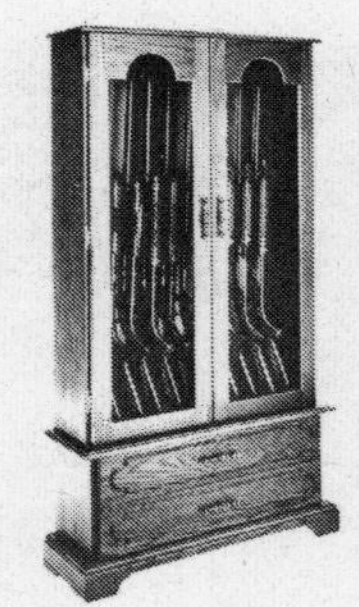

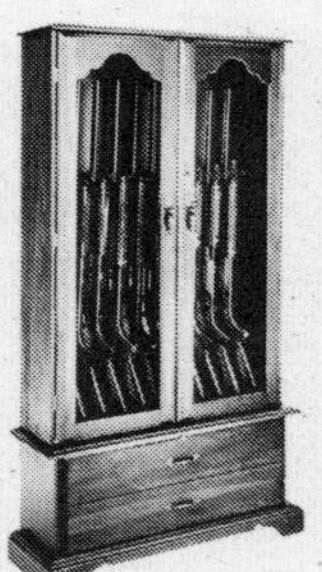

RIFLE/SHOTGUN CABINET

This Brenik gun cabinet is the Model 7910; it holds ten guns. The 7910 is made from solid oak and sports a "distressed Mediterranean finish." Features two glass-fronted (hinged) doors and lock. Also comes with a large storage compartment that's lockable.

Price: $432

From Brenik, Inc.

GUN CABINET

Brenik's Model 9910, 10-gun cabinet holds 10 rifles or shotguns in vertical position. It comes with handy storage compartment; and, that compartment plus the cabinet itself, are both lock-secured. The Model 9910 is made from selected hardwoods complemented with a hand-rubbed fruitwood finish. Measures 37¾ inches wide by 70½ inches high by 12½ inches deep.

Price: $376

From Brenik, Inc.

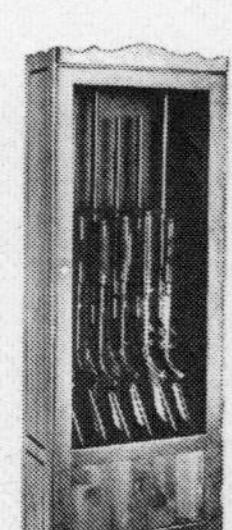

RIFLE/SHOTGUN CABINET

Brenik's Model 3006, six-gun cabinet is constructed of knotty pine. Comes with large storage compartment, hinged door and glass panel. (Optional light unit with push-button switch available.) Comes with a hand-rubbed medium walnut finish.

Price: $190

From Brenik, Inc.

GUN CABINET

Brenik's Model 3026, six-gun cabinet is made of solid knotty pine with hand-rubbed medium walnut finish. Measures 55½ inches wide by 32¼ inches high by 11½ inches deep. Features hinged doors with lock, glass panels. (Optional light unit with pushbutton switch available.)

Price: $184

From Brenik, Inc.

PISTOL CABINET

Brenik's Model 2014 pistol cabinet is made of solid hardwood with a hand-rubbed walnut finish and scarlet felt backing. Comes with 12 hooks for mounting pistols. This model features 3/16-inch thick sliding glass doors complete with ratchet lock and two keys.

Price: $74

From Brenik, Inc.

Prices shown are subject to change.

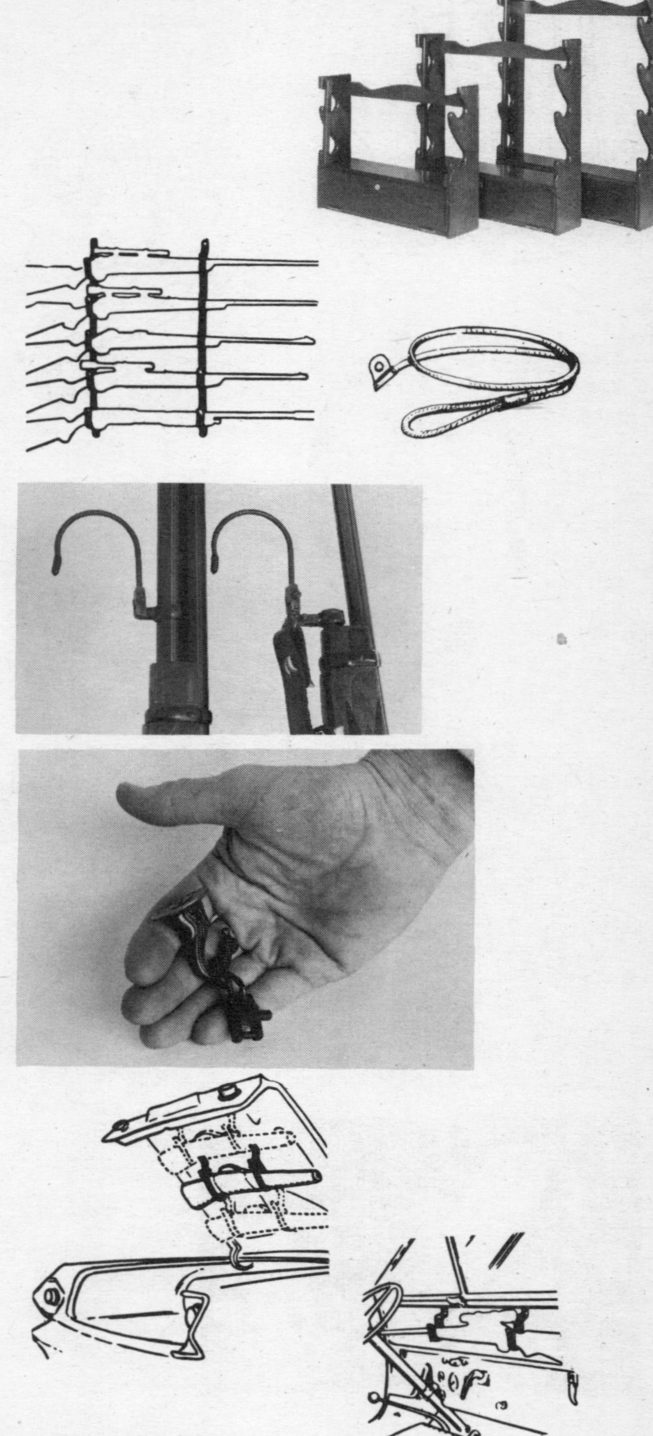

RIFLE/SHOTGUN RACKS

Shown nearby, from left to right, are Brenik's Models 3782, 3783 and 3784 gun racks—2, 3 and 4-gun capacity, respectively. Each rack features a hand-rubbed walnut finish, a locking bar for the guns and a good sized (lockable) storage compartment.

Price: 2-gun $31.95; 3-gun $36.95; 4-gun $40.95.

From Brenik, Inc.

WALL-TYPE GUN RACK

This rack holds 2, 3, 4 or 5 guns. Construction is plastisol coated steel and a handy locking cable is available for multiple units.

Price: 2-gun $5.95; 3-gun $6.95; 4-gun $8.95; 5-gun $9.95; Write company direct for a price on the locking cable.

From San Angelo Co.

SWIVEL-MOUNT GUN HANGERS

These ingenious gun hangers mount quickly on sling swivel studs to permit a rifle or shotgun to be hung, muzzle up or down, on a closet pole, over a tree branch, or on the edge of a duck blind.

Price: $4.95 (standard); $8.95 (Deluxe, for use with sling in place.

From Michaels of Oregon

QUICK DETACHABLE WALL GUN HANGER

This handy item comes with everything you'll need to attach this hanger to any wall. Unit consists of hanging hook, Q-D lock and all necessary mounting hardware.

Price: See your local dealer or write maker direct.

From Edmisten Co., Inc.

CAR TRUNK GUN RACK

These are plastisol-coated steel hangers that can be easily mounted in the trunk of your car. Holds guns securely and out of sight. Each unit holds one gun—up to three can usually be mounted.

Price: $5.95

From San Angelo Co.

DASHBOARD GUN MOUNT

Consists of two plastisol coated steel hangers. Holds gun within arm's reach. Holds one gun.

Price: $4.95

From San Angelo Co.

WALL HANGER HOOKS

These handy items are designed to easily, quickly, lock into ⅛- or ¼-inch pegboard. You can hang guns on these plastic-coated hooks without fear of having them damage your gun, or, pop out of the board when you least expect it. They come in a wide variety of sizes and shapes. Write maker direct for more information.

Prices: Range from 12¢ each up to 40¢ each, depending on style.

From Roman Products.

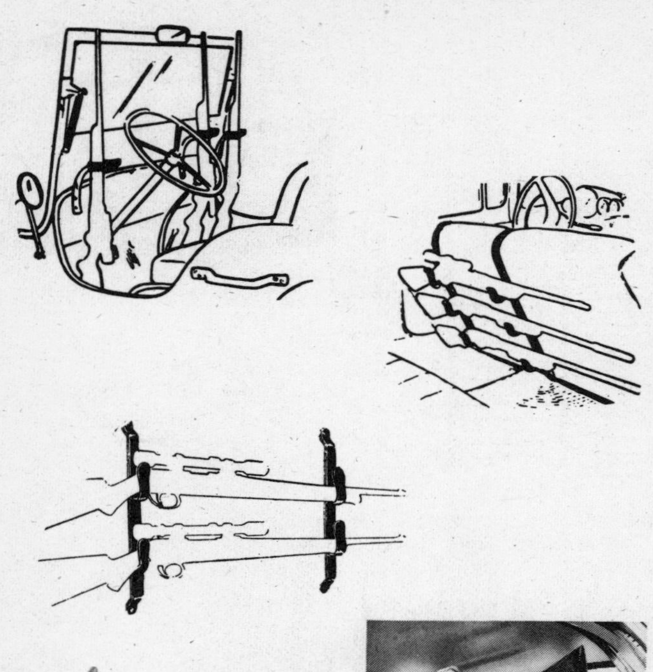

UPRIGHT DASHBOARD GUN RACK

Top bracket mounts on dash, bottom on floor. Locks gun firmly in place—no rattle or bounce in rough country. Constructed of plastisol coated steel.
Price: $7.95 each set.
From San Angelo Co.

OVER-THE-SEAT CAR GUN RACK

Holds three guns securely in place. Easy to mount—not a permanent installation. May be moved from car to car with ease.
Price: $12.95
From San Angelo Co.

PICKUP TRUCK WINDOW RACK

Consists of plastisol coated steel construction; holds two guns. Mounts easily and length is adjustable for large or small windows.
Price: $6.95
From San Angelo Co.

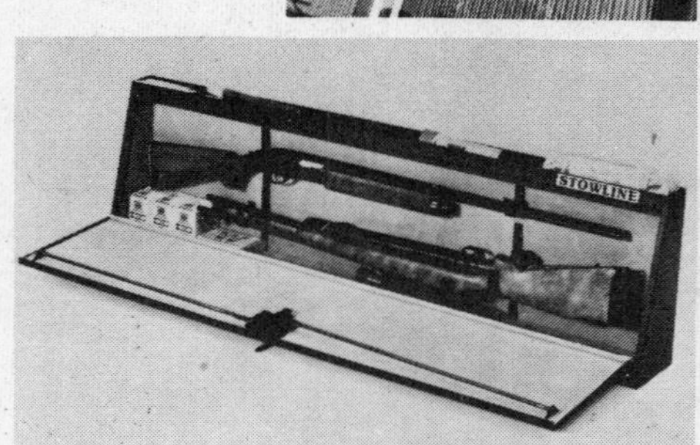

PICKUP TRUCK GUN RACK

E-Z Mount's pickup gun rack in a snap to install—no drilling, no screws. Installs in just a few minutes.
Price: See your dealer or write maker direct.
From E-Z Mount Corp.

PICKUP TRUCK GUN SAFE

The Stowline truck safe comes with a plush interior lining to prevent your guns from being damaged. Each safe holds up to four guns, comes with 3-way keyed locking mechanism and is made of heavy-gauge steel. It's expressly made for all light trucks with a tilt-forward seat and no in-cab gas tank.
Price: $160
From Stowline (Trik-Truk, Inc.)

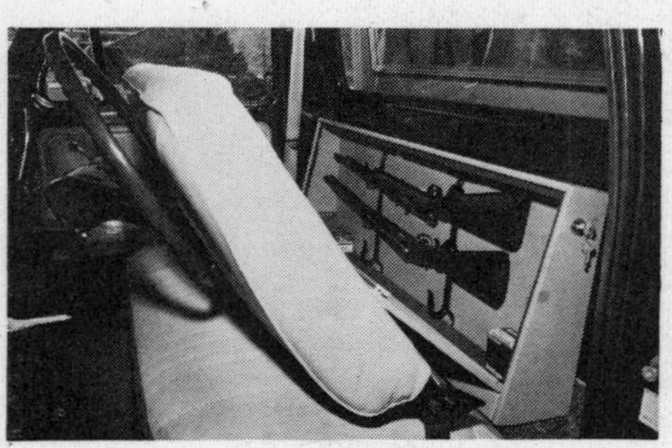

BEHIND-THE-SEAT PICK-UP SAFE

Holds up to 3 rifles or shotguns and other valuable gear. (Model 302 has 3-gun capacity. The 302 is made for Dodge, Ford and similar model pickups. The Model 312 has 2-gun capacity and is made for Chevy, GMC and similar pickups). Comes with racks and "Medeco" lock and 2 keys.
Price: Model 302 $176; Model 312 $170.
From Tread Corporation.

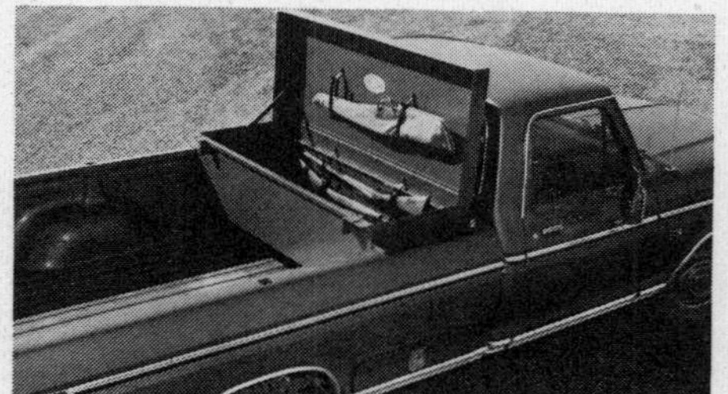

PICK-UP TRUCK SAFE

Comes in 3 different sizes to accommodate the bed of your particular pick-up truck. It holds 5 guns when the optional racks are purchased. Bottom of chest is covered with red indoor/outdoor carpeting. Also features a full piano-type hinge, sliding steel pin locks with "Medeco" security inner cylinders.
Price: From $332 to about $400; racks $28.75.
From Tread Corporation.

Prices shown are subject to change.

RUMBLE-SEAT SAFE

Treadlok's new Rumble Seat takes the place of the rear seat in the Chevy Blazer and other comparable models made by GMC, Dodge, Plymouth and others. It's made of 13-gauge welded steel and has sliding pin locks with "Medeco" security inner cylinders. Holds 3 rifles or shotguns and comes with seat and back cushions.

Price: $523

From Tread Corporation.

GUN VAULT

The Pro-Steel 2436 vault features 12-gauge construction with a 3/16-inch steel door. The door and frame are fully reinforced and 6 chrome finished locking pins secure the door—the lock is a combination type. Depending upon the type of rack you purchase, the vault will hold up to 23 guns. Weighs 425 pounds empty, stands upright.

Price: $735 with shelving; 23-gun rack $145; 11-gun rack and 4 shelves $180.

From Provo Steel & Supply Co.

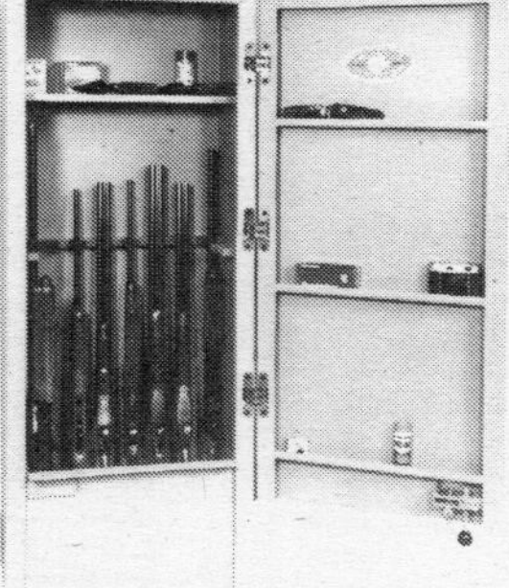

GUN STORAGE SAFE

Holds 12 guns; stands upright. Treadlok's Model 601 features 12-gauge welded steel construction, is 24-inches wide, 17-inches deep and is 63-inches high. The 601 also comes with three heavy-duty concealed hinges and a 2-point sliding bar lock secured by one "Medeco" high security lock. Weighs 225 pounds empty.

Price: $472; with racks and shelves $488.

From Tread Corporation.

GUN VAULT

Se-Cur-All gun cabinets have double wall construction of heavy 14 and 18 gauge welded steel. It has a high-security door lock, double swinging doors, plug welded full length piano hinges and comes with shelving as shown. These vaults come in 6- and 12-gun models—12-gun models do not have the extensive shelving the 6-gun model has.

Price: $459 for either the 6- or 12-gun vault.

From A&A Sheet Metal Products, Inc.

GUN STORAGE SAFE

The Treadlok Model 101R gun safe (as shown) comes complete with gun storage racks. This is the model that rests on the floor in a horizontal position. It's made of 12-gauge welded steel, comes with a set of locks and keys and features a full, piano-type hinge. May be bolted to the floor for additional security. Holds 16 guns. Weighs 180 pounds empty.

Price: $345; $400 with racks.

From Tread Corporation.

See the Directory for complete company addresses.

GUN SAFE

This Dara-Nes gun safe is made of heavy 14-gauge steel. All chests are gasketed and supplied with several soft sheet plastic or sponge rubber separators. The Dara-Nes safe shown in the Colonial Bench Chest Model 60-G which measures 14 inches high by 18 inches wide by 60 inches long. Comes with rubber pad and vinyl cover and features a dual locking system.

Price: $304.50

From Dara-Nes, Div. of Nesci Enterprises, Inc.

GUN LOCK

Master Lock's No. 90 gun lock is designed to fully enclose the trigger guard on most rifles, shotguns and handguns. Prevents tampering during storage or while in the field. Cushioned pads prevent any marring of the gun's finish.

Price: $6.49

From Master Lock Company.

GUN SAFES

The Dara-Nes gun safe line offers the sportsman protection for his guns at a reasonable price. Each safe is made of 14-gauge steel, has rubber gaskets to keep out dust and moisture. The padlock area of the chest is fully enclosed.

Prices: See below.

No.	Item	Size	Wgt.	Price
1224	Pistol Chest	12Wx12Hx24L	45#	$117.60
1630	Pistol Chest	16Wx16Hx30L	65#	$127.00
1836	Pistol Chest	18Wx18Hx36L	90#	$163.80
2042	Firearms Chest	20Wx20Hx42L	115#	$189.00
2448	Firearms Chest	24Wx24Hx48L	150#	$219.45

From Dara-Nes, Div. of Nesci Enterprises, Inc.

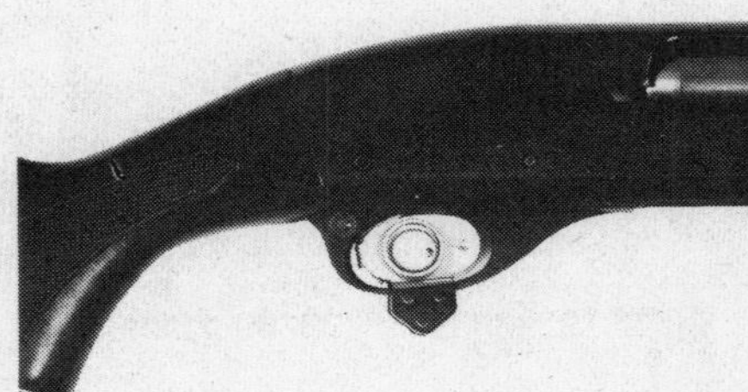

GUN TRIGGER LOCK

Each lock is designed to fit practically every domestic and foreign firearm. It helps hide the trigger from inquisitive fingers. Uses a 2-pronged key that effectively prevents the trigger from being pulled. Won't harm the gun.

Price: See your local dealer.

From Cesco (Central Specialties Co.).

TRIGGER-GUARD GUN LOCK

The "trigger lock" securely blocks the trigger guard of a rifle, pistol or shotgun with which it is used, preventing the trigger from being pulled intentionally or accidentally. Cushioned pads protect the gun's finish from the lock, which can be locked in place without its key.

Price: $7.25

From Michaels of Oregon

Prices shown are subject to change.

Target & Bench Shooting Accessories

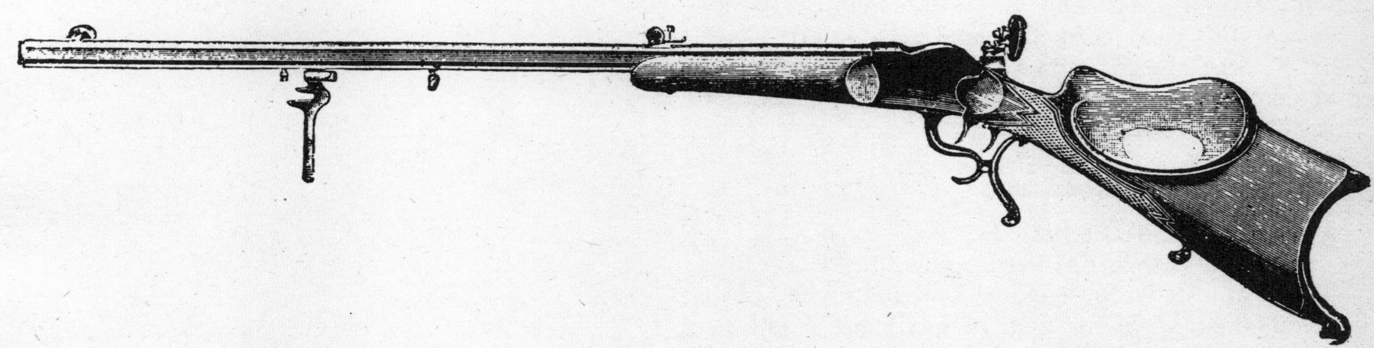

Target and bench rest shooting are particularly demanding areas of the shooting sports, and as a result have developed a unique group of specialized accessories. In this section we've assembled quite a cross-section of these items for shooters ranging from the beginning paper puncher through the most sophisticated bench rest competitor.

Leading off the section you'll find a variety of replacement or add-on gun components specifically aimed at the target or bench rest shooter. Next come rests, stands, and shooting bags, followed by spotting scopes and their accessories. Pistol caddies for range use are next, followed by shooting glasses and ear muffs to protect the shooter's eyes and ears. Sights, a very crucial part of every target shooting rig, have their own sections; 3, *Metallic Sights,* and 4, *Telescopic Sights,* while the next section after this one covers targets and range equipment.

Although many of the basic needs of target shooting will be found on the shelves at most any well-equipped gun shop, many of the more sophisticated accessories are available only from shops that cater specifically to the precision shooting fraternity or, in some cases, the makers themselves.

See the Directory for complete company addresses.

SLING KEEPER

It's made specifically for a 1¼-inch military/target sling. This keeper is made of gold anodized aluminum and comes with a stainless steel slipper.

Price: $3.25

From Freeland's Scope Stands.

FORE-END STOP

Freeland's FSBV "Jumbo" fore-end stop comes with a quick-detachable Viking 1½-inch swivel and stud. It's available for the Winchester 52B, 52C, 52D and Model 70 Target; BSA Mark I and Mark II; Remington 40X Early Model 37 Remington and old 540X Remington. Specify right or left hand.

Price: $19.50

From Freeland's Scope Stands.

FORE-END STOP

The Freeland FSCV "Jumbo" Fore-end stop comes with clamping bar and quick-detachable 1½-inch swivel. Fits channel for Freeland 52D, 40XB, 40XR, 540X, BSA Mark III, BSA ISU and also all Anschutz channels. Specify gun and channel type, right or left hand, when buying.

Price: $20

From Freeland's Scope Stands.

ADJUSTABLE BUTT PLATE

Freeland's Model 61 International Butt Plate is completely adjustable for length of pull and up and down positioning. Made for right or left hand shooters—specify when buying. Shoulder plate comes fitted for replaceable rubber pad.

Price: $86.50 complete.

From Freeland's Scope Stands.

SWISS-TYPE BUTT PLATE

Available for most target rifles. Fully adjustable for up and down positioning.

Price: $43.50 complete.

From Freeland's Scope Stands.

REPLACEMENT TRIGGER

The Hart 2-ounce trigger is for target shooters *only*; it has no *safety*. Pull is clean, sharp and consistent. Fits most modern Remington rifles including the 40X and 40XB. (Also fits all Hart actions.)

Price: $57

From Hart Products.

BOB PEASE ACCURACY

This outfit is included in this section because of the tremendously wide variety of benchrest items they offer. If you are a benchrest shooter in need of specialized shooting equipment, we suggest you write this firm direct.

Price: N/A.

From Bob Pease Accuracy.

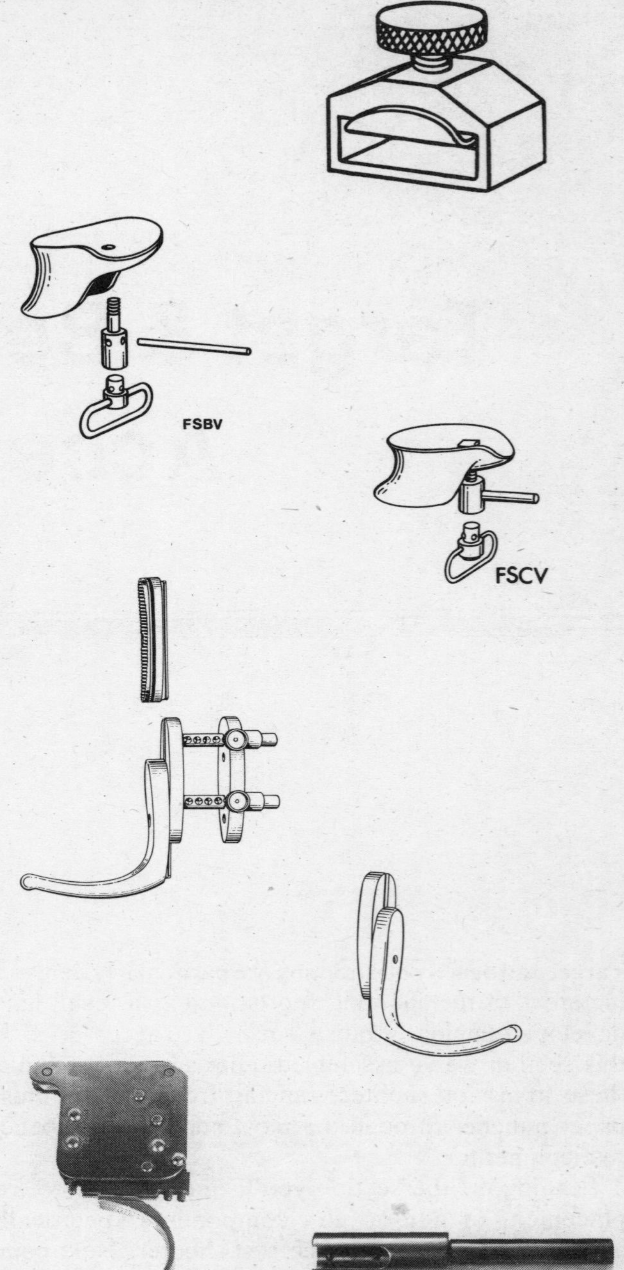

MINI-14 MUZZLE BRAKE

For those who've had a chance to bench a Ruger Mini-14, you might be interested in this item. It's Wichita's new muzzle brake, expressly made for the Mini-14. It adds 3¼ inches more length to the barrel and installs easily. This item has been included here due to the number of shooters who've been highly surprised with the Mini-14's excellent 100-yard accuracy. The Wichita brake may just improve your already excellent groups.

Price: $10.95

From Wichita Engineering & Supply.

Prices shown are subject to change.

MINI PISTOL REST FOR THE COLT .45 AUTO

Made by B-Square, this pistol rest eliminates the use of cumbersome sandbags. It's deltoid in shape and is fully adjustable for windage and elevation. An upright post at the rear of the unit slides into the butt of any 1911-type Colt auto and serves to replace the magazine and fully lock the gun in place through two Allen screws. Base is black crackle finished; upright post is gold anodized. This unit enables the bench shooter to fire *exceedingly* tight groups without investing in an expensive pistol rest.

Price: $29.95

From B-Square, Inc.

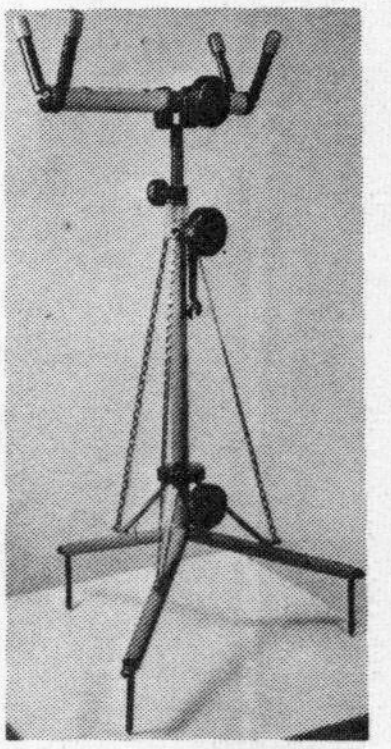

MICRO-REST SHOOTING STAND

Featuring all-steel construction, this rest is an extremely rigid set up via an adjustment wheel and three chains. Those chains run from the top of the post to each leg at a 120-degree angle. Total adjustment height is 5 inches; and a heavy-duty spring, inside the main post, is capable of lifting a heavy-barreled varmint rifle to desired height. Can be quickly adjusted for right- or left-hand use, and, the main shooting post can be removed for prone shooting. Lifetime guarantee.

Price: $75

From Cravener's Gun Shop.

TWO-PIECE RIFLE REST

This 2-piece rest is *solid*. It's made of steel. Front foot extends 9 inches; total width 14 inches. Windage and elevation travel is 3 inches in each direction (up, down, left and right). Forked prongs are completely covered with nylon tubing. Since the nearby photos were taken, the V-prongs on the rear stabilizer were modified and are now adjustable to fit the width of any rifle stock. Wrench is provided. Comes with a lifetime guarantee.

Price: $75 plus shipping.

From Cravener's Gun Shop.

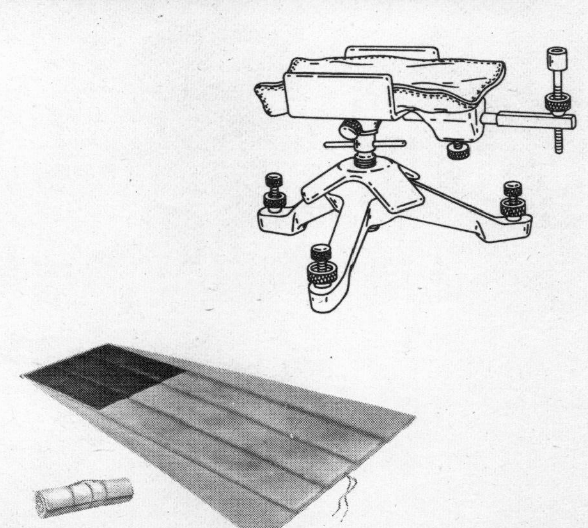

BENCHREST STAND

This one's for the benchrest rifleman. Freeland's "Supreme" benchrest stand features a wide saddle, lots of elevation, adjustable forend bumper. Comes with a gray wrinkle finish; smaller parts are blued. Each stand has two small, and one large empty sandbags.

Price: $42.50

From Freeland's Scope Stands.

SHOOTING MATS

Each Freeland shooting mat is waterproof and mildew proof. They roll up quickly and each one has a carrying handle. Olive drab color. The "AR" mat has double thick padding, the "BR" mat has a single layer of padding.

Price: AR mat $48; BR mat $42.50.

From Freeland's Scope Stands.

INTERNATIONAL SHOOTING STAND

Invented by A.I. Freeland, this unique shooting stand has a base that's spiked for deep-earth penetration. (The legs of the base are reversible so the shooter may use rubber-padded cups on a cement surface.) The upright shaft is 2 inches in diameter and is made of high-tensile alloy. Has a neoprene bar support, ammo block. Can be quickly adjusted for use in kneeling, off-hand or prone-position shooting. Gray wrinkle finish.

Price: $127.85; carrying case $35.

From Freeland's Scope Stands.

BENCHREST STAND

This tripod stand is fully adjustable and may be locked into position once the desired height, and a level position, are obtained. Weight: About 13 pounds.

Price: Varmint $59.95; Heavy Bench $63.50; Combination $71.50.

From Hart Products.

SHOOTING STOOL

This portable stool is adjustable (as can be seen in the nearby photo) for different heights. You can take this item to the range and always be assured of having a spot to sit or a small table for extra gear. Sturdily made. Order direct.

Price: $24.50, plus postage.

From Anthony Hidalgo.

SAND BAGS

These canvas bags come unfilled and feature a funnel-type flap on the bottom for filling. They are contoured to hold the rifle firmly.

Price: $10.00

From Kolpin Gun Cases

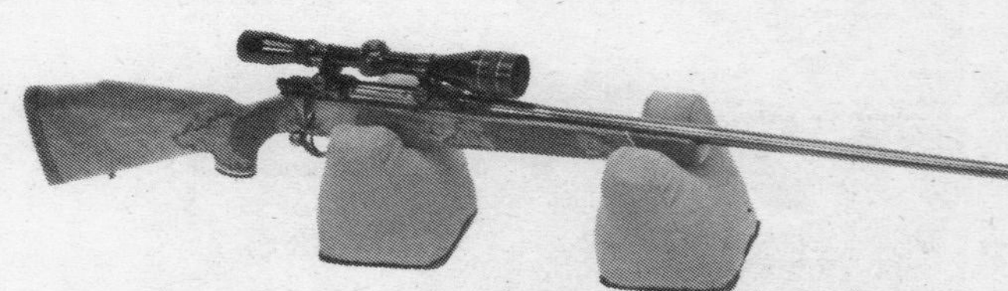

PORTABLE SHOOTING TABLE

A shooter will have to have to see this unit to appreciate it's heft, ruggedness and workmanship. Called the ''Earth Anchor,'' this rest folds up small enough to fit into the smallest car trunk. When set up, the three steel legs are fully adjustable for overall heights of between 14 and 21 inches. A turnbuckle attaches to an anchor stake to pull the bench firmly down to the ground. Measures 36 by 16 by ¾ inches.

Price: $69.95 complete.

From T.W. Menck, Gunsmith.

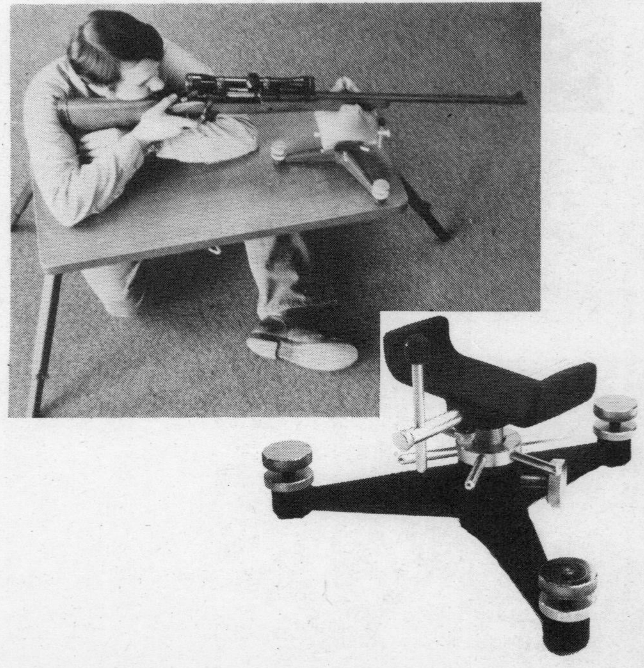

FULLY ADJUSTABLE RIFLE REST

These Wichita rests help eliminate the use of makeshift forend supports. Adjustment requires no tools and each of the three legs come with leveling screws. Padded forend stop insures the gun returns to the same position, shot after shot. Hardware is chromed.

Price: Cast alloy and steel $39.95; cast iron and steel $49.95.

From Wichita Engineering & Supply.

Prices shown are subject to change.

BAUSCH & LOMB DISCOVERER SPOTTING SCOPE

This 15X - 60X zoom spotting scope features a 60mm objective lens. The scope has precision ground optics and comes with protective lens caps. Top quality.

Price: $375

From Bausch & Lomb Optical Company

BUSHNELL ANGLED EYEPIECE SPOTTING SCOPE

If you're a competition shooter, this scope (with its 45-degree angled eyepiece) allows you to shoot and spot your target without changing your position. Comes with protective lens caps. Available in 15X, 20X, 22X wide angle, 25X, 40X and 60X. Extra eyepieces in the above powers are available.

Price: $294; 22X wide angle $299; extra eyepieces are $39.95 for 15X, 20X, 25X, 40 X and 60X; 22X wide angle $44.

From Bushnell Optical Company.

BUSHNELL SPACEMASTER ZOOM SPOTTING SCOPE

This Bushnell spotting scope is zoom adjustable from 20X to 45X at the flick of a wrist. All lenses are achromatic color corrected and hard coated. Protective lens caps come with each scope. Standard thread tripod mount quickly attaches to a camera tripod or shooter's stand.

Price: $320

From Bushnell Optical Company.

BUSHNELL "COMPETITOR" 20X SPOTTING SCOPE

This is a reasonably priced spotting scope for most handgun and rifle shooting. Comes with dovetail tripod mount for Bushnell's 78-3003 tripod. Has protective lens caps. Fully coated, color corrected optics. (The size of this scope lends itself for pistol-box mounting.) 5-year warranty.

Price: $79.50; Tripod, $24.95.

From Bushnell Optical Company.

BUSHNELL "TROPHY" 16-36X ZOOM "ARMORED" SPOTTING SCOPE

If you need a spotting scope that's built to take heavy use, this is the item for you. The entire scope is green-rubber protected. Accessory eyepieces for 20X, 32X and 48X are available. Has a tripod mounting base.

Price: 20X, 32X and 48X . . . $199
16X - 36X Zoom . . . $259.

From Bushnell Optical Company.

REDFIELD'S REGAL SPOTTING SCOPE

This spotting scope is available in either 15X-45X or 15X-60X zoom configuration. An American-made spotting scope, it's fully fog proof and features the highest quality precision ground optics. Fully adjustable tripod available.

Price: 15X-45X . . . $317; 15X-60X . . . $351; Tripod . . . $55.

From Redfield.

SWIFT ANGLE EYEPIECE SPOTTING SCOPE

The eyepiece on the scope is angled 45 degrees so the shooter can actually check his target without changing his shooting stance or position. A 22-power eyepiece comes standard; however, 30X, 40X and 50X eyepieces are available. Comes with removable tripod adapter. Fully coated lenses.

Price: $195; 30X or 40X eyepieces $32; 50X eyepiece $38; Tripod $15.

From Swift Instruments, Inc.

See the Directory for complete company addresses.

SWIFT MARK II 20X SPOTTING SCOPE

This spotting scope may also be used for telephotography when combined with Swift's 841PA, T-System adapter. Features built-in sunshade. Eyepieces are available in 15X, 30X, 40X, 50X and 60X. 120-foot field of view at 1000 yards with 20X eyepiece.

Price: 20X - $245; 15X, 30X, 40X, 50X and 60X eyepieces - $35 each; Tripod - $15.

From Swift Instruments, Inc.

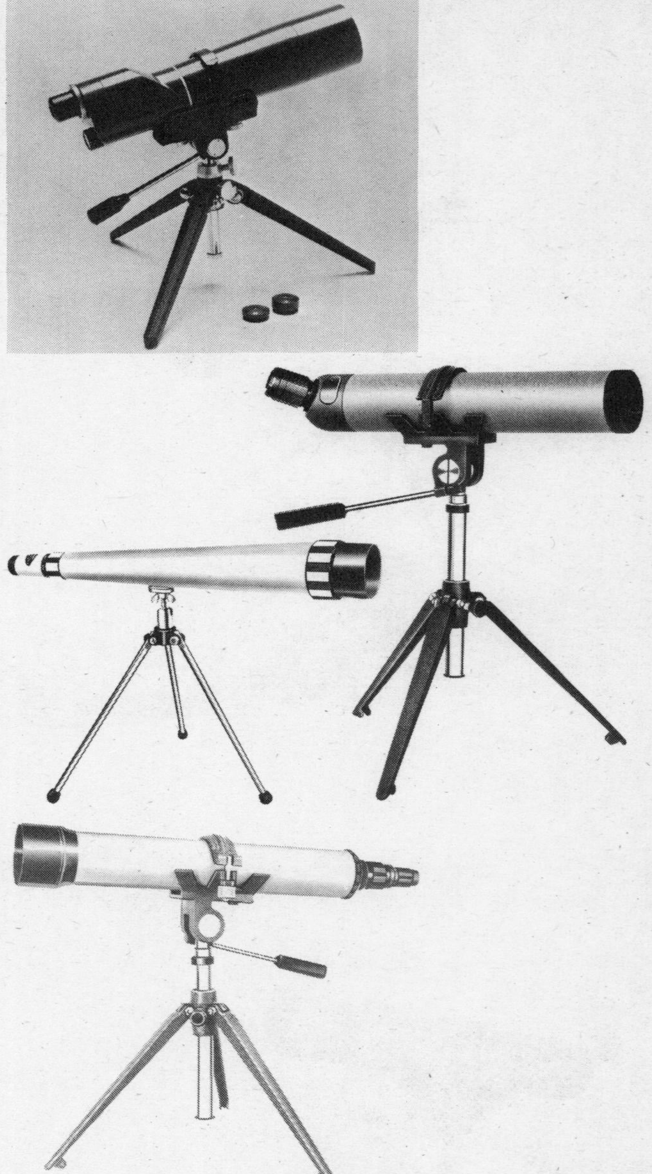

TASCO NO. 27T ANGLE EYEPIECE SPOTTING SCOPE

Featuring a 10-foot field of view at 100 yards, this spotting scope focuses down to 33 feet. The angled eyepiece allows you to shoot and check your target without changing your shooting position. Comes with tripod and adjustable center post. Also, this spotting scope comes with a camera tripod adapter. Accessory 30X, 40X and 50X eyepieces are available.

Price: See your local dealer.

From Tasco Sales, Inc.

TASCO NO. 22T ZOOM SPOTTING SCOPE

This spotting scope zooms from 15 to 45 power and features a 40mm objective lens. All lenses are color corrected. Comes with rubber tipped tripod legs.

Price: See your local dealer.

From Tasco Sales, Inc.

TASCO NO. 18E ZOOM SPOTTING SCOPE

If you want power, this spotting scope has it. It instantly zooms from 20 to 60X. It comes with adjustable tripod, single panhead lever and built in camera tripod adapter. Has a 60mm objective lens.

Price: See your local dealer.

From Tasco Sales, Inc.

UNERTL 100mm TEAM SCOPE

The 100mm Spotting Scope is a large instrument which was designed to meet the requirements of team coaches to enable critical spotting of long range big bore matches.

The coated prismatic optical systems, with a 100mm aperture objective and four element orthoscopic oculars, is critically tested and hand corrected so that the final system will yield matchless resolution. The objective cell has a sunshade which can be extended about 5 inches when required and the eyepiece is screw focused with a fast over-running push-pull travel. Dust covers are provided for each end. Workmanship is of the highest quality and the body of the instrument is made from aluminum alloy and finished in a light gray wrinkle.

The yoke mounting enables easy insertion and removal of the telescope from the yoke and tripod. By tensioning the binding screws the scope can be fixed by locked in position or so set to permit scanning of a series of targets. The lower portion of the yoke fits the cylindrical column of a floating action metal tripod. Within the tripod ram is a helical spring which counterbalances the scope so it can be raised or lowered with ease.

A wooden carrying case of substantial construction houses the telescope, yoke, tripod and extra interchangeable eyepieces. Standard oculars are 16X, 24X and 32X.

Price: $638

From the John Unertl Optical Company.

Prices shown are subject to change.

UNERTL SPOTTING SCOPES

These top quality spotting scopes fulfill the most critical spotting and observation requirements. The objective lens cells on all Unertl spotting scopes come with sun shades. Dust caps of the screw-on type are provided as well. The "24X63" model is good for any range spotting use while the "20X54" model was designed for pistol shooters. The "24X63 Right Angle" spotting scope has, as its name implies, a right angle eye piece. It has become popular with match shooters as you can set the scope up and use it without changing body position. Well made.

Price: "20X54" - $141; "24X63" - $168; "24X63" Right Angle - $199.

From the John Unertl Optical Company.

WEATHERBY "SIGHTMASTER" 20X TO 45X ZOOM SPOTTING SCOPE AND TRIPOD

All optics are fully coated for maximum clarity and brightness. Perfect for scoring.

Price: Scope alone . . . $305.95; Scope & Tripod . . . $359.95; Tripod alone . . . $65.95.

From Weatherby, Inc.

ZEISS DIALYT 40X60 SPOTTING SCOPE

This is a new offering from Zeiss. It comes complete with protective lens cap, clamping device and tripod adapter. This scope is for the serious shooter, shooting club or shooting team. The optics are superior. The brilliance and clarity have to be seen to be fully appreciated.

Price: $899.95

From Carl Zeiss, Inc.

SPOTTING SCOPE TRIPOD & SADDLE

This lightweight spotting scope tripod is made of aluminum and is *fully* adjustable. It's the perfect mount for your favorite spotting scope. Specify brand and scope when ordering.

Price: $35

From Freeland's Scope Stands.

SPOTTING SCOPE BIPOD

This Freeland product is called the "Regal Bipod" and comes with either the *zoom* or *saddle* head. Accommodates many different spotting scopes with varying diameters. Available are 12-, 18-, or 24-inch extensions. Gray wrinkle finish.

Price: Saddle or Zoom Head Models $41; 24-inch extension $9.85; 12-inch extension $6.30; 18-inch extension $8.50.

From Freeland's Scope Stands.

SPOTTING SCOPE CASE

This case has been especially designed for the target/benchrest shooter who is looking for the best storage or transport case for a spotting scope. It's made of russet top-grain, oil-treated cowhide. Has a protective center divider. Measures 17¼"x10½"x4" inches.

Price: $59

From Freeland Scope Stands.

SPOTTING SCOPE CASE

Outers' Model 2200 carrying case is especially designed for the transport of precision optics. Measures 22x10x5¼ inches. Features an aluminum frame, piano hinge and full foam lining.

Price: $44.82

From Outers Laboratories, Inc.

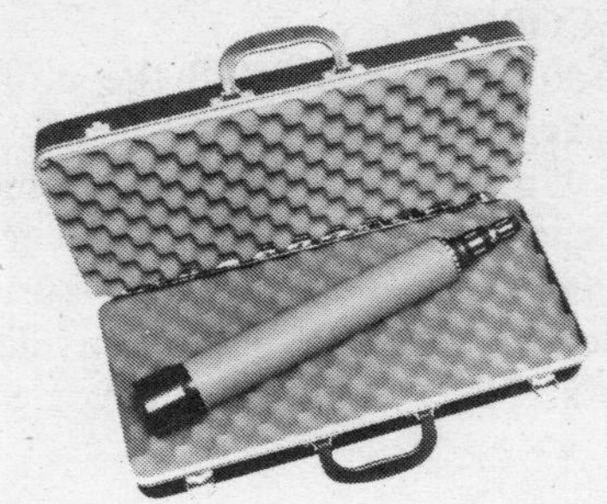

SPOTTING SCOPE MOUNT

Comes with extruded rubber strip to prevent marring of scope body. Black anodized finish. Easy to install on any pistol box.

Price: $10

From Pachmayr Gun Works.

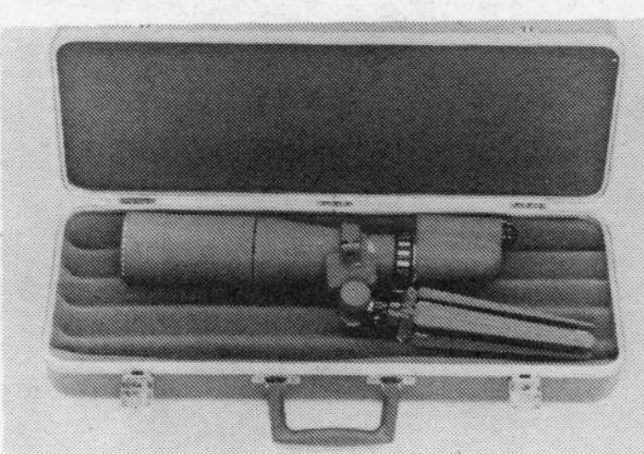

SPOTTING SCOPE CASE

This handy case helps insure that your spotting scope will arrive at the range in top shape. It measures 8″x22″x4½″ deep and weighs 4 pounds. Case is made of high-impact plastic and fully lined. Color is green.

Price: $35.75

From Protecto Plastics, Div. of Penguin Inc.

FIVE-GUN COMPETITIVE PISTOL SHOOTERS BOX

This is Gun-Ho's Model No. PC5 gun box. It holds 5 autos or revolvers in a rubber-padded pistol vise—no bouncing around during transport. The case is fully lockable, has a washable interior and is accessible from either the right or left side—it has 2 doors. Holds lots of accessories. (Optional carrying strap available).

Price: 5-gun $85; carrying strap $13.

From Gun-Ho Sport Cases.

FOUR-GUN COMPETITIVE PISTOL SHOOTER'S BOX

This lockable hard-shell pistol case is Gun-Ho's Model No. PC4. It holds 4-guns in a rubber-padded pistol vise that keeps the guns from bouncing around during transport. The interior is completely washable and the case comes with a heavy duty luggage-type handle. (Optional carrying strap—as shown—is available). Holds lots of accessories.

Price: 4-gun $80; Carrying strap $13.

From Gun-Ho Sport Cases.

COMPETITION PISTOL BOX

This case comes in 3- 4- and 5-gun sizes. It comes with a lok-grip tray that insures a stable ride for your fine target pistols. There's plenty of space for ammo, shooting accessories and spotting scope. Comes in black or brown color.

Price: 3-gun $63; 4-gun $70; 5-gun $72. (The 4- and 5-gun cases with Lok-Grip trays are also available with a "back-door" compartment at $77 and $84, respectively.)

From Pachmayr Gun Works.

RIFLEMAN'S COAT

Bob Allen's new "Top-Shot" rifleman's coat is made from a long wearing fabric which is 65% polyester and 35% cotton. It features split-leather shoulder and sling pads, coat/sleeve butt pad, plus high-cut armholes, seamless elbows and shaped elbow pads. It's offered in sizes 36-48 and comes in right or left styles. This tan color coat is fully dry-cleanable and comes in its own zippered gear bag.

Price: $69.95

From Bob Allen Sportswear.

Prices shown are subject to change.

HOLDEN SHOOTING GLASSES

J. B. Holden's new "Three-In-One" shooting glasses come with interchangeable green, amber and vermilion lenses. The lenses lock into place quickly and firmly. Nose pieces are adjustable and the frames are made of gold-plated monel spring steel.
Price: $39.95
From J. B. Holden Company.

SHOOTING GLASSES

These Olympic Optical shooting glasses are available in a *wide* variety of styles and lens colors. They help sharpen your sight picture while, at the same time, protect your eyes from dangerous gasses and flying brass. The pair shown nearby is Olympic Optical's Model 357. They come in smoke-tint, yellow and vermillion colored lenses.
Price: Any color $25.
From Olympic Optical Co.

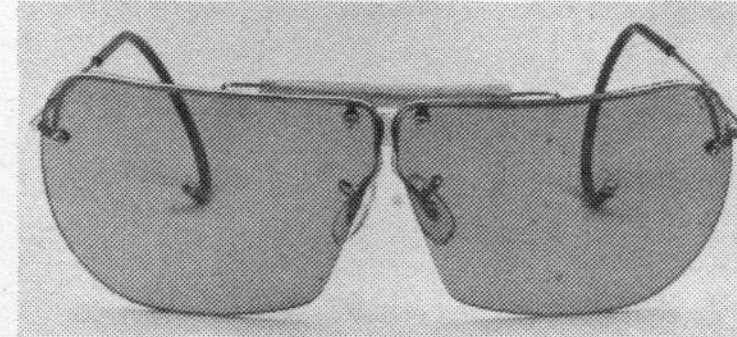

EAR MUFFS

Used by most competitive shooters, ear muffs deaden the sound of gunfire and protect the shooter's eardrums from possible damage.
Price: $10.25 (Model RBW-71).
From Safety Direct, Inc.

BUSHNELL SHOOTING GLASSES

These Bushnell shooting glasses are offered in 6 different lens colors—yellow, green, gray, vermilion, Polarized gray and Photochromic gray. All lenses are optically ground, polished and tempered to withstand shock. The glasses feature lightweight frames and adjustable nose pads. Each pair comes with a case.
Price: Yellow - $41.95; Green, Gray and Vermilion - $34.95; Polarized Gray - $42.95; Photochromic Gray - $49.95.
From Bushnell Optical Company.

TASCO ADVENTURER SHOOTING GLASSES

These glasses feature chrome frames with plastic encased ear grips. The lenses are made of precision ground and polished glass, are shock resistant and come in yellow, gray tint, green, brown tint, vermilion and polarized gray. Comes with a hard case that may be worn on the belt.
Price: See your local dealer.
From Tasco Sales, Inc.

TASCO SURE GRIP SHOOTING GLASSES

These glasses feature gold plated frames and flexible soft ear grips. All lenses are of optically ground and polished glass and are fully shock resistant. Come in yellow, gray tint, green, brown tint, clear, polarized gray, vermilion and photosun. Come with a hard case that may be worn on the belt.
Price: See your local dealer.
From Tasco Sales, Inc.

SHOOTING GLASSES

Zeiss shooting glasses feature lightweight alloy frames (black) and precision ground plastic lenses. These well-made glasses help keep gasses and flying brass out of the shooter's eyes. Available with yellow, vermilion or green or gray lenses.
Price: Yellow $39.95; Vermilion $45; Green or Gray $49.95.
From Carl Zeiss.

EAR MUFFS

These "Silencio" muffs feature a super soft padded headband, liquid filled ear cushions and comfort-oriented styling.
Price: $24.95
From Safety Direct, Inc.

See the Directory for complete company addresses.

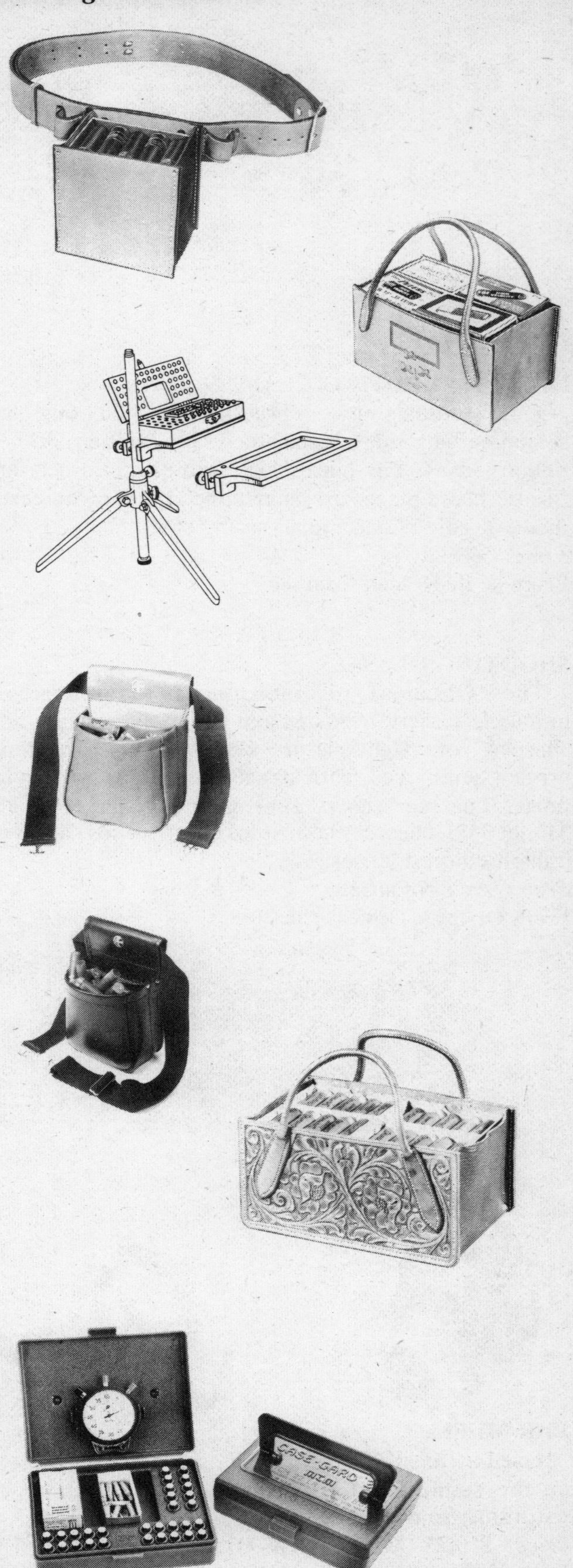

SHOTSHELL CARRIER

Perfect for the Skeet or trap shooter, Boyt's shell carrier holds one box of shotshells. Features all leather construction and comes with a leather belt that's adjustable from 30 inches through 46 inches and is 1¾ inches wide.

Price: $29.70

From Boyt (Div. of Welsh Sporting Goods Corp.).

4-BOX SHOTSHELL CARRIER

This Boyt shell carrier is made of solid leather and is well made. It holds 4 boxes (100 rounds) of your favorite shotshell ammo.

Price: $24.10

From Boyt (Div. of Welsh Sporting Goods Corp.).

.22 AMMO BLOCK HOLDER

Freeland's Position-Master puts your .22 ammo right where you want it. The holder mounts on any tripod, and attaches to your own cartridge block with two wood screws. Made of lightweight aluminum. Ammo block also available.

Price: Ammo Block and Holder $19.25; Holder only $11.

From Freeland's Scope Stands.

LEATHER SHELL CARRIER

This one's made of brown, oil-tanned, top grain cowhide. Holds 25 loose, loaded shells and a generous bundle of empty hulls. Comes with an adjustable belt. Model No. 77-2P.

Price: $31.75

From Kolpin Manufacturing, Inc.

BLACK VINYL SHELL CARRIER

Kolpin's Model No. 74-2P shell carrier comes with an adjustable belt. It holds 25 loaded shells and a good supply of empty hulls.

Price: $12.20

From Kolpin's Manufacturing, Inc.

SHOTSHELL CARRIER

Lawrence's No. 67 shotshell carrier holds 4 boxes (100 rounds) of ammo. Perfect for the trap or skeet range. Sports deluxe leather construction, rounded carrying handles, soft leather gussets and leather lined sides. (Specify gauge when buying.) Unoiled.

Price: Plain - $45.90; Basketweave - $55.50; Flower carved - $74.45.

From The George Lawrence Co.

AMMO BOX

MTM's Case-Gard ammo box was designed by and for competitive shooters. It holds 30 rounds of ammo (projectile down) in individual recesses, and has additional space for boxed ammo. The lid is equipped to hold a stop watch (not included). Comes in either green or dark brown.

Price: $3.99

From MTM Molded Products Company.

Section 11

Targets & Range Equipment

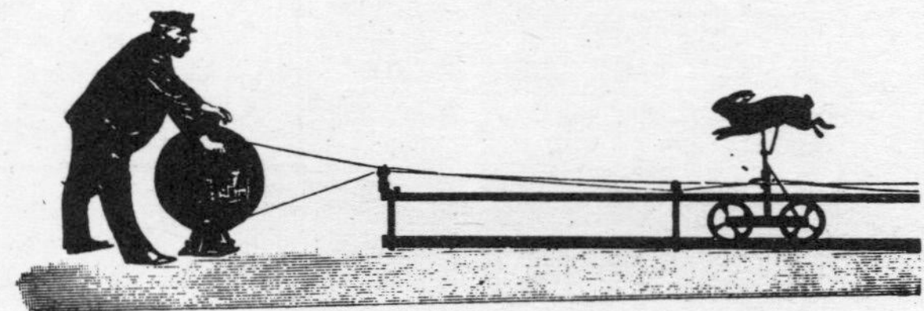

Unquestionably more rifle, pistol and shotgun ammunition is fired at "formal" targets—paper, metallic and clay—each year than at all other objects put together. Much of this "target" shooting is informal, noncompetitive plinking, of course, but it still means that targets and range equipment are a necessary and vital part of most shooters' kits.

Paper targets come in many forms beside the traditional "bullseye" in the middle of a sheet of paper, and we've included a great many of these variations in the opening pages of this section. In those same pages you'll also find metallic silhouette targets, both big-bore and .22, and some mechanical "spinner" plinking targets. Bullet traps and target carriers come next, followed by trap and Skeet shooting range equipment and clay birds.

Targets, both paper and clay, are stocked by most gun shops, and a number of them also carry a limited variety of bullet traps and hand traps for throwing clay birds. For many of the more unusual paper targets and more sophisticated range equipment, you'll have to go directly to the manufacturer.

OFFICIAL 200-YARD N.R.A. RIFLE TARGET

This is the official standard target for 200-yard rifle shooting and is used in matches sanctioned or conducted by the National Rifle Association.
Price: $8 per 100.
From National Target Company.

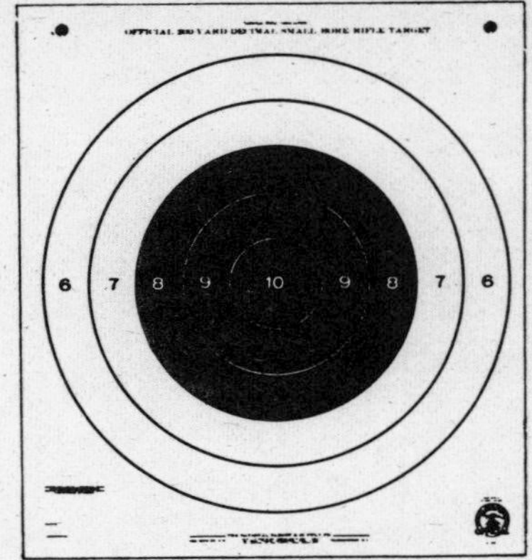

OFFICIAL INTERNATIONAL 200-YARD N.R.A. RIFLE TARGET

Most U.S. ranges have a maximum of not more than 200 yards. This target is an exact reduction of the 300-meter rifle target reduced for 200-yard matches and practice.
Price: $20.30 per 100.
From National Target Company.

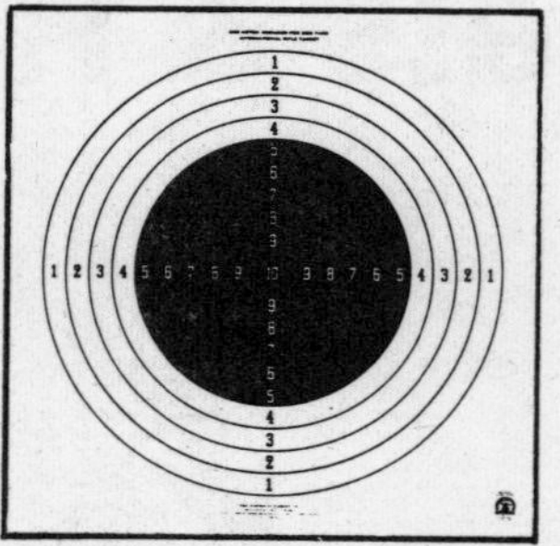

OFFICIAL 100-YARD N.R.A. RIFLE TARGET

This 100-yard target (No. A-15) is official in all dimensions and is made of special "tagboard." This target is used for all official N.R.A. competition. Measures 14″x14″.
Price: $5.10 per 100.
From National Target Company.

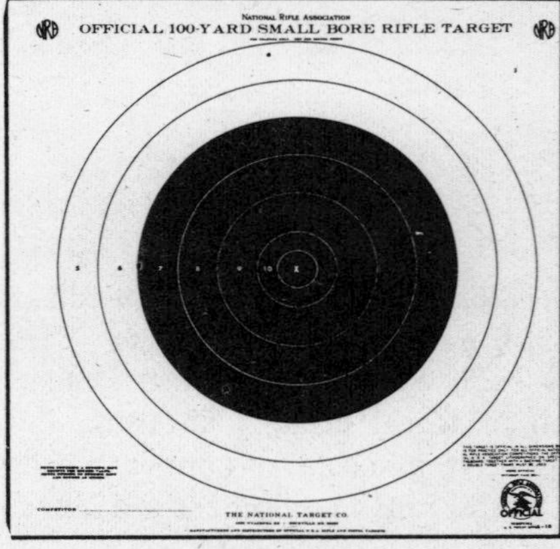

OFFICIAL 50-YARD N.R.A. PISTOL TARGETS

These 50-yard slowfire pistol targets are centers only with scoring rings running from 7 to X. They are official N.R.A. targets and come 100 to the package.
Price: $2.40 per 100; full target $7 per 100.
From National Target Company.

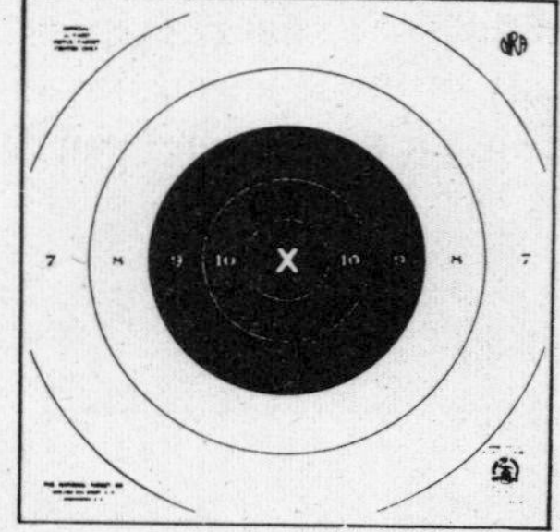

OFFICIAL 25-YARD N.R.A. PISTOL TARGET

These 25-yard rapid-fire targets, are centers only with scoring rings running from 7 to X. They are official N.R.A. targets and come 100 to the package.
Price: $2.40 per 100; full target $7 per 100.
From National Target Company.

Prices shown are subject to change.

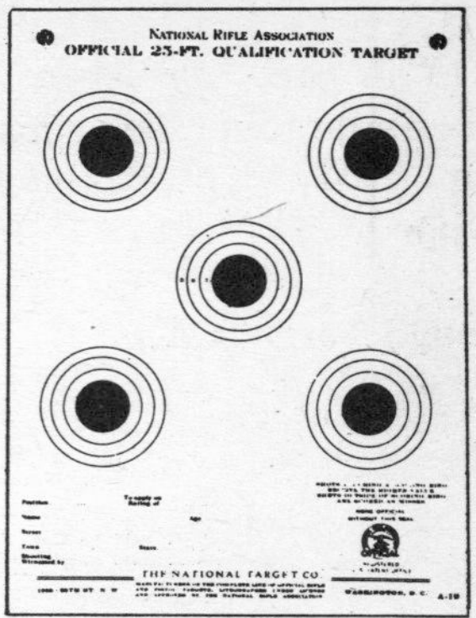

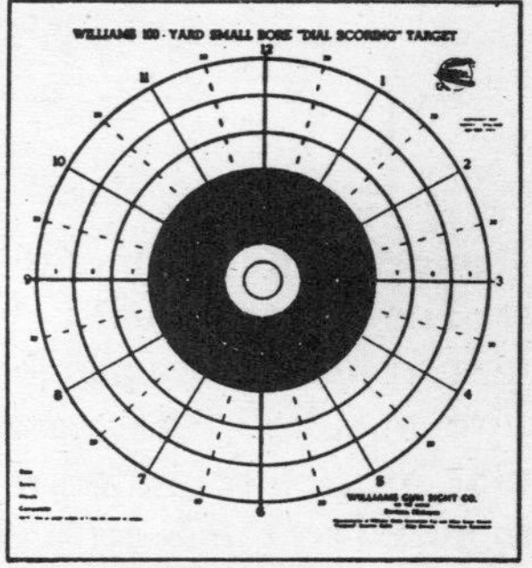
100 Yd. Small Bore DS

100 Yd. Small Bore WC.

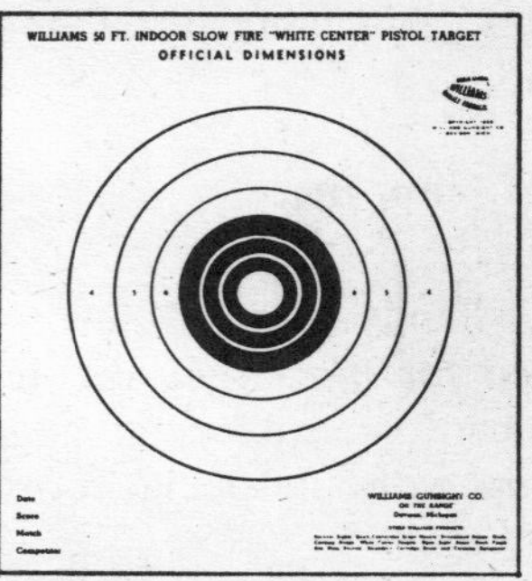
50 Ft. Indoor Slow Fire Pistol

25 Yd. Outdoor Center Only Pistol

OFFICIAL N.R.A. AIR RIFLE TARGETS

These official N.R.A. air gun targets are available for 10-meter (33 feet), 15-foot and 25-foot ranges. (Shown nearby is the 25-foot target.) They come 100 to the package.

Price: 25-foot (A-19) $1.15; 10-meter (AR-2) $2.40; 15-foot (A-45) $2.40—all per 100 targets.

From National Target Company.

PAPER TARGETS

Unique white-centered target design provides better aiming point, while clock-like overlay "Dial Scoring" (D-S) style facilitates calling shots. Printed on NRA target paper.

Price:

Per 100:

200-Yard Small Bore D.S. Targets	$14.35
100-Yard Small Bore D.S. Targets	6.60
100-Yard Small Bore W.C. Targets	6.60
50-Foot Small Bore 10-Bull Targets	5.45
50-Yard Small Bore D.S. 2-Bull Targets	5.45
25-Yard Outdoor Slow Fire Pistol Targets	5.45
50-Foot Indoor Rapid Fire Pistol Targets	5.45
50-Foot Indoor Slow Fire Pistol Targets	5.45
25-Yard Outdoor Center Only Pistol Targets	5.45

From Williams Gun Sight.

NRA RIFLE AND PISTOL TARGETS

A very wide variety of NRA rifle and pistol targets are offered in packs of 12 or 100 targets each.

PISTOL TARGETS	12	100
25-foot slow fire	$1.11	$2.89
50-foot slow fire	$1.11	$4.67
20-yard timed & rapid	$1.11	$4.98
25-yard timed & rapid	$1.11	$2.98
25-yard slow fire	$1.11	$4.67

RIFLE TARGETS		
50-foot Junior (one-bull)	$ .56	$1.91
50-foot Junior (five-bull)	$ .56	$1.91
50-foot Single Bullseye	$ .56	$1.56
50-foot Five Bullseye	$1.11	$4.11
75-foot Single Bullseye	$ .56	$1.67
50-yard Single Bullseye	$ .56	$1.91
50-yard Two Bullseye	$1.11	$3.31
50-yard Five Bullseye	$1.11	$4.73
100 yard Single Bullseye	$1.11	$4.49
50-foot 10 Bullseye	$1.11	$4.98
50-foot 11 Bullseye	$1.11	$4.67
25-foot Single Bullseye	$ .50	$2.16
15-foot Junior	$ .50	$2.07

From Outers.

See the Directory for complete company addresses.

SIGHTING-IN TARGETS

These large Redfield sighting-in targets measure a large 16"x16", have flame-red sighting diamonds and come with complete instructions.

Price: $7.50 per 100.

From Rocky Mountain Target Co.

REPLACEMENT BULLSEYES

The Data-Targ self-sticking bullseyes are 3 inches in diameter and are designed to be used on the standard 50-foot pistol target. They come 80 to the roll.

Price: $1.75 per roll.

From Data-Targ (Rocky Mountain Target Co.).

TARGET STAMP

These stamps allow the shooter to easily turn out his own targets. Made of varnished solid walnut, the stamps may be used with any ink pad. Stamps come two to a set—1-inch and 2-inch sizes.

Price: Two stamps $8.45; two stamps and an ink pad $9.75.

From Ranging, Inc.

PISTOL PRACTICE UNIT

"Light Load" is designed for those handgunners who want to practice their skills without incurring the expense of regular ammo. Light Load is actually an electronic conversion kit for dry-firing practice. When installed—it takes less than a minute—and fired, a stroboscopic burst of light is sent through a barrel mounted lens which registers on the target as a bullet-shaped image. (You get over 1000 "shots" from a pair of 1.5 V "N" batteries). Light Load is available for many popular handguns.

Price: About $90.

From Jafin Products.

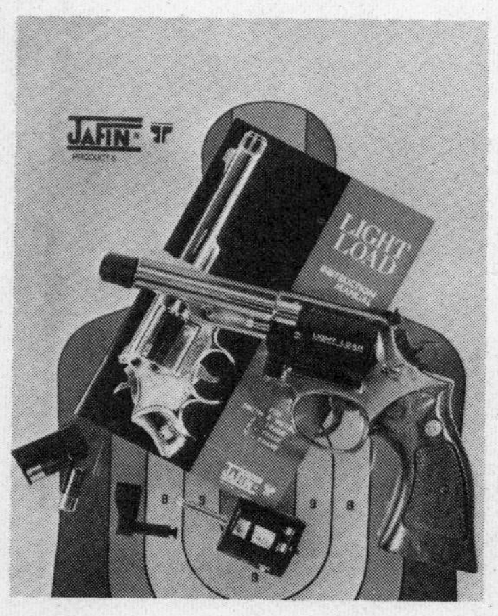

PORTABLE TARGET STAND

Holds any target up to 15"x15" in size. Consists of a sturdy welded steel frame and six target-holder clips. Handy, easy to store and transport. With a proper back stop you can quickly create your own range.

Price: $6.95

From Data-Targ (Rocky Mountain Target Co.).

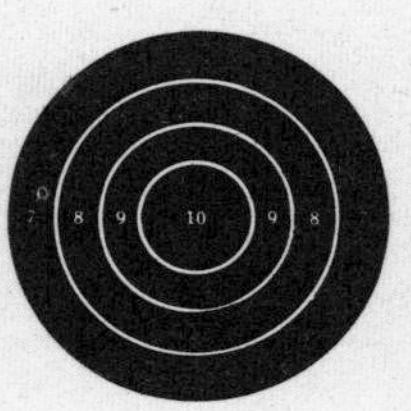

RIG EZE SCORERS

These target scorers are made for the competitive pistol, rifle and airgun shooter. The scorers consist of a spring mounted precision plug surrounded by a piece of optical-quality lucite. The entire unit allows the user to determine the exact point value of each round on the target. These scorers are recognized by the N.R.A. as *the official scoring device* for all competitive target shooting in the United States. Available in calibers ranging from .177 through .45.

Price: $3.50, any caliber.

From Rig Products, Div. of Mitann, Inc.

PORTABLE TARGET STAND

Called the "Plink-Kit," this handy item isn't just for "plinking." It's ideally suited for the target shooter who needs to practice, yet, doesn't have a formal range facility nearby. Easily sets up without special tools. Holds targets up to 15" x 24".

Price: $8.95

From Safety Direct, Inc.

ELECTRONIC TRAP BOY

This item is designed for automatic trap and Skeet fields. Each unit is voice-activated; and, when the user calls for his bird with the familiar "Pull," the unit electronically signals the trap and a bird is thrown. This unit isn't cheap, nor are there too many individual shooters who'll be installing them in their backyards. However, we've included it because your local club may just feel that the Electronic Trap Boy is just the sort of item worth investing in. If you're interested, we would strongly urge you, or your club's Secretary to write the manufacturer for full details.

Price: From about $300 for a practice unit up to about $950 with 7 microphones; Electronic Trap Boys available for Traps of European manufacture—price on request.

From Electro Ballistic Laboratory.

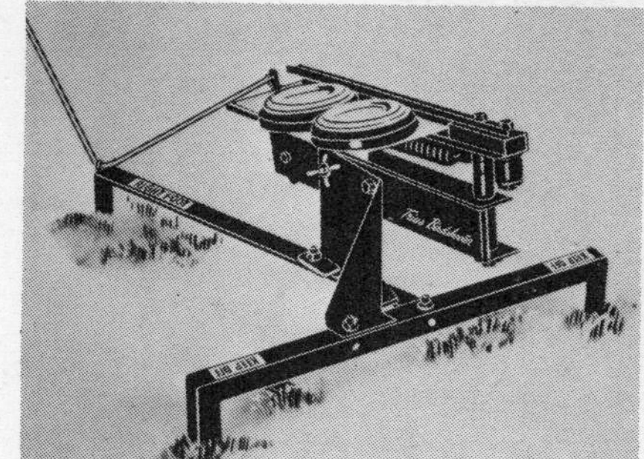

CLAY BIRD TRAPS

Mechanical, ground-mounted traps have been around for years; however, the "Trius" series of traps are well known to most shooters. The original "Trius Foot Trap" features a high-angle clip, can thrower and patented ground anchor—it throws regulation singles 65 yards. The "Trius Bird Shooter" comes with a T-base for a foot hold, plus a tire mounting bolt. A new Trius offering, the "Trapmaster," offers the operator sit-down comfort and good pivot action.

Prices: Foot Trap $49.95; Birdshooter $43.95; Trapmaster $99.95.

From Trius Products, Inc.

CLAY PIGEONS

Clay birds for skeet and trap shooting are principally the products of four major manufacturers. Because of their fragility it is strongly recommended that they be purchased locally rather than through the mail, as some broken birds are almost certain in a carton handled by parcel post. The standard clay birds, as they come from all four makers, feature a yellow dome. Other colors are available for night and competition shooting.

Price: $5-$6 (carton of 135 birds.)

From Champion (Federal), Eclipse, Remington and Winchester.

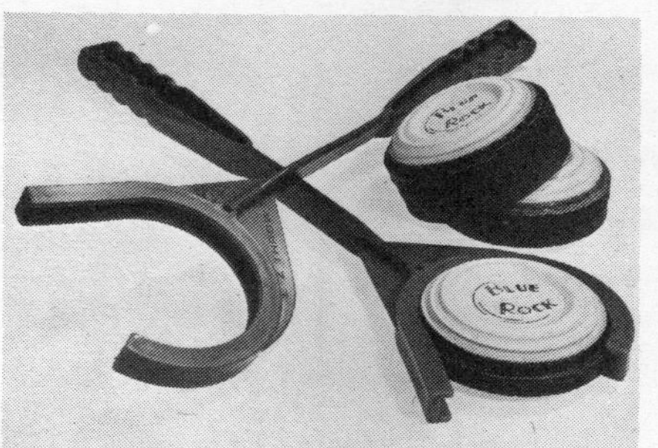

CLAY-BIRD THROWER

May be used with either hand. Channeled throat reduces breakage to a minimum.

Price: $2.99

From MTM Molded Products Company.

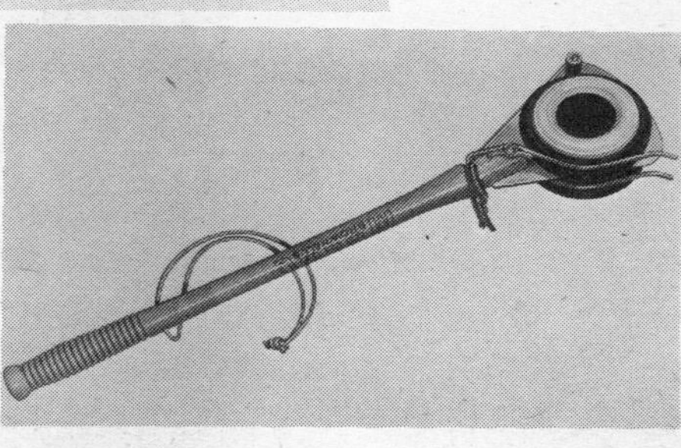

HAND TRAP

The Metro Hand Trap is designed to toss clay birds in either single or double fashion. Features a hardwood handle and wrist thong.

Price: $6.25

From Brownell's, Inc.

SHOTSHELL CARRIER

The Case-Gard 100-round shotshell case is a versatile accessory especially designed for the competitive shotgunner. Features include a rust-proof stainless steel hinge pin and center balanced handles. It can be padlocked for security. Contents are fully protected from dust and moisture. Comes in black. Shell tray is removable.

Price: 12, 16 or 20 gauge $9.49.

From MTM Molded Products Company.

See the Directory for complete company addresses.

SHOTGUN PATTERNING TARGET

These large targets measure 35"x45" and help the shotgunner determine which load patterns best in his own shotgun.

Price: 20¢ each.

From National Target Company.

RUNNING DEER TARGET

This measures 28"x42" and is lithographed on brown kraft paper. Comes with "vital-hit" scoring system. Available in packages of 4. (Two have deer facing left; two facing right).

Price: $1.60 per 4.

From National Target Company.

TARGET PASTERS

Come in black or white, 250 per roll. Each roll is packed in a handy dispensing box. These pasters are pressure sensitive and help increase target life.

Price: 75¢ per roll; $15 per 20 rolls—specify black or white.

From National Target Company.

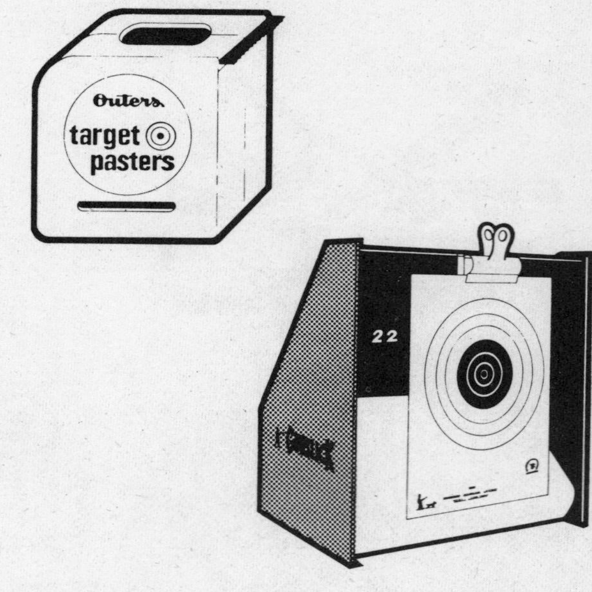

TARGET PASTERS

350 one-inch target pasters, in a roll in a polypropylene dispenser. In black or white (specify).

Price: $1.22 (specify black or white).

From Outers.

BULLET TRAP

Compact bullet trap for .22 rimfire only has 10x11-inch target area.

Price: $25.96

From Outers.

METALLIC SILHOUETTES

Available in full scale for centerfire rifles; ½ scale for pistols and 1/5 scale for rimfires. The silhouettes are made of Jalloy 360 steel; and, if placed over 100 yards from the firing point, they will withstand the largest magnum. A 1/5-scale set of silhouettes is also available in mild steel; but, these are *strictly* for the .22 S, L and LR rounds *only*. Each set contains one ram, chicken, hog and turkey.

Price: Full-scale $349.95; Half-scale $149.95; One-Fifth scale $39.49; One-Fifth scale mild-steel $24.95.

From South West Metallic Silhouettes.

Prices shown are subject to change.

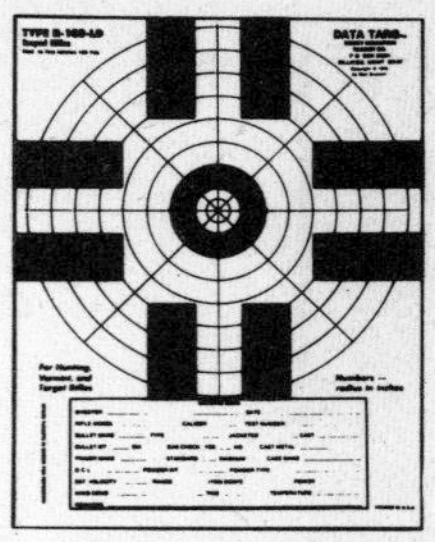

R-100-LD

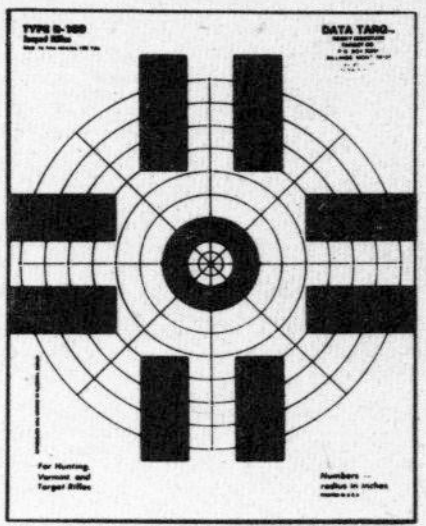

R-100

R-200-LD

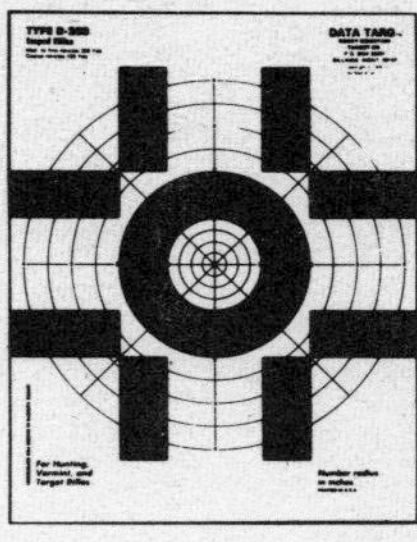

R-200

VARMINT/HUNTING TARGETS

Made for 100- and 200-yard ranges, these "Data-Targs" are designed for varmint and game hunters who need to sight their rifles in for a specific range. The R-100-LD and the R-200-LD (100- and 200-yard targets) come with a handy log that lets you keep track of your load development.

Price: $6.50 per 100.

From Data-Targ (Rocky Mountain Target Company).

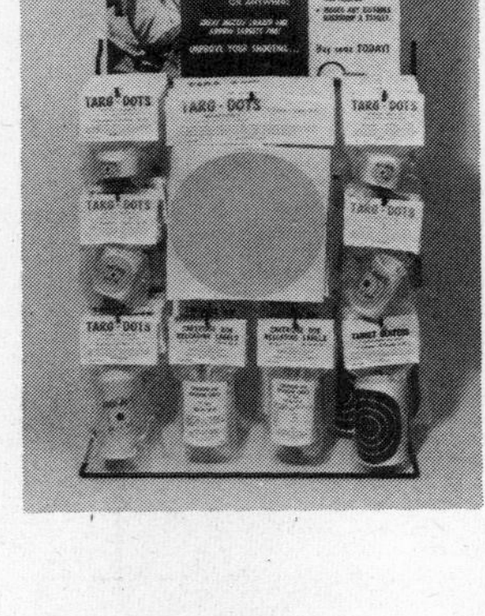

TARG-DOTS

Self-sticking Targ-Dots come in many different sizes. The basic Targ-Dot is a brilliant blaze red/orange and is designed to be pasted on the center bullseye. It really shows up at almost any range.

Price: See below for quantity and price.

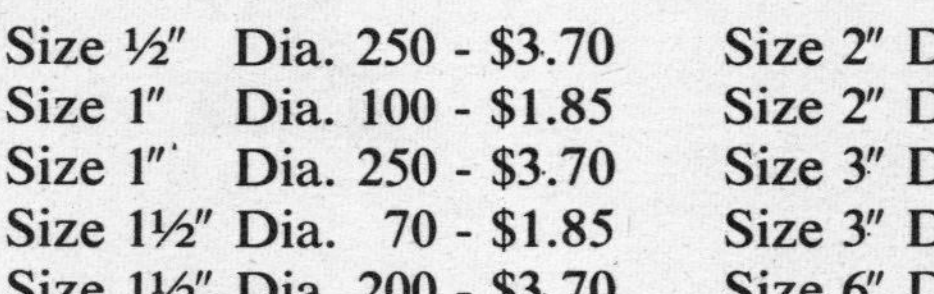

Size ½"	Dia. 250 - $3.70		Size 2"	Dia. 45 - $1.85	
Size 1"	Dia. 100 - $1.85		Size 2"	Dia. 175 - $5.25	
Size 1"	Dia. 250 - $3.70		Size 3"	Dia. 25 - $1.85	
Size 1½"	Dia. 70 - $1.85		Size 3"	Dia. 100 - $5.25	
Size 1½"	Dia. 200 - $3.70		Size 6"	Dia. 15 - $1.85	

From Peterson's Labels.

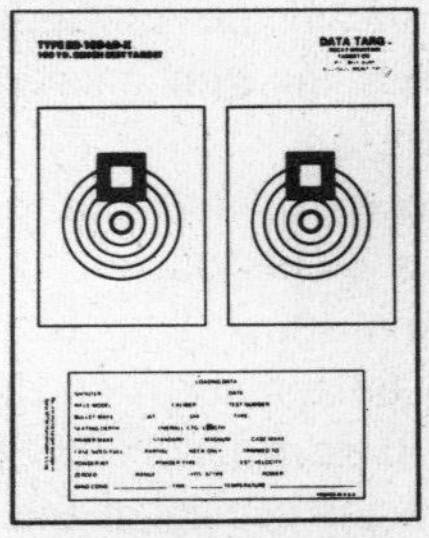

BR-100-LD-X

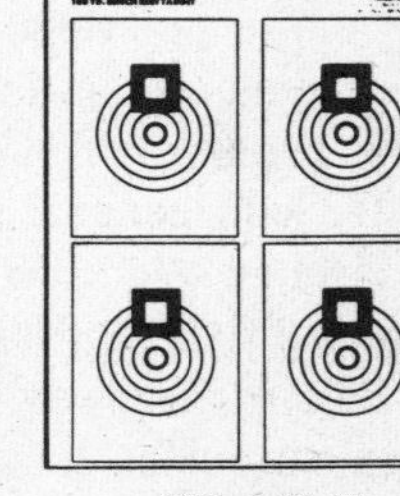

BR-100-X

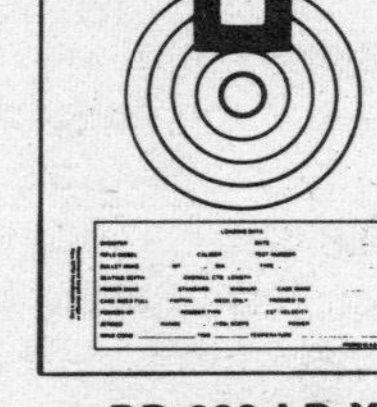

BR-200-LD-X

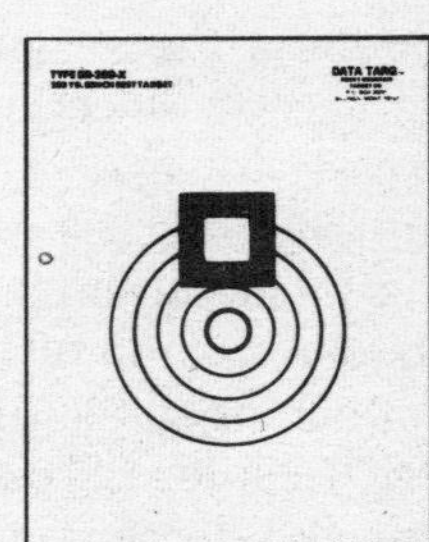

BR-200-X

BENCHREST TARGETS

"Data-Targs" are made for 100- and 200-yard benchrest shooting. The BR-100-LD-X and the BR-200-LD-X (100- and 200-yard targets) come complete with a handy log on which you can record your load development.

Price: $6.50 per 100.

From Data-Targ (Rocky Mountain Target Company).

See the Directory for complete company addresses.

Section 12

Air Gun Accessories

Air gun shooting is almost certainly one of this nation's fastest growing shooting sports, both for its economy and convenience. Although many of the accessories used by cartridge shooters are entirely appropriate for air gun shooting, the air gun fraternity has also been developing a good selection of specialty items of all kinds expressly for that sport.

As air gun shooting is a very specific sport in its own right, we've included those accessories for the air gun enthusiasts in a section of their own rather than interspersed with comparable items aimed at the cartridge gun shooter. Leading off the section you'll find quite a comprehensive selection of air gun ammunition, darts and special hunting projectiles as well as a large variety of pellets for all types of shooting. Air gun targets, pellet traps, and even air gun games are next, followed by both metallic and telescopic sights specifically designed for air gun use. Cleaning and maintenance equipment, including some very unusual newly developed items, follow, while holsters and other air gun carrying and storage items conclude the section.

As yet relatively few gun shops are catering to the air gun buff, with general sporting goods outlets often offering a better selection of air gun items. For the serious air gun enthusiast, there's no better sources than Air Rifle Headquarters and Beeman's Precision Airguns—their fat catalogs are the bibles of the sport!

AIRGUN PELLETS
Beeman's "Kodiak" weighs over 50% more than standard .22 pellets for maximum impact and wind-bucking ability.
Price: No. 3250 (tin of 500), $6.95.
"Bruin" is an extra heavy .20 caliber pellet for Sheridan air rifles.
Price: No. 3180 (tin of 500), $3.75.
From Beeman's.

AIR GUN PELLETS
.177 and .22 caliber Super Pells are made of 100 percent soft, virgin lead, come in a unique clip-on Belt-Pak plastic box for easy use.
Price: .22 caliber Belt-Pak (175), $1.00; .177 caliber Belt-Pak (250), $.70.
From Crosman Airguns distributors.

AIR GUN BBs
Steel Super BBs are precision ground and copper plated to eliminate rusting.
Price: 200 Pak, 19¢; 400 pack, 30¢; 1500 pack, $1.15; 2500 pack, $1.85; 5000 pack, $3.75.
From Crosman Airguns distributors.

H&N POINTED MATCH PELLETS A
Pointed pellet for greatest accuracy in long-range shooting for Sheridan (.20) as well as conventional bore air guns.
Price: .177 cal., $3.95 (500); .20 cal., $3.95 (200); .22 cal., $3.95 (200).
From K.J. David.

H & N ENGLISH STYLE PELLETS B
High quality pellet for accurate mid- and long-range shooting.
Price: .177, $3.65 (500).
From K.J. David.

Z & S DIABLO PELLETS C
Inexpensive but well-made pellet for all 'round shooting.
Price: .177, $2.90 (500).
From K.J. David.

H & N MATCH PELLETS D
Made for highest accuracy, available with either ribbed or smooth skirt, .177 caliber.
Price: $3.85 (500 bulk packed tin, or 200 in foam lined box).
From K.J. David.

AIRGUN PELLETS
"Silver Jet" pellets are designed as a field pellet for maximum velocity and accuracy at longer ranges.
Price: No. 3070 (.177, per 500), No. 3075 (.20 Sheridan, per 300), or No. 3080 (.22 per 250), $4.75.
From Beeman's.

LEAD BBs
Precision lead BBs provide greater impact, less rebound than steel shot in any BB rifle or pistol.
Price: No. 3450 (.177 per 500), $2.59; No. 3470 (.20 per 500), $3.99; No. 3472 (.22, per 500), $4.99.
From Beeman's.

PELLET SAMPLER
About 25 each of seven different pellets provide easy means for determining which is the best performer in a given .177 airgun.
Price: No. 3300 Pellet Sampler, $5.98.
From Beeman's.

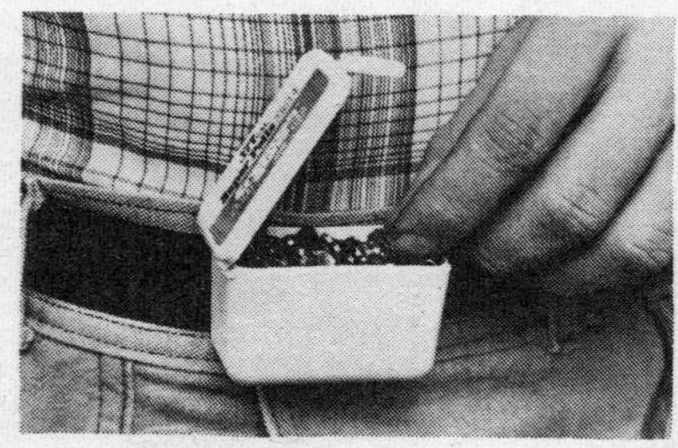

AIRGUN PELLETS
Daisy pellets have a wad-cutting nose and are designed for general purpose use.
Price: 177 (500); .22 (250), $1.50.
From Daisy distributors.

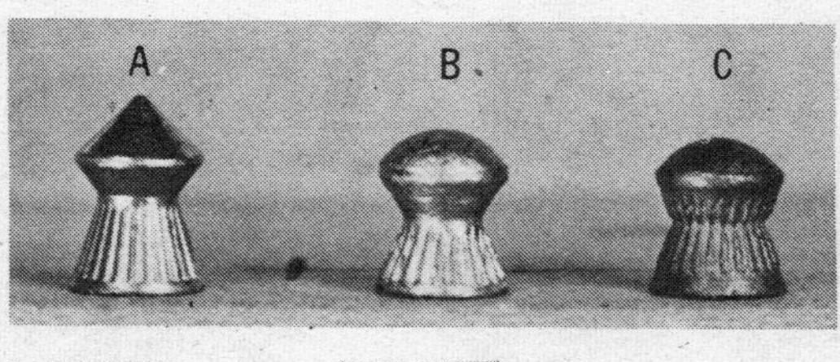

D

E

F

SILVER JET PELLETS E
Unique head design for long range accuracy, available in .177, .20 (Sheridan) and .22.
Price: $4.45 for 500 .177; 300 .20 or 250 .22.
From K.J. David.

BIMOCO NEVE SPITZ PELLETS F
Unique design promotes high velocity.
Price: .177, $3.65 (500); .22, $6.50 (500).
From K. J. David.

MATCH-GRADE AIR GUN PELLETS

Manufactured to precise standards and packed in a special protective plastic box to avoid damage in shipping and handling, RWS match pellets provide top accuracy in .177 target rifles and pistols.

Price: $1.70 (Box of 100); $5.80 (carton of 500 on snap-in cards).

From Eastern Sports International.

AIR GUN PELLETS

RWS .177 (4.5mm) "Meisterkugeln" are manufactured to the same standards as their Match pellets, but are bulk packed for economy.

Price: $1.10 (tin of 200); $2.30 (tin of 500).

From Eastern Sports International.

ECONOMY AIR GUN PELLETS

For economical air gun shooting, RWS "Hobby" pellets are available in both .177 and .22 caliber.

Price: 75¢ (.177, box of 200); $1.65 (.177, box of 500); $1.25 (.22, tin of 200); $2.65 (.22, tin of 500).

From Eastern Sports International.

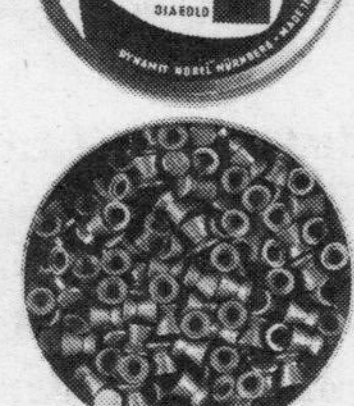

RWS NEW "HOBBY GRADE" PELLETS

Lightweight, low cost pellet ammunition from RWS in both .177 (7.0 gr.) and .22 (11.9 gr.).

Price: .177 caliber: 200, 70¢; 500, $1.75; .22 caliber: 500, $2.99.

From Fanta Air Rifles.

RWS MATCH GRADE PELLETS

Match grade pellets in .22 caliber from RWS, packed 500 to a tin.

Price: $3.99. Same, except .177 caliber. 100, 70¢; 200, $1.35; 500, $2.60.

From Fanta Air Rifles, K.J. David.

AIRGUN PELLETS

These pellets are 5mm (.20 caliber) in size and are meant to be used in Sheridan airguns. Come in either cylindrical or diablo-type configurations.

Price: $3.75, either style (500).

From Sheridan Products.

MARKSMAN AIR GUN PELLETS

Manufactured from 99% pure lead to insure best grip on rifling and maximum seal in bore. Supplied in polycon plastic container to protect pellets during shipping and handling.

Price: .177, $1.16 (200), $2.16 (500); .22, $1.66 (200), $2.57 (500).

From Marksman Products distributors.

AIR GUN DARTS

Darts for air gun games or competition feature colored mohair feathers for effective air seal, stability, contoured steel points for penetration.

Price: .177, $1.66 (12); .22, $2.08 (12).

From Marksman Products distributors.

MARKSMAN BBs

Copper coated BBs for use in all makes of air pistols and rifles.

Price: 65¢ (approx. 435).

From Marksman Products distributors.

PRECISION .177 AND .20 SIZING DIES

Sizing air gun ammo promotes uniformity in velocity, tightens groups, and makes loading easier. Available in three sizes to permit experimentation for optimum performance. Plunger (for all sized dies): $9.50; dies (.178, .179 or .180 - specify): $8.50 each. Sizing die set for .20 caliber Sheridan air rifles improves accuracy and velocity: $18.50 (complete set).
From Air Rifle Headquarters.

CO^2 AIRGUN CYLINDERS

12-grain CO^2 cylinders are plated, contain oil to internally lubricate airgun mechanisms.
Price: No. 3740 (five per box), $2.29.
From Beeman's.

CO^2 PELLET GUN CARTRIDGES

12.5-gram capacity. Powerlets are chrome finished to prevent rusting. 8.5 gram capacity cartridges are also available for those guns requiring the smaller size. $1.70 per pack of five.
From Crosman Airguns distributors.

CO^2 CYLINDERS

12-gm. self-oiling cylinders, packed five to a box.
Price: $1.75 (5).
From Daisy distributors.

CO^2 Pellet Gun Cartridges

12-gram capacity CO^2 gas cartridges, made with welded seams to avoid leaks.
Price: $2.50 per pack of 5.
From Nittan (U.S.A.) Distributors.

CO^2 CARTRIDGES

These are the standard 12.5 gram size and may be used in any gas-operated airgun calling for this size of gas cartridge. Each carton contains 5 cartridges.
Prices: $2.60
From Sheridan Products.

AIR GUN SHOOTING GLASSES

Wrap-around shooting glass design provides maximum eye protection, and unique center hinge lets one size fit youngsters and adults alike. Smoke-tinted lenses are provided for sunny days, amber for cloudy days or indoor shooting.
Price: $3.75
From Crosman Airguns distributors.

BALLISTIC PUTTY

Used to monitor pellet and airgun performance, this special putty will stop a pellet in as little as one inch and is reusable.
Price: Half pound package $2.50.
From Air Rifle Headquarters, Beeman's.

PELLET MOLD

English-made brass mold casts a sharp point (spitzer) pellet heavier than factory pellets.
Price: No. 7195 (.177) or 7196 (.22), $27.95.
From Beeman's.

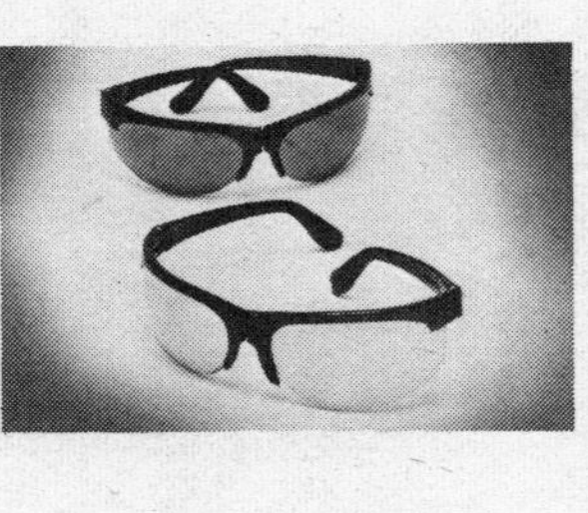

PELLET TRAPS

Wood-framed and filled with ballistic putty, these traps are quiet to use and almost entirely free of "bounce-back."
Price: Model 677, 6⅝x6⅜x2½" o.a., $12.50; Model 678, 8¾x9½x21.2", $16.50; Model 679, 10¾x10¾x2½", $27.50.
From Air Rifle Headquarters, Beeman's.

5-METER AIRGUN TARGETS

Various style rifle and pistol targets reduced to 5-meter dimensions for short-range practice. In 50 target pads (except No. 4329, 25 per pad).

Price: No. 4419, 5-bull rifle target; No. 4402; ISU 5-bull rifle target, $3.65. No. 4332, single bull ISU pistol target; No. 4329, silhouette pistol target, $1.99.

From Beeman's.

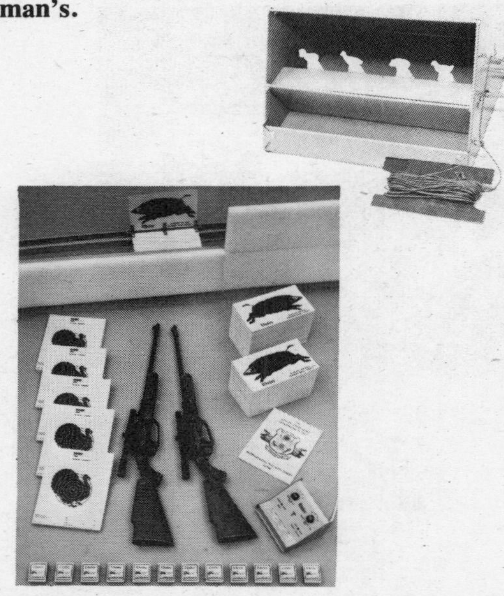

PELLET TARGET TRAP

Heavy steel front, sheet steel side panels. 9″ w x 9⅞″ h x 10″ d.

Price: Model 879, $7.95.

From Daisy distributors.

AIRGUN SILHOUETTE TARGETS

Set of 20 steel silhouette targets designed for scaled down, 20-50 meter, silhouette course.

Price: No. 4040 (set of 20), $49.95.

From Beeman's.

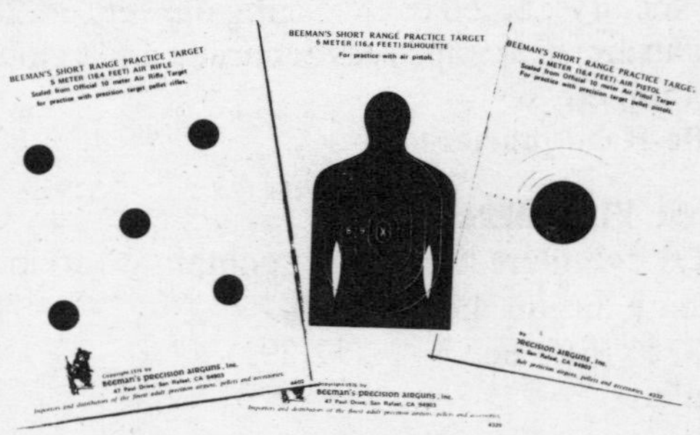

METALLIC SILHOUETTE TRAP

Welded steel trap has four yellow painted animal silhouettes, which can be reset from the firing line by pulling a cord. Scaled for use at 10 meters.

Price: No. 4020, $39.95.

From Beeman's.

AIR GUN SHOOTING GAMES

Shooting games include BB baseball, Shoot Par, Air Raid, five others on forty 8½ x 11-inch targets.

Price: $1.75 per pack of 40.

From Crosman Shooting Games, Box 290, Rochester, New York 14601.

AIR GUN RUNNING TARGET PROGRAM

Kit includes two Model 1917 pellet rifles with 4X scopes, electronically-controlled variable speed target system, targets and pellets.

Price: Model 5828, $525.00.

From Daisy distributors.

BB TRAPS

Light duty traps stop BBs without ricochet. Double target Model 168 has canvas insert.

Price: Model 878 (single target), $4.50; Model 168 (double target), $4.50; Model 168 (double target), $11.95.

From Daisy distributors.

AIR GUN TARGET RUNNERS

Target runners with trap, made specifically for 10-meter airgun shooting indoors or outdoors.

Price: Model 873 (Spieth, Germany), $88.95; Model 877, $47.95.

From Daisy distributors.

SILHOUETTE TARGET TRAP

Four animal silhouette targets are scaled for 10-meter pellet rifle shooting. Trap has heavy steel front, pellet stopping back and base, sheet metal side panels. 24″ w x 18¾″ h x 10″ deep.

Price: Model 5874, $23.95

From Daisy distributors.

AIR GUN SHOOTING GALLERY

110 VAC operated motor provides moving duck or animal targets; a variety of conventional targets is also included. 18-gauge steel backstop, trap in base. No. 2020.

Price: $36.52

From Marksman Products distributors.

AIR RIFLE AND PISTOL TARGETS

Both one- and five-bull air rifle and one bull air pistol 10-meter (33-foot) targets are offered in 100-target packages.

Price: $4.38 (one-bull pistol); $2.96 (one-bull rifle); $5.04 (five-bull rifle).

From Outers.

AIRGUN PELLET TRAP

Can be used indoors or out. Features a snap-clip target holder and is designed to be used with pellets *only*.

Price: $13.95

From Sheridan Products.

CUSTOM AIR RIFLE PEEP SIGHTS

Specially made Williams peep sight clamps to cylinder grooves or scope ramp of air rifle, has flush adjustments for field use. Available for (specify) Weihrausch. Feinwerbau, Wischo, BSF, Diana, Hy-Score and Winchester rifles.

Price: $18.50

Similar to above, except target model with knob adjustments.

Price: $24.50.

From Air Rifle Headquarters, Beeman's.

VARIABLE POWER AIRGUN SCOPE

Features 1" tube with 32 mm objective lens; designed to focus at extreme short ranges.

Price: No. 5004, $89.95.

From Beeman's.

LIGHTWEIGHT VARIABLE POWER AIRGUN SCOPE

Compact, lightweight 3-7X scope provides excellent performance in the medium price range.

Price: No. 5003, $49.95.

From Beeman's.

2.5X AIRGUN SCOPE

A 32mm objective lens highlights this fixed power, one-inch tube, scope. Designed for optimum performance in the medium price range.

Price: No. 5002, $59.95.

From Beeman's.

1.5X AIR PISTOL SCOPE

Made especially for "Hurricane" air pistol, but can be adapted to others. Eye relief, 11-16 inches.

Price: No. 5010, $32.95.

From Beeman's.

"AUTOMATIC" AIR GUN FIRING RANGE

18-Gauge steel backplate angles pellets and BBs into base trap. Ducks fall or spin when struck; supply of heavy duty paper targets also included.

Price: No. 2040 $26.50.

From Marksman Products distributors.

AIR RIFLE ACCURIZING KIT

Set of necessary chemicals, application tools for periodic maintenance or accurization of Feinwerkbau, Weihrausch and Wischo air rifles, priced considerably below cost of individual components.

Price: Kit $16.50.

From Air Rifle Headquarters.

AIR GUN CARE KIT

Complete set of chemicals, lubricants and cleaning equipment necessary for proper air rifle or pistol maintenance, priced well below cost of individual components.

Price: $24.50

From Air Rifle Headquarters.

AIR GUN SCOPE

Four-power scope with ring mount features a turret-type sight adjustment with focusing eyepiece, image moving fixed reticles and coated optic lenses. Fits most Crosman, other make air rifles.

Price: $10.50

From Crosman Airguns distributors.

MICROMETER-ADJUST RECEIVER SIGHT

Though specifically designed for Daisy's Model 99 BB gun, the Model 5800 sight can be adapted to other air guns.

Price: Model 5800, $9.95.

From Daisy distributors.

AIR RIFLE SCOPE

4-power scope fits air rifles with grooved receivers, cross-hair reticule is adjustable for windage and elevation. No. 808, fits all grooved receivers.

Price: $11.95.

From Daisy distributors.

AIR RIFLE SCOPE SIGHT

4-Power scope has mounts to fit all grooved rifle receivers.

Price: No. 4010, $14.94.

From Marksman Products distributors.

AIRGUN SCOPE MOUNT

Designed to fit on Sheridan air rifles and will accept any scope and mount made to fit the ⅜-inch standard dovetail. Also available with Weaver D-4 scope.

Price: $8.95 for mount alone; $26.70 for above scope and mount.

From Sheridan Products.

AIR GUN REBUILDING/SPARE PARTS KITS

Complete set of key parts to rebuild or repair most spring type air guns (specify).

Price: $12.50 to $14.95.

From Air Rifle Headquarters.

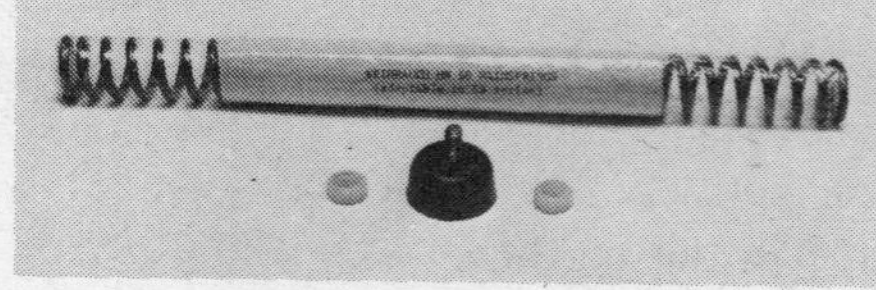

AIR GUN TRIGGER SHOE

Custom trigger shoes make for easier trigger pull, improved accuracy in both field and target work. Available to fit a wide range of air rifles and pistols.

Price: $5.95

From Air Rifle Headquarters, Beeman's.

AIRGUN REPAIR SERVICES

A wide range of airgun repair, maintenance and custom rebuilding or modification services are offered by Beeman's. Many of these services are described and priced in Beeman's catalogue—contact them regarding specific needs.

From Beeman's.

AIR GUN CLEANING PELLETS

Heavy felt cylindrical pellets expand to wipe rifling clean when fired. Can be moistened with cleaner, degreaser or light oil.

Price: No. 3860 (approximately 100 .177 pellets), 2.79; No. 3862 (approximately 80 .22 pellets), $2.79.

From Beeman's.

AIRGUN LUBRICANTS A

Beeman's carries a wide range of airgun lubricants, both liquid and dry. They also carry airgun greases, both lubricating and spring dampening. Consult Beeman's catalog for specific needs.

From Beeman's.

LUBRICANT APPLICATOR B

Four-inch hypo needle slides on spouted dispensers to permit putting lubrication where it belongs without mess or waste.

Price: No. 9110, $.99.

From Beeman's.

FLEXIBLE AIRGUN CLEANING ROD

"Roll-Up" plastic rod complete with .177 jag and brush stores in compact case.

Price: No. 9013, $6.98.

From Beeman's.

AIR GUN LUBRICANT

Special silicone formula oil is formulated for airgun seals, moving parts and pump actions.

Price: Tube, 38¢.

From Crosman Airguns distributors.

PELLET POUCHES C

Open top fabric pellet pouches designed for fast reloading. Available in brown, blue or red.

Price: $2.50; pouch belt clip, $1.50.

From Air Rifle Headquarters.

BELT POUCH

Cowhide, with soft vinyl lining and one-hand operated spring-action top, sturdy belt loop. Holds up to 1500 pellets, or use for CO² cartridges, conventional .22 or larger ammunition.

Price: No. 7290 (black) or 7291 (brown), $10.98.

From Beeman's.

AIR PISTOL HOLSTER

8-oz. top grain leather holster with smooth oil finish, designed for Daisy Model 1200 or Model 188 pistols but usable with many other air guns.

Price: Model 7200, $7.25.

From Daisy distributors.

AIRGUN HOLSTER

Designed for the Sheridan E.B. gas powered air pistol. Genuine leather with snap buttons on belt loop and safety strap.

Price: $8.95

From Sheridan Products.

AIR GUN CLEANING RODS

Stainless steel one-piece rods feature barrel bushing to protect bore, brass jag and bronze brush, adjustable rod stop; .177 caliber only.

Price: No. 9001 (rifle), $16.98; 9002 (pistol), $15.98; No. 9003 .177 jag, $.99; No. 9004 .177 brush. $1.49.

From Beeman's.

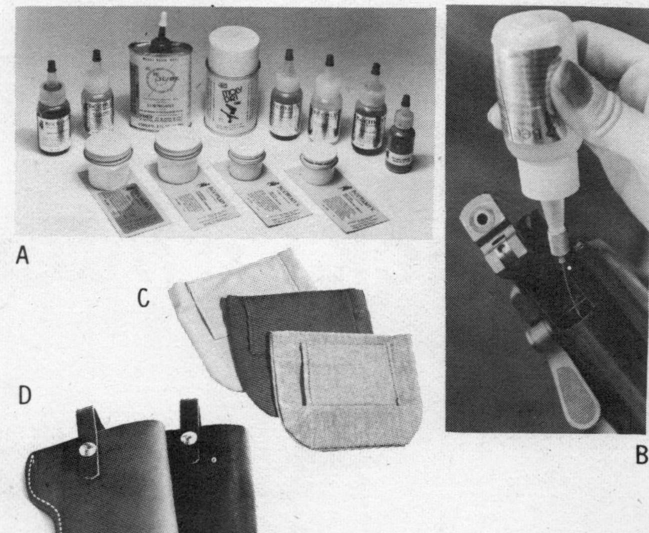

AIR PISTOL HOLSTERS D

Model FWB fits F-65 PG, F-65M, Webleys, BSA Scorpion, Walther LP-53, is made from black leather. Model D-56 fits Winchester 353 and 363, Diana 5 and 6, Hy-Score 815 and 816, GeCado, Beeman, Wischo, all BSF models, is brown leather.

Price: $12.50

From Air Rifle Headquarters.

AIR PISTOL CASES, HOLSTERS

Top-grade cowhide leather holsters for every model Crosman air pistol or revolver. Naughahyde pistol case features fur-type interior, double lockable zipper and dual carrying straps, holds any Crosman handgun except Models 1322, 1377.

Price: Any model holster, $8.25; carrying case, $7.50.

From Crosman Airguns distributors.

Section 13

Black Powder Accessories

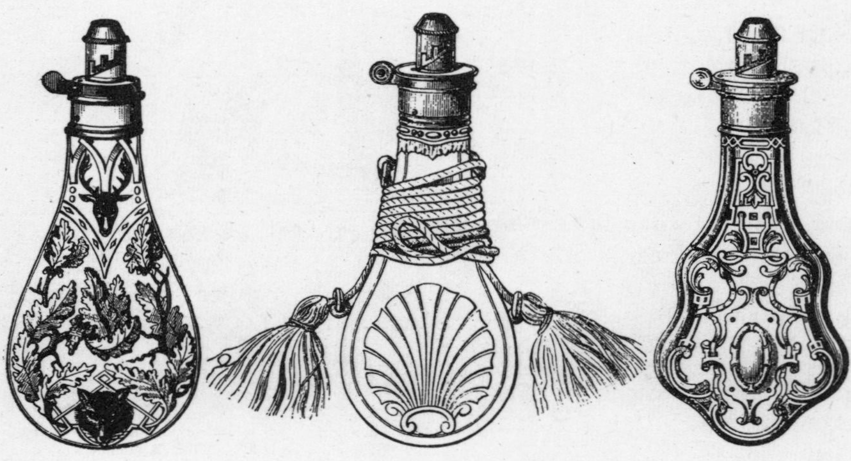

In this section you'll find practically everything needed to make black powder shooting more fun, safer and economical. Because so much of the equipment used by black powder shooters is unique to that fast growing sport, we've elected to group it all into one easy-to-refer-to section instead of adding it into the appropriate other sections pertaining to fixed ammunition accessories and shooting. This isn't to say, of course, that many of the things throughout the remainder of the *Gun Digest Book of Gun Accessories & Services* won't be valuable to the black powder enthusiant.

Black powder shooters, like their counterparts of yesteryear, are often innovators and do-it-your-selfers. For that reason we've included a fair number of custom parts suitable for upgrading, repair or even building a black powder gun from scratch. Using such items, a reasonably handy black powder shooter can usually substantially improve both the performance and appearance of his arm, especially a lower cost import.

Since cleaning is about the least agreeable and yet most necessary chore facing the black powder shooter, we've led off the section with cleaning and lubricating accessories. Next comes ammunition components and basic loading equipment, followed logically by flasks and horns. Next is bullet molds, with parts—repair and custom—closing the black powder section.

Many of the larger gunshops now maintain a black powder department, and a good deal of what we've included here is available from them. A number of black powder specialty suppliers now cater—sometimes exclusively—to black powder shooters. We strongly recommend that you get catalogs from several of these. As is the case with every item in this book, the maker listed with each item can provide that item if it is not available from other sources. When writing be sure always to include a self-addressed, stamped envelope. It's a nice courtesy that usually will greatly expedite a reply.

Prices shown are subject to change.

BLACK POWDER BORE MIRRORS

Each Borebrite mirror kit comes with five different size mirrors that allow you to readily inspect the bore of any muzzle loader. Simple to use. Instructions included.
Price: See your local dealer or write maker direct.
From The Gun House.

BLACK POWDER BORE SOLVENT

This solvent dissolves bore residue, removes and prevents rust, corrosion and leading. Comes in a 4-ounce applicator bottle.
Price: $1.98
From New Method Manufacturing Co.

LUBE KIT FOR MUZZLE LOADING RIFLES

Each kit contains bore wiping solvent, patch lube, bullet lubricator, bullet lube and an attractive shoulder patch. Available in .44, .45, .50, .54, or .58 caliber (specify).
Price: $9.95
From Gussert Bullet & Cartridge Co., Inc.

LUBE KIT FOR MUZZLE LOADING REVOLVERS

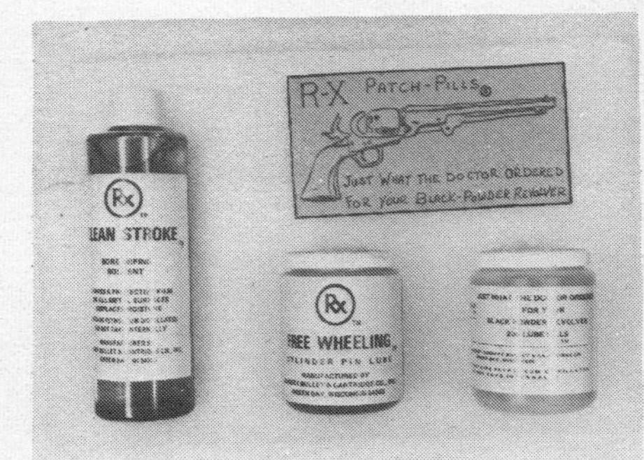

Each kit comes with bore wiping solvent, cylinder pin lube, 200 patch lube pills and an attractive shoulder patch. Comes in either .36 or .44 caliber (specify).
Price: $7.95
From Gussert Bullet & Cartridge Co., Inc.

4-PIECE BRASS CLEANING JAG

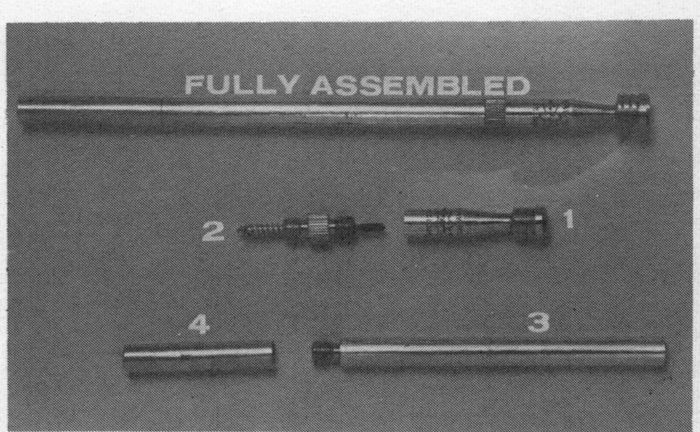

Not only does this jag serve as a patch holder, it may also be used as a "worm," or stuck-ball remover. The extension shaft and base section are threaded to accept the standard shotgun cleaning brush, while the ball removal screw may be removed and its socket is threaded to accept the standard pistol size cleaning brush. Comes in either .45, .50, .54 or .58 caliber (specify).

Components:

1. Precision machined jag tip caliber adjusted for .45, .50, .54 or .58 caliber.
2. Drill bit—for cutting screw entry hole in ball also effective patch puller. Opposite end screw tip for ball removal.
3. 4-inch extension shaft to make work rod out of ordinary ramrod.
4. Base section for attachment to ramrod.

Price: $7.50
From The Hawken Shop.

See the Directory for complete company addresses.

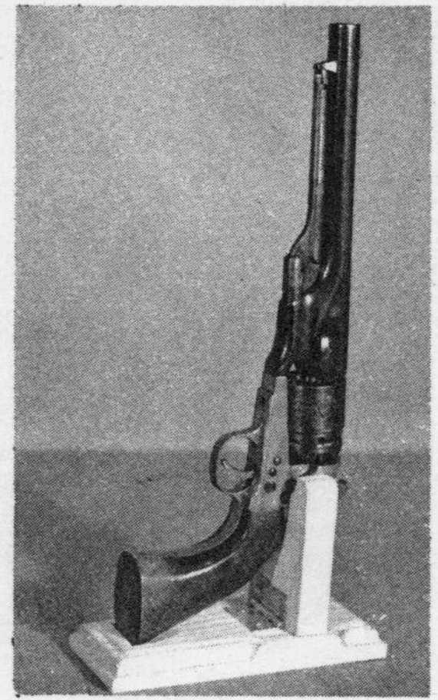

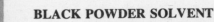

PERCUSSION REVOLVER LOADING STAND

This solid pine loading stand is designed for the .36 caliber Colt Navy; .44 caliber Colt Army (and Remington Old Army); .44 caliber Ruger (old model only) and the .31 caliber Colt Baby Dragoon. Helps simplify, speed up and make more safe the loading process for the above guns. Comes with complete instructions (specify gun when ordering).
Price: $4.25 each.
From M. Sporting Arms Co.

BLACK POWDER SOLVENT

This solvent has been especially formulated to completely dissolve black powder fouling. It also prevents rust, lubricates and may be used as a patch lube.
Price: $2
From Green River Forge, Ltd.

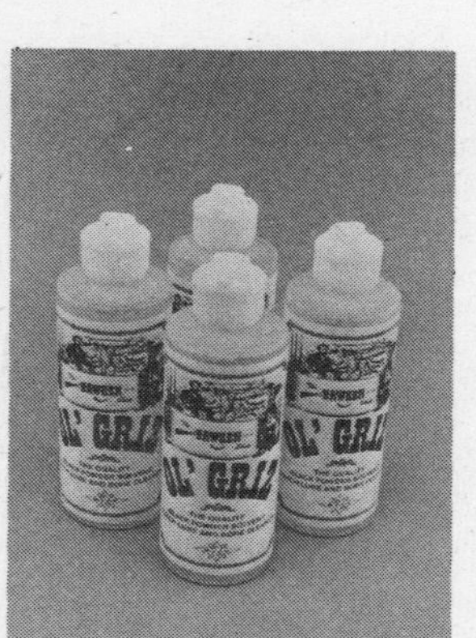

PATCH LUBE & BORE CLEANER

Ol' Griz may be used as both a patch lube and bore cleaner. Helps keep black powder from adhering to the bore. In freezing weather this solution may be cut 50 percent with alcohol to reduce the possibility of freezing and still perform well. Comes with a flip-top dispenser.
Price: $2 per 4½-ounce bottle.
From The Hawken Shop.

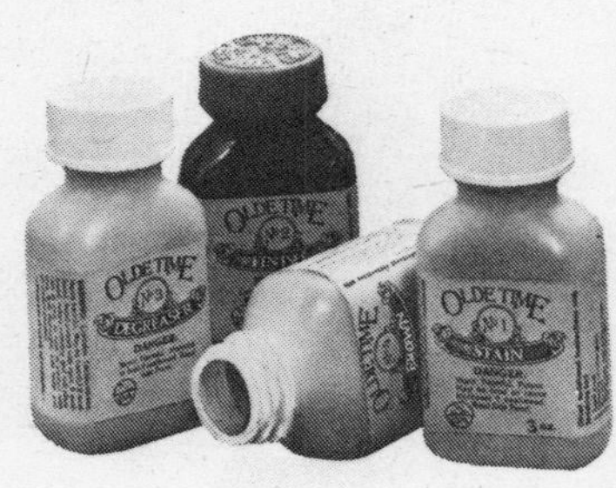

BROWN AND FINISH KIT

CVA's Olde Time Brown and Finish Kit contains enough chemicals to finish a single rifle or a number of pistols. Comes with complete instructions.
Price: $5.95
From Connecticut Valley Arms, Inc.

BARREL FLUSHER KIT

These kits are available to fit a large number of nipple thread sizes to include the Parker-Hale Enfield musket. The complete Barrel Flusher Kit consists of a special cleaning adapter that replaces the nipple, a 24-inch length of special rubber tubing, a one-ounce bottle of Bore Guard rust inhibitor concentrate, and three Rust Rag patches in sealed foil packets.
Price: $3.95 per kit.
From Michaels of Oregon.

STAINLESS RAMROD

Uncle Mike's stainless steel ramrods fit any muzzleloader. Featuring a round hardwood, removable ball handle with a knurled brass fitting, the new stainless steel ramrods are offered as a single 30-inch ramrod or in three 10-inch sections that screw together. A 10-inch extension is also available to fit either style ramrod for muzzleloaders that have a barrel more than 30 inches long. All are made of centerless ground stainless steel. These stainless steel ramrods fit all calibers, and they are tapped to accept fittings with a 10-32 thread.

Price: 1-piece $9.95; 3-piece $12.95; 10-inch extension $3.95.

From Michaels of Oregon.

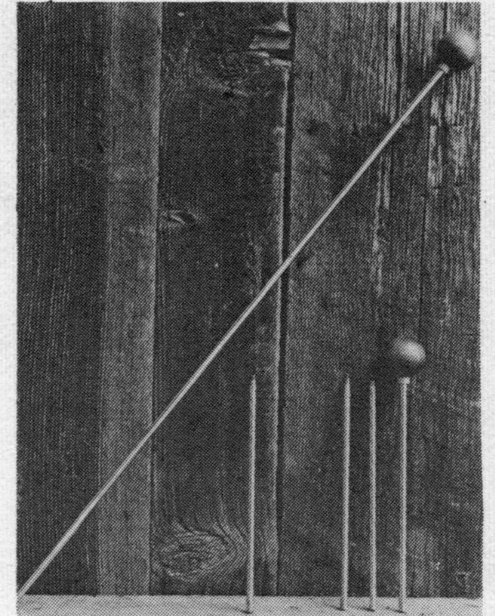

EBONY LOADING MALLET AND CLEANING ROD

These ebony accessories are made by Ken Steggles in England and are of the finest workmanship. The Pistol Loading Mallet has an overall length of 8 inches with a head diameter of 1½ inches. The face of the mallet's head is leather covered. The wood is polished, then hand rubbed for an excellent matte finish. The Pistol Cleaning Rod is 12 inches long and .480 in diameter. It is made with the same precision as the abovementioned mallet and rubbed to a matte finish. The rod is equipped with a brass tip which is threaded to accept a solid brass loading tip or a uniquely machined brass cleaning jag. The rod can be shortened by simply removing the knob, cutting to desired length and replacing the knob.

Price: Mallet $28; Rod $28.

From Dixie Gun Works, Inc.

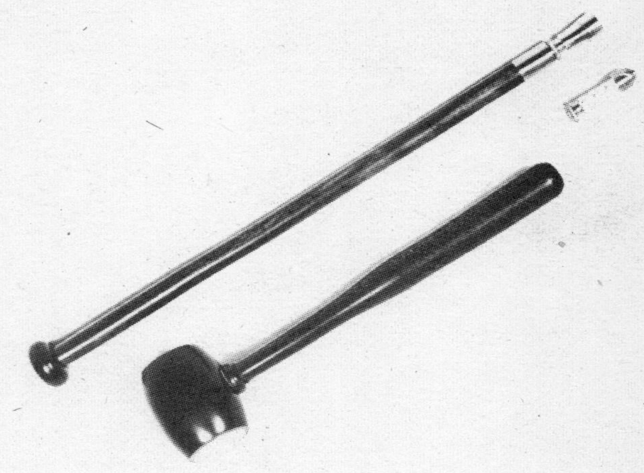

CUSTOM OIL BOTTLES

Each bottle is made by James Dixon & Sons, Sheffield, England, of Britannia metal (highest quality pewter), polished to a silver-like shine, and marked with the maker's cartouche and style number on the bottom. The bottles feature a leak proof screw on cap with oil dropper, and are available in two styles and three sizes: The two square bottles measure 2 inches high x 2 inches wide x 1¾ inches deep on the larger; and 2 inches high x 1½ inches wide x 1½ inches deep on the smaller bottle. Round bottle is 2 inches high and 1¾ inches around.

Prices: Large Square Bottle $26.95; Small Square Bottle $22.95; Round Bottle $18.95.

From Dixie Gun Works, Inc.

BULLET PATCHES

These patches come in .50 to .59 caliber size and are sold 100 to the bag. They are .010″ thick and come dry or pre-oiled.

Price: Dry $1.25; Oiled $1.50.

From Ox-Yoke Originals.

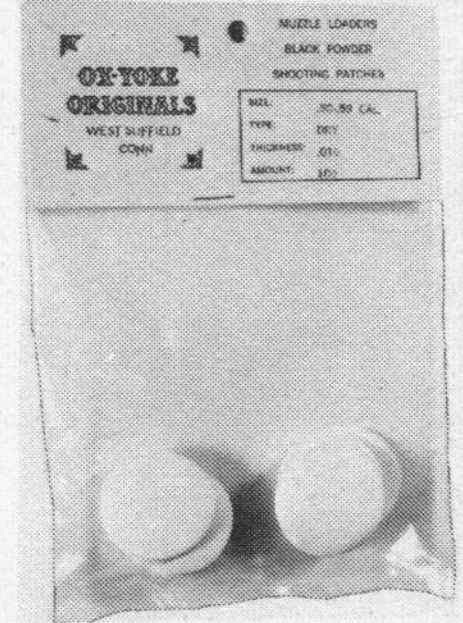

See the Directory for complete company addresses.

SEMI-WADCUTTER HANDGUN SLUGS

These projectiles come in .44, .36 and .31 calibers—from left to right in the nearby photo. Slugs are made from a special alloy and come prelubed. They feature hollow bases to help seal the bullet to the bore and avoid gas blow-by.

Prices: Not available at publication. Write maker direct or see your local dealer.

From L&W Casting Company.

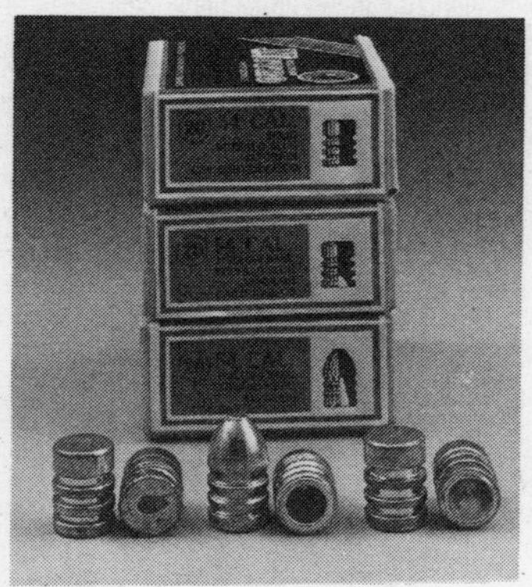

SHARPS PERCUSSION BULLETS

Each box contains 20 bullets. Available in original Sharps .54 caliber are: Solid Buffalo Slug 425-grain; Hollow Base Buffalo Slug 380-grain and Hollow Base Conical Minie 415-grain. Also available are .45 and .50 caliber bullets in Buffalo Slug Style and solid or hollow base styles.

Price: $4.50 per box of .45 or .50 caliber slugs; See your dealer for cost of .54 caliber slugs.

From The C.W. Cartridge Company.

CAP AND BALL WADS

These wads are made from high density 100% wool fabric that's been designed to safely seal percussion revolver chambers and prevent multiple discharges. The wads are impregnated with a dry lubricant making it possible to attain excellent accuracy. They come in 2 sizes: No.1 fits all .44-.45 caliber revolvers; No.2 fits all .36 caliber revolvers.

Price: $2.45 (either size).

From Ox-Yoke Originals.

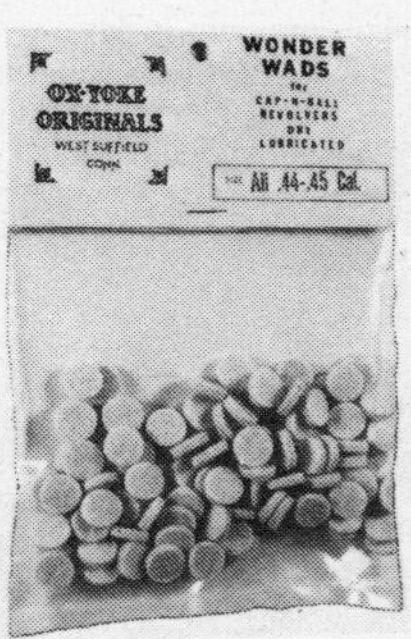

BALL/BULLET STARTER

"Uncle Mike's" new Oregon Ball/Bullet Starter for muzzleloaders protects the firearm ball or bullet and the shooter's hand as it starts a ball or bullet down the muzzle. The Oregon Ball/Bullet Starter has a shank of centerless ground stainless steel with a built-in-self-centering brass muzzle guard that prevents the steel rod from touching the muzzle and/or deforming soft lead balls and bullets. At the same time the muzzle guard assures that the rod will align perfectly on top of the ball. A brass stop beneath the wooden ball handle prevents pinching the hand between the ball starter and the muzzle guard. The Oregon Ball/Bullet Starter is available in two sizes, one to fit .44 to .50 caliber muzzleloaders, the other to fit .54 to .58 caliber guns.

Price: $5.95

From Michaels of Oregon.

PATCH LUBE

Minute Man Mini-Maxi patch lubricant is designed to reduce build-up and fouling. Also provides protection against rust and corrosion.

Price: $1.98

From New Method Manufacturing Co.

POWDER HORN

These horns come fully polished, are about 10 inches long and come fitted with a carved wooden cap and stopper.
Price: $9
From Connecticut Valley Arms, Inc.

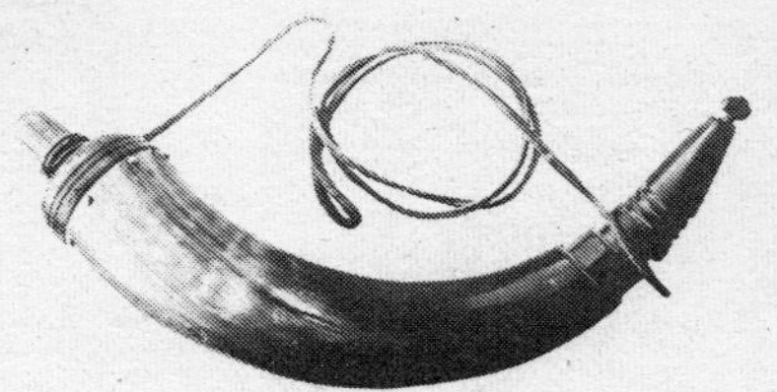

COPPER POWDER FLASK

These unique powder flasks for cased gun sets are made in England by Westley/Richards. The copper body of the flask is compartmented to accept powder, caps and balls. The brass flask head is equipped with a non-adjustable 12-grain spout, and has a small slide cover which opens to reveal the compartment for the lead balls. The capbox is made of brass and its lid is a large knurled screw which forms the bottom of the flask. The flask is available in two sizes—3 inches high x 1½ inches oval diameter x 4 inches around the body on the larger flask. The smaller one is 2⅜ inches high x 1½ inches oval diameter x 3⅜ inches around the body.
Price: $61, either size.
From Dixie Gun Works, Inc.

MOLDED LEATHER SHOT POUCH

Made of high quality russet leather in the "hot sand mold" fashion. The leather is stitched around the outside edges and filled with hot sand to expand the sides and form the shape of the flask. A hunting dog scene is embossed on the side and the flask is equipped with a brass ring at the bottom for attaching a carrying strap. The brass flask head of English style, is adjustable for 1¼ ounces of shot. The pouch could hold up to ½-pound of black powder and the head will throw 80 grains.
Price: $31
From Dixie Gun Works, Inc.

STRAIGHT LINE CAPPER

This all steel capper has a machined channel of close tolerance to keep cap from rotating within the shaft. Two standard models are available—one for Remington, Navy Arms and German No. 11 caps; one for Italian No.11 caps. Each style has a screw-off tip for complete disassembly and cleaning. (On special order this capper can be had with special narrow tip designed for use with .31 caliber Colt and some models of the Remington New Model 1858 revolvers.)
Price: $8.50; specify type desired.
From The Hawken Shop.

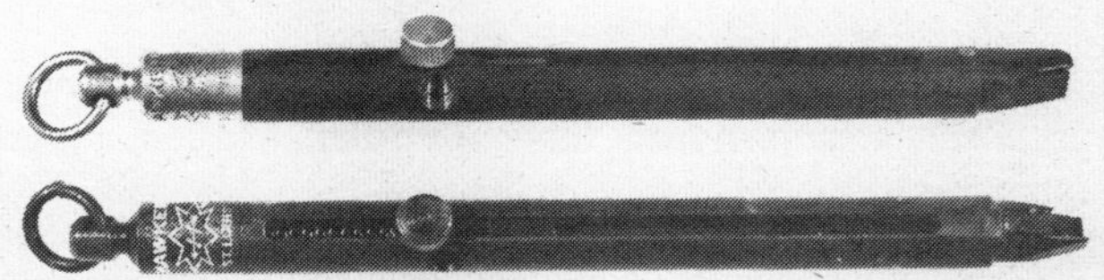

FLINTS AND AGATES

These come in bundles of 1 dozen—your choice of flint or agate—and are of medium size.
Price: Flints $3.75; Agates $5.50—both per dozen.
From the Golden Age Arms Co.

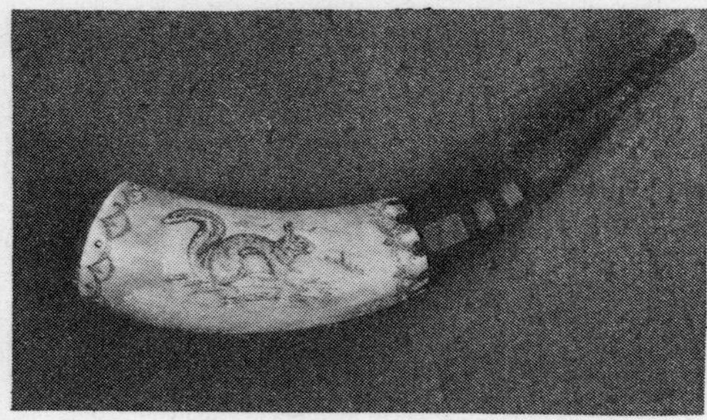

CUSTOM POWDER HORN

This hand made powder horn is strictly a custom item. It's beautifully crafted of the best materials. The horn itself was made by Michael McCormick while the scrimshaw was done by Marcia Woodzick.

Price: $100 and up; write for more information.

From Cache La Poudre Rifleworks.

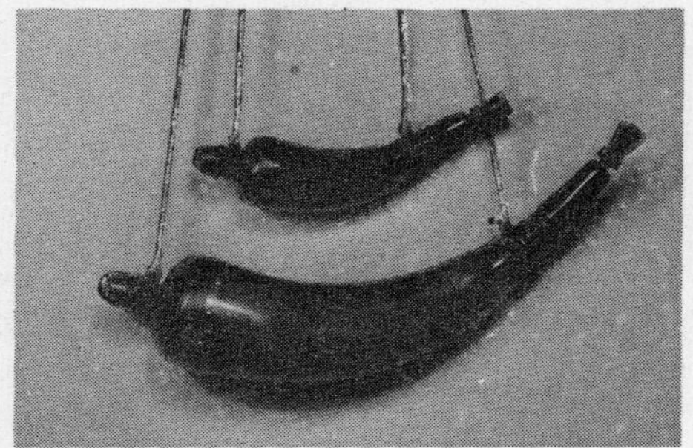

HAND CRAFTED POWDER HORNS

Shown nearby are two of Earl Cureton's powder horns. Each horn is made of quality materials. The nearby photo is of a combination matched set of horns—powder horn and priming horn.

Price: Standard Priming & Powder Horns $24.15; Deluxe $36.10—other sizes available; write maker direct.

From Earl T. Cureton

FLINTS

Green River Forge's new Forge Flints are unique in that they can provide the user with upwards of 1000 shots on one edge. They come with one or two striking edges depending upon the size ordered.

Prices: See below:

1. 2 Striking edges ¾"x¼"	$5.75
2. 1 Striking edge ¾"x¼"	5.25
3. 1 Striking edge ½"x³/₁₆"	4.25

From Green River Forge, Ltd.

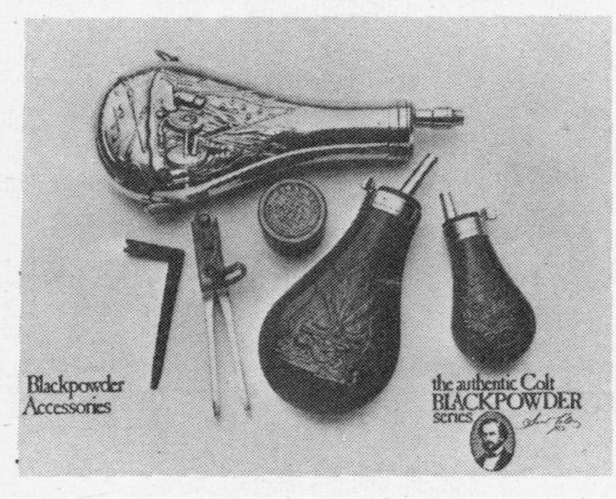

AUTHENTIC COLT ACCESSORIES

Colt recently announced a line of accessories for their black powder revolvers. Included are flasks, 2-cavity bullet molds (.36 or .44 caliber), nipple wrenches and a reproduction Ely Bros. cap box. The flasks molds and wrenches are available in appropriate sizes for the full line of Colt Black powder revolvers. Top quality accessories.

Prices: See your local dealer.

From Colt Patent Firearms (Colt Industries).

POWDER HORNS

These deluxe powder horns feature turned wood, horn and leather construction. Each horn comes with a leather strap.

Price: $14.95 each.

From D. Schneider Horns, Inc.

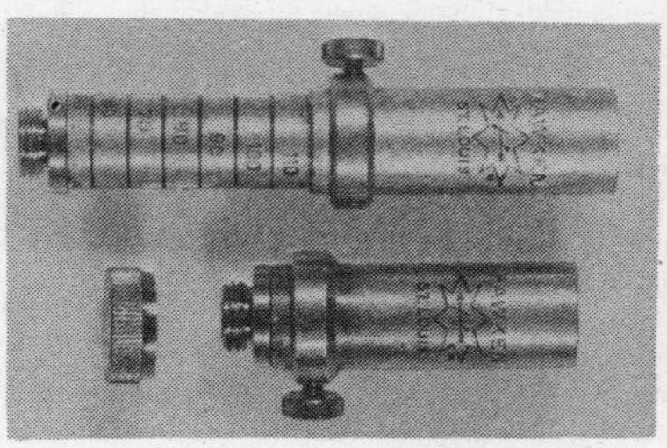

FLASK SPOUT MEASURE

Graduated from 45 to 110 grains, this solid brass spout fits any standard flask or horn. Makes loading fast, simple.

Price: $6.25

From The Hawken Shop.

PRIMING HORN SPOUT

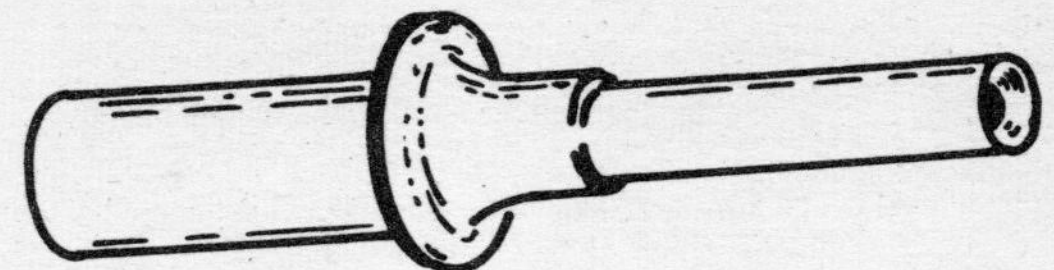

This item is designed to replace existing priming-horn spouts. It easily epoxys into place. The spout is spring loaded; and, you simply push the spout into the priming pan, lift up, and the pan is properly charged. Fast. Made of solid brass.
Price: $6
From Green River Forge, Ltd.

BLOWING HORN

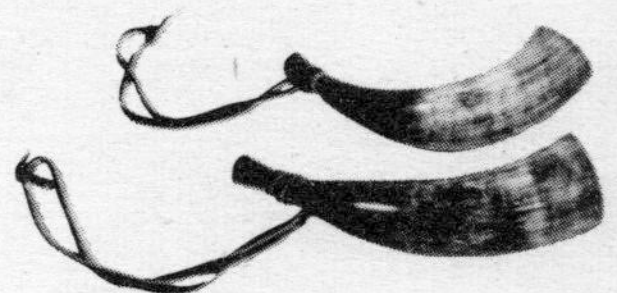

This horn is for the black powder boys who want to add a touch of authenticity to a hunt. Each horn is made of real polished steer horn and comes in lengths running from about 10 to 14 inches.
Price: $6.95 (style MBH).
From The Eutaw Company.

PRIMING HORN

This horn features a push-button valve and a pre-measured powder spout. It's fast, handy and easy to use. Comes with carrying thong.
Price: $20.95
From The Eutaw Company.

POWDER HORN KIT

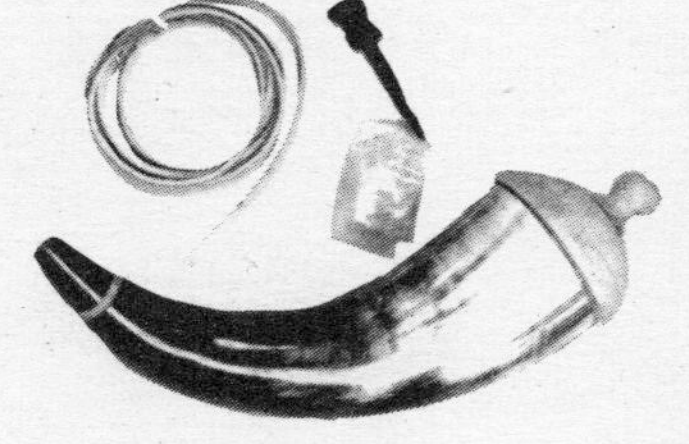

This kit comes with everything you'll need to assemble an authentic frontier-style horn. All that is needed to complete the kit is to stain the wood and assemble per directions.
Price: $9.95 (style STB-FPOS).
From The Eutaw Company.

CYLINDRICAL POWDER FLASK

This flask features a screw-off cap to facilitate loading. Its cylindrical construction enables the flask to stand upright on the shooting bench. Takes all standard spouts. For .45 and .50 calibet guns. (Specify 30- or 22-grain spout.)
Price: $6.95
From Connecticut Valley Arms, Inc.

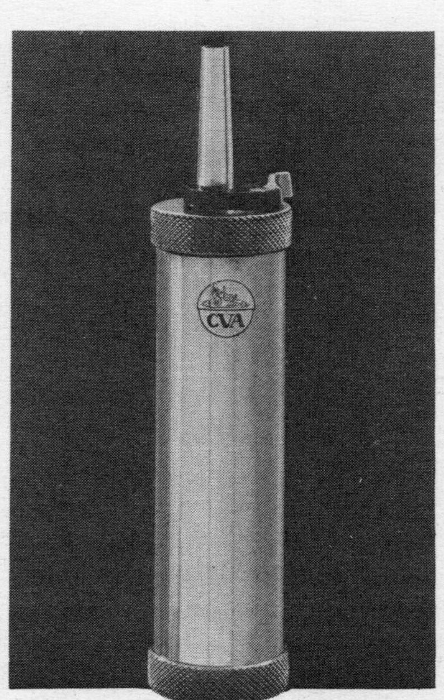

SAWED FLINTS

These are new, modern-style flints cut on lapidary saws from the finest European and American flint. Available for pistols, rifles and muskets: come three to a pack.
Price: $2
From The Eutaw Company.

KNAPPED FLINTS

These standard knapped flints are made of the best American flint. They have been knapped in the same way the frontiersmen used. Available for pistols, rifles and muskets. Come seven to the pack.
Price: $2.20
From The Eutaw Company.

See the Directory for complete company addresses.

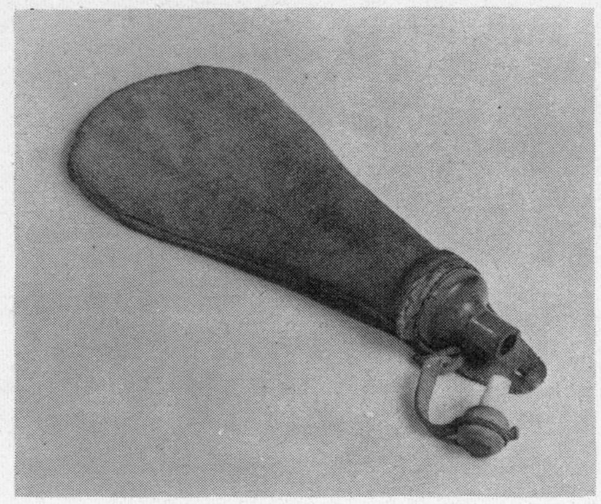

WATERPROOF SHOT AND POWDER FLASK

A waterproof suede leather flask muzzleloaders can use for either shot or powder is new from Michaels of Oregon. The traditionally buckskin-hued flask has a waterproof inner liner that keeps moisture out and powder dry. Capacity is half a pound of black powder or Pyrodex replica black powder, or an equal volume of shot. There are no metal parts to rust or corrode. The tip is hardwood, and a wooden peg covers the opening, which is sized to fit "Uncle Mike's" graduated powder measure. The peg is attached to the flask by a leather thong, and the flask has a leather belt loop.
Price: $10.95
From Michaels of Oregon.

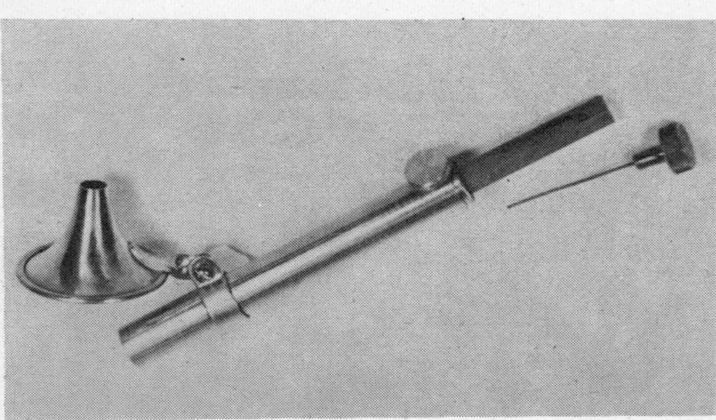

ADJUSTABLE POWDER MEASURE WITH FUNNEL

This brass powder measure will enable you to quickly select any granulation of black powder or Pyrodex from 5 to 135 grains, in 5-grain increments. The funnel is attached so that it will swivel and will fit any size barrel. By unscrewing the knurled nut at the base of the measuring staff, you will find attached a pick of fine spring wire. Use this pick to clean clogged nipples and flintlock vents. (Wipe pick and oil it occasionally, to keep it in good condition.) Order number on the measure is B14-4-2.
Price: $7.50 (postpaid).
From Dixie Gun Works, Inc.

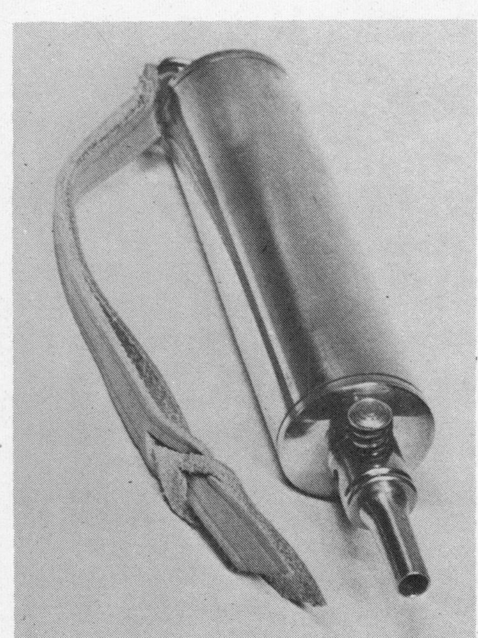

BRASS CYLINDER POWDER FLASK

The flask is made of solid brass and shaped into a perfect cylinder. It has a lanyard ring permanently attached to the bottom of the flask and a 9-inch piece of leather braided into place for attaching to your belt, possibles pouch, etc. The head is the push and release type, which is completely removable for ease in filling the flask. The head is equipped with a 12-grain spout, but other sizes are available. The body is 5⅛ inches high x 1⅜ inches diameter x 4½ inches around.
Price: $8.95
From Dixie Gun Works, Inc.

MUZZLE LOADING PARTS & ACCOUTREMENTS LISTING

If you're in need of specific parts for your own black powder firearms, we suggest you contact the firm below. They supply both antique and modern parts.
Price: Free listing.
From Muzzleloaders Etcetera, Inc.

STRAIGHT-LINE CAPPER

This particular capper is designed for use with No. 11 caps. Its design keeps the caps in a straight line, ready for use, when you need one. Made of shined solid brass.
Price: See your local dealer or write maker direct.
From Lakeview Gun Shop.

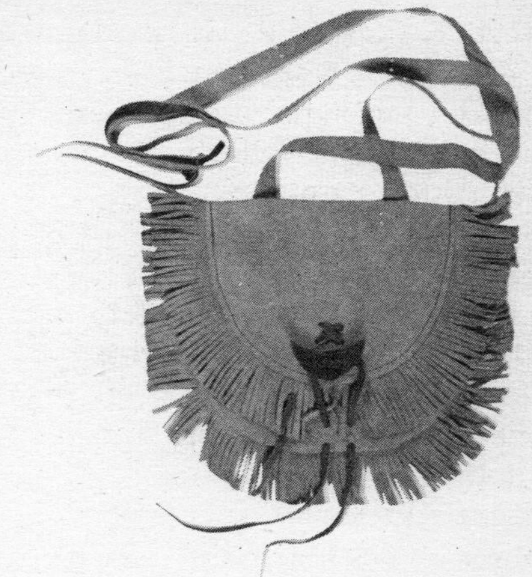

POSSIBLES BAG

Made of quality suede this possibles bag has a fully adjustable shoulder strap. Features leather fringe and flap front.
Price: $12.95 (style STB-FPOS).
From The Eutaw Company.

.36 CALIBER ROUND BALL/BULLET MOLD

This all brass 2-cavity mold casts a .375 diameter ball and bullet for all .36-caliber guns.
Price: $11.99
From Hopkins & Allen.

PATCHES

These large-bore patches are 1¾ inches in diameter and are designed for bores over .45 caliber.
Price: $.99 per package.
From Hopkins & Allen.

RUSSET LEATHER HAVERSACK

This item is well made of the best quality leather. It's ideal for the black powder shooter who's got some gear to haul.
Price: $65.62
From Ordinance Park Corp.

.44/.45 CALIBER ROUND BALL MOLD

Comes complete with wood handles. This mold is of the double-cavity type and casts two .437 caliber balls for .44 or .45 caliber guns.
Price: $12.99
From Hopkins & Allen.

NITRATED PAPER

These papers are made for the black powder shooter who wants to "roll his own." Come in .45, .50, or .54 caliber sizes; 100 sheets to the pack.
Price: $4.50 per pack.
From C.W. Cartridge Company.

FORMING DOWEL

Black powder shooters who make up their own paper loads will find these dowels more than handy. They come in .45, .50 or .54 caliber.
Price: $4.50 per dowel.
From C.W. Cartridge Company.

POSSIBLES BAG

Made of the best suede leather, this bag is fully fringed, comes with a leather shoulder strap. Holds a little bit of everything the black powder shooter may want to carry afield.
Price: $12.95 (style STB-FPOS).
From The Eutaw Company.

See the Directory for complete company addresses.

BLACK POWDER ACCESSORY KIT

Each kit comes generously stocked with a deluxe powder measure, straight line capper, deluxe nipple wrench and the following items:

100 cotton Patches
Stainless steel nipples
Flints
Lead Flint Covers for Safety
Deluxe Wooden Ball Starter
Wire Brush
Fiber Brush
Cloth Brush
Muzzle Protector
Stuck Bullet Jag
Patch Puller Worm
Slotted Patch Jag
Cleaning Jag
Ball Starter Jag
Complete 3-piece-cleaning rod

These kits are available for .44, .45, .50 and .54 caliber black powder guns. For .58 caliber guns, the kit comes with a musket patch puller, worm, stuck-ball jag and straight line musket cap loader. Available for either flint or percussion guns.

Price: .44, .45 or .50 $42.50; .54 $47; .58 $52.

From Armsport, Inc.

NITRO PAPER CARTRIDGE FORMING KIT

Each kit contains 200 precut, nitrated paper sheets, easy to use cartridge adhesive stick and 7-inch plastic forming dowel. Specifically made for .45, .50 and .54 caliber cartridges. (Specify caliber when purchasing.)

Price: $12.50 per kit; Refill pack of 500 nitrated papers and 2 cartridge adhesive sticks $20.

From C.W. Cartridge Company.

SHARPS COMBUSTIBLE CARTRIDGES

These nitrated paper cartridges are available in .54 caliber with 425-grain Buffalo Slug (solid); 380-grain Buffalo Slug (hollow base) and 415-grain Conical Minie (hollow base). Come lubed, sized, 10 to the box. Each cartridge has charge capacity line.

Price: Buffalo Slug (solid) $7; others $6.50 — all prices per 10-round box.

From C.W. Cartridge Company.

DELUXE SHOOTER'S KIT

CVA's Deluxe Shooter's Kit contains everything you'll need but the black powder. Comes with Grease Patch lube, patches, caps and capper (or flints), powder measure, brass tubular flask and a 120-page book on black powder shooting. Comes in .45 or .50 caliber percussion or flint and .54 or .58 caliber percussion.

Price: $21.95

From Connecticut Valley Arms, Inc.

BULLET SEATER

Lakeview Gun Shop's bullet seater is a tool specifically used to start tight fitting balls into the barrel of a muzzleloader. This sturdy bullet seater is made of fine hardwood and brass.

Price: See your local dealer or write maker direct.

From Lakeview Gun Shop.

ROUND AND CONICAL BALL BULLET MOLDS

Made by Armsport these molds are made of the best materials. They are available in .44, .45, .50, .54 and .58 calibers. The .44, .45 and .50 caliber molds come in round ball only; the .54 and .58 caliber molds come in conical ball. Hardwood handles.

Price: .44, .45, and .50 $14.95; .54 and .58 $19.95.

From Armsport, Inc.

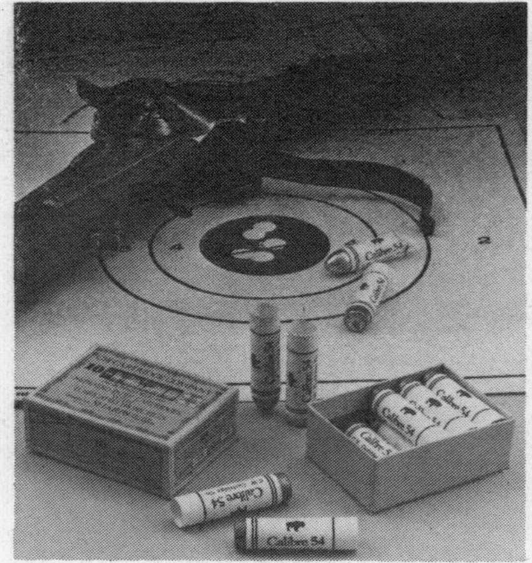

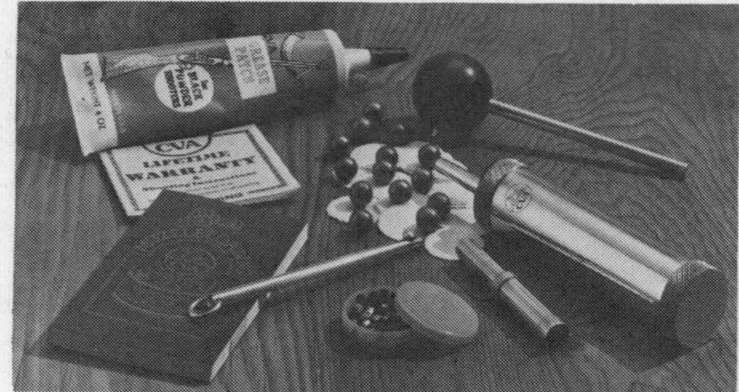

PARTS CATALOG FOR MUZZLE LOADING FIREARMS

The Upper Missouri Trading Company has a catalog that's loaded with parts, kits, and other goodies for just about every popular black powder firearm. We suggest you write for more information.

Prices: Write for catalog.

From Upper Missouri Trading Company.

Prices shown are subject to change.

STAINLESS STEEL NIPPLE FOR PARKER-HALE 1861 ENFIELD MUSKET

This nipple is made of heat-treated stainless. You get less burn out and longer life; plus, they reduce flashback and mushrooming.
Price: $1.25 each
From Michaels of Oregon.

HOT SHOT NIPPLES

These nipples were designed by the late Dan Pawlak, the inventor of Pyrodex. The nipple delivers consistent results with either Pyrodex or black powder. Prevents hammer blowback as well; and, laboratory tests have found that these nipples give more consistent muzzle velocity and better accuracy.
Price: $1.95 each
From Michaels of Oregon.

CUSTOM MUZZLE LOADING RIFLES & PISTOLS

Cache La Poudre Rifleworks is a small shop that prides itself on turning out custom black powder Hawkens, Trade guns, and Trappers. Prices can range from about $225 on up to what the customer is willing to pay for "extras." Shown nearby are some examples of this outfit's work. We sincerely suggest that you write the maker direct for more information.
Prices: Write maker direct.
From Cache La Poudre Rifleworks.

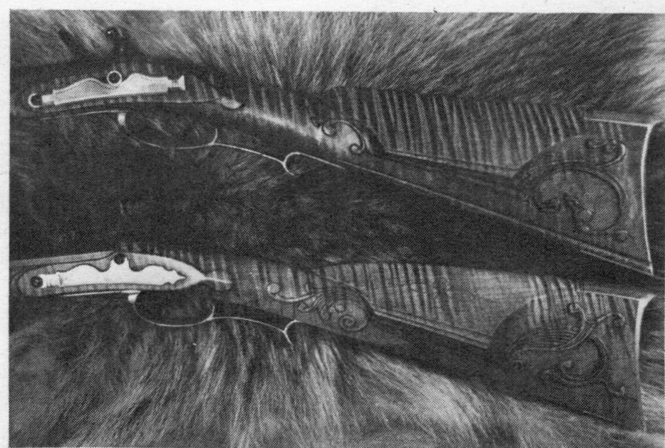

HAWKEN RIFLE SET TRIGGER ASSEMBLY

The Hawken Shop of St. Louis is offering a set trigger assembly for Hawken-type rifles. Shown nearby (No. 1) is an original Hawken trigger unit with the new one (No. 2) pictured just below. The triggers themselves have been hand fitted and hardened to resist wear. Overall length is 9 inches, height, 2½ inches.
Price: $47.50
From The Hawken Shop.

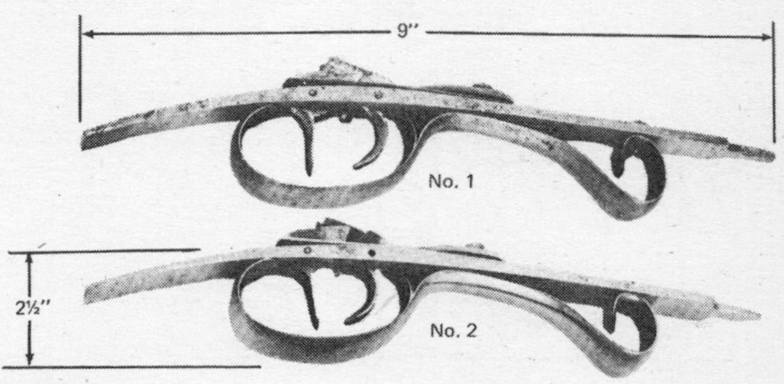

PERCUSSION LOCK

Reasonably priced, and well made in a post-1820 style. It features leaf springs made of the best tool steel.
Price: $19.50
From C.E. Siler.

MUZZLE LOADING PARTS CATALOG

This catalog contains 33 cutaway views of percussion and early cartridge Colts, Remingtons, Starrs, Derringers and other flint and percussion martial pistols. Comes with detailed list of parts and prices for flint and percussion firearms.
Price: $4.50
From C.H. Weisz.

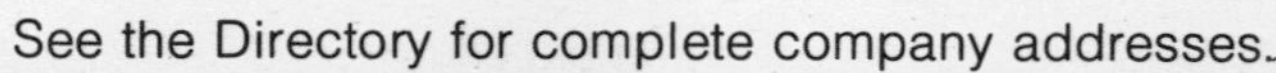

See the Directory for complete company addresses.

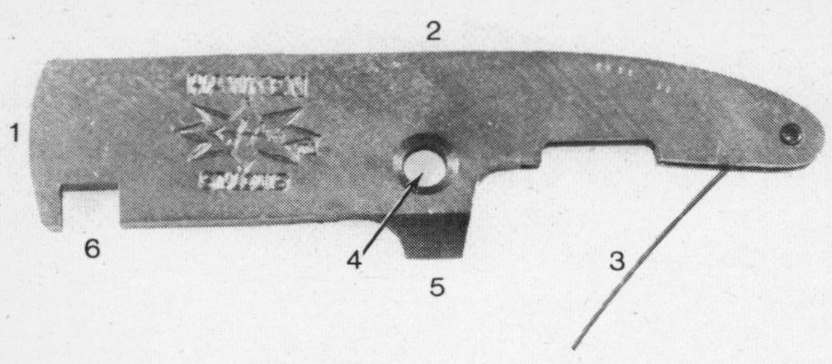

HAWKEN-TYPE BUTT PLATE

This one-piece annealed cast steel butt plate is of authentic and accurate styling. It reflects the style used on middle and late period S. Hawken rifles. Pre-shaped to correct contour, the butt plate is virtually ready to install. Original screw holes marked on inside of butt plate but not drilled.
Price: $9.50
From The Hawken Shop.

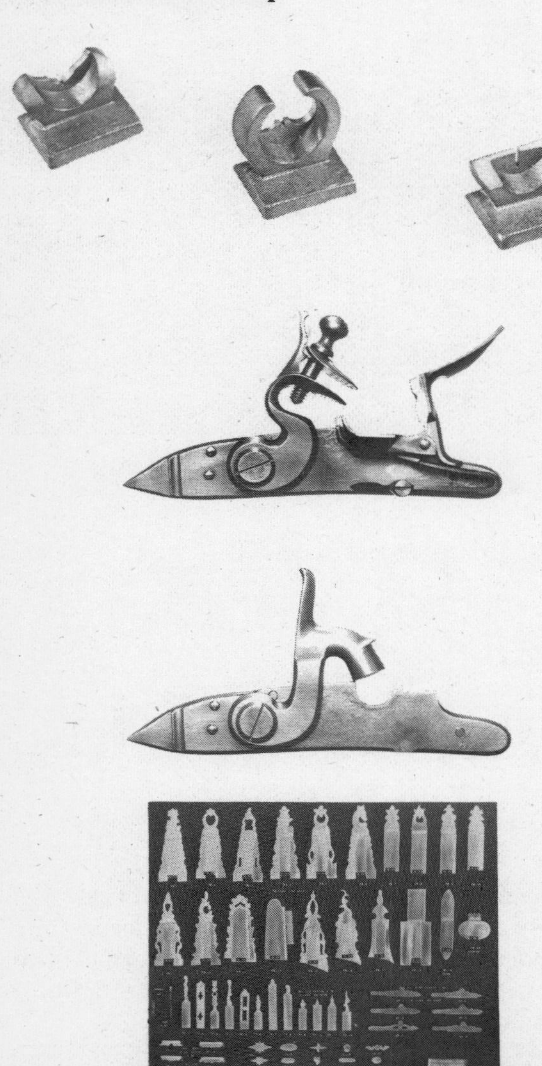

FLINTER'S TOOL

This unique 6-in-1 tool was specifically designed for the shooter of flintlock guns. The face surface (1) may be used to "knap" the gun's flint and even the striking edge for better sparking. The long backside (2) of this tempered, high carbon tool has been specially prepared to throw a shower of sparks for fire starting competition. A touch hole pick (3) has been fitted in the rear section, ready to fold out and use. (4) A hole has been drilled for inserting leather thong making the tool easier to hold when acting as flint and steel fire starter. A durable screwdriver (5) is always a handy item to have, and the ¼″ cut (6) in the front lower section (which may be enlarged if necessary) may be slipped over a tensed mainspring to hold it for easy removal and lock repair.
Price: $9.95
From The Hawken Shop.

HAWKEN-TYPE REAR SIGHTS

Here are just a few of the Hawken-type rear sights available from the Hawken Shop. When ordering be sure to specify style. From left to right in the nearby photo are semi-buckhorn, full buckhorn and flat-top sights.
Price: $4.75 each.
From The Hawken Shop.

FLINT LOCK

This Siler flint lock measures 5¼ inches long by 1 inch high. The style is from America's revolutionary period. Leaf springs are made of the best tool steel.
Price: $32
From C.E. Siler.

PERCUSSION LOCK

This particular Siler lock was patterned after the converted flint-style locks that were so prevalent in the last century. The leaf springs are made of the best tool steel.
Price: $19.50
From C.E. Siler.

PATCH BOXES, SIDE PLATES & TOE PLATES

The Hawken Shop's selection of these items—as can be seen nearby—is extensive. We suggest you write them direct for a complete listing of available items and prices.
Prices: Write company direct.
From The Hawken Shop.

MUZZLE LOADING ACCESSORIES

Richland Arms company offers a wide selection of quality accessories for the black powder shooter. Shown nearby is a photo with each item numbered in accordance with the prices and descriptions listed below.

Prices: See Below:

1.	Nicky Hard Leather Shot Flask—English	$33.00
2.	Kentucky-Michigan Rifle Wood Handle Nipple Wrench	3.40
3.	Nicky Hard Leather Shot Flask—Irish	33.00
4.	Straight Line Capper	4.00
5.	Nicky Powder Measure with funnel	8.00
6.	Nicky Powder Measure	5.00
7.	Adjustable Powder Measure—50 to 110 grains	3.50
8.	Colt Brass Circular Capper	12.50
9.	Cleaning Kits .45 or .58 caliber Wood Box	14.00
10.	Mainspring Vise	4.50
11.	Bullet Mold, Wood Handle .44 or .36 caliber pistol	10.00
12.	Bullet Mold, Wood Handle .45 or .50 caliber rifle	10.00

From Richland Arms Company.

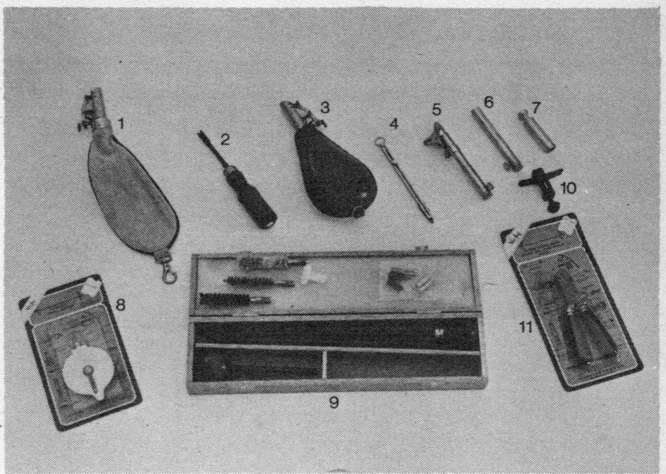

POSSIBLES BAG

Green River Forge calls this offering the "Wilderness Trail Bag." It's made of full-grain cowhide that's been oil tanned. Features a wide 2-inch carrying strap and a special bullet starter compartment.

Price: $26.50

From Green River Forge, Ltd.

PATCH KNIFE

This Green River Forge patch knife may also be used for hunting purposes. Each knife is made by W.L. Goddard and comes serial numbered and dated by the maker. Blade is made of Swedish high carbon tool steel, is 4-inches long and ⅛-inch wide. Has stag slab handles.

Price: Knife $43; Sheath $12.95.

From Green River Forge, Ltd.

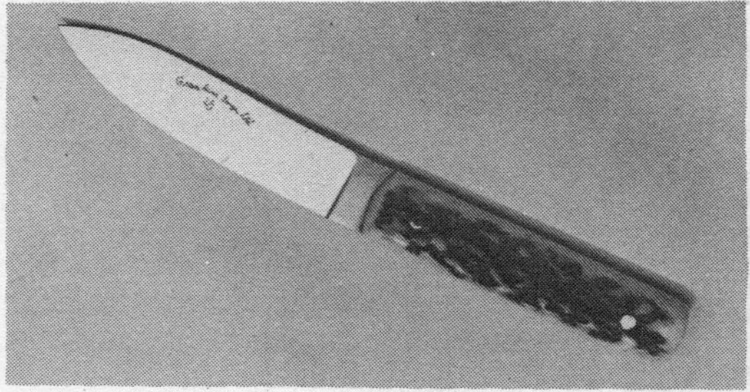

BALL BAG

This suede leather bag features a large round bottom and draw-thong closure. It holds a good supply of round-ball or conical-ball slugs.

Price: $3.75

From The Eutaw Company.

CANNON FUSE

Water resistant. Packed in 15-foot lengths. May be trimmed to desired length. Perfect for all black powder cannons.

Price: $1.75 per 15-foot coil.

From Connecticut Valley Arms, Inc.

NIPPLE WRENCH

This item is used for the removal of nipples for cleaning or replacement. It's made of hardened tool steel and will not break under normal use.

Price: See your local dealer or write maker direct.

From Lakeview Gun Shop.

MUZZLE LOADER PARTS DIGEST

Contains detailed schematic drawings of the entire CVA line of firearms. Has a comprehensive list of parts and prices.

Price: $1

From Connecticut Valley Arms, Inc.

REVOLVER PRESENTATION CASES

The wooden cases are for Colt and Remington Army or Navy models and feature a hand rubbed oil finish and compartments for powder flask, nipple wrench, mould, caps and balls. They are carefully lined with velvet in assorted colors; and the corners, edges, hinges, locks, joints and partitions are well fitted. Locks and hinges are brass and they have pierced brass keys. Dimensions of these cases are 15x7x1½ inches. Although designed for muzzleloading revolvers, because of the compartment for the powder flask, the Colt Single Action Army with 7½-inch barrel will fit perfectly into this case.

Price: Deluxe $38.50; Standard $18.50.

From Dixie Gun Works, Inc.

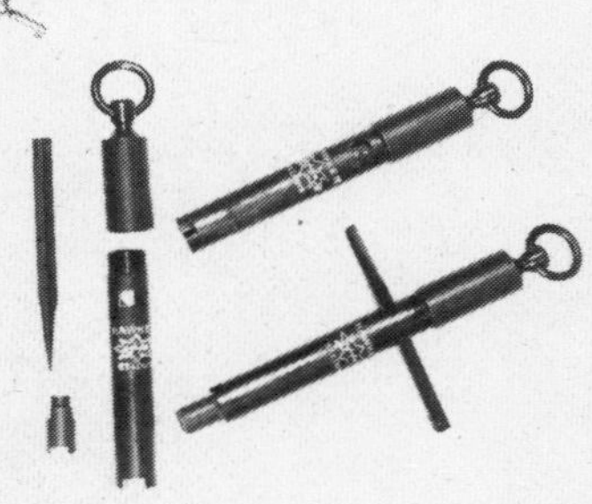

NIPPLE WRENCH

The Hawken Shop's combination nipple wrench tool features a hollow body in which a screwdriver/nipple-pick bar is stored. Pick may be inserted in the wrench, at right angles, as shown nearby. The screw-off cap section contains an adapter for use on pistol nipples of cap and ball revolver.

Price: $7.50

From The Hawken Shop.

MUZZLE LOADERS HANDBOOK

CVA's *Start Muzzleloading* handbook contains a wealth of information for the novice black powder shooter. Contains detailed loading, shooting, cleaning and safety instruction.

Price: $1.95

From Connecticut Valley Arms, Inc.

HAWKEN PARTS CATALOG

This 40-page illustrated catalog features authentic Hawkens Plains Rifle components as directly copied from the original guns in this firm's private collection. For the black powder shooter who has a preference for Hawken rifles, we would suggest you consider their catalog.

Price: $2

From The Hawken Shop.

STANDARD POWDER MEASURE

This measure is made of shined, solid brass. It accurately measures out from 10 to 120 grains of black powder.

Price: See your local dealer or write maker direct.

From Lakeview Gun Shop.

BLACK POWDER MEASURE

Lakeview Gun Shop's Deluxe Powder Measure is made of solid brass. Comes complete with funnel that swivels to cut off charge. Measures from 10 to 120 grains of black powder.

Price: See your dealer or write maker direct.

From Lakeview Gun Shop.

CUSTOM BARRELS

Mr. W.M. Large, of the JJJJ Ranch, Gun and Machine Shop advises us he intends to make barrels until he is, "100 years young." Mr. Large offers but one line of products: Match grade muzzleloader barrels.

Prices: We suggest you write maker direct for both prices and delivery schedule.

From The JJJJ Ranch, Gun & Machine Shop.

Prices shown are subject to change.

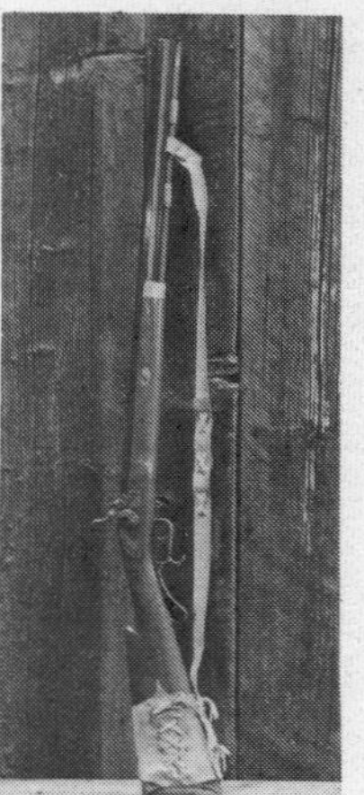

MUZZLE LOADER SLING

Michaels of Oregon calls this item their "Slinger." It needs no hardware for installation. Fashioned of buckskin-hued suede leather, the Slinger, a swiveless muzzleloader carrying system, has a boot that laces over the gun stock. The other end slips over the ramrod. Strap length is adjustable, utilizing traditional leather thong laces. There are no metal parts, either on the Slinger or attached to the muzzleloader. In addition to serving as a carry strap, the Slinger provides protection for the butt of a fine antique or replica firearm. It is easily removable, but can be left on during shooting if desired.
Price: $9.95
From Michaels of Oregon.

CARTRIDGE BOX, BLOCK AND TIN

This well made item features an embossed eagle and U.S., marking on the front flap. Made of top quality leather. Block is .69 caliber.
Price: $35
From Ordinance Park Corp.

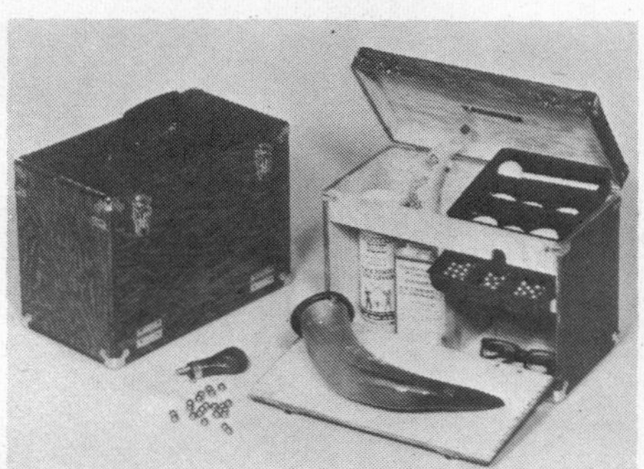

MUZZLE LOADER'S CARRY ALL

Gun Ho's "Muzzle Loader Kit" comes with handy drop-in and slide-out trays that hold everything from conical balls to caps. All corners on this solid wood box are metal covered. Hinges are quality made and allow for easy, stress-free opening.
Price: $44
From Gun-Ho Sport Cases & Equipment Mfrs.

FLINTS

CVA's flints come packaged by the pair and are specifically knapped for all CVA flintlocks.
Price: $2.25
From Connecticut Valley Arms, Inc.

POSSIBLES BAG

This large suede leather possibles bag comes complete with shoulder strap—brown color. Holds all of those items a black powder shooter may need in a hurry.
Price: $9.99
From Hopkins & Allen.

CUSTOM FLINT & PERCUSSION LOCKS & ACCESSORIES

William Roberts, II, specializes in both custom guns and accessories. All of the accessories listed below are produced by the maker.
Prices: See below

Dixon small style pewter bottles	$20
British-style screwdriver	20
British-style nipple wrench	20
Platinum-lined nipples	16
Joseph Braziier percussion locks (in the white, not carved)	350

(Note: Roberts also makes custom front and rear sights for muzzleloaders. We suggest you write the maker direct for more information on his complete line of custom accessories.)
From William A. Roberts, II.

See the Directory for complete company addresses.

POWDER HORN

Each horn is individually hand formed and polished to a high sheen, and features a brass tip measure which is the push and release type. It has a turned wooden plug in the leather covered butt that can be removed for easy filling. Overall length is approximately 10 inches. Comes with a 36-grain non-adjustable spout, but other sizes are available.
Price: $10.95
From Dixie Gun Works, Inc.

CUSTOM POWDER HORN

The Bydoc custom powder horn shown is hand made from elk antler and German silver. The scrimshaw work was personally done by Glen Stearns. Prices can vary for this horn depending upon the amount of scrimshaw desired.
Price: Start at about $125; write for more information.
From Ladow Johnston, Bydoc, Inc.

MUZZLE LOADING FLASKS, SPOUTS & HORNS

Richland Arms Company offers a wide selection of quality accessories for the black powder shooter. The nearby photo shows some of those accessories; and, the numbers alongside of each item correspond to the descriptions and prices below.
Prices: See Below:

1.	Ideal Circular Brass Flask—3 spouts	$14.00
2.	Flat Horn—36-grain spout	17.00
3.	Powder Horn—70-grain spout	22.00
4.	Bag Flask—12 gr.	7.00
5.	Diamond Flasks	10.75
6.	Walker Powder Flasks	13.00
7.	Zouave Powder Flasks	10.75
8.	Pocket Baby Flasks	7.00
9.	Florentine Flask—Silver	10.00
10.	Remington Powder Flasks	7.75
11.	Colt Army Powder Flasks	9.00

From Richland Arms Company.

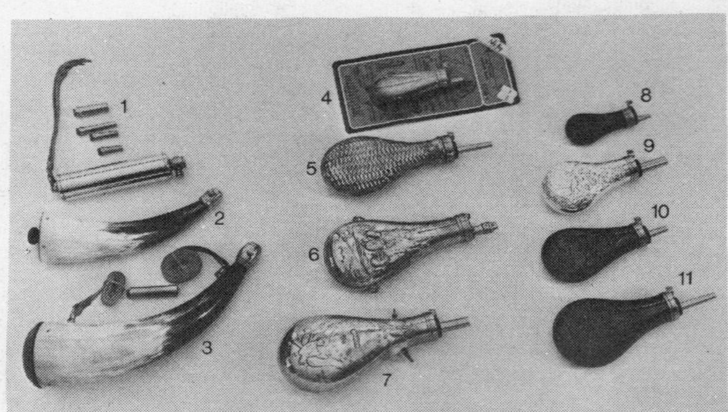

MUZZLE GUARD

This is a new improved muzzle guard that accurately centers a ramrod in most caliber muzzleloaders to protect the crown and muzzle from wear and lead ball or bullet from loading damage. The tapered lower tip of the new style muzzle guard is self-centering in any bore from .36 to .62 caliber. The edge is knurled for a secure grip.
Price: $1.50
From Michaels of Oregon.

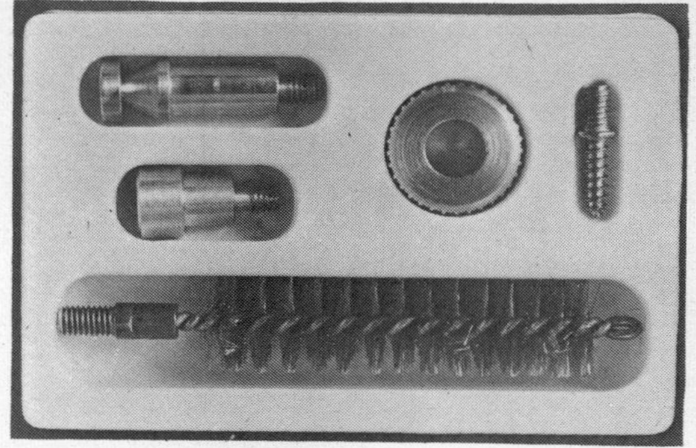

RAMROD ESSENTIALS

Parts are packaged in a fitted plastic tray. Parts include a "Barrel Scrubber" phosphorous bronze cleaning brush, a combination ramrod tip that is a ball seater, accepts a patch/ball puller worm and allows for adaption of rod for different attachments. Also included, a new style muzzle guard and a brass cleaning jag. All parts are threaded 10-32 to fit "Uncle Mike's" ramrods. Four different sets are offered to fit .45, .50, .54, or .58 caliber muzzleloaders.

Price: $5.95

From Michaels of Oregon.

CANNON SHOOTERS KIT

CVA's Cannon Shooter's Kit comes with everything but the black powder. It contains lube, .69 caliber balls, flask and fuze.

Price: $16.95

From Connecticut Valley Arms, Inc.

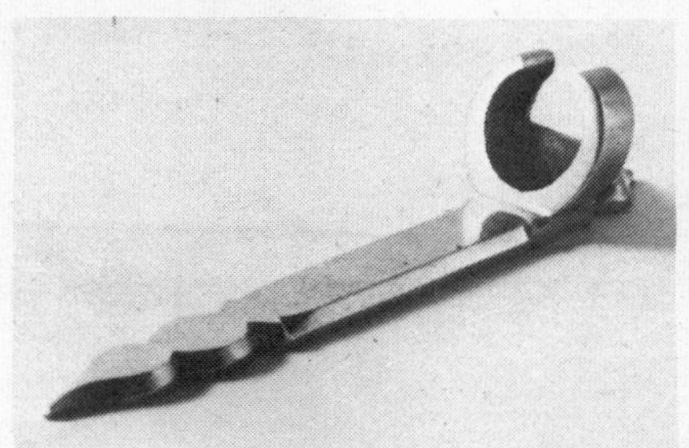

T-C REPLACEMENT SIGHT

This rear sight unit consists of a Hawken-type rear sight mounted on a rear base. The whole unit enables Thompson Center rifles (and other similar guns) to adopt this item by merely drilling the long base to correspond to the holes in the barrels.

Price: $8.50

From The Hawken Shop.

MUZZLE LOADING SUPPLIES CATALOG

If you are in need of special black powder parts or tools, you might want to check out Golden Age Arms Company's current No.11 catalog. This 178-page catalog covers the black powder parts field quite nicely.

Price: $2

From Golden Age Arms Co.

TRIGGER GUARDS

Lakeview Gun Shop offers a *wide* selection of trigger guards for both percussion and flintlock firearms. Most are made of brass; and, again, we emphasize this outfit's wide selection. We suggest you write them direct for more information.

Price: Write maker direct.

From Lakeview Gun Shop.

SPECIAL BLACK POWDER SERVICE

Marshall F. Fish offers repair work on all muzzle loading firearms. He also offers a special lapping and slugging of muzzle loading barrels to insure the best accuracy.

Price: Write gunsmith direct for more information and price quotes.

From Marshall R. Fish, Gunsmith.

MUZZLE LOADING FIREARMS PARTS CATALOG

Patch Box Arms offers an extremely wide selection of just about all muzzle loading firearms parts. These include locks and related parts, barrels, triggers, bands—everything.

Price: Write direct for catalog.

From Patch Box Arms.

See the Directory for complete company addresses.

POWDER HORN

The horn features a measuring device, with a 65-grain non-adjustable spout, which is the push and release type. Other spouts are available. It has a turned wooden base plug which is threaded and can be removed for easy filling of the horn. Two brass lanyard rings are attached to the body of the horn for your rawhide thong. Length is approximately 12 inches and colors vary.
Price: $15
From Dixie Gun Works, Inc.

COLT-TYPE FLASK

This is a traditional flask with a body of formed copper and a cap of polished brass. Spout throws approximately 30 grains black powder. For all .45 or .50 caliber guns.
Price: $9.95
From Connecticut Valley Arms, Inc.

STRAIGHT-LINE CAPPER

This is Uncle Mike's straight-line capper. It holds 20 or more No. 10 or No. 11 Remington caps, No. 11 CCI caps or foreign-made caps. It's made of solid brass and comes with lanyard loop. Makes loading caps a one-hand operation.
Price: $9.95
From Michaels of Oregon.

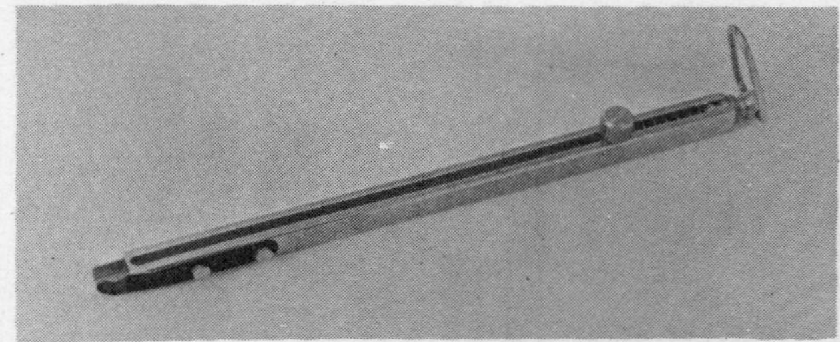

PRESENTATION TOMAHAWK

This unique item has been included because of its traditional styling and decoration—something important to both the black powder shooter and collector. The brass blade has an all-steel bit that's been fully tempered and perfectly dovetailed into the blade. The handle is made of maple inlayed with sterling silver and fitted with a solid bone stem. It's hand engraved, handmade—a truly collectible item. Comes mounted on weathered barn wood. Special limited edition of 100 pieces only.
Price: $495
From Lawrence R. Mrock.

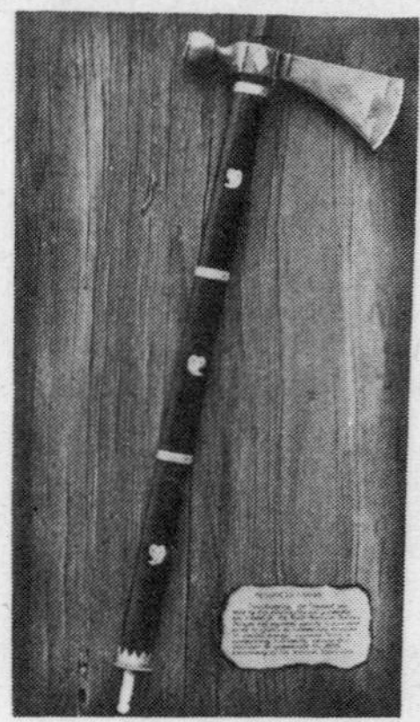

LEATHER HAT

This hat is made of top quality leather. Features an extra-wide brim. Comes in dark brown with braided leather band.
Price: $12.95 (style MMH).
From The Eutaw Company.

RAIDER HAT

Made of the best Latigo leather, this hat is of the type worn by some of the frontier scouts. Hand tooled.
Price: $19.95 (style RDH).
From The Eutaw Company.

AUTHENTIC PLAINS MOCCASIN

While not a direct gun-related accessory, proper garb such as the nearby moccasin is an important item for black powder shooter who fancies himself a purist. This moccasin is the hard-soled type and is made of quality leather. It's a machine-sewn version of the traditional plains moccasin worn by the Cheyenne and Sioux Indians.
Price: $25 (Model SM-3).
From Salish House, Inc.

Holsters, Scabbards & Slings

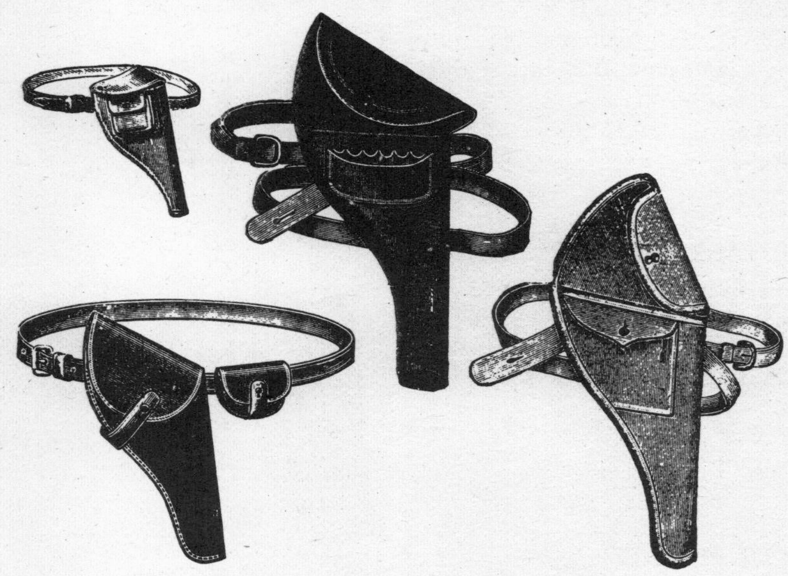

Good leatherwork can be both beautiful and utilitarian. A well-designed holster or scabbard both protects and compliments the gun it holds, and the artistry of some of our top leather workers challenges that of the top artists in other mediums.

In this section we've assembled a great variety of leather goods, from strictly utilitarian to "high art." In order of appearance, you'll find holsters, scabbards, slings, and other leather-made gun and shooting accessories.

A fair-to-good assortment of holsters and slings can usually be found at your local gun shop. Scabbards are stock items only in shops serving areas such as the Southwest, where there's a lot of range riding and horseback hunting, while the more exotic leatherwork is generally made to order on a direct customer-to-artisan basis.

CUSTOM COMBAT RIG FOR AUTOMATICS

Made of the best materials available, the Davis "Usher International" Combat rig is hand made for the .45 Auto. Each rig consists of holster, belt and magazine pouch. Give exact measurements when ordering.
Price: Complete Rig $90; Holster Only $51.
From G. Wm. Davis, Maker.

CUSTOM COMBAT RIG FOR AUTOMATICS

Made for .45 Autos, the Davis "Realist" rig is quite simple in design; yet, is made of top-quality leather. The entire rig consists of belt (give size when ordering) holster and magazine pouch.
Price: Complete Rig $84; Holster only $51.
From G. Wm. Davis, Maker.

CUSTOM HOLSTER FOR AUTOMATICS

Made by G. Wm. Davis, this high rise .45 Auto holster is made of the best materials. Butt tilts slightly forward for those who favor this style.
Price: Plain $23.50; Basketweave $25.50.
From G. Wm. Davis, Maker.

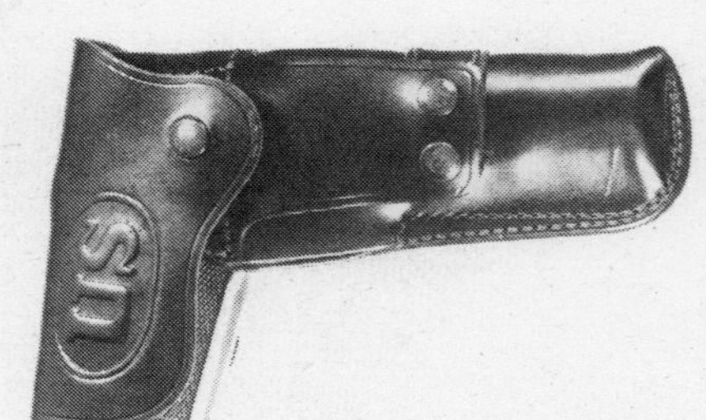

AMBIDEXTROUS MILITARY HOLSTER

Made for the Colt .45 Auto, Colt Commander and Browning High Power. Can be worn on either right or left side. The holster is made of the best quality leather and comes in plain black only. Easily snaps on and off the belt.
Price: $27
From Bianchi Gunleather.

FULL-FLAP AUTOMATIC HOLSTER

If you need a rugged holster, this one will fill the bill. Each Eutaw Model FH-45 is made of heavy-duty leather and comes fully lined with glove leather or buckskin suede. Available for 2-, 4- and 6-inch autos. Comes in plain or basketweave styles.
Price: $14.95, plain or basketweave.
From The Eutaw Company.

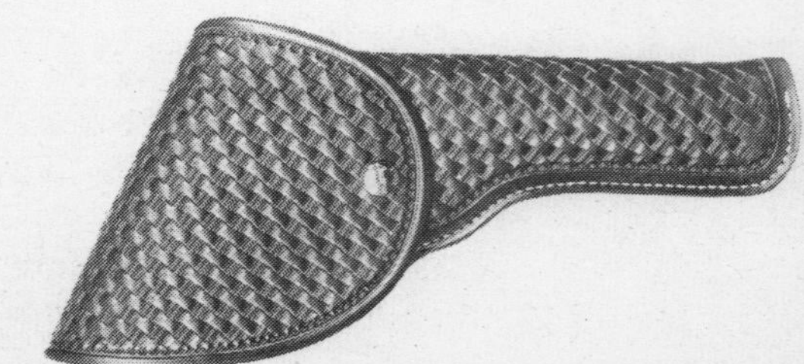

FULL FLAP HANDGUN HOLSTER

Lawrence's Model 14 holster comes with a full flap (snap closure) and 2½-inch belt loop. Keeps your favorite handgun completely protected. For revolvers and autos.
Price: Plain $31.35; Basketweave $37.25; Flower Carved $49.95. Also available with pocket for spare magazine: Plain $43.95; Basketweave $52.25; Flower Carved $64.85.
From Lawrence Leather.

Prices shown are subject to change.

AUTOMATIC PISTOL HOLSTER

Available for Colt-type autos and the S&W Model 52. This holster features a snap-strap, open bottom and heavy-duty construction. Fully lined.
Price: $13.98 (Model K-45).
From American Sales & Mfg. Co.

AUTOMATIC PISTOL HOLSTER

Lawrence's Model 52 holster is made for most large and medium frame autos. It features a spare magazine pouch, open top and snap strap. Fits most belts.
Price: Plain $32.75; Basketweave $38.45; Flower Carved $44.95.
From Lawrence Leather.

AUTOMATIC HANDGUN HOLSTER

This is Brauer's Model FB auto holster. Fits all large and medium frame autos. Comes in black; smooth or basketweave styling. Has an over-the-hammer snap strap.
Price: $11
From Brauer Bros.

AUTOMATIC PISTOL SPEED HOLSTER

Made of 2-ply leather with heavy machine stitching. Designed to fit .25, .380, .32 and .45 autos. Specify caliber and make of gun when ordering. Model B69.
Price: Plain $6; Basketweave $6.50.
From American Sales & Mfg. Co.

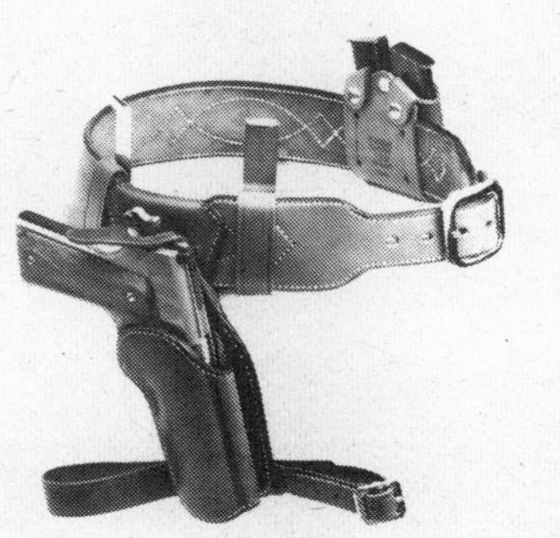

COMBAT AUTO RIG

Bianchi's Model 45 "Pistolero" assembly comes with keepers, belt, holster and magazine pouch. The entire unit is made of the finest leather obtainable. It features a buckle-type leg strap, low-cut muzzle holster that also sports a muzzle-forward rake. The Pistolero is fully lined and steel reinforced. Made for the Colt .45-ACP, Colt Gold Cup and AMT Hardballer.
Price: $125 complete.
From Bianchi Gunleather.

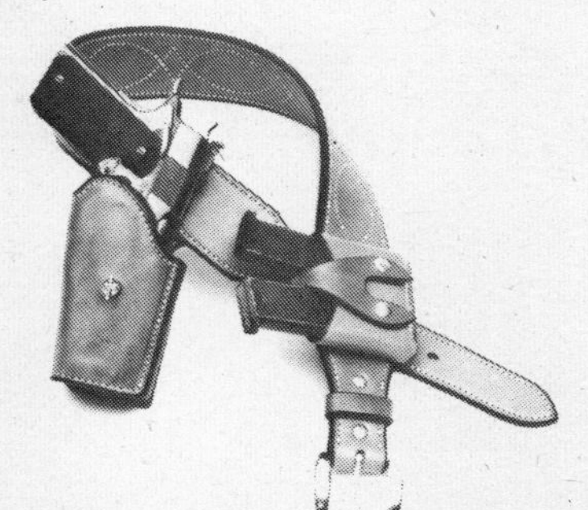

CUSTOM COMBAT RIG FOR AUTOMATICS

Called the "Championship," this rig is made of the finest leather and hardware obtainable. It consists of belt, holster and magazine pouch. Holster is of the muzzle forward design and has adjustable tension screw. Give exact measurements when ordering. *Well made.* Made for the .45 Autos.
Price: Complete Rig $127; Holster Only $65.
From G. Wm. Davis, Maker.

See the Directory for complete company addresses.

LUGER (P.08) HOLSTER

This replica holster has been manufactured from *original* W.W. II dies. It fits all standard 4-inch barreled Lugers. Features full-flap cover and spare magazine pouch. Made of solid black leather.
Model R546.
Price: $27.95
From Replica Models, Inc.

P.38 HOLSTER

This is Replica Model's No. 514D universal military style holster. It's made of heavy duty black leather and comes with a full flap and spare magazine pouch. Fits all P.38 autos.
Price: $9.95
From Replica Models, Inc.

PPK/HSc BELT HOLSTER

Designed to fit all PPK or HSc type autos, this holster comes with a full flap and spare magazine pouch. It's made of solid black leather.
Price: $14.95.
From Replica Models, Inc.

CROSS DRAW HOLSTER FOR AUTOS

Comes with spring-action opening, safety strap, rear-sight recess and a closed muzzle. Available for the Colt Commander, S&W Mdls. 59/39 and the Browning High Power. Comes in tan or black; plain or basketweave.
Price: Plain $25.95; Basketweave (shown) $27.95.
From Bianchi Gunleather.

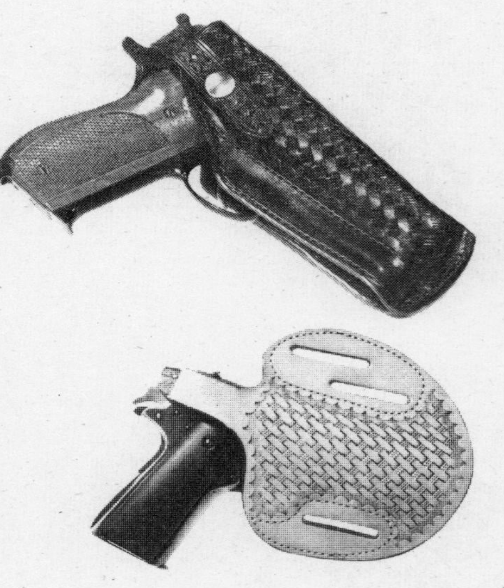

THUMB-SNAP AUTO HOLSTER

Comes in plain or suede-lined models. Also available in plain or basketweave styling. This holster is one of Roy Baker's Pancake designs and comes with belt-loop cuts that allow the user to position his holster to taste.
Price: Plain, unlined $19.95; Plain, lined $25.95; Basketweave, unlined $21.95; Basketweave, lined $27.95.
From Roy's Custom Leathergoods, Inc.

HIGH-RIDE AUTOMATIC HOLSTER

This is Triple K's Style 19 auto holster. Features minimum bulk and maximum exposure. For large frame autos. Has open bottom. Comes in black or cordovan; plain or basketweave styling.
Price: Plain $16; Basketweave $18.
From Triple K Manufacturing Company.

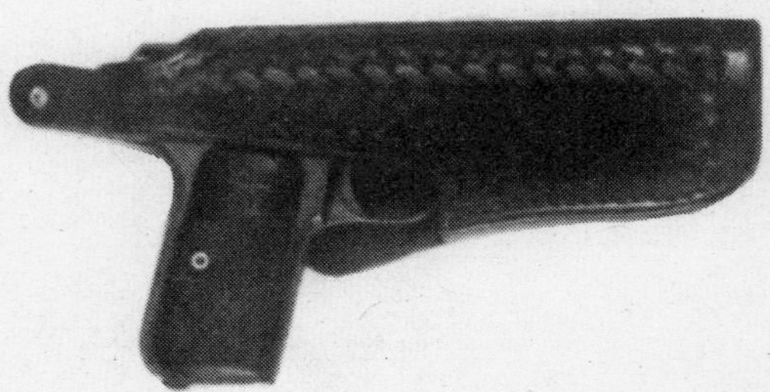

SUEDE LINED AUTOMATIC HOLSTER

Comes in basketweave or plain; cordovan, black or golden oak. Holster features thumb-break snap, open bottom and full suede lining. Made of top-quality leather. Style 77A-SL. Matching belt available.
Price: Plain $21; Basketweave $23; Plain Belt $23; Basketweave $25.
From Triple K Manufacturing Company.

HEAVY-DUTY FLAP HOLSTER

This Bianchi holster is available for many Colt, S&W and Ruger revolvers and autos. It features a full silicone suede lining and snap closure. Made of the best leather. Rear sight recess clears adjustable rear sight. Comes in plain or basketweave styling.

Price: Plain (shown) $34.95; Basketweave $38.95.

From Bianchi Gunleather.

RIMFIRE AUTO HOLSTER

Solid leather construction with attractive floral design. Comes with thumb-snap strap and closed bottom. Comes in plain oil or black. Fits most .22 auto pistols.

Price: Oiled Model 3100 $12.95; Black Model 3100 B $13.40.

From The Hunter Company.

RIMFIRE AUTO HOLSTER

Comes with a nickel finished buckle and snap. Features hand rubbed and creased edges. Full welt construction. Available for barrel lengths up to 7 inches. Fits .22 auto Colts, Brownings, High Standards and Rugers. Specify barrel length and make of gun when ordering. Model 101.

Price: $12.98

From American Sales & Mfg. Co.

RIMFIRE AUTO HOLSTER

A high-ride holster for the following .22 auto pistols: High Standard Victor and Citation; Colt Woodsman and Match Target; S&W Mdl. 41; Ruger Standard and Target Model Autos. Handles barrel lengths ranging from 4 inches to 7⅜ inches. Comes in plain tan only and has a steel reinforced sight channel. Features a full silicone suede lining and snap strap.

Price: $26.95

From Bianchi Gunleather.

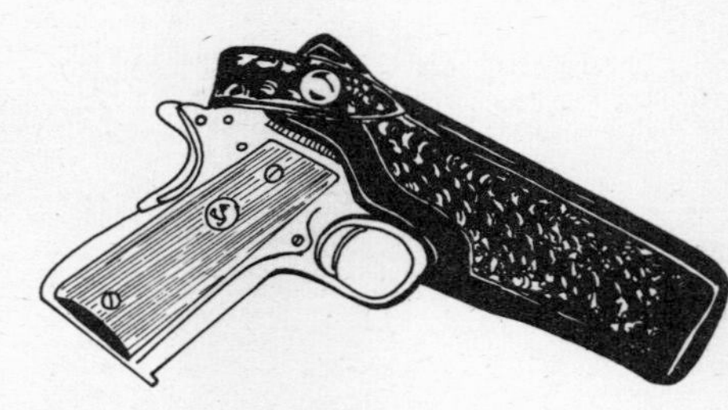

AUTOMATIC PISTOL HOLSTER

The Bucheimer Series T auto holster has a wide, detachable swivel hammer strap and comes in black only. Available in right- or left-hand version, in plain or basketweave styles. Comes unlined. Quality leather. May be used with either 1¾- or 2¼-inch belts. For large frame autos.

Price: $14 (plain, unlined).

From J. M. Bucheimer.

COLT OR BROWNING .25 AUTO HOLSTER

This is one of Roy Baker's Pancake holsters; and, it's made for the smallest autos. Comes with or without suede lining and can be had in plain or basketweave (shown) styles.

Price: Plain, unlined $14.95; plain, lined $20.95; Basketweave, unlined $15.95; Basketweave, lined $21.95.

From Roy's Custom Leathergoods, Inc.

See the Directory for complete company addresses.

CAMOUFLAGE HOLSTERS AND SLING

Shown nearby, from top to bottom, are Ranger Leather Products new automatic pistol rig, revolver rig and carrying strap. All are made of heavy top-grain cowhide and come in a unique green and brown camouflage pattern. Perfect for hunters. The auto pistol rig comes with magazine pouch while the revolver outfit features cartridge loops—both are available for a good selection of popular revolvers and autos. Sizes available up to 44 inches. The sling is foam padded for comfort and is tapered to fit 1-inch swivels.

Price: For Revolver or Auto holster alone $24.95 (suede lined $30.95); Belt (Auto) $26.95; Magazine Pouch $18.50; Revolver Belt w/loops $30.95—specify caliber; Sling $15.50.

From Ranger Leather Products.

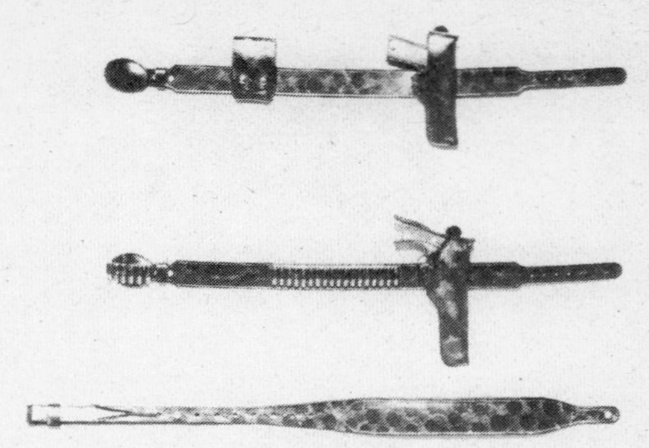

FLAT PROFILE REVOLVER AND AUTOMATIC HOLSTERS

Called the "Challengers" these holsters handle most popular handguns with barrels ranging from 2 inches up through 6½ inches. Each holster is wet-molded to conform to the shape of a particular style of handgun. Comes with thumb-break snaps and double-row nylon stitching. From left to right: Models C52, C60 and, again, C-52. Come in black or brown.

Price: See below.

	Lined	Unlined
C-52 2″ revolvers	$21.00	$15.00
C-53 2½″ revolvers	22.00	16.00
C-54 4″ heavy frame revolvers	23.00	17.00
C-55 46 small & med. frame revolvers	23.00	17.00
C-56 6 & 6½″ heavy frame revolvers	25.00	19.00
C-57 6 & 6½″ small & med. frame D.A. revolvers	25.00	19.00
C-58 32-380 automatics	21.00	15.00
C-59 .45 automatics	23.00	17.00
C-60 9mm automatics	23.00	17.00
C-61 Lugers & P38s	24.00	18.00

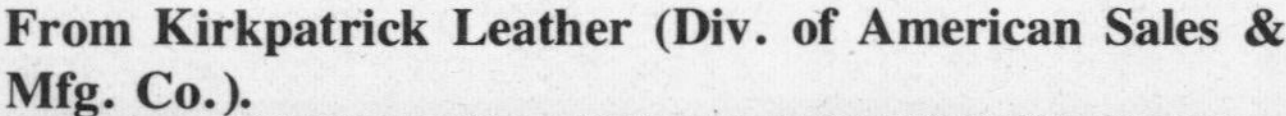

From Kirkpatrick Leather (Div. of American Sales & Mfg. Co.).

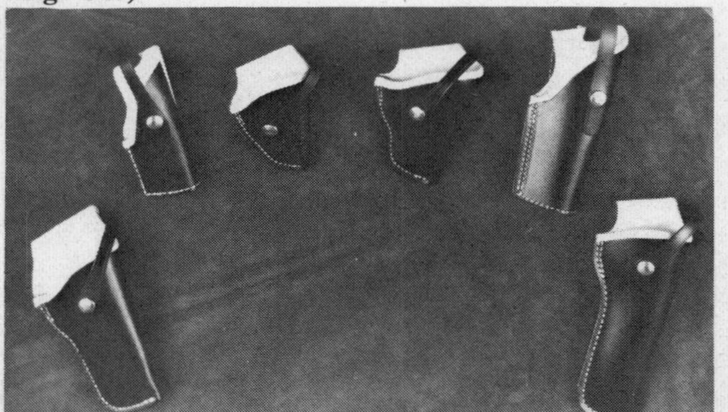

AUTO & REVOLVER HOLSTERS

In the nearby photo you can see a super selection of Kirkpatrick's new "Rolled-Edge" holsters. The rolled edge is simply a continuation, and overlap of, the high quality glove leather used to line these holsters. These holsters are available for most popular revolvers and autos with barrels ranging from 2 inches to 8⅜ inches. From left to right: Model R-25, A-3, R-20, $-23, A-5 and R-30.

Price: From $16 to $26, depending upon model ordered.

From Kirkpatrick Leather (Div. of American Sales & Mfg. Co.).

AUTO & REVOLVER HOLSTERS

From left to right, Kirkpatrick Leather's Models M-2, M-4, M-45 and M-46. Each holster is molded to your style of handgun. Made of top-quality leather. Available for most popular revolvers and autos.
Price: See below.

Style	Lined	Unlined
M-2	$16.95	$12.95
M-4	$18.95	$14.95
M-45	$17.95	$13.95
M-46	$18.95	$14.95

From Kirkpatrick Leather (Div. of American Sales & Mfg. Co.).

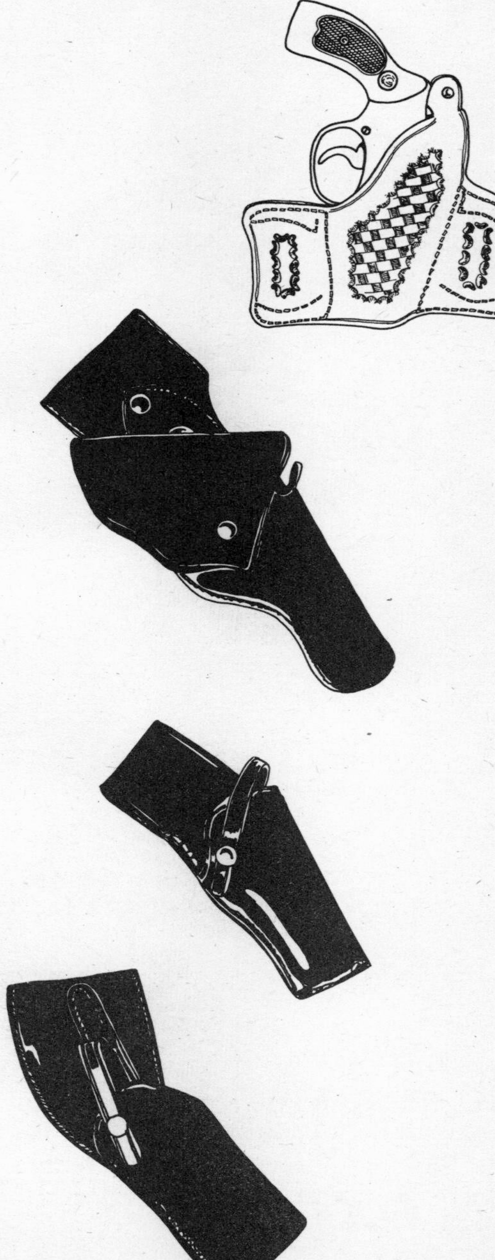

REVOLVER & AUTOMATIC HOLSTER

This is Bucheimer's Series C belt holster made for 2- and 4-inch revolvers; and, medium and large frame autos. Has a metal-reinforced thumb-break safety release. It's made for 1¾-inch belts but is available for 2¼-inch uniform belts. Made of excellent leather. Comes in black or russet; plain or basketweave; right or left hand in a lined or unlined version.
Price: $16
From J. M. Bucheimer Co.

FULL FLAP REVOLVER OR AUTOMATIC HOLSTER

Bucheimer's Series 18 holster features a full flap, has snap closure and swivels. Accommodates large frame autos and 4-inch barreled revolvers. Comes in black, plain or basketweave styling. Not offered with lining. Available in right- or left-hand styles.
Price: $32 (plain, unlined).
From J. M. Bucheimer.

AUTOMATIC/REVOLVER HOLSTER

This is Bucheimer's Series 179, butt-forward leather holster. It comes in right- or left-hand models, black only, in plain unlined configuration. Features an over-the-hammer snap strap.
Price: $27 (plain, unlined).
From J. M. Bucheimer.

AUTOMATIC PISTOL AND REVOLVER HOLSTER

Bucheimer's Series 15 holster is made for 4-inch barreled revolvers and large-frame autos. Features muzzle-forward tilt. Comes in black, in right or left hand styles and comes plain, unlined. Quality leather.
Price: $38 (plain, unlined).
From J. M. Bucheimer.

REVOLVER OR AUTOMATIC HOLSTER

Bucheimer's Series FM holsters are available in left- or right-hand versions. You have your choice of black or russet colors, lined or unlined. Closed bottom. Quality leather. Plain or basketweave patterns available. Has a thumb-break strap.
Price: $15 (plain, unlined).
From J. M. Bucheimer.

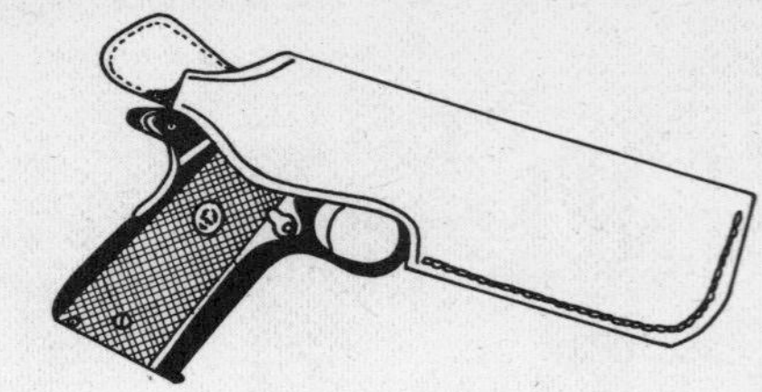

REVOLVER AND AUTOMATIC HOLSTER

Original snap-off design. Available for most handguns. Made of the best-quality leather and is available in black or brown smooth or basketweave styling. Model H.
Price: $10
From Brauer Bros.

FULL FLAP HANDGUN HOLSTER

This is Brauer Bros. Model FH holster. Features a full protective flap and belt loop. Made of smooth black cowhide.
Price: $17.10
From Brauer Bros.

SKELETON HOLSTER

Three sizes fit 97% of all handguns. Features a slim profile and minimum bulk and weight. Comes with snap strap, loops and has a black finish. Model G.
Price: $10
From Brauer Bros.

OPEN-TOP HANDGUN HOLSTER

Comes in top grain dark russet leather. Features basketweave design and snap strap. Open bottom. Comes in 15 popular sizes. Model 100.
Price: $8.55
From Brauer Bros.

WOOL-LINED HANDGUN HOLSTER

Made of bark tanned leather, Brauer's Model C holster comes with a full flap and wool lining. Features 100% leather construction. Fits most handguns.
Price: $15.55
From Brauer Bros.

CARTRIDGE/HOLSTER BELT

This Lawrence belt is 2½ inches wide and comes with a removable nickel buckle. Comes in oiled, plain; basketweave or flower carved styles. Has 30 cartridge loops.
Price: Plain $32.45; Basketweave $43.85; Flower Carved $64.65.
From Lawrence Leather.

ANKLE HOLSTER FOR SMALL AUTOS

Rogers No. 4-303 holster is specifically made for the Walter PPK and other autos of similar frame size. Features a thumb-release strap over hammer. Has a hook-and-loop fastening system.
Price: $14.95
From Rogers Holsters.

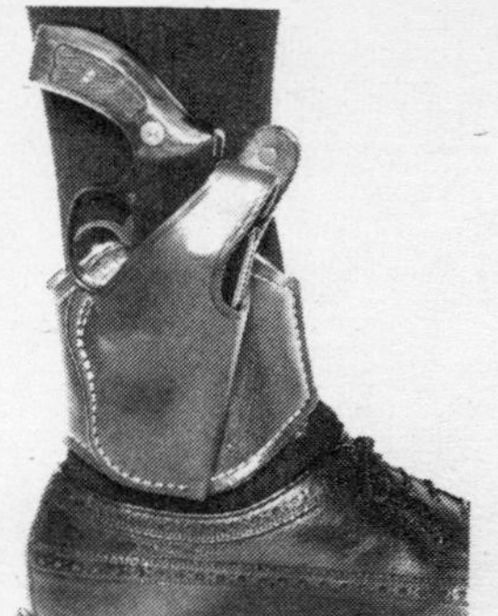

ANKLE HOLSTER

This one's for the policeman. It's Bianchi's Model 12. It's fully padded on the ankle side of the holster with shearling wool and attaches to the ankle with Velcro straps. Also features a thumb-break strap. Tan color only.

Price: $23.95

From Bianchi Gunleather.

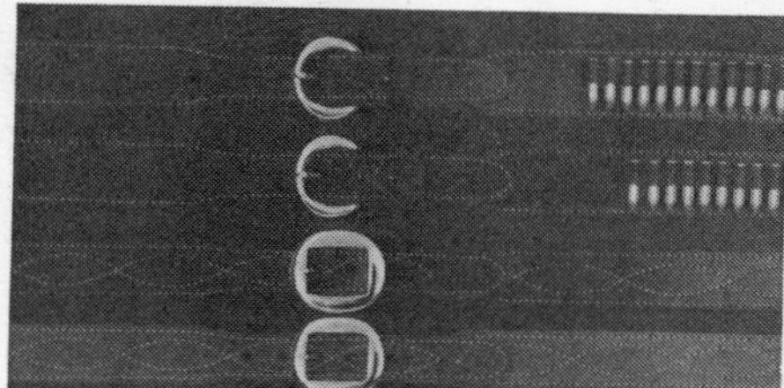

HOLSTER AND SPORTSMAN'S BELTS

From top to bottom in the nearby photo, Kirkpatrick Leather's Model B-30; Model B-30 (basketweave); Model B-40 black; Model B-40 Tan. All feature nickel finished brass buckles. Model 30 belts are 2 inches wide while the Model 40 belts are 1¾ inches wide. Made of the best leather.

Price: B-30 Plain $24.95, B-3 Basketweave $28.95; B-40, Plain Black or Tan only, $18.95.

From Kirkpatrick Leather (Div. of American Sales & Mfg. Co.).

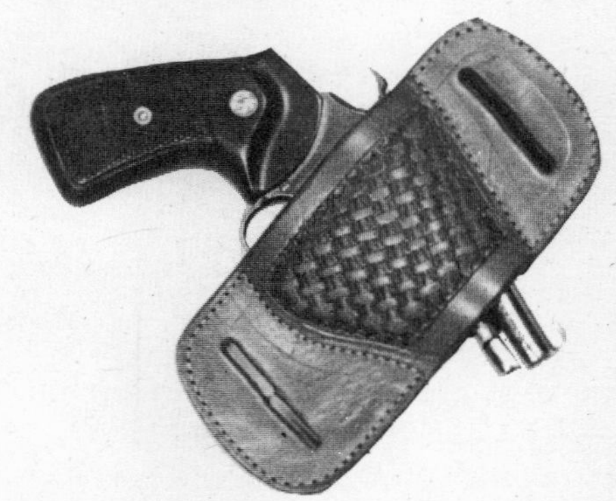

BELT HOLSTER

Eutaw Company's new "NFH" belt holster features a simple design that adapts to all medium and large frame handguns. Comes lined or unlined. Available in plain or basketweave; brown or black color.

Price: Lined $9.95; unlined $8.95.

From the Eutaw Company.

KEITH-TYPE REVOLVER HOLSTER

Lawrence's Model 120 holster was personally designed by gun writer Elmer Keith. Holster is cut with exposed sight, trigger and hammer. Features snap-strap closure. Fits 2½-inch wide belt. (Holster only.)

Price: Plain $18.65; Basketweave $22.95; Flower Carved $34.95.

From Lawrence Leather.

JORDAN-TYPE HOLSTER

Designed by lawman Bill Jordan, this holster/belt combo is made by Don Hame Leathergoods. The belt is fully lined, stitched, and comes in either black or brown color; plain, basketweave, or black clarino styling. The holster rides well, is made for 4-inch barrels and features a forward rake. Comes with an over-the-hammer snap strap.

Price: Belt (plain) $24; Basketweave $25.95; Clarino $29.75. Holster (plain) $26.35; Basketweave $28.95; Clarino $31.30.

From Don Hume Leathergoods.

See the Directory for complete company addresses.

LARGE-FRAME HANDGUN HOLSTER

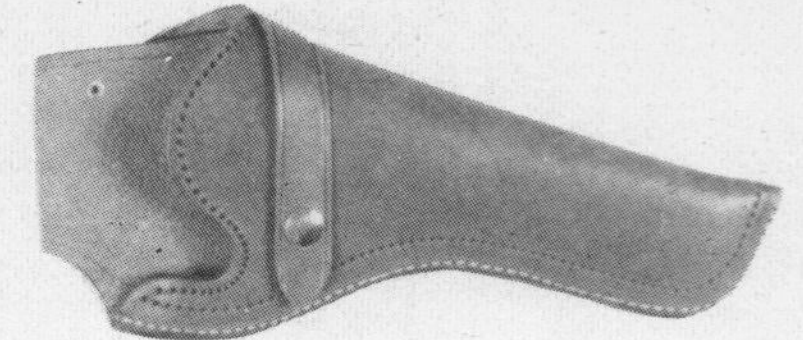

This is Eutaw's Model PLFR-6 holster. Comes in plain or basketweave styles and is made of the highest quality top-grain cowhide. Handles revolvers with barrel lengths of up to 6 inches and features a sturdy over-the-hammer snap.
Price: Contact your local dealer or write the maker.
From The Eutaw Company.

CUSTOM REVOLVER HOLSTER

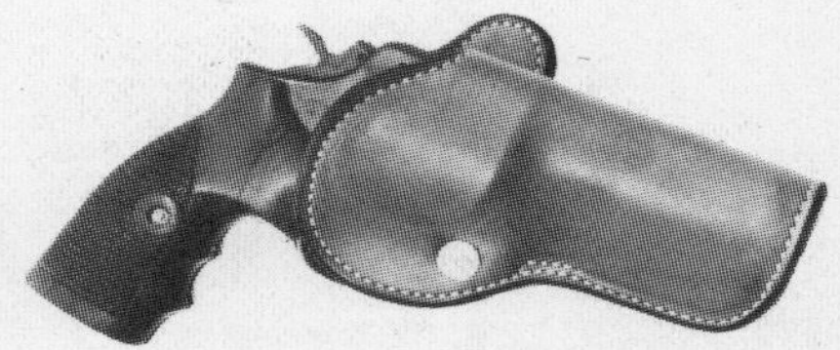

This holster is hand made by G. Wm. Davis. It's made of the finest leather. Called the DA challenger, this holster is designed for both speed and comfort; and, it was made for the competitive combat pistol shooter. Available for all popular revolvers.
Price: Plain $60; Basketweave $65.
From G. Wm. Davis, Maker.

REVOLVER HOLSTER

This Lawrence holster is made to accommodate most popular S/A and D/A revolvers with 4-inch, or longer, barrels. Open bottom. Sights and hammer are fully protected and the holster comes with snap-strap closure. Made of the finest leather.
Price: Plain $26.35; Basketweave $35.95; Flower Carved $43.45.
From Lawrence Leather.

SUEDE-LINED REVOLVER HOLSTER

Triple K's Style 18SL holster comes with a full suede lining and plain or basketweave design. Available in black, cordovan or golden oak. Matching belt—style 27—available, too.
Price: Plain $21; basketweave $23; Belt (plain) $23; basketweave $25.
From Triple K Manufacturing.

HIGH-RIDE, FORWARD-TILT HOLSTER

Made for most auto pistols. This is Triple K's Style 77A. It positions itself high on the hip for maximum comfort. Features a thumb-break snap and comes in black or cordovan, plain or basketweave. Features an open bottom and is made of top-quality leather.
Price: Plain $16; Basketweave $18.
From Triple K Manufacturing.

REVOLVER HOLSTER

Made for Ruger Security Six, Smith & Wesson Mdls. 14 & 19 and similar models with 6- or 6½-inch barrels. Comes fully lined. Model K72-6.
Price: $15.50
From American Sales & Mfg. Co.

FORM-FIT REVOLVER HOLSTER

Made of quality leather with a thumb-break strap. Closed bottom. It has been molded to universally fit a large number of popular D.A. revolvers.
Price: Plain Oiled $12.95; Lined $16.95; Black Plain $13.50; lined $17.50.
From The Hunter Co.

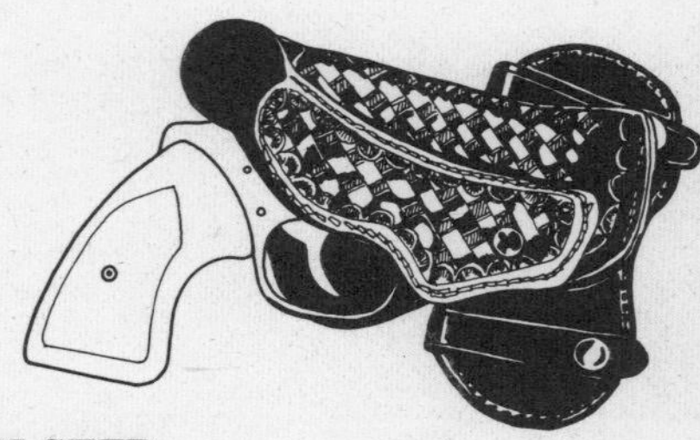

REVOLVER HOLSTER

Bucheimer's Series 10 holster is made for most 2- to 4-inch barreled revolvers. Comes in black, plain or basketweave, lined or unlined in right or left hand styles. Features an adjustable spring retaining clamp. Detachable hip plate fits 1¾-inch belts. Holster may be used without plate.
Price: $17 (plain, unlined).
From J. M. Bucheimer.

Prices shown are subject to change.

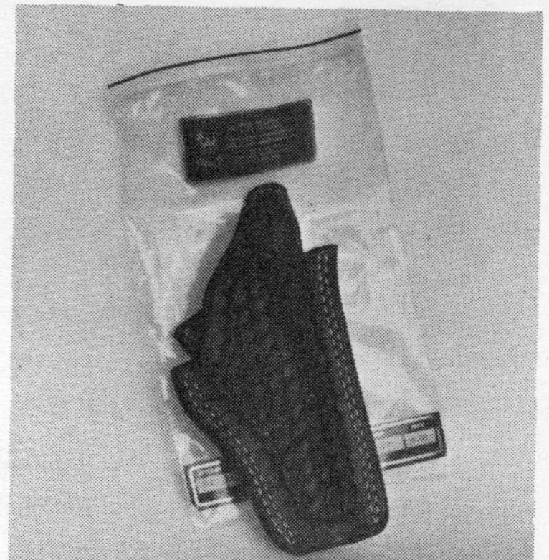

REVOLVER HOLSTER

This is the Jackass Model D.R. 40 holster. It's made for 4- to 5-inch barreled revolvers and is offered in plain or basketweave (shown) styling. Comes lined or unlined and can be had with the F.B.I. butt-forward cant; or in a straight up and down style. Made of the best materials; brown or black color.

Price: Plain $24.95; Basketweave $26.95; Plain-lined $30.95; Basketweave lined $32.95

From Jackass Leather Company

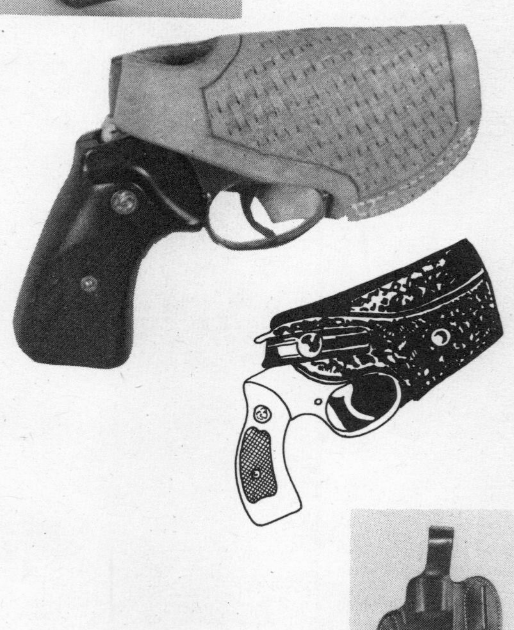

SNUB-NOSE CROSS DRAW REVOLVER HOLSTER

Made for most small-frame revolvers, Eutaw's Model SFSH holster comes in plain or basketweave styling. It features a thumb-snap strap. Made of the best quality leather.

Price: $7.95

From the Eutaw Company.

HIGH-RIDE REVOLVER HOLSTER

May also be used for cross draw. This leather holster is Bucheimer's Series 85 for 2- to 4-inch revolvers. It comes in black, plain or basketweave, unlined style. Also available in right- or left-hand model. Features an over-the-hammer snap strap.

Price: $15.50 (plain, unlined).

From J. M. Bucheimer.

BAKER PANCAKE HOLSTER

Roy Baker's famous Pancake holster is available for most popular revolvers and autos. It's designed to be worn with belts up to 2 inches wide in any one of three different positions. All Baker holsters are made of the finest leather available. They come in black, brown, russet, mahogany, clarino-black and are offered in plain or basketweave styles.

Price: 2- and 3-inch revolvers or autos $19.95; write maker for more information.

From Roy's Custom Leather Goods, Inc.

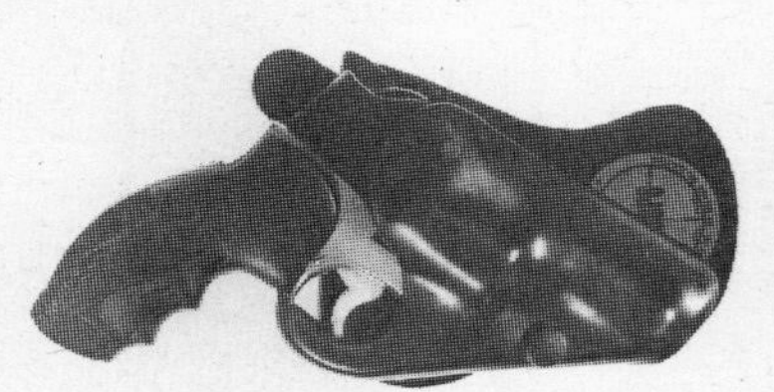

"PADDLE HOLSTER" FOR SMALL, MEDIUM AND LARGE FRAME REVOLVERS

Rogers' Type II Paddle Holster has a full leather lining and nylon post to adjust clamping tension on gun. Comes with thumb-break snap. Fits S&W, Colt and Ruger D/A revolvers.

Price: $20.95

From Rogers Holsters.

SWIVEL-TYPE REVOLVER HOLSTER

Called the "El Capitan," this El Dorado holster features a 3-position swivel. It's made of heavy top grain cowhide with real suede leather lining. This model is available for all medium and heavy frame revolvers.

Price: Plain (shown) $27.95; Basketweave $29.95.

From El Dorado Leather.

See the Directory for complete company addresses.

SWIVEL-TYPE HOLSTER FOR REVOLVERS

Made for the S&W Models 19 & 28; Colt Python; Ruger S.S. (.357) and Dan Wesson .357. Available for 4- or 6½-inch barrel lengths and comes black only; plain or basketweave styling. Consists of a Bianchi No. 104M swivel holster attached to a belt loop fitted with 12 cartridge loops. Loops are hand molded for .38/.357 cartridges. Each holster has a rear sight guard, snap strap and open muzzle.
Price: $33.95; Basketweave $35.95.
From Bianchi Gunleather.

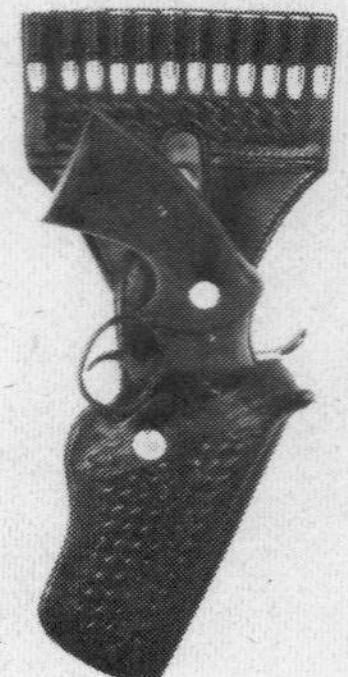

DUTY HOLSTERS

In the photo nearby, at top left is Kirkpatrick Leather's Model 16DA; bottom left, Model 229 Border Patrol; Middle right, Model 211 Swivel Holster. All are made of top-quality leather. The 16DA gives full sight protection coupled with a handy thumb snap. The Model 229 features butt-forward carry while the Model 211 swivels or locks as desired. All are available with glove lining and come in either black, brown or russet color.
Price: Model 16DA unlined $21, lined $25; Model 229 unlined $23, lined $27; Model 211 unlined $27, lined $31. Basketweave $2 extra.
From Kirkpatrick Leather (Div. of American Sales & Mfg. Co.).

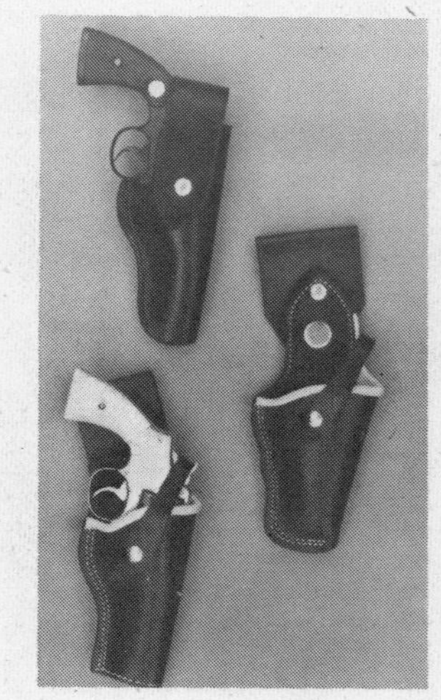

CROSS DRAW REVOLVER HOLSTER

Made for the S&W .41 & .44 Magnums with 6½-inch barrel; 6½- or 7½-inch barreled Colt and Ruger Single Actions. Features top-grain leather lining, spring opening and snap strap. Comes in tan or black; plain style only.
Price: $31.95
From Bianchi Gunleather.

CROSS-DRAW HOLSTER

Called the "Crossfire," this Eutaw holster (Model CRF) is made of top-quality leather and is a new concept in cross-draw, high-ride holsters. It can be worn on the right or left side and comes in plain or basketweave styles. Features an over-the-hammer snap. Designed for short barreled revolvers.
Price: $13.95, plain or basketweave.
From the Eutaw Company.

FULL-FLAP REVOLVER HOLSTER

Comes with suede or buckskin suede lining; plain or basketweave styling. Handles all 2-, 4- and 6-inch large frame revolvers. Made of heavy-duty leather. It's Eutaw's Model FH-4.
Price: $14.95, plain or basketweave.
From The Eutaw Company.

Prices shown are subject to change.

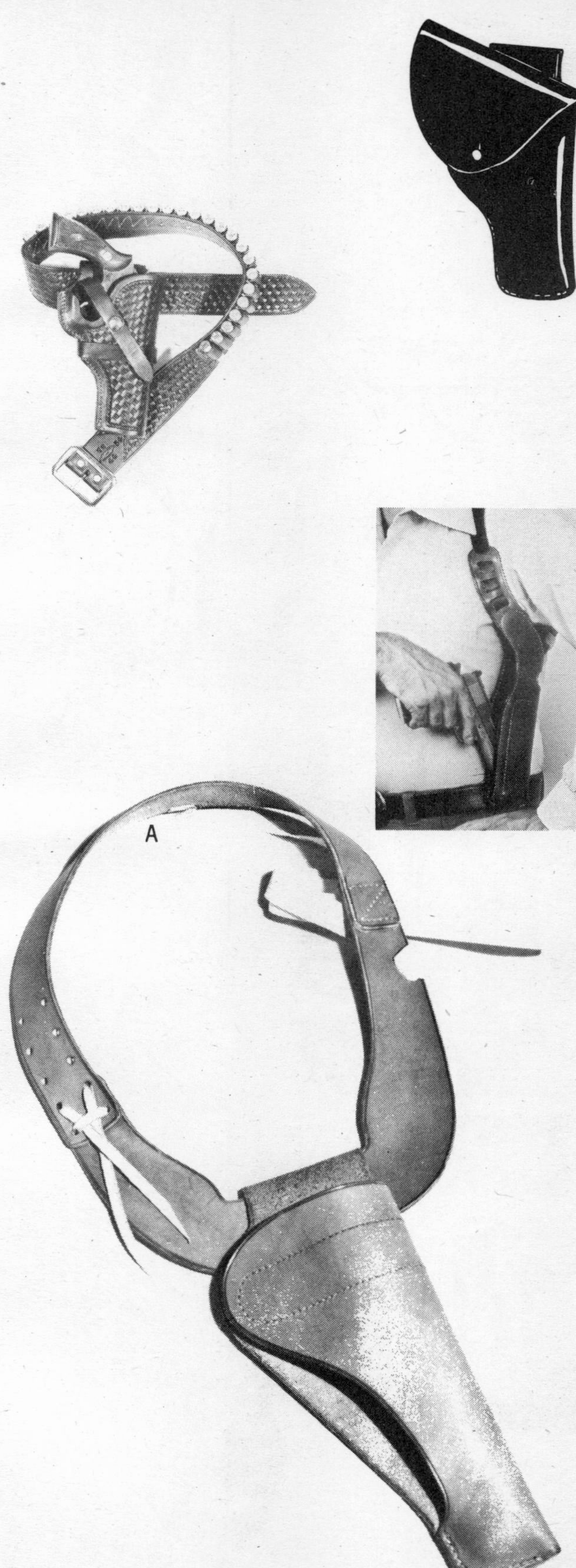

FULL FLAP REVOLVER HOLSTER

Made for 4-inch barreled revolvers, the Bucheimer Series AH leather holster features a full flap with snap closure. Fits 2¼-inch belts and comes in black only. Not available lined or with basketweave. Quality leather.

Price: $18 (plain, unlined).

From J. M. Bucheimer.

HOLSTER/BELT COMBO

Lawrence's Model 1C holster is made for D/A revolvers and comes with open bottom. Holster also features snap-strap closure. Belt is 2 inches wide and comes with 25 sewn cartridge loops. Specify gun, cartridge and waist size when purchasing. Russet or black.

Price: Holster Plain $10.45; Basketweave $16.45; Belt Plain About $15. For black color, on both belt and holster, add $10.

From Lawrence Leather.

SHOULDER HOLSTER FOR AUTOMATICS

Fits many Colt, S&W, Browning, Star and AMT autos. Bianchi's "Phantom" shoulder rig comes fully lined with silicone suede and is available in plain tan styling only. Gun is held securely by a carbon wire spring of special design. Premium quality leather used throughout.

Price: $44.95

From Bianchi Gunleather.

SHOULDER HOLSTER/HARNESS COMBO

The Lawrence Model 9 shoulder harness is a universal item designed to fit most holsters. It's shown here with the Lawrence Model 9 holster. Rig is fully adjustable and is made of quality leather. Holster features spring retention.

Price: Complete rig $32.90; Holster $21.95; Strap (harness) $10.95.

From Lawrence Leather.

SMALL FRAME AUTOMATIC SHOULDER HOLSTERS

Bucheimer's Series 342 shoulder holster is fully adjustable, features quality leather construction and is specifically designed for small-frame .25 caliber (and similar) autos. The cotton web harness is removable for laundering. Comes in natural color, plain finish and is unlined. Available in right or left-hand style.

Price: $12

From J. M. Bucheimer Co.

G.I. STYLE SHOULDER HOLSTER

This is the standard leather G.I. shoulder holster as issued during World War II. Comes with snaps. Light brown color. Fits all 1911-type Colt and other auto pistols.

Price: $14.95. (Model R543).

From Replica Models, Inc.

See the Directory for complete company addresses.

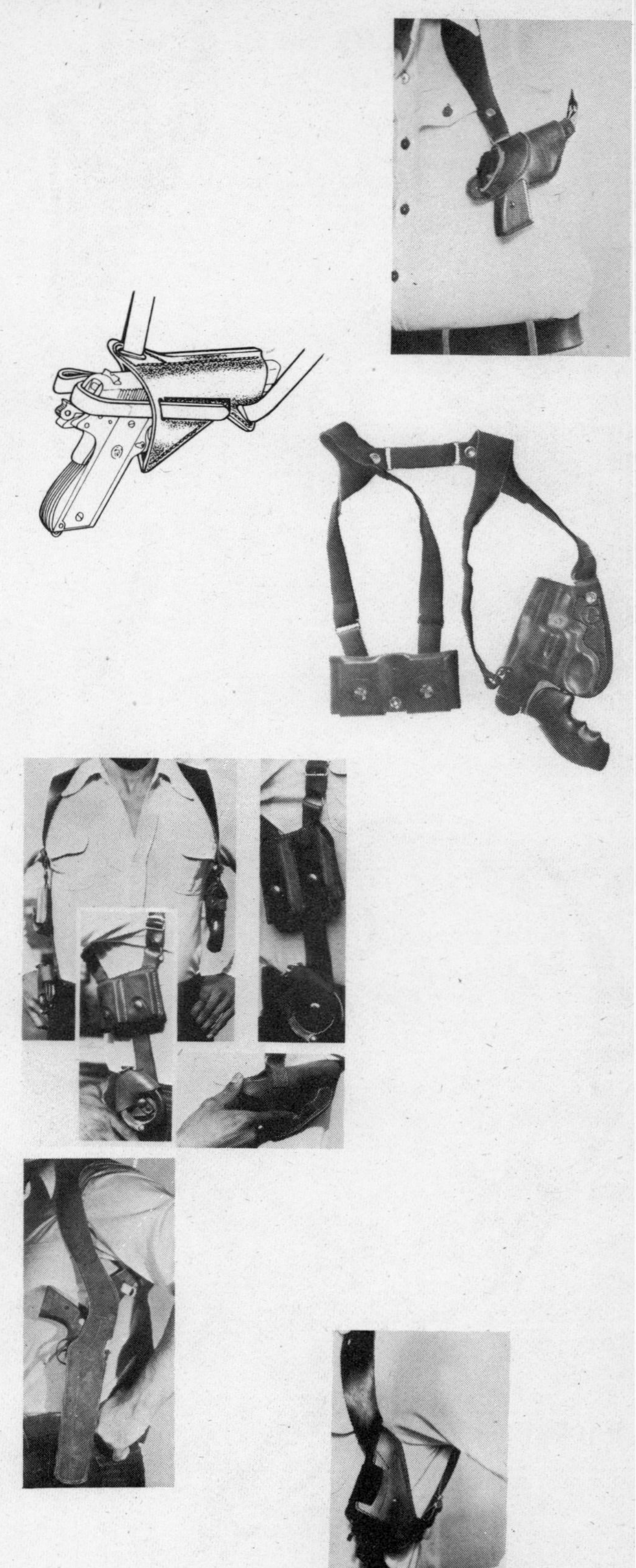

SMALL-FRAME AUTO SHOULDER HOLSTER

Carries small automatics in a horizontal position. Comes with a fully adjustable leather harness and thumb-break snap. Fits Walther PP, PPK; Mauser HSc; OMC Backup .380; Sterling and Colt .25 autos. Madé of top quality leather. Plain tan only.

Price: $24.95

From Bianchi Gunleather.

SHOULDER HOLSTER RIG

Called the "Double Agent II," this Rogers shoulder holster system holds your favorite auto or revolver in the horizontal position. Comes in right- or left-handed models. Has an adjustable thumb-release snap. Available with clip case (autos), ammo pouch (revolvers) or speed loader case. Comes complete with harness. Available for most popular autos and revolvers.

Price: $36.95

From Rogers Holsters.

SHOULDER HOLSTER RIG

This Rogers holster rig is made for most popular handguns—auto or revolver. Features full adjustment and comes complete with harness and ammo pouch (revolvers) or clip case (autos)—speed loader case also available.

Price: $34.95

From Rogers Holsters.

COMPLETE SHOULDER-HOLSTER SYSTEM

Called the Model 1180 "Shoulder-Holster System" this rig consists of several pieces of leather gear—6 to be exact: 1. Holster; 2. Left Harness Strap; 3. Elastic Connecting Strap; 4. Right Harness Strap; 5. Double Drop Case (clip or cartridge); 6. Cuff Case. Made for revolvers or autos. Top-quality leather.

Price: $42

From Old West, Inc.

SHOULDER HOLSTER

Comes in five different sizes to accommodate a wide selection of handguns. It's made of heavy rough-out cowhide complete with suede lining. It also features an open-sight cut out and belt strap to keep this gun close into your torso. Fully adjustable shoulder strap.

Prices: Range from $19.90 to $27.90 depending upon size.

From Old West, Inc.

SHOULDER HOLSTER

Made for small and medium frame revolvers, Old West's Model 2130 shoulder holster features the popular butt-down style. Fully adjustable shoulder strap. Fully lined.

Price: $22.95

From Old West, Inc.

Prices shown are subject to change.

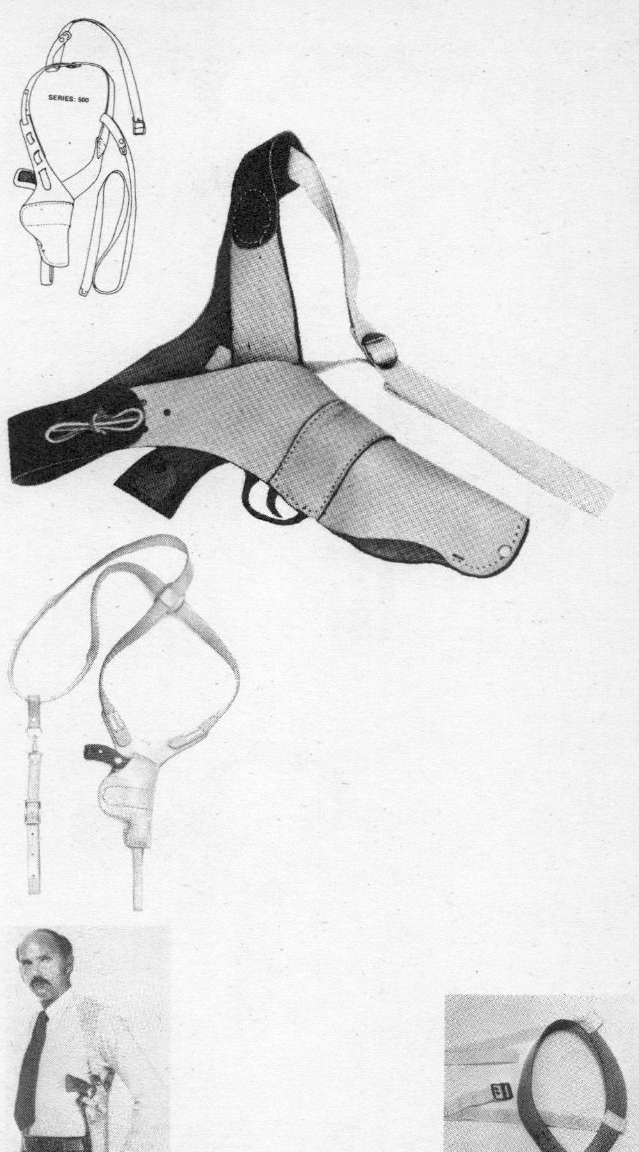

SHOULDER HOLSTER FOR REVOLVERS & AUTOMATICS

Made for 2- or 6-inch revolvers, and medium or large-frame autos, this Bucheimer shoulder holster comes in right- or left-hand models, is fully adjustable and features spring-clip retainment. Cotton web harness is removable for laundering.

Price: $20 (Series 500).

From J. M. Bucheimer.

SHOULDER HOLSTER

Brauer's No.K shoulder system is fully adjustable and fits just about all handguns. Made of best quality leather and comes with spring-clip retention. Oil finished.

Price: $20; 8⅜-inch model $22.25; 7½-inch model $22.25.

From Brauer Bros.

SHOULDER HOLSTER

Lawrence's Model 7 shoulder holster fits most D.A. revolvers and autos; except for .25 caliber guns. It's made of the best leather, is fully adjustable and features spring retention. (Shown with optional underarm strap and snap closures.)

Price: $38.60.

From Lawrence Leather.

ROY BAKER SHOULDER HOLSTER

Baker's new "Out-of-Sight" shoulder rig features a soft suede harness that's fully adjustable with Velcro fasteners, broad shoulder straps and off-side clip pouch or cartridge dump. Comes in both large and small sizes. Both sizes handle all popular revolvers or autos.

Price: Small $32.95 (unlined); Small $38.95 (lined); Large $48.95 (unlined); Large $54.95 (lined).

From Roy's Custom Leather Goods, Inc.

SNUB-NOSE REVOLVER SHOULDER HOLSTER

Carries the gun in a modified butt-down position. Features a carbon wire (internal) spring that holds the gun securely in place. Has a fully adjustable shoulder harness. Comes in plain tan only.

Price: $38.95

From Bianchi Gunleather.

SNUB-NOSE REVOLVER SHOULDER HOLSTER

This Series 600 Bucheimer shoulder holster is for 2-inch barreled revolvers only. Features a fully adjustable, washable harness. Carries the gun in a butt-down position. Comes in russet color, unlined. Interchangeable for right- or left-hand use.

Price: $16

From J. M. Bucheimer.

SHOULDER HOLSTER HARNESS

For use with many of Hunter's holsters. Fully adjustable elastic straps. Comes in either right- or left-hand versions.

Price: $11.45

From The Hunter Co.

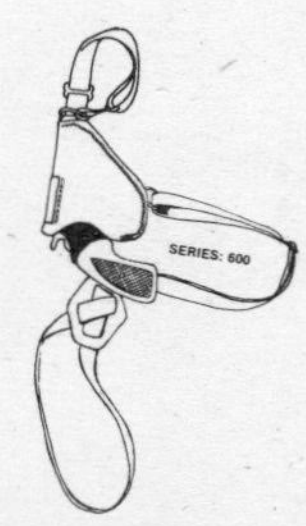

See the Directory for complete company addresses.

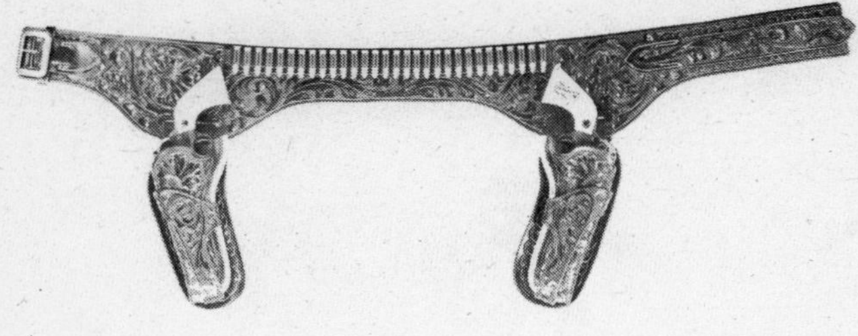

BUSCADERO RIG

Shown nearby is the complete Lawrence Buscadero Belt and Holster Rig. The entire two-gun outfit is made of premium oak-tanned saddle leather. Comes oiled, plain, or basketweave or flower carved styles. Has 30 sewn cartridge loops (specify caliber); and, the belt itself is 3 inches wide. Well made.

Price: As shown, with flower carved style $225.70; In the same style, but for one gun $160.50. For the plain holster/belt combo in one- or two-gun style $111.70 (one-gun); $146.65 (two-gun).

From Lawrence Leather.

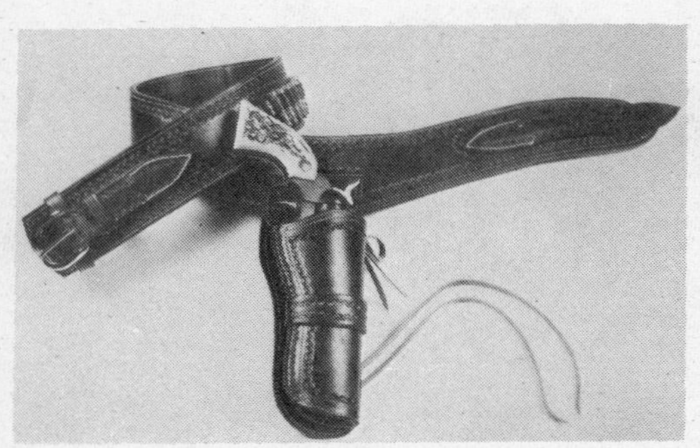

FAST DRAW SET

Each set comes with holster, belt hammer loop, tie down thong and nylon stitching. Comes in black or brown and handles up to 6½-inch barrels (5½-inch holster also available). Left-hand version available at *no extra charge*. Cartridge loops available in .22, .38/.357, .44/.45 calibers.

Price: $37.50 as shown.

From American Sales & Mfg. Co.

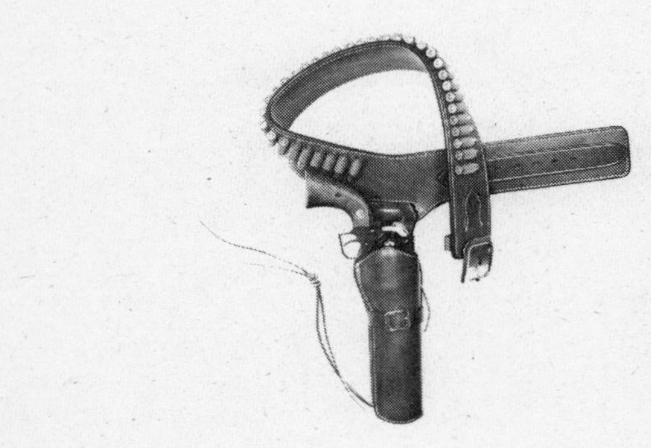

"1890 FAST DRAW RIG"

Consists of a holster/belt combination. Comes with 36 cartridge loops. The belt is a generous 3 inches wide, is fully lined and contoured. The holster features a hammer thong, metal reinforcing and a nylon stitched belt. Comes in waist sizes 32 to 46 inches and cartridge loops come in .38/357 and .44/.45 only.

Price: $106.90 for the total assembly; belt alone $59.95; holster alone $46.95.

From Bianchi Gunleather.

SINGLE ACTION REVOLVER HOLSTER

Bianchi's "Lawman" holster comes in left- or right-hand versions, is made of premium cowhide and is available with silicone suede lining. Comes in tan, plain finish only. Available to fit 4¾-, 5½-, 6½-, and 7½-inch barrels.

Price: $27

From Bianchi Gunleather.

"OLD WEST" S.A. REVOLVER HOLSTER

The holster itself is woven through a carefully cut back flap—its styling is right out of yesteryear; a real plus for the western folklore buff. Each holster is made of top-quality leather that's wet molded to fit the following guns. Colt SAA .45, 1851 Navy, 1860 Army; Remington 1858 Army; Ruger Blackhawk .357, .44 and Old Army. Available barrel lengths: 4¾-, 5½-, 6½-, 7½-, and 8-inches. Comes in plain tan only.

Price: $25.95

From Bianchi Gunleather.

WESTERN STYLE HOLSTER

The Eutaw Company offers a well-made traditional western holster/belt rig that comes fully lined with best-quality suede or glove leather. Each set is hand-tooled and comes in either black or brown. Designed for the fast draw competitor. Made for, .22, .38, .357, .44 or .45 caliber single action revolvers.

Price: Model BR-1 $31.95.

From The Eutaw Company.

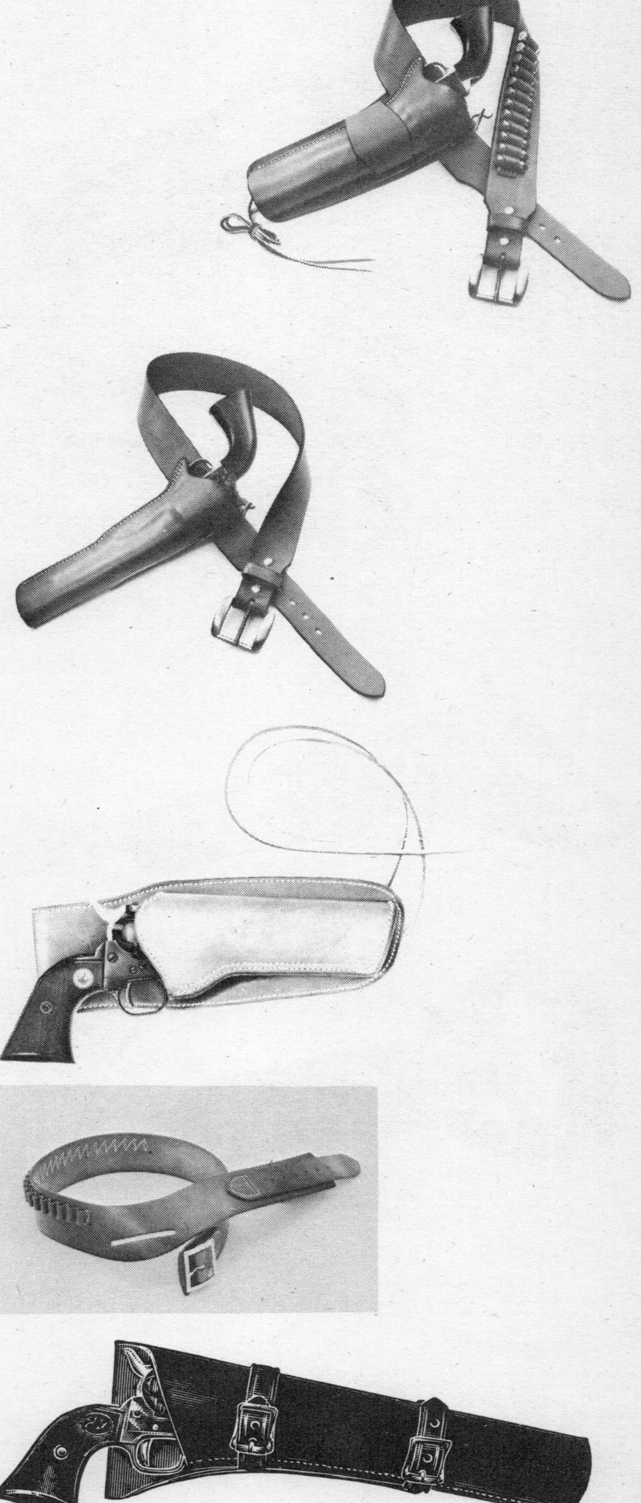

CUSTOM WESTERN S.A. RIG

Made for single action revolvers, this Davis design represents a modern look of days gone by. The "Grizzly Rig" is made of heavy leather and comes with 12 cartridge loops sewn for .38/.357, .41 or .44/.45 cartridges. Give waist size and cartridge when ordering. (Not made for .22's.)

Price: Complete Rig $60; Holster Only $31.

From G. Wm. Davis, Maker.

CUSTOM OLD-WEST STYLE S.A. HOLSTER

While this holster is made of the best materials, it's also made in the simplistic style so popular in the frontier West. Rig consists of belt and holster complete with hammer thong. It's called the "Shiloh."

Price: Plain Holster $23.50; Basketweave Holster $25.50; Plain Belt $12.50; Basketweave Belt $17.50. (Give belt size when ordering.)

From G. Wm. Davis, Maker.

WESTERN-STYLE S.A. HOLSTER

Comes with tie-down thong and accommodates most popular S.A. revolvers. Features 3-ply construction. Also comes with hammer thong.

Price: Oiled $29.35, Black $29.90.

From The Hunter Co.

WESTERN-STYLE S.A. HOLSTER BELT

May be used in conjunction with one of Hunter's western style holsters. Comes in a plain oiled russet finish with cartridge loops available in .22, .38 or .45 calibers.

Price: Plain Oiled $22.60; Plain Black $23.50.

From The Hunter Co.

BUNTLINE-STYLE S.A. REVOLVER HOLSTER

This Brauer holster has been specifically made for H&R, Colt and Ruger S.A.'s. Specify make, model and barrel length when buying. Comes in oiled brown or black color and has brass buckle straps.

Price: From $17.80 to $20 depending on gun.

From Brauer Bros.

See the Directory for complete company addresses.

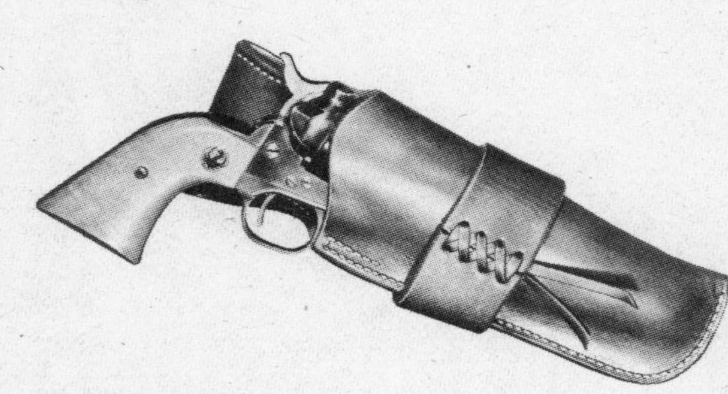

S.A. HOLSTER RIG

Fits most S.A. revolvers with barrel lengths up to 6½ inches. Belt and holster are made of top-grain cowhide; belt is fully lined. You can get this one in black or brown. Basketweave styling. Specify belt length and make and model of handgun (barrel length, too) when purchasing. Model 100.

Price: $37.70; Model 101 for small and medium frame guns same price.

From Brauer Bros.

WESTERN STYLE S.A. HOLSTERS

Lawrence's Model 121 holster is specifically made for single action revolvers—handles most models of popular single actions. Fits all belts.

Price: Plain $33.55; Basketweave $38.95; Flower carved $46.50.

From Lawrence Leather.

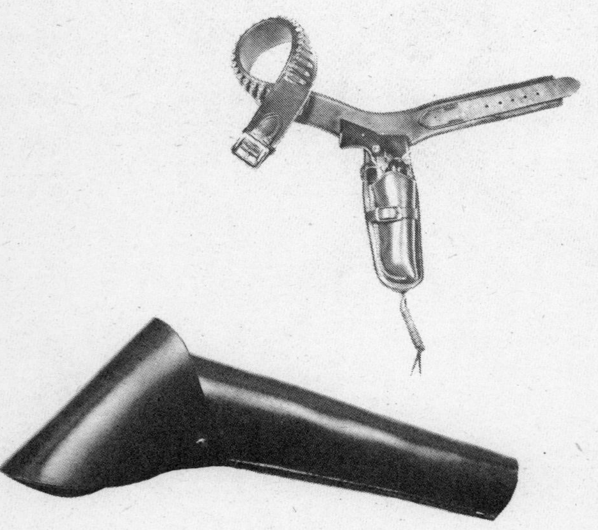

FAST DRAW S.A. REVOLVER RIG

Fully crafted of saddle leather, the Lawrence Model 79 fast draw rig comes complete with cartridge loops and nickeled hardware. Also has tie-down and hammer thongs. Comes in russet or black. Specify waist size, barrel length and your gun's caliber.

Price: Plain $52.70; Basketweave $72.30.

From Lawrence Leather.

CAP & BALL HOLSTER

Features full-flap design of the best top-grain cowhide. Comes in black or russet and fits all cap and ball handguns. Model F-50.

Price: $14.70

From Brauer Bros.

BLACK POWDER PISTOL HOLSTER

This is Brauer's Model 103 and fits all .44 and .36 caliber cap and ball revolvers. Solid leather construction.

Price: $37.70

From Brauer Bros.

CIVIL WAR TYPE HOLSTERS

Available for Walker Revolver; 1st, 2nd, and 3rd Mdl. Dragoon; Army and Navy Revolvers; Sheriff Model 1851 Revolver; Baby Dragoon 4-inch barrel and Baby Dragoon 6-inch barrel. All come in black leather and full flap style. Brass-stud closure.

Price: Walker $16.60; 1st, 2nd, and 3rd Dragoon $14.85; Army & Navy $14.30; Sheriff $12.20; Baby Dragoon $12.20.

From Old West, Inc.

Prices shown are subject to change.

HOLSTER FOR THOMPSON CENTER SINGLE SHOT

Comes in oiled russet. Made for T/C single-shot with or without scope. Available in 10- or 14-inch barrel lengths.

Price: 10-inch $13.20; 14-inch $17.75; 10-inch with scope $17.00; 14-inch with scope $20.90.

From The Hunter Co.

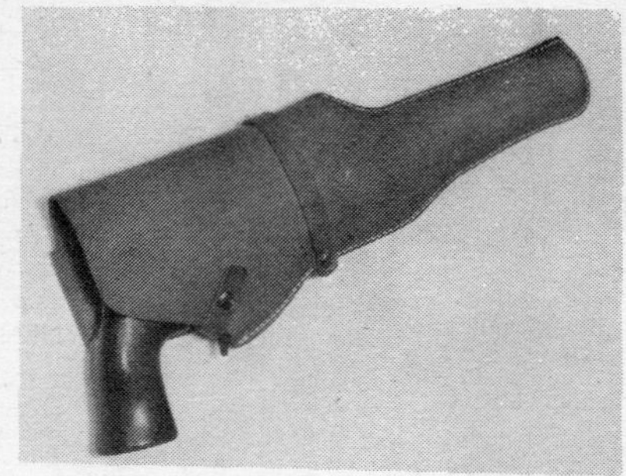

CONTENDER HOLSTERS

Custom holsters for Thompson-Center Contender, shoulder or hip carry, with scope or iron sights.

Price: $38.95 (iron sights); $39.95 (scope).

From Marsh Al's.

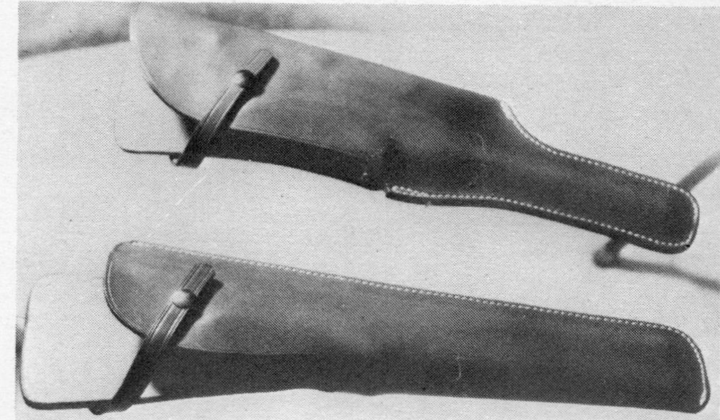

WALLET-TYPE DERRINGER HOLSTER

The Jackass Leather Company is currently offering a handy wallet-type holster made especially for the High Standard rimfire Derringer. Holster is made of the finest leather and holds two spare rounds of ammo. Comes in plain finish.

Price: $14.95

From Jackass Leather Company.

WALLET HOLSTER

This wallet shaped holster holds the High Standard 2-shot D/A Derringer and loops (inside) for 2 spare rounds of ammo. Available in black or brown.

Price: $14.50

From Steven E. Henigson.

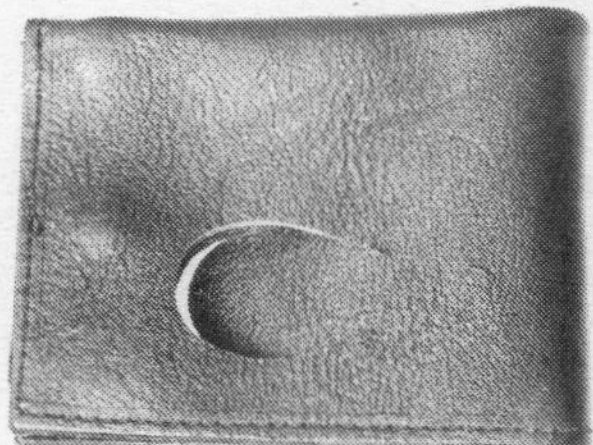

RIFLE SCABBARD FOR UNSCOPED RIFLES

Comes fully lined and is made of the best oak-tanned saddle skirting. Basketweave trim is standard; walnut-oil finish only. Model 120.

Price: $65 (specify barrel length when ordering).

From Triple K Manufacturing Company.

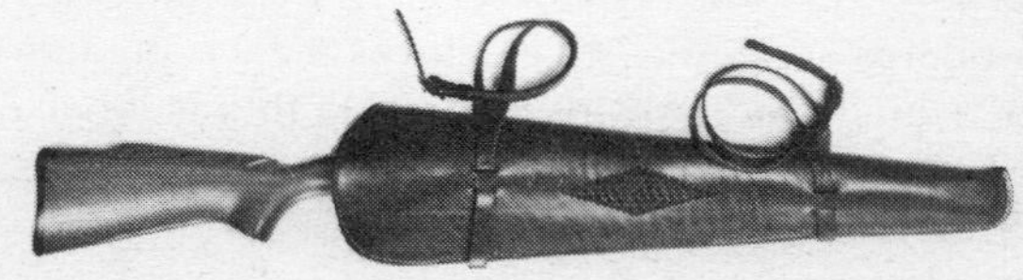

See the Directory for complete company addresses.

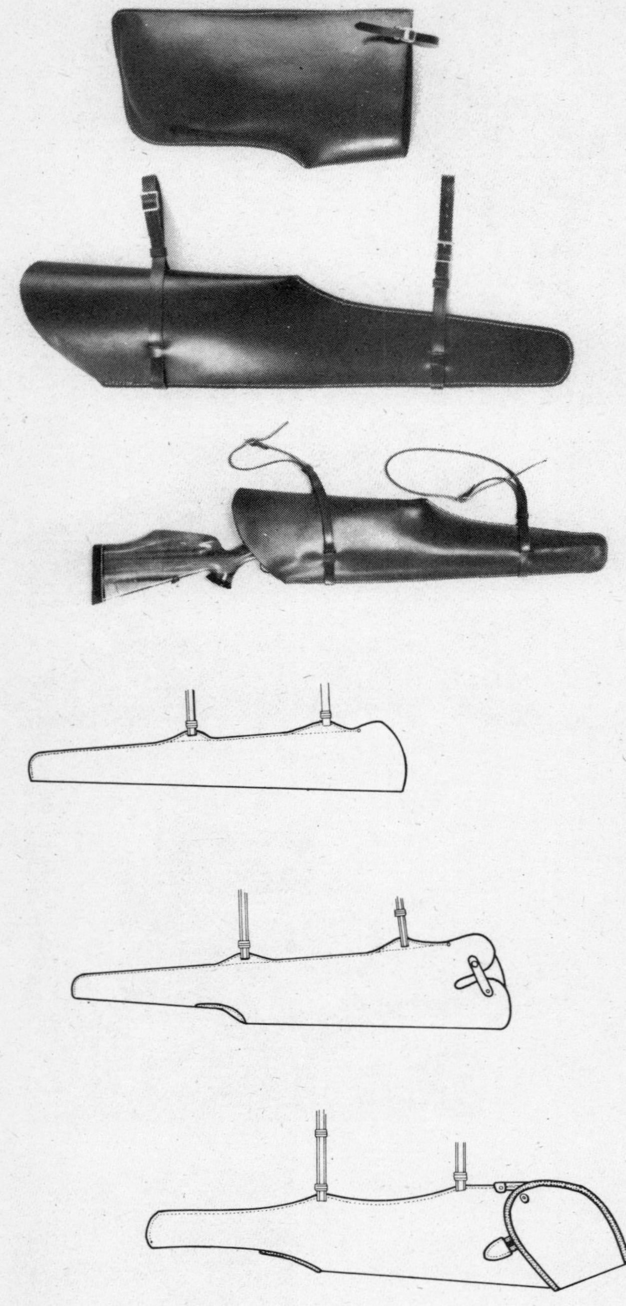

SCABBARD WITH HOOD

Triple K's Model 128 Scabbard is available with matching Model 129 hood. Scabbard and hood are made of heavy strap leather and will accommodate all scoped rifles. It's made for rifles with barrel lengths of up to 26 inches.

Price: $45 for the scabbard; $20 for the hood (specify barrel length when ordering).

From Triple K Manufacturing Company.

RIFLE SCABBARD FOR SCOPED RIFLES

Triple K's Model 121 scabbard is specifically made for scoped rifles and is available in sizes that will handle 20-, 22-, 24- or 26-inch barrel lengths. Made of the best oak-tanned saddle skirting. Walnut-oil finish only; comes with basketweave trim as standard.

Price: $70

From Triple K Manufacturing Company.

CARBINE SCABBARD

This Model 100 Bucheimer scabbard features all-leather construction and is designed for carbine-length firearms. Made of heavy, full-grain cowhide. Natural color. Hood available.

Price: Model 100 $44.50; Hood $31.50.

From J. M. Bucheimer.

RIFLE SCABBARD

The Bucheimer Model 104 scabbard is expressly made for scoped bolt action rifles. Comes with straps; hood available. Made of heavy, full-grain cowhide. Natural color.

Price: $62

From J. M. Bucheimer.

LINED RIFLE SCABBARD

Bucheimer's Model 107 is fully lined with acrylic pile and accommodates all scoped rifles. Comes in natural color, but black is also available. Comes with straps and snap hood. Made of the best full-grain cowhide.

Pride: $89

From J. M. Bucheimer.

SCABBARD & HOOD

Available for 20-, 22-, 24- and 26-inch barrel lengths. Solid, durable item that's made of the finest materials. Accommodates scoped rifle. Features a carrying handle. Two 23-inch saddle straps come with this scabbard. *Well made.*

Price: $100 (Model No. 27-179).

From The Hunter Co.

SCABBARD FOR REMINGTON 600 AND 660 RIFLES

This scabbard has been specifically made for the legion of hunters who swear by the Remington 600 series bolt action rifle. This scabbard is beautifully made. It comes with two 23-inch saddle straps. Made of the best materials.

Price: Plain $36.35; Scoped $43.40.

From The Hunter Co.

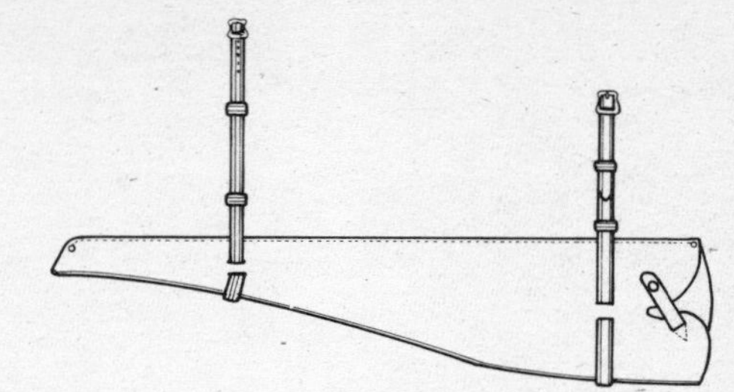

RIFLE SCABBARD

Fits all scoped rifles and comes complete with hood. Made of the best full-grain cowhide. Comes in natural color. Straps included. This is Bucheimer's Model 200 scabbard.

Price: $115.50

From J. M. Bucheimer.

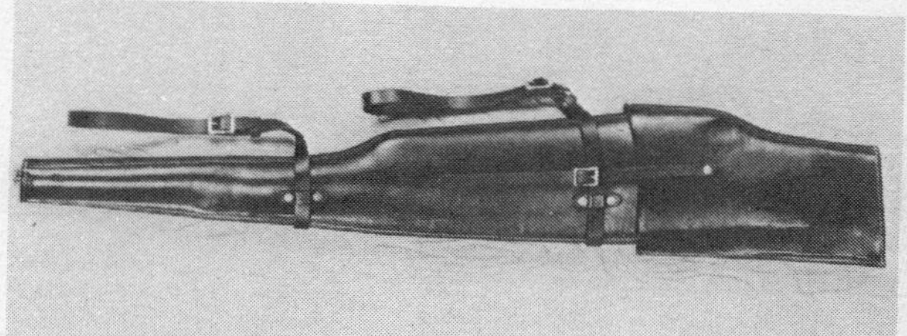

LEATHER SCABBARD

This Lawrence product was designed by one of the top gun writers in the U.S.—Jack O'Connor. It's made from 9-10 ounce saddle leather and is hand molded to accommodate any scoped rifle. Comes with two extra long carrying straps; buckle-down hood or snap flap. Polished nickel hardware. Comes oiled, plain, or, basketweave or flower carved styles. Send tracing of your rifle when ordering. Available with carrying handles, soft leather lining and hand carved initials. *Well made.*

Price: Plain with flap $108.85; with hood $162.75—prices go up to about $300 depending on style and options ordered. (Model 55.)

From Lawrence Leather.

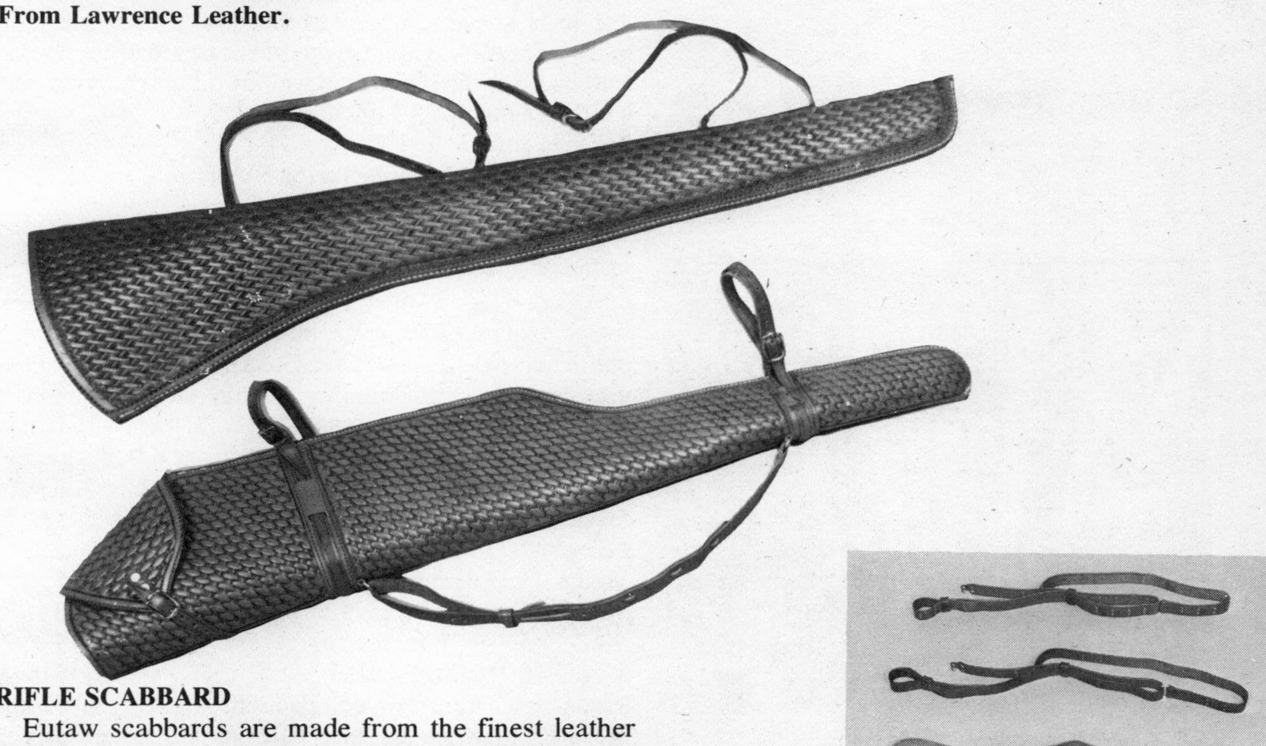

RIFLE SCABBARD

Eutaw scabbards are made from the finest leather obtainable. They come completely lined with glove leather or buckskin suede leather. Two saddle straps are included with each scabbard. Shown nearby (top) is Eutaw's Model 30 Scabbard; just below is that firm's Model 40 scabbard which is designed for scoped rifles and comes with a hood. Both come in either brown or black and are available in plain, basketweave or floral pattern styles.

Price: Model 30 $34.95; Model 40 $69.95.

From The Eutaw Company.

BOYT LEATHER SLINGS

Shown nearby, from top to bottom are Boyt's 1-inch natural russet military-type sling; the same sling, only oiled; and, the Boyt 1-inch oiled carrying strap. All are made of the best materials available.

Price: 1-inch natural russet $11.30; oil version $11.35; carrying strap $9.35.

From Boyt (Div. of Welsh Sporting Goods Corp.).

See the Directory for complete company addresses.

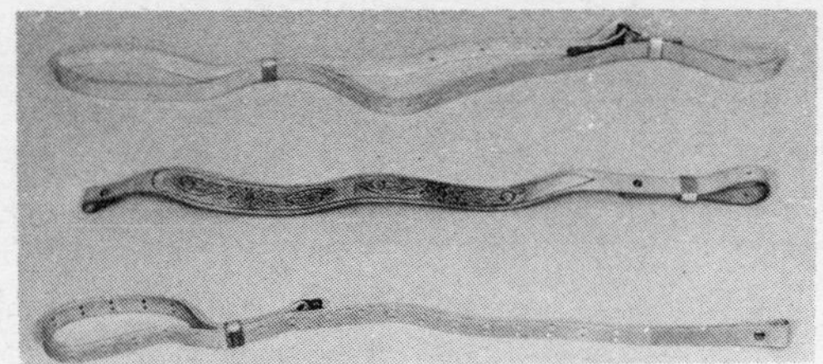

BOYT LEATHER SLINGS

From top to bottom, as shown nearby, the Boyt Fast-Adjust sling; Boyt wide-shoulder carrying strap; and, the Boyt Standard Carrying Strap. All are made of the best materials available.

Price: Fast-adjust $11.30; Wide-shoulder carrying strap $13.20; Standard carrying Strap $9.35

From Boyt (Div. of Welsh Sporting Goods Corp.).

"KWIKFIRE GUN SLING"

Allows the shooter to keep his hands free at all times. However, the Kwikfire sling allows the shooter to get his favorite rifle into action instantly. Comes completely assembled. Made of 1-inch nylon web—all metal parts are bronze finished.

Price: $6.75

From Wayne Products Company.

MILITARY-TYPE SLING

This is Triple K's Style 64 Sling—it's made for durability and utility. Comes with keepers and brass hooks. Fully adjustable. Comes in walnut-oil finish. Available widths: 1-inch or 1¼-inch.

Price: 1-inch $10; 1¼-inch $11.

From Triple K Manufacturing Company.

SLINGS & CARRYING STRAPS

All are made from sturdy saddle leather and come in russet, brown and tan. From left to right, in the nearby photo, Model 40, 41, 42, 42, 43, 43, 43, 44, 45, 46, 46. As you can see, these quality leather slings come in a variety of styles—all are tapered to fit 1-inch swivels.

Price: See below.

Model 40 (Personalized Sling)	$16.95
Model 41 (Plain Finish, Suede-Lined)	$12.95
Model 42 (100% Hand Tooled)	$16.95
Model 43 (Diamond Stitched)	$14.95
Model 44 (Basketweave)	$14.95
Model 45 (All Purpose Sling)	$ 8.95
Model 46 (Plain, Padded)	$16.00
Model 46 (Hand Tooled, Padded)	$20.00

From Kirkpatrick Leather (Div. of American Sales & Mfg. Co.).

RIFLE SLINGS

Hunter's Military Sling comes in both 1-inch and 1¼-inch sizes. These slings are made of beautiful leather that seems to resist cracking over long periods of time. They are well recognized by the experienced shooter. Come with brass hardware and leather keepers. Fully adjustable. *Well made.*

Price: 1-inch $8.25; 1¼-inch $9.95. (Model 200 slings).

From The Hunter Co.

QUICK-FIRE SLING

This Hunter sling has no hooks, buckles or laces. Instantly ready for fast rifle action. Adjusts in seconds to any length. *Well made.* (Comes in 1-inch or 1¼-inch sizes.) Model No. 230.

Price: 1-inch $7.95; 1¼-inch $9.15.

From The Hunter Co.

SHOTGUN SLING

You simply slip the loops over the barrel and butt—it's that easy. Comes with a suede liner. Model 65-531. Well made.

Price: $10.20.

From The Hunter Co.

SLING

Features solid brass hardware and top-quality natural color leather. Fully adjustable. One inch width; stitched keepers.

Price: $10 (Model 244).

From J. M. Bucheimer.

LATIGO QUICK-SET SLING

Brownell's Latigo sling is made of top-quality leather and has an excellent reputation with hunters and sportsmen. It's quickly adjustable for almost any desired length. Well made, reasonably priced. Sling is 1 inch wide.

Price: $11.95

From Brownell's Inc.

MILITARY SLING

Comes in either 1-inch or 1¼-inch widths. Features basketweave styling and is fully adjustable. Oil finish. Model 112 (1¼-inch), Model 113 (1-inch).

Price: 1-inch $5.10; 1¼-inch $7.30.

From Pioneer Products (Div. of King & Priest).

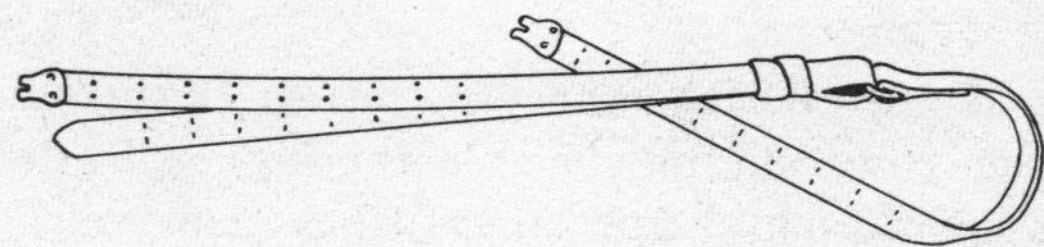

CARRYING STRAP

The Model BSS Eutaw carrying strap features suede lining and an attractive stitching pattern. It comes with Latigo laces at both ends and is tapered to fit 1-inch swivels.

Price: $11.95

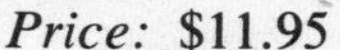

From The Eutaw Company.

CARRYING STRAP

Eutaw's Model BSP carrying strap is fully lined with suede leather. It's made of the best leather, Latigo laced, and is tapered to fit 1-inch swivels.

Price: $11.95

From The Eutaw Company.

See the Directory for complete company addresses.

CARRYING STRAP

Eutaw's Model BSBK carrying strap features basketweave styling and full suede leather lining. Both ends are Latigo laced and tapered to fit 1-inch swivels. Made of the best quality leather.
Price: $11.95
From The Eutaw Company.

CARRYING STRAP

This is Pioneer's Model 550 strap. It's fully adjustable for all rifles and is made of the best leather. Constructed of bridle leather overlayer and lined with plush suede.
Price: $17.78
From Pioneer Products (Div. of King & Priest).

CARRYING STRAP

These suede-lined leather carrying straps really take a load off the shooter's shoulder. Come in stitched or basketweave pattern. *Well-made item.*
Price: See your Browning dealer.
From Browning Arms Company.

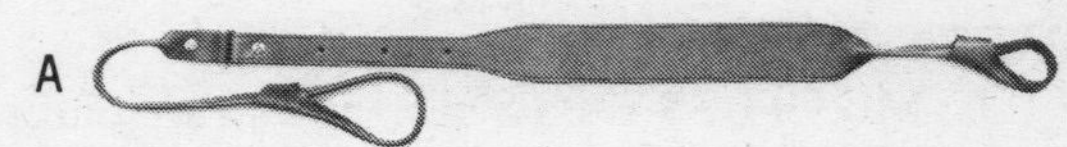

SHOTGUN CARRYING SLING A

No swivels, no hooks, no fuss. This Eddie Bauer sling just slips over the butt and barrel of your favorite shotgun. It's made of full-grain cowhide and is fully lined with suede leather. Features a wide shoulder strap. *Well made.*
Price: $12.95
From Eddie Bauer.

DELUXE CARRYING STRAP

This is a tapered carrying strap of *exceptionally* high quality. It's made of top quality cowhide doubled and stitched with a tough non-slip cowhide lining. *Well made.*
Price: $8.80
From The Hunter Co.

CARRYING STRAP

Triple K's Style 57 carrying strap comes lined, is hand carved and sports an oil finish. Available in saddle tan or walnut. It's tapered at both ends to accommodate the use of sling swivels.
Price: $18
From Triple K Manufacturing Company.

CARRYING STRAP

Triple K's Model 60 carrying strap is tapered at both ends to accommodate the use of swivels. Comes in walnut or tan finishes and sports an attractive stitch pattern.
Price: $12
From Triple K Manufacturing.

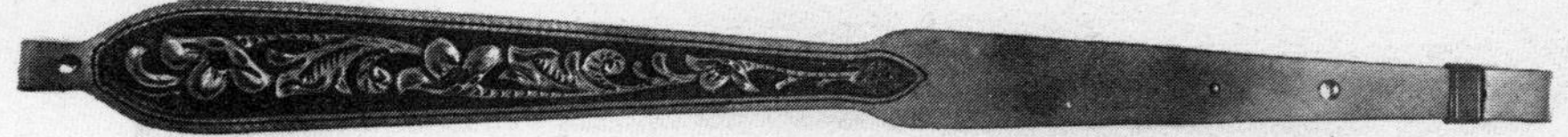

CARRYING STRAP

This is Pioneer's Model 105 carrying strap. It comes tapered for 1-inch swivels, features flower design and is suede lined with padding. Best leather.
Price: $17.94
From Pioneer Products (Div. of King & Priest).

CARRYING STRAP

This is a cobra-style sling made by Pioneer Products. It's tapered at both ends to accommodate 1-inch swivels. Features basketweave styling—made of quality leather; suede lined.
Price: $7.78 (Model 101).
From Pioneer Products (Div. of King & Priest).

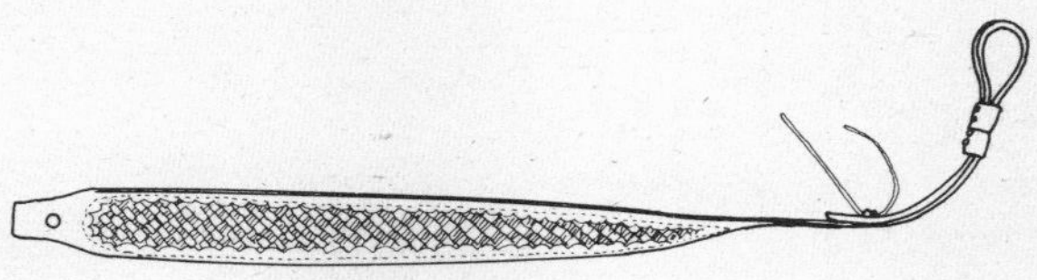

CARRYING STRAP

Called the "Cobra" this carrying strap tapers to 1 inch at either end. Comes in natural color, plain or basketweave styles. Lined with suede leather.
Price: $13.50 (Model 77 or 77 Basketweave).
From J. M. Bucheimer.

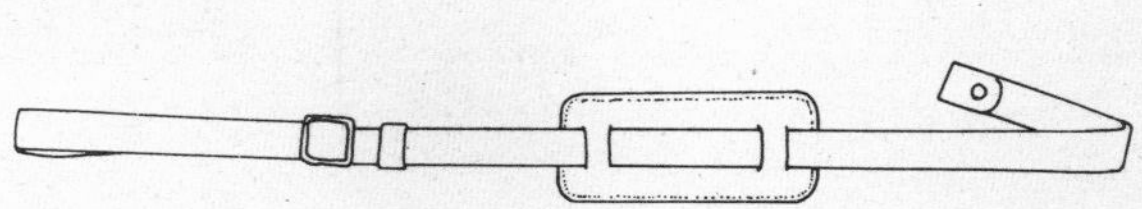

PADDED CARRYING STRAP

Basic strap is 1 inch wide; however, it comes with a generous cushioned shoulder pad. Natural color. Comes with keeper and speed-slide buckle.
Price: $13.50 (Model 222).
From J. M. Bucheimer.

SHOTGUN SLING

No swivels are necessary for this model. It simply slips over the barrel and butt of your favorite shotgun. Made of the best latigo leather, this strap is suede lined and comes with buckle adjustment.
Price: $17.30 (Model 560).
From Pioneer Products (Div. of King and Priest).

CARRYING STRAP

Pioneer's Model 700 carrying strap is figure-8 stitched on mahogany latigo leather. It's fully lined with suede and comes with an adjustable buckle.
Price: $13.90
From Pioneer Products (Div. of King & Priest).

See the Directory for complete company addresses.

CARRYING STRAP

This is Pioneer's Model 430 carrying strap. It's foam padded and comes in brown suede.
Price: $6.96
From Pioneer Products (Div. of King & Priest).

CARRYING STRAPS

In the nearby photo from top to bottom are Lawrence's Models 2, 2F, and 2B carrying straps which represent plain, flower carved and basketweave styles. Straps taper to 1 inch at either end. Suede lined.
Price: Plain $11.95; Flower Carved $17.55; Basketweave $14.25.
From Lawrence Leather.

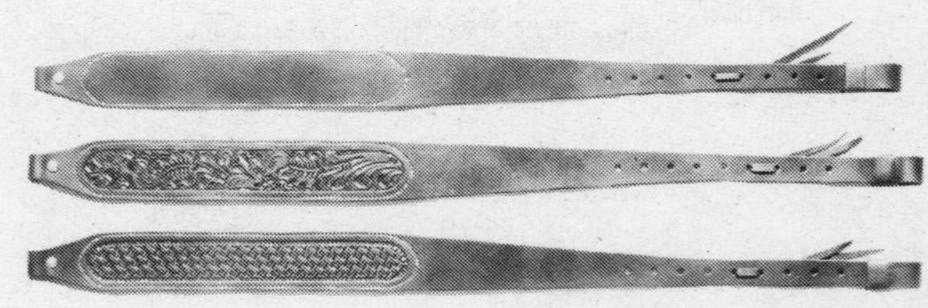

CARRYING STRAP

Model 520. Made of bridle leather with a sliding pad. Features a padded suede liner that slips over a 1-inch suede-lined strap. Adjustable brass buckle.
Price: $15.96
From Pioneer Products (Div. of King & Priest).

SPORT BELT

This Lawrence belt is designed for the man who wants a *quality* leather belt. Comes in 1¼- or 1½-inch widths. Comes unoiled in plain, basketweave or flower carved design. Specify size when purchasing.
Price: Plain $17.95; Basketweave $24.95; Flower Carved $42.85.
From Lawrence Leather.

ADJUSTABLE SHOTSHELL BELT

Holds 24 shotshells, any gauge. Full 2-inch width. Web construction with leather trim. (Model 995.)
Price: $6.50
From J. M. Bucheimer.

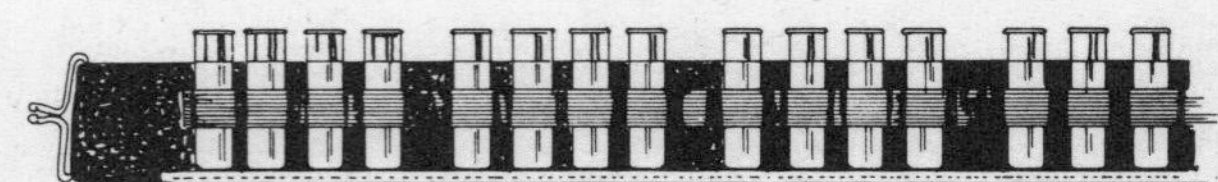

RIFLE CARTRIDGE BELT

Bucheimer's Model 985 cartridge belt is made of solid leather and comes in 2¼-inch width. Holds 30 rounds. Fits most popular calibers.
Price: $22
From J. M. Bucheimer.

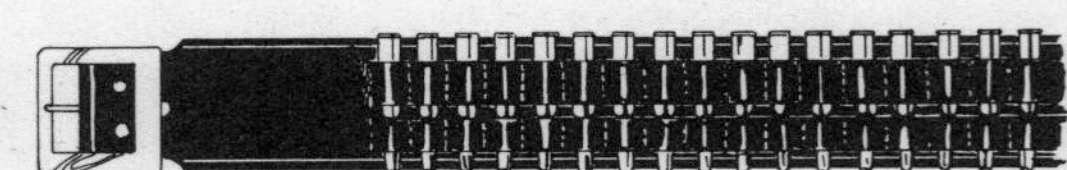

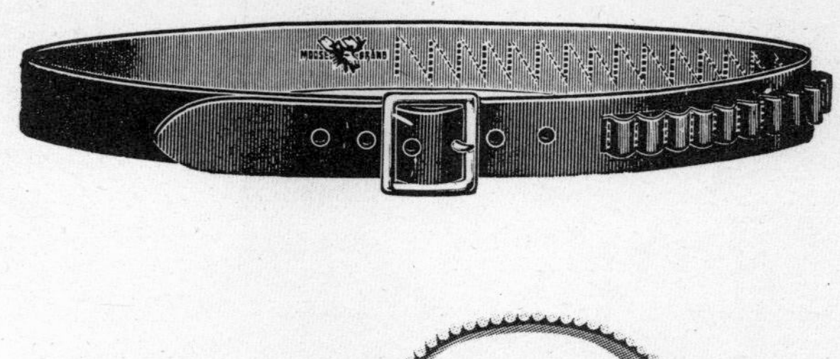

CARTRIDGE BELT
Made of the finest quality, top-grain cowhide. Comes in brown or black and has 30 cartridge loops for any caliber. (Specify caliber and waist size when ordering.) Is 1¾ inches wide.
Price: $14.70 (Model 50).
From Brauer Bros.

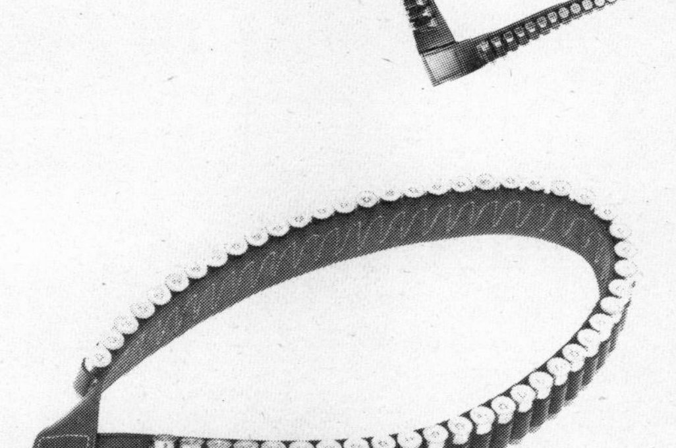

CARTRIDGE/SHOTSHELL BANDOLEER
Lawrence's Model 17 bandoleer is a stitched, one-piece item that's available for several rifle, pistol and shotshell calibers or gauges. Features a hand-rubbed oil finish. Specify caliber or gauge when ordering.
Price: .22 $35.95; .38 $29.65; .44 $27.45; Rifle $51.65; 12 or 20 gauge $33.95.
From Lawrence Leather.

SHOTSHELL BANDOLEER
Eddie Bauer's 2½-inch wide shotshell bandoleer holds two full boxes of regular or magnum loads. Comes in 12 or 20 gauge. Made of oiled, cowhide saddle leather. Shell loops are lock stitched with waxed linen thread. Color is brown. (Specify 12 or 20 gauge when purchasing.)
Price: $26.50
From Eddie Bauer.

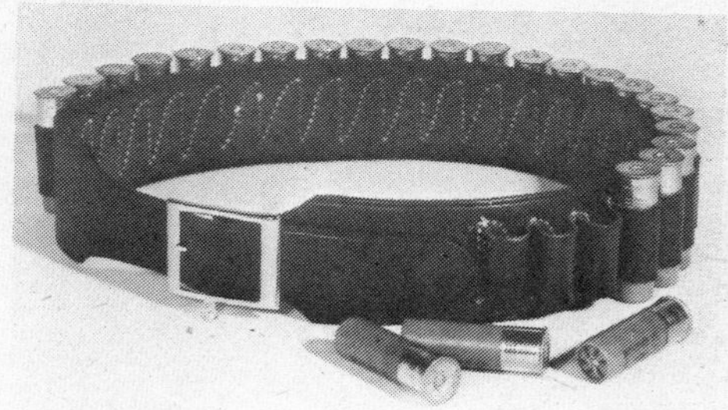

SHOTSHELL BELT
Eddie Bauer's 2½-inch wide shotshell belt holds one full box of magnum or regular shotshells. The belt is made of oiled, brown cowhide saddle leather. Comes in Small (28-32), Medium (33-37), Large (38-42) or Extra Large (43-47). (Specify size when ordering; also, specify 12 or 20 gauge.)
Price: $19.50
From Eddie Bauer.

CENTERFIRE CARTRIDGE BELT
This Hunter belt is 2½ inches wide and comes in oiled russet. Available for all '06-based cartridges; or, H&H Magnum (belted) cartridges. Comes in plain or tooled-leather versions.
Price: Plain $21.50 (Black $21.90) for '06-based rounds; Flowered Russet $27.75 (Black $28.15)—same price for the H&H-based cartridge belt.
From The Hunter Co.

DOUBLE CLIP POUCH FOR AUTOMATICS
Old West's double clip pouch is made of quality leather, features individual pocket snaps and comes with belt loop. Specify make and model of magazine when purchasing.
Price: Plain $10.35; Tooled $11.35.
From Old West, Inc.

CLIP POUCH
Brauer's Model 7 clip pouch is made of black leather cowhide and fits any 2¼-inch belt. Holds 2 clips. Specify make and caliber when ordering.
Price: $12
From Brauer Bros.

CARTRIDGE/SHOTSHELL BANDOLEER
This Old West bandoleer is made of solid, stitched leather. It is available for .22, .38, .45, .30-06; 12, 10, .410 and 20 gauge ammo. (specify when purchasing). You wear this item over the shoulder and across the chest — ammo is easy to get at. Comes in russet, plain leather only.
Price: $21.50.
From Old West, Inc.

See the Directory for complete company addresses.

SPARE CYLINDER POUCH

Lawrence's Model 3 cylinder pouch is made of top quality pliable leather. Fits all belts up to 2½ inches in width. Features snap flap closure.
Price: $7.95.
From Lawrence Leather.

SPARE CYLINDER POUCH

This leather pouch holds your spare cylinder and may be worn on the belt. Features basketweave styling and snap closure. Made of solid leather. Model 12587.
Price: $6.65.
From Old West, Inc.

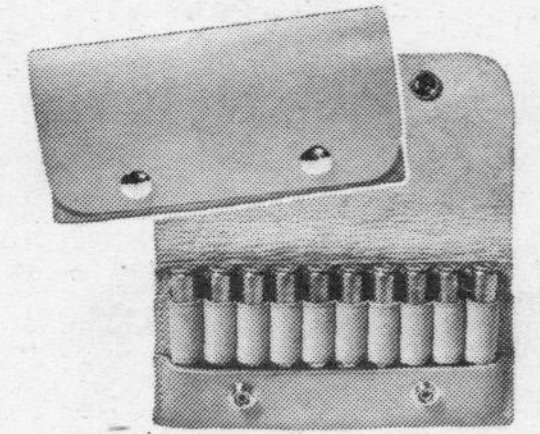

CARTRIDGE POUCH

This Lawrence Model 25 cartridge case holds 10 rifle cartridges. It features snap closure and is made of the best leather. Fits most belts.
Price: Plain $15.35; Basketweave $21.20; Flower Carved $24.75.
From Lawrence Leather.

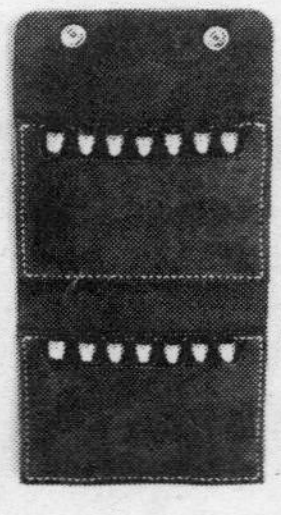

AMMO WALLET

Hunter's Model 22-204 Ammo Pouch is made of quality leather. It features snap closures and holds 14 centerfire rifle cartridges.
Price: See your local dealer or write maker.
From Hunter Leather.

PERCUSSION CAP POUCH

Made of solid leather. Features brass stud closure. Full inner and outer flaps. Model 3148.
Price: $8.45; plain only.
From Old West, Inc.

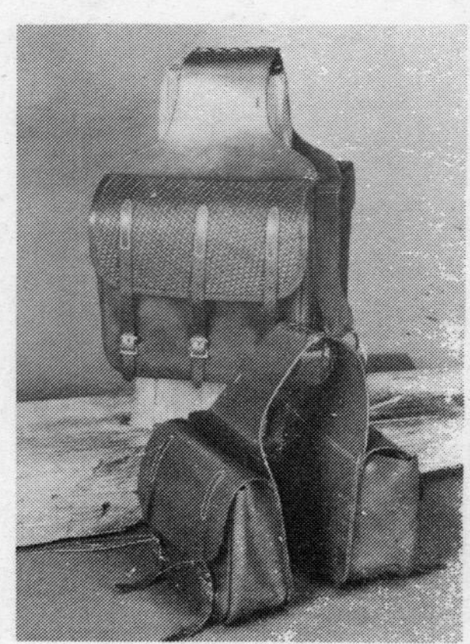

PREMIUM LEATHER SADDLE BAGS

This item is sometimes hard to find. Triple K's Style 1 saddle bag measures 12 inches by 14 inches by 5 inches and is made from the finest oil treated select grade saddle leathers. Comes with extra long straps and Latigo ties. Flaps have triple straps and plated buckles. Comes in plain or basketweave flaps; walnut oil only.
Price: Plain $75; Basketweave $85.
From Triple K Manufacturing Company.

CARTRIDGE BELT

May be used in around-the-waist fashion or over the shoulder. Features 25 calfskin loops. Available in small, medium and large sizes—brown only. May be used with holster.
Price: With .22 Cal. loops $8.20; .38 cal. loops $8.60; plain (no loops) $6.90.
From The Hunter Co.

BOOT WATERPROOFING

Birchwood Casey's Perma-Dri is a spray-on silicone preparation that waterproofs the boot, yet, allows the leather to breathe. For all leather gear. Comes in 8-ounce aerosol can.
Price: $2.19
From Birchwood Casey.

MINK OIL

If you haven't used this leather preparation you ought to give it a try. A lot of hunters swear by this one. Mink Oil is a totally natural product—it's made from 100% mink fat. Original Mink Oil comes in a number of different sized containers; however, the 3-ounce size is, perhaps, the handiest.
Price: About 65¢ per 3-ounce tub.
From Original Mink Oil, Inc.

LEATHER DRESSING KIT

Bianchi's Leather Dressing Kit includes a sheep's wool applicator and an 8-ounce bottle of professional leather dressing. It's the same formula used at the Bianchi factory. Excellent for all holsters and leather goods.
Price: $3
From Bianchi Gunleather.

LEATHER SOFTENER

Primeol leather softener is designed to be mixed with warm water. It penetrates rapidly into the leather leaving the surface free of any tackiness. Lubricates the collagen (protein) fibers of the leather. Helps restore old leather slings, holsters, cases and related equipment.
Price: about $2.50 per 8-ounce container.
From Prime Leather Finisher Co.

LEATHER DRESSING

Old West's Leather Dressing comes in an 8-ounce, applicator-type bottle. Keeps leather soft and pliable. Good for slings, holsters, scabbards and related gear.
Price: $2.10.
From Old West, Inc.

MINK OIL LEATHER PRESERVATIVE

Outer's prime mink oil comes in grease, liquid and spray configurations. Helps keep leather soft, pliable and water resistant. Contains Vitamin E oil.
Price: See your local dealer.
From Outers Laboratories.

See the Directory for complete company addresses.

Section 15

Hunting Accessories

In this section you'll find all or most of those gun accessories that are related to hunting and didn't seem to have a proper home in any other part of the book. Although the section's emphasis is definitely on the hunting theme, you'll find an occasional camping or hiking item that, though not really for hunting, was too unusual and worthwhile not to include.

However, such unmistakably hunting items as decoys and game calls lead off the section, followed by blinds and other game stalking materials. In the remainder of the section you'll find hunting clothing, game drags and a variety of other outdoor items.

Large gun shops and sporting goods outlets are the best local sources for hunting accessories like decoys and calls, and some have a good selection of hunting garb as well.

GOOSE DECOY

This is Carry-Lite's Model 5500 full-bodied Canadian goose complete with leg stand. Each decoy is made of blow-molded polyethylene and individually hand painted. Impervious to freezing weather. Available in Canadian, blue or snow goose configuration.
Price: $118.80 per dozen.
From Carry-Lite Decoys.

GOOSE DECOY

This is Carry-Lite's floating goose decoy. You can get this in snow, blue or Canadian configuration. Hand painted and impervious to freezing.
Price: $98.80 per dozen.
From Carry-Lite Decoys.

GOOSE DECOY

Available in snow, blue or Canadian goose configuration, this Carry-Lite decoy is designed for field use. It's hand-painted and impervious to freezing.
Price: $62.57 per dozen.
From Carry-Lite Decoys.

MALLARD DECOY

This Carry-Lite decoy is that firm's "Aqua-Keel" model that actually uses water for ballast; it reduces carrying weight by 25%. This style of decoy is "self-righting," even in rough weather.
Price: $32.87 per dozen.
From Carry-Lite Decoys.

PINTAIL DECOY

This Carry-Lite pintail decoy is "oversized" for the best visibility. From the tip of the bill to the tip of the tail, the drake pintail (shown) measures a generous 24 inches. It comes with a sealed, weighted keel.
Price: $46.20 per dozen.
From Carry-Lite Decoys.

FLOATING SNOW GOOSE DECOY

This G & H decoy is a full 22 inches long, lightweight, and made of high impact polyethlene. Weighted keel insures self righting. Snap-on heads make for easy transportation. Authentically hand-painted.
Price: $120.95 per dozen.
From G & H Decoy Manufacturing Company.

FIELD-STAKE SNOW GOOSE DECOY

This G & H decoy is hollow, features super-impact plastic construction and comes with removable, folding reinforcement stakes. Each decoy is authentically hand painted. Comes with detachable heads in long, short and feeder configuration.
Price: $67.95 per dozen.
From G & H Decoy Manufacturing Company.

FIELD OR FLOATER CANADIAN DECOYS

The floater is made of high-impact polyethlene while the field decoy comes with removable stakes and is made of high impact plastic. Both feature hand painting and snap-on heads—9 short and 3 long for the floater; 4 each in long, short and feeder configuration for the field decoy.

Price: Floater $120.95 per dozen; Field $67.95 per dozen.

From G & H Decoy Manufacturing Company.

MALLARD DUCK DECOY

These 16-inch decoys are made of high-impact polyethlene, have raised feathers and are hand detailed with non-glare paint. Weighted keel assures self righting in the roughest weather.

Price: $48.95 per dozen.

From G & H Decoy Manufacturing Company.

BLUEBILL (SCAUP) DECOY

This one is for the lake hunters. G & H's Bluebill Decoy features quality hand painting, raised feathers and self righting, line adjustment hook reel. Come by the dozen with 6 drakes, 6 hens.

Price: $48.95 per dozen.

From G & H Decoy Manufacturing Company.

GREEN-WING TEAL DECOYS

Each decoy is 11 inches long, has raised feathers and is hand-painted for detail. Good for the early teal seasons. Come by the dozen—six drakes, six hens.

Price: $45.95 per dozen.

From G & H Decoy Manufacturing Company.

CANADIAN AND SNOW GOOSE DECOYS

These field decoys come with detachable heads that easily pivot into any desired position. Made of tough molded plastic that will not crack, tear or shatter. Come by the dozen along with 12 metal stakes.

Price: Canadians $70; Snows $65.

From Tuff-Lite Decoy Co.

DECOY CARRYING BAGS

Seen nearby, from left to right: the "Paperboy" bag (holds 16 magnum decoys); the "Standard" bag (holds 18 magnum decoys) and the "Extra Large" bag (holds 24 magnum decoys). The Paperboy bag is ideal for the lone hunter. It balances nicely and frees up the hands for other carrying chores.

Price: Paperboy $25.50; Standard $19.95; Extra Large $14.95.

From Sports Haven, Inc.

DECOY ANCHOR CORD

Olt's DAC-100 decoy cord is made of rot-proof nylon. It's dark green in color; and, while it's thin and pliable, this cord is stronger than needed for even the largest decoys. Comes in 100-foot loops.

Price: See your local dealer.

From the P.S. Olt Company, Inc.

Prices shown are subject to change.

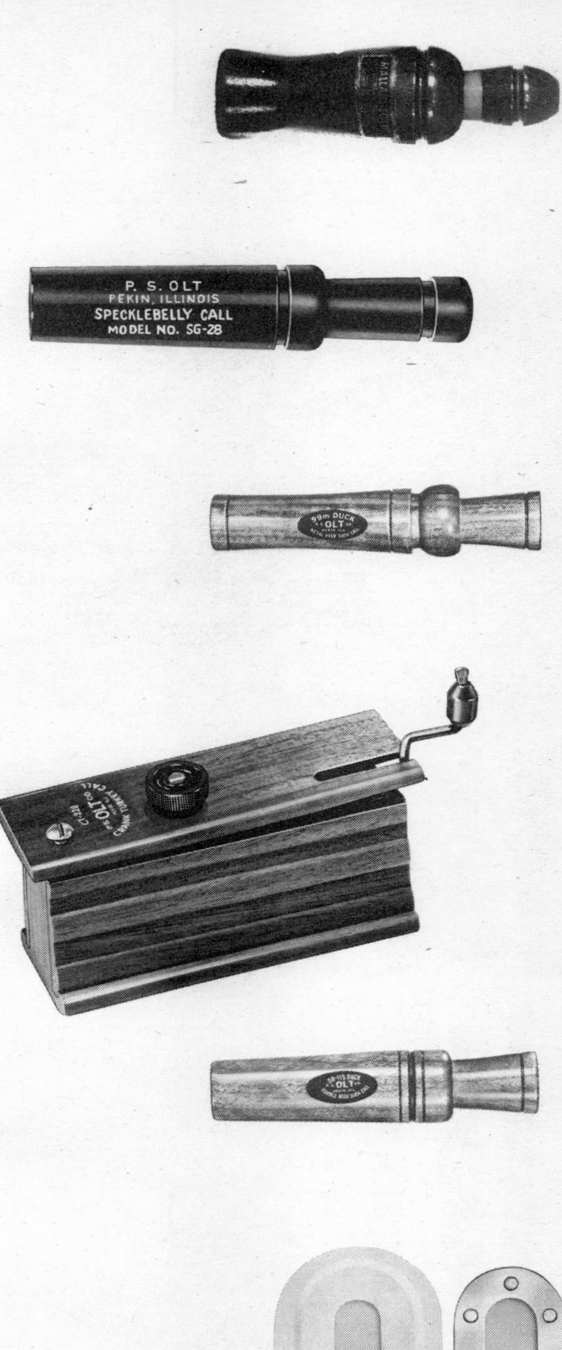

DOUBLE-REED DUCK CALL

This particular call is Mallardtone's latest offering. It features an American black walnut body and has been designed to produce the most realistic sound, tone and "scratch" possible.

Price: $11.95 each.

From Mallardtone Game Calls.

SPECKLEBELLY GOOSE CALL

This Olt reed-type call produces the high pitched calls and cackle of the white-fronted goose. Has a black barrel and a brown tone bell.

Price: $5.95 (cassette instructions $8.95).

From the P.S. Olt Company, Inc.

METAL REED DUCK CALL

This is one of Olt's newest offerings. It comes pre-tuned for the average caller; however, it can be easily adjusted for easier or harder blowing and a finer or coarser tone. The reed material is phosphor bronze while the call is made of the best selected walnut.

Price: $16.95

From the P.S. Olt Company, Inc.

CRANK-OPERATED TURKEY CALL

Olt's CT-220 turkey call has an easy-to-use crank mechanism that produces perfect hew yelps and clucks. The box and lid are made from American walnut while the sound board is made of select cedar. Comes with complete instructions.

Price: $16.95

From the P.S. Olt Company, Inc.

DOUBLE REED DUCK CALL

Olt's DR-115 duck call has a double reed that eliminates "blow-down" and other tone distortions. A heavy reed over the main tone producing reed keeps the tonal reed from vibrating too wildly and distorting. All wood construction with a red cedar reed.

Price: $9.95

From the P.S. Olt Company, Inc.

DIAPHRAGM TURKEY CALLS

Shown nearby, to the left, is the Olt DT-2 call; to the right is the DT-1. Both calls have a latex diaphragm and have extremely realistic tone coupled with motionless operation. The DT-1 has an aluminum frame; the DT-2 has a larger, plastic frame that's better suited to beginners.

Price: $2.95 each.

From the P.S. Olt Company, Inc.

VARMINT CALL

The Crit'r-call reproduces authentic jackrabbit, cottontail and mouse calls. The sounds produced vary with the amount of reed used by the caller. A 30-minute cassette instructional tape is also available.

Price: $7; cassette instruction tape $5.75.

From Rocky Mountain Wildlife Products.

HAND CARVED AND CHECKERED DUCK OR GOOSE CALL

These calls are made one-at-a-time, of the best walnut. Each call is numbered and registered; and, a certificate of origin will be provided upon purchase. Allow 8 weeks for delivery.
Price: $86.95
From Royal Game Call Co., Ltd.

DUCK CALL

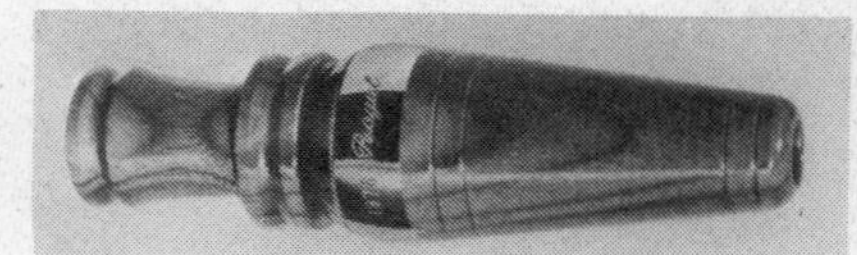

The Royal Duck Call is made from the best materials. A copper band encircles the call and may be engraved with the owner's name and date of purchase.
Price: $24.95
From Royal Game Call Co., Ltd.

GOOSE CALL

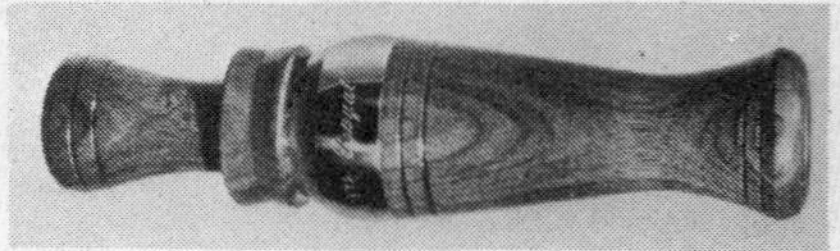

Royal's Goose Call, like their other waterfowl calls, is made of the best materials. Call features a single reed design that allows the call to easily ride from low to high tones. Copper band may be engraved with owner's name and date of purchase.
Price: $27.95
From Royal Game Call Co., Ltd.

WATER FOWL CALLS

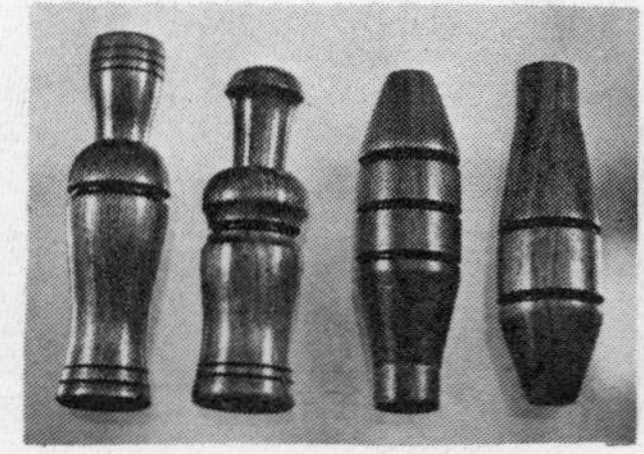

From left, #1655 Goose Call; #1451 Mallard call; #1481 Double Reed Duck Call; #1685 Goose Call. All are designed to give the best tonal quality and are made from American walnut.
Price: $8.29 each.
From Scotch Game Call Company, Inc.

HAND OPERATED GAME AND VARMINT CALLS

From left to right, #1401 Duck Call; #1605 Goose call; #1503 Predator call. All are hand operated, won't freeze-up; will provide consistent tonal quality.
Price: Duck call $9.29; goose call $9.95; predator call $8.95.
From Scotch Game Call Company, Inc.

TURKEY CALL

This call is hand crafted to reproduce the yelp, whine and putt of the wild turkey. Tuned for low-volume control.
Price: $10.95
From Scotch Game Call Company, Inc.

PREDATOR CALL

The Stewart PC-1 varmint call features patented rubber button pitch control that produces "pup" squeal, high-pitch squeaks, mid-range squeals or loud, long-range squeals.
Price: $7.95
From Johnny Stewart Game Calls, Inc.

DUCK CALL

This Johnny Stewart duck call features a double reed. It never needs tuning and may be disassembled for cleaning without fear of upsetting tone or pitch. All plastic construction.
Price: $11.95; Lanyard $1.25
From Johnny Stewart Game Calls, Inc.

DELUXE DUCK CALL

All plastic construction. Never needs tuning. Comes with a double reed and special mouthpiece and sounding bell. Unconditional 1-year warranty.
Price: $19.95; Lanyard $1.25.
From Johnny Stewart Game Calls.

RECORD-TYPE GAME CALLER

For use with 45 RPM game call records. This hi-fi unit runs on 12 "D" cell batteries and is fully portable. Designed to be used in the field to lure in coyotes, crows and other varmints. Controls are outside mounted. Comes with 8-ohm speaker.
Price: $149.95, 8-watt unit; $169.95, 25-watt unit.
From Johnny Stewart Game Calls, Inc.

CASSETTE-TYPE GAME CALLER

This unit is similar to Stewart's Record-Type Game Caller with the exception it uses handy cassette cartridges, not records. Uses 12 "D" cell batteries for power and is fully portable. Comes with shoulder strap.
Price: $189.95, 8-watt unit; $209.95, 25-watt unit.
From Johnny Stewart Game Calls, Inc.

DEER CALL KIT

Each kit contains deer calling booklet, information on age of deer, dressing/skinning instructions, extra reeds and the call itself. Helps bring deer in close, halts running deer and gets bucks out of hiding.
Price: About $10.
From Sport-Lore, Inc.

DUCK CALL RECORDING

Comes in 45 RPM recording and is designed to instruct duck hunters in the art of calling.
Price: $2.50
From Sure-Shot Game Calls.

PREDATOR CALL

Made from selected black walnut. Tone attracts various varmints.
Price: $4.95
From Sure-Shot Game Calls.

GAME CALL LANYARD

Spring loaded lanyard grips call firmly and allows the user to drop the call, at a moment's notice, without fear of losing it in the brush.
Price: Single 89¢; double $1.09.
From Sure-Shot Game Calls.

"APPLE LURE" FOR DEER HUNTERS

Simply put, Kolpin's Apple-Lure smells like apples to deer. It's their favorite food. Put a few drops around your stand or on your clothes. Comes in a leak-proof bottle with self-dispensing cap.
Price: $2.50 per 1-ounce bottle.
From Kolpin Manufacturing, Inc.

"DOE-IN-RUT" BUCK LURE

This is Kolpin's No. 69 deer lure. Contains undiluted doe secretions and urine collected when the season's right. Comes in a leak-proof bottle with self-dispensing cap.
Price: $4.95 per 1-ounce bottle.
From Kolpin Manufacturing, Inc.

DEER LURE

Buck Stop's new Acorn deer lure combines one of the deers' favorite foods with pure deer musk. Squeeze a few drops on your clothes or around your stand; it's effective in any weather condition.
Price: See your local dealer.
From Buck Stop Lure Company.

DOG TRAINING SCENTS

Available in rabbit or pheasant scents, these items help train your favorite hunting dog to trail the appropriate game.
Price: See your local dealer.
From Buck Stop Lure Company

DEER DRAG

The "Easy Way" deer drag helps ease the chore of getting your venison out of the woods. It's made of 2-inch wide blaze orange webbing and comes with 8 feet of nylon rope. (Field dressing instructions are on the reverse side of each package.)
Price: $3.70 each.
From D & H Products.

TREE-CLIMBING SPIKES

Each "step" screws in and out by hand and is used to get the deer hunter up high, into his tree stand. In short, each set of steps is a portable tree-ladder.
Price: 8-step $25.95; 6-step $19.95; 4-step $14.95.
From Deer Me Products.

"NO. 88 BUCK LURE"

Strong enough to overcome human odor, this scent will attract all big game; such as deer, moose, elk or deer. Contains pure musk. Comes in a leak-proof bottle with self-dispensing cap.
Price: $3 per each 1-ounce bottle.
From Kolpin Manufacturing, Inc.

HOT SEAT

All you do is "sit-on-it"—the seat does the rest. Body pressure creates an instant heat source. Perfect for the waterfowler. Made of heavy vinyl and comes with belt hanger hook. Blaze orange or blaze orange/camouflage patterns available.
Price: Regular size $4.50; XL Size $5.50; Blaze-orange and camouflage combo $4.75.
From Kolpin Manufacturing, Inc.

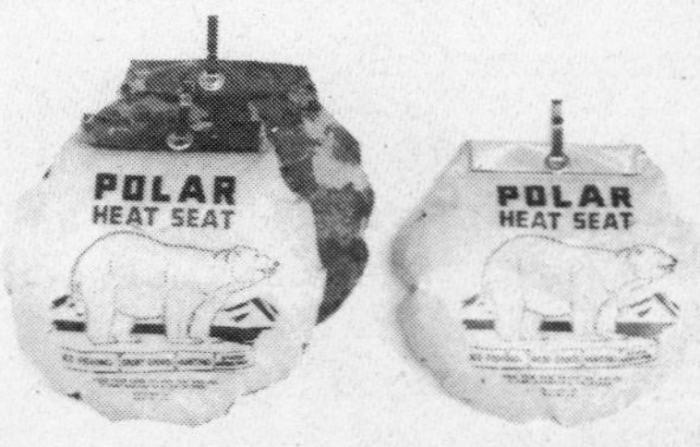

Prices shown are subject to change.

CAMO FACE MASK

Penn's Camo face mask helps eliminate face reflection for the varmint, turkey or deer hunter. It's built around solid eyeglass frames. One size fits all.

Price: $5.50

From Penn's Woods Products.

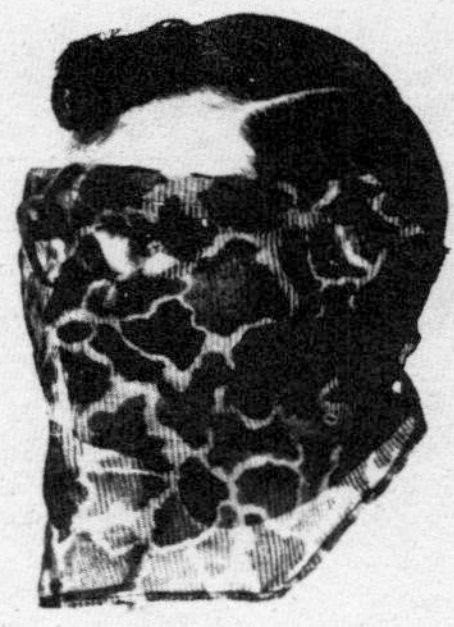

CAMO FACE CREAM

Comes in handy plastic tubes in brown, green or black colors. Easily applied to the face and hands. Helps insure the game won't see you first.

Price: $2.49 per 2-tube package.

From Penn's Woods Products.

DEER LURE

Pete Rickard's "Indian Buck Lure" was the first buck lure to be offered commercially (1945). Made from pure musk, this preparation effectively hides human scent and attracts game even in a down-wind situation.

Price: $3.39 for a 1¼-ounce squeeze bottle.

From Pete Rickard, Inc.

DEER LURE

Super-Doe Buck Lure is made from 100% doe-in-heat musk in a special quality odorless anti-freeze.

Price: $5

From Pete Rickard, Inc.

CAMOUFLAGE BLINDS

Each blind includes one cover, three support legs and six body sections. Twelve interchangeable covers are offered to fit each of the two available frame sizes. Fabrics are cotton duck, nylon taffeta, nylon mesh and marsh mat. Come in green or brown camouflage, snow white or natural corn (for the marsh mat).

Price: Starts at $49.95

From Sports Haven, Inc.

GAME STRAP

The strap is made of polyester with a suede-leather overlay; and, has six individual D-ring loops.

Price: $5.95

From Sports Haven, Inc.

HUNTER'S PORTABLE SEAT

This rugged seat has a sturdy aluminum frame with a base that won't sink into the ground. Comes in two fabrics (your choice): cotton duck or nylon mesh. Your choice of green or brown camouflage.

Price: $22.75

From Sports Haven, Inc.

"HOT SEAT" HUNTER'S CUSHION

This is one item duck hunters will flock to. It features cloth-backed vinyl construction. The seat itself is filled with a material that naturally warms up when you sit on it.

Price: Jumbo Camouflage $6.10; Jumbo Blaze Orange $7.20

From Weather Shield Sports Equipment Co.

FOLDING HUNTER'S SEAT

Holds up to 250 pounds. Features a light-weight durable steel frame, support chains and double-stitched seat. Folds to 10″ x 7″ x 1½″.

Price: See your local dealer

From Woodstream Corp.

See the Directory for complete company addresses.

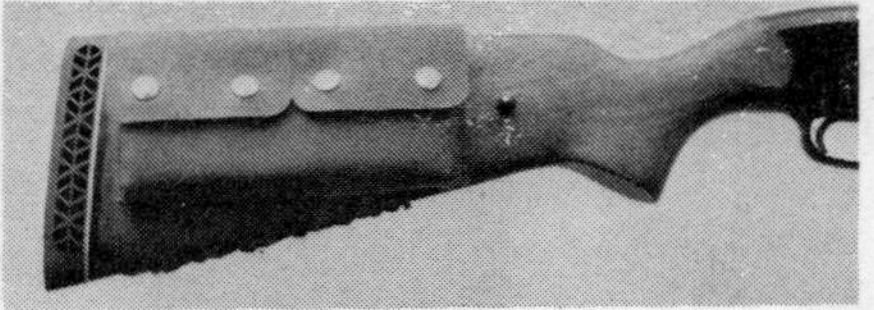

STOCK-MOUNTED AMMO CARRIER

Designed to hold a good supply of shotgun ammo. Lace-on feature insures firm fit; snap closures keep shells securely in place. Made of top quality leather.

Price: $15.88

From BDU Enterprises.

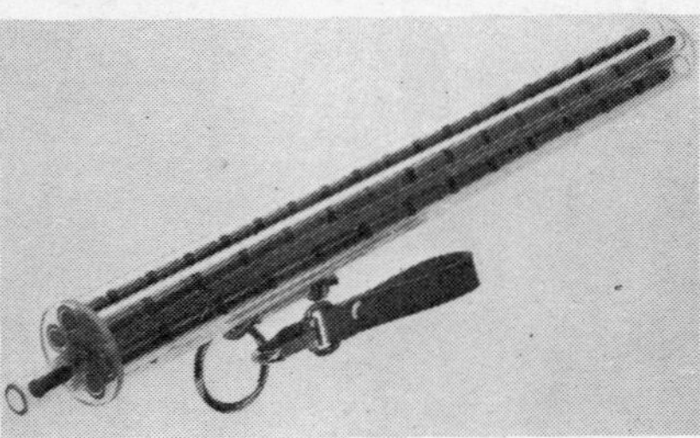

RIMFIRE AMMO DISPENSER

The E-Z Loader holds a tremendous amount of rimfire ammo. Dispenses 13 rounds of Long Rifle ammo at the twist of a wrist. Perfect for loading any tube-fed rimfire rifle. Comes with belt loop and snap and it's well made.

Price: $14.95

From Del Rey Products, Ltd.

SHOTSHELL BANDOLEER

Shown nearby (top left) is Kolpin's No. 5 Deluxe Web Shell Belt. Instantly adjustable from 28- to 46-inch waist size, this belt features 20 elasticized shell pouches. Marsh tan in color. To the lower right you'll see Kolpin's No. 4 Web Shell Belt. It adjusts to fit all waist sizes and features elasticized shell loops. Both belts accommodate 12, 16 or 20 gauge shotshells.

Price: No. 5 $9.50; No. 4 $6.50.

From Kolpin Manufacturing, Inc.

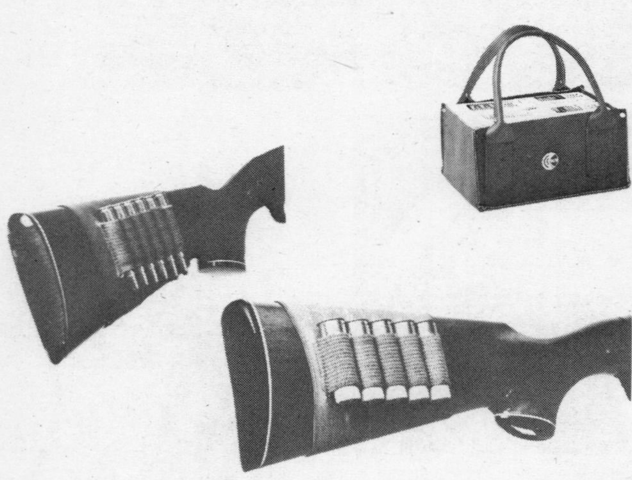

SHELL CARRIER

This one's made of heavy black expanded vinyl that won't soak up moisture in the field or in a wet duck blind. Holds 4 boxes of shells.

Price: $7.50

From Kolpin Manufacturing, Inc.

AMMO CARRIER

Made of strong surgical elastic, this slip-on ammo sling comes in two sizes. Style "S" holds five 12, 16, 20 or 28 gauge shotshells. Style "R" holds six centerfire cartridges or .410 shotshells.

Price: $3.99

From Perry's Ammo Sling Co.

CAMOUFLAGE CARGO, AND GUN CARRYING CASES/BAGS

The camouflage design has been done by wildlife artist Maynard Reece. This one-of-a-kind camouflage pattern was donated to Ducks Unlimited; and, a percentage of all sales goes directly to D.U.

Maynard Reece is shown with the entire line which includes: clockwise from top left, 1) Gun Case; 2) Back/Carry Pack; 3) Medium Duffle; 4) "Hands Free" Valet/Travel Pack; 5) Sportsman's Travel Tote; 6) Bob Allen (Medium) Cargo Bag; 7) Bob Allen (Large) Cargo Bag. Free Bob Allen Sportswear Catalogs are available by writing the company.

Prices: See your local dealer.

From Bob Allen Sportswear.

CAMPAIGN COAT AND SLACKS

New from Bob Allen Sportswear, these items are available in both men's and ladies' styles and sizes. The coat and slacks are made of 65% polyester, 35% cotton. Jacket has epaulets, large pockets and belt. Slacks feature cargo-type pockets full cut for comfort, large belt loops and rubberized inner waistband. Ladies' sizes 8-18 for slacks; 32-40 for the jacket. Men's sizes 32-44 for slacks; 38-50 for the jacket.

Price: Jacket $39.95; slacks $32.95.

From Bob Allen Sportswear.

CAMOUFLAGE WILD FOWL PARKA

This Bob Allen offering is insulated with polar-guard, a high-loft fiber-fill. (Readily cleans or launders.) The outer material comes in brown/green/tan camouflage, is water repellent and is made of 65% polyester, 35% cotton. Other features include cargo pockets, draw-string hood, heavy-duty zipper and slash-style hand-warming pockets.

Price: $119.95 in S, M, L and XL sizes.

From Bob Allen Sportswear.

SAFARI BUSH JACKET

Made of 50% cotton, 50% polyester. Features two Naughasuede recoil patches, four expandable bellows pockets and adjustable button sleeves.

Price: $38.94

From Game Winner.

BLAZE ORANGE HUNTING VEST

Comes in solid blaze orange for maximum safety and hunter recognition. Has a blood-proof nylon game bag, shell loops and shell pockets.

Price: $12.44

From Game Winner.

CAMOUFLAGE COVERALLS

This one-piece green or brown camouflage hunting suit has a two-way zipper, two large front pockets and other features. It's made from 50% polyester and 50% cotton. Available in all sizes.

Price: $20.86 in either color.

From Game Winner.

2-PIECE LIGHTWEIGHT CAMOUFLAGE SUITS

Available in either green or brown camouflage. Designed to be used over other clothes if so desired. Jacket has two large pockets and button front. Pants have two front and two rear pockets. Available in all sizes.

Price: $20.86 in either color

From Game Winner.

BRUSH CHAPS

These chaps are made of tough featherlight nylon—they're *waterproof*. Helps keep the thorns, burrs and brush off your legs. Chaps are held up by adjustable straps that fit through your belt. Available in all sizes.

Price: $15.42

From Game Winner.

See the Directory for complete company addresses.

SLEEVELESS HUNTING COAT

This one represents a smart marriage between the full coat and vest. It's made of 50% dacron and 50% cotton. It's stain and rain repellent. This coat has a full width, expandable blood-proof game bag on the back with front entrance on either side of the front zipper. Elastic shell loops are sewn to the inside of the pockets. Available in most sizes.

Price: $27.12

From Game Winner.

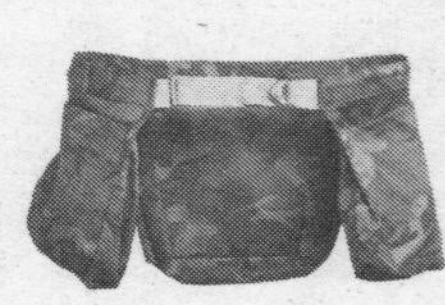

DELUXE BRUSH PANTS

Super-tough nylon facing turns away the most stubborn brush. Thistles and burrs won't cling to the facing. The nylon facing extends ¾ of the way up the front and about ½-way up the back of the legs. Features leg zippers, four pockets and high-rise cut for best comfort afield. Available in most popular sizes.

Price: $32.12

From Game Winner.

WAIST GAME BAG

Perfect for dove hunters, this bag has side pockets that are designed as shell carriers. Comes in green camouflage duck that's water repellent. Extra-large game bag is blood-proof and has snaps and a convenient flap. Available in all waist sizes.

Price: $8.34

From Game Winner.

BOOT INSOLES

Kolpin's Polar Comfort Insoles are made of foam material with a cotton surface—they reflect body heat and can be trimmed to fit any shoe or boot.

Price: $2.25 per pair.

From Kolpin Manufacturing, Inc.

LICENSE BACK TAGS

Both feature plastic construction and a sturdy safety pin for fastening to the back of your hunting coat. Blaze orange in color.

Price: Top tag 85¢; bottom tag 90¢.

From Kolpin Manufacturing, Inc.

CAMOUFLAGE PARKA

While it weighs a light 32 ounces, this parka is 100% waterproof. Marathon's Weather King Parka comes in either green or brown pattern camouflage. The quilted lining insures warmth, yet reduces condensation as well. Available in all sizes.

Price: $54.95

From Marathon Rubber Products.

KNEE-LENGTH PARKA

Comes in either green or brown pattern camouflage and weighs only 16 ounces. It's 100% waterproof, and puncture/tear-resistant too. Comes with a draw-string hood and elastic wrists. Available in all sizes.

Price: $34.95

From Marathon Rubber Products.

JACKET/PANTS/HOOD CAMOUFLAGE RAINGEAR

It's 100% waterproof. Called the "Huntsman," this outfit comes in either brown or green camouflage pattern. The entire suit weighs a light 20-ounces; yet, is puncture and tear resistant, even at 15 degrees above zero. The jacket has elastic wrists, drawstring hood and zipper front. Pants have a drawstring waist and snap cuffs.

Price: Jacket $29.95; pants $19.95.

From Marathon Rubber Products.

BRITISH-TAN POPLIN TROUSERS

These trousers are perfect for early season hunts where heat, not cold, is an important consideration. They are made from crease-resistant poplin, have a heavy-duty zipper, large belt loops and slash pockets.
Price: $14.99
From Saf-T-Bak, Inc.

HUNTING LICENSE BACK TAGS

Available in green, orange or clear plastic. Comes complete with tag, pin and sew-on tab.
Price: 95¢, green or orange; 55¢ clear.
From Scotch Game Call Company, Inc.

CAMOUFLAGE DECOY MITTENS

These are waterproof mittens that eliminate cold, wet hands when setting or retrieving decoys. They come in brown camouflage and have extra long cuffs.
Price: $7.95
From Sports Haven, Inc.

REVERSIBLE GOOSEDOWN JACKET

The Stearns Mark V goosedown jacket has a water repellant suede-finish nylon outer shell. It also features full-knit cuffs and 3-layer construction. The Mark V offers Velcro closures, reversible zipper and cargo pockets as well.
Price: $87.50, in tan/camouflage or camouflage/blaze.
From Stearns Manufacturing.

LADIES HUNTING BOOTS

The Royal Red Ball Vac Morgan boot is now available in ladies' sizes. This 12-inch rubber boot comes in marsh brown color, is non-insulated and lightweight. Has a cushioned insole, steel shank and is 100% waterproof. All ladies' sizes are available.
Price: $30
From Uniroyal, Inc.

HUNTING SUIT

Royal's new "Go-Suits" come in 5 solid colors and two camouflage patterns. (Available solid colors are blue, red, yellow, green and white; camouflage patterns come in green or brown.) The jacket comes with hood and visor, heavy-duty zipper and seams. Matching trousers feature a shock-cord waist and zipper fly. Women's styles and sizes are also available. S, M, L and XL.
Price: Men's or women's suit about $65.
From Uniroyal, Inc.

WATERPROOF CAMOUFLAGE SUIT

The jacket comes with hood and visor, heavy-duty zipper, large pockets and license holder on the back. Trousers have draw-cord and elasticized waist. Camouflage is of random pattern to insure best results. S, M, L, XL and XXL.
Price: Jacket $42; Trousers $24
From Uniroyal, Inc.

HUNTING VEST

Forest Green in color, this vest comes with shell loops, detachable game bag, flap pocket, shoulder pad and flap pockets. It's made of water-repellent 8.65-ounce army duck.
Price: $12.99
From Saf-T-Bak, Inc.

BIB OVERALLS

These handy overalls are 100% waterproof, have an elasticized waist and come with heavy-duty suspenders. Perfect for wet-morning hunts. S, M, L, XL.
Price: $32.50
From Uniroyal, Inc.

See the Directory for complete company addresses.

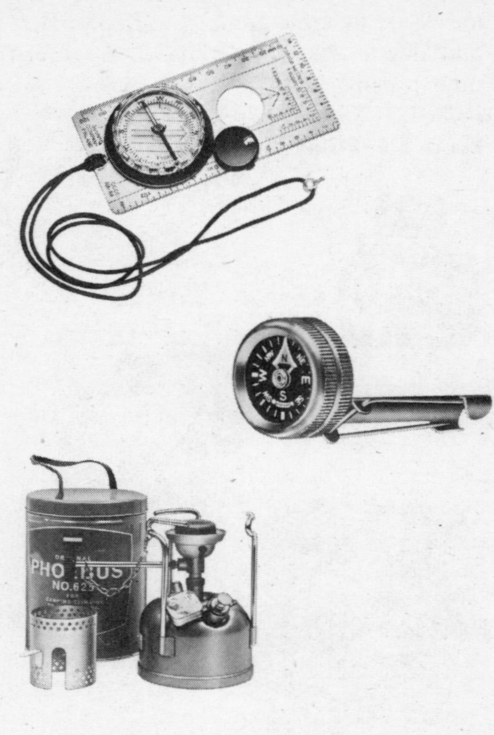

INSULATED BOOT LINERS

Made of 100% nylon shell; dacron filled for maximum warmth. Quilted construction. Bright red in color, these liners are available in all popular sizes.

Price: $6.10

From Weather Shield Sports Equipment Co.

COMPASS

Comes complete with straight-plate protractor and carrying thong.

Price: $15.95

From Precise.

COMPASS

This particular compass is made in Germany. It's made to be pinned on the front of the coat so the hunter can easily glance down to see which direction he's headed in.

Price: $7.95

From Precise.

PORTABLE CAMP STOVE

Weighing slightly under 3 pounds, this handy stove runs on white gas. Solid construction.

Price: $47.60

From Precise.

FIRST-AID KIT

Sigma's FA-2 Trail-Aid Kit provides enough first-aid gear for the treatment of field injuries. Handles everything from sunburn to bone breaks. See below for a complete list of the kit's contents:

1 Carrier box	12 Aspirin
1 Eye Irritation Solution	2 Disposable Soap Pads
1 Wire Splint	1 Tube, Burn Ointment
6 Salt Tablets	1 Gauze Bandage 1″x6 yds
3 Ammonia Inhalants	2 Gauze Pads 2″x2″
12 ¾″ plastic Bandage Strips	3 Gauze Pads 3″x3″
1 ½″x2½ yds. Adhesive Tape	1 Single Edge Razor Blade
1 Presun Gel	6 Safety Pins

Price: $14.95

From Sigma Scientific, Inc.

FIRST-AID KIT

The FA-3 first-aid kit is designed for camp use. This kit has a broad array of first-aid creams, gels, bandages, etc. For a list of the Kits' contents see below:

1 Carrier Box	1 First Aid Cream
1 Elastic Bandage 2″x5 yds	1 Presun Gel
1 Gauze Bandage 1″x5 yds	1 Wire Splint
1 Gauze Bandage 2″x5 yds	1 Sting-Eze (for bites)
1 Gauze Bandage 3″x5 yds	12 Aspirin
5 Gauze Pads 2″x2″	6 Salt Tablets
5 Gauze Pads 3″x3″	2 Tubes Burn Ointment
5 Gauze Pads 4″x4″	1 Eye Irritation Solution
12 ¾″ Plastic Bandages	1 Emergency Blanket
6 Antiseptic Swabs	6 Safety Pins
2 Disposable Soap Pads	1 Single Edge Razor Blade
3 Ammonia Inhalants	1 Adhesive Tape-Waterproof

Price: $34.95

From Sigma Scientific, Inc.

SPORTSMAN'S SIGNAL KIT

If you ever find yourself "lost" one of these kits may save your hide. Contains a 10-mile mirror, red smoke cannister, fire-starter kit, two aerial flares—all packaged in a handy belt pack.

Price: $14.95 each.

From Sigma Scientific, Inc.

AERIAL FLARES

Each Skyblazer flare pak contains three red flares that weigh a light 1 ounce each. They burn at 20,000 candle power and burn out while still in the air; and, will float on water while burning. Visible over 20 miles.

Price: $10.95 per 3-pak; also available with white flares at the same price.

From Sigma Scientific, Inc.

DISTRESS PANEL MARKER

Comes in distress-orange color and measures 4′x8′. Also serves as a temporary shelter. Easy to Store.

Price: $2.95

From Sigma Scientific, Inc.

AUTOMATIC DUCK/GOOSE PICKER

This electric plucker features 4-inch rubber fingers that pick a duck or goose clean (in minutes) without harming the flesh. Runs off of regular house current. Comes with ⅓-hp. motor and bag attachment for feathers. No muss, no fuss.

Price: $324.95

From G & H Decoy Manufacturing Company.

JONAS BROTHER'S GAME SKINNING GUIDE

This handy field guide was written by the folks who figuratively "wrote the book" on taxidermy. Tells you how to field dress small and large game; also, how to prepare your animal for trophy mounting. An invaluable pocket-sized book.

Price: $1

From Denver Jonas Bros., Inc.

TAXIDERMY KITS

These Kits are a do-it-yourself item—they come with *complete* instructions. Available for birds, fish and mammals. See the following list for prices and available kit types.

Item Number	Description	Suggested Retail
1005	Fish Mounting Display Pack Includes: 8 Fish Mounting Kits 6 Extension Kits	$109.30
1015	Fish Mounting Kit	9.95
1025	Bird Mounting Kit	9.95
1035	Mammal Mounting Kit	9.95
1045-A	Extension Kit	4.95
1045-B	Universal Fish Eyes (18 Pcs.)	48.95
1055	Bird Head & Rugging Kit	9.95
1065	Antler Mounting Kit	9.95
1075	Tanning Kit	9.95

From E-Z Mount, Inc.

See the Directory for complete company addresses.

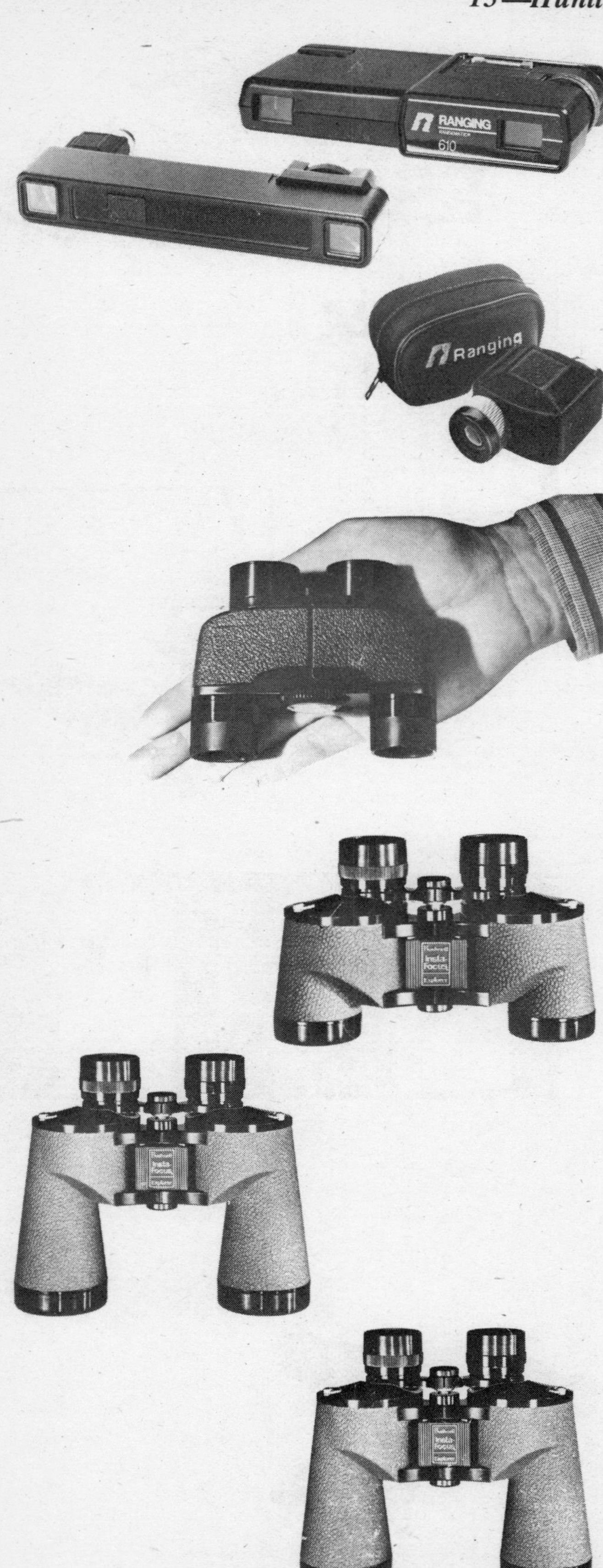

RANGEFINDERS

The Ranging Model 610 Handgun rangefinder is a new item designed specifically for the handgun hunter. The 610 instantly tells the distance to objects and game out to 200 yards. Ranging's Model 1000 Rangemaster MK-5 provides accurate range information from 50 to 1000 yards. Both of these units are well suited for game or varmint hunters.

Price: $49.95 for the 610; $69.95 for the 1000 MK-5
From Ranging, Inc.

MONOCULAR

This 6x18 Ranging monocular is a real weight saver—it weighs a scant 4 ounces and comes with its own belt-loop carrying case.

Price: $24.95
From Ranging, Inc.

BUSHNELL 6X AND 7X CUSTOM COMPACT BINOCULARS

These lightweight 11-ounce field glasses are perfect for the hunter who has to haul a lot of gear. Features fully coated lenses and roll down eyecups. Field of view at 1000 yards is 420 feet (6X) and 368 feet (7X). Easily fit in the pocket. Center focus.

Price: 6X — $189.50; 7X — $199.50 (*20-year* warranty).
From Bushnell Optical Company.

BUSHNELL EXPLORER 7X35 EXTRA WIDE ANGLE BINOCULARS

These field glasses also come with Bushnell's Insta Focus feature. The field of view at 1000 yards is a generous 578 feet. These binoculars are a good bet for plains and Western-region hunters. Fully coated lenses.

Price: $140 (5-year warranty).
From Bushnell Optical Company.

BUSHNELL "EXPLORER" 7X50 EXTRA BRIGHT BINOCULARS

You'll get all the light you need when you use these field glasses. They are specifically designed for extreme low-light situations—perfect for early morning and late afternoon hunting. Field of view at 1000 yards is 420 feet. Features fully-coated lenses and Bushnell's Insta Focus.

Price: $150 (5-year warranty).
From Bushnell Optical Company.

BUSHNELL EXPLORER 10X50 BINOCULARS

When it comes to varmint hunting, these big 10X50's really fill the bill when it comes to long range spotting. Lenses are fully coated and the field of view at 1000 yards is 368 feet. Comes with Insta Focus feature.

Price: $155 (5-year warranty).
From Bushnell Optical Company.

Prices shown are subject to change.

BUSHNELL 6-18X, 35mm ZOOM BINOCULARS

Bushnell's Insta Focus feature and roll down eye cups are standard with these glasses. Power range is instantly adjustable from 6X to 18X and the field of view at 1000 yards ranges from 230 to 205 feet, depending upon the power selected.

Price: $176 (5-year warranty).

From Bushnell Optical Company.

BUSHNELL 7-21X, 40mm ZOOM BINOCULARS

This set of field glasses are ideal for spotting and confirming game at medium to long ranges. Bushnell's Insta Focus feature is standard with these glasses. Lenses are fully coated and the eyepieces have fold down rubber cups. Field of view ranges from 288 feet to 172 feet (at 1000 yards) depending on the power selected. Instant power change.

Price: $186 (5-year warranty).

From Bushnell Optical Company.

BUSHNELL 8-24X, 50mm ZOOM BINOCULARS

Within Bushnell's zoom binocular lineup, these 8X to 24X field glasses provide the most power. If you are a hunter or guide who must spot and quickly confirm game at long ranges then these field glasses should rate high on your list of accessories. The field of view at 1000 yards ranges from 247 to 150 feet. Bushnell's Insta Focus is standard. Fully coated optics. Roll down eye cups.

Price: $199 (5-year warranty).

From Bushnell Optical Company.

JASON/EMPIRE 3X28 BINOCULARS

These 3X binoculars feature center focus adjustment. The weight is an amazingly slim 4.6 ounces. Comes with wrist strap and case. Model 233.

Price: $22

From Jason/Empire, Inc.

JASON/EMPIRE WIDE ANGLE ROOF PRISM BINOCULARS

Two models are available, one with 8X optics, the other with 10X optics. Weighs only 7½ ounces. The 10X model has a 262-foot field of view while the 8X version has a 425-foot field of view (both at 1000 yards). Both have rubber eyecups. Models 122 (8X) and 123 (10X).

Prices: 10X — $150; 8X — $135.

From Jason/Empire, Inc.

SWIFT MARK I "SPORT KING" 7X35 BINOCULARS

These binoculars feature light weight (26 ounces) and an *extra wide* field of view (600 feet at 1000 yards). Perfect for spotting and tracking fast moving game.

Price: $158

From Swift Instruments, Inc.

See the Directory for complete company addresses.

SWIFT ARMORED 7X50 ''SWIFT-FOCUS'' BINOCULARS

This is a good glass for low-light situations—something all hunters are faced with. The hard black rubber armoring makes these glasses both shock and water resistant. They weigh 32 ounces and come with neck strap. The super fast ''Swift Focus'' allows you to instantly focus on your target.
Price: $118.50
From Swift Instruments, Inc.

SWIFT MARK III RUBBER ARMORED 7X50 BINOCULARS

If you spend a lot of time in the field, these binoculars might just be for you. The rubber armoring helps make these binoculars shock and water resistant. Clear, crisp focusing to 20 ft. is possible. Comes complete with carrying case and strap. Field of view at 1000 yards is 372 feet.
Price: $232
From Swift Instruments, Inc.

SWIFT ARMORED STORM KING MARK II 7X50 BINOCULARS

If you're a duck or goose hunter these glasses will fill the bill. They're *waterproof, fog proof* and shock resistant. They can accompany you on your roughest foul-weather hunt. They focus right down to 21 feet. Come with rain guard and neck strap.
Price: $365
From Swift Instruments, Inc.

SWIFT "AEROLITE" 8X40 WIDE ANGLE BINOCULARS

For hunting purposes, where a wide field of view is necessary, these binoculars are invaluable. At 1000 yards your field of view is a generous 498 feet—perfect for the antelope or western mule deer hunter. They weigh a light 30 ounces and feature roll away eye cups. Comes with luggage quality hard case and carrying straps.
Price: $72
From Swift Instruments, Inc.

SWIFT "AEROLITE" 8X40 WIDE ANGLE BINOCULARS

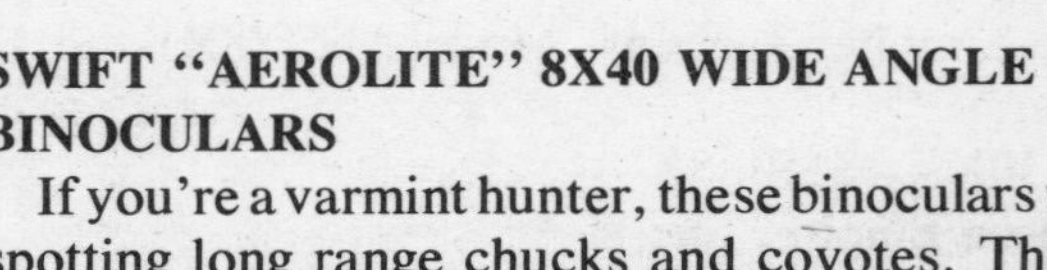

If you're a varmint hunter, these binoculars will aid in spotting long range chucks and coyotes. The field of view is 341 feet at 1000 yards. When in the field, these binoculars will serve well—the rubber armoring helps make them both shock and water resistant. Comes with carrying case and strap.
Price: $238
From Swift Instruments, Inc.

Prices shown are subject to change.

SWIFT "NIGHTHAWK" 8X40 EXTRA WIDE ANGLE BINOCULARS

These binoculars, because of their wide lens separation, provide the hunter with superior depth perception. All lenses are hard magenta coated. You get a 499-foot field of view at 1000 yards and the ocular lenses have roll away eyecups. Weighs 28 ounces and comes with cowhide grain case. Model 771.
Price: $60.25
From Swift Instruments, Inc.

SWIFT "AUDUBON" MARK II 8.5X44 WIDE ANGLE BINOCULARS

One of the ruggedest glasses a shooter can buy; the optical brilliance is superb and is coupled with a 445-foot field of view at 1000 yards. Model 804.
Price: $230
From Swift Instruments, Inc.

SWIFT "AEROLITE" 10X50 BINOCULARS

These glasses are not a bad bet for the long range varmint hunter who needs to find his target fast. The precision ground optics help you see the smallest details of the objects within view. Comes with carrying case and straps. Weighs only 35 ounces.
Price: $71
From Swift Instruments, Inc.

TASCO 7X35 "ZIP" FOCUS BINOCULARS

These lightweight (21-ounce) binoculars are well suited for the hunter with a heavy load. The field of view is 525 feet at 1000 yards. Eyepieces come with fold down rubber cups and the lenses are fully coated. The "Zip" Focus feature enables the user to instantly focus with the flick of a finger. Comes with case.
Price: See your local dealer.
From Tasco Sales, Inc.

TASCO 7X50 "ZIP" FOCUS BINOCULARS

You get a full 372-foot field of view at 1000 yards. All optics are fully coated and the eyepieces come with rubber (fold down) cups. The "Zip" Focus feature is darned handy for field use on moving game. Comes with a case.
Price: See your local dealer.
From Tasco Sales, Inc.

TASCO 8X30 RUBBER ARMORED BINOCULARS

These binoculars feature achromatic lenses. The green rubber armor body absorbs shock. Field of view at 1000 yards is 392 feet. This is a good choice for the hunter or shooter who is looking for a durable pair of field glasses.
Price: See your local dealer.
From Tasco Sales, Inc.

See the Directory for complete company addresses.

TASCO ZOOM 6-12X32 BINOCULARS

You can quickly find your game with the 6X setting and instantly zoom in to 12X for a better look. Not bad when you're looking for a once in a lifetime trophy. Lenses are fully coated and the field of view ranges from 314 feet to 183 feet (at 1000 yards) depending upon the power selected. Case and straps included.
Price: See your local dealer.
From Tasco Sales, Inc.

WEATHERBY ROOF PRISM 7X35 BINOCULARS

Weighing in at 17 ounces, these Weatherby binoculars are perfect for the hunter who's packing a lot of gear. Features fully coated lenses.
Price: $164.95
From Weatherby, Inc.

ZEISS DIALYT 3X30 B-GA BINOCULAR

These small, handy binoculars are ideal for the hunter. They feature center focus, superior optics and come with their own carrying case.
Price: $699.95
From Carl Zeiss, Inc.

ZEISS 8X30 B-GA ARMORED BINOCULARS

If you're in need of a good set of field glasses with enough magnification for general use, you should consider these superb binoculars. The brilliance and clarity are hard to beat. They come water proofed, shock proofed and have integral carrying modules. *Superior* optics.
Price: $599.95
From Carl Zeiss, Inc.

ZEISS DIALYT 8X56 B-GA, "UHLT" BINOCULARS

The "UHLT" stands for "Ultra High Light Transmission." If you do a lot of hunting in the disappearing lights of dusk or dawn then these glasses will be helpful. Exhibits superior brilliance and clarity. Has center focus; comes with case.
Price: $899.95
From Carl Zeiss, Inc.

ZEISS 10X40 B-GA ARMORED BINOCULARS

These binoculars are water proof, shock proof and virtually noiseless. The clarity of these binoculars has to be seen to be appreciated. Comes with a B-type eyepiece for use with eyeglasses or naked eye and with a pouch. Center Focus. *Superior* optics.
Price: $829.95
From Carl Zeiss, Inc.

Prices shown are subject to change.

Knives & Knife Accessories

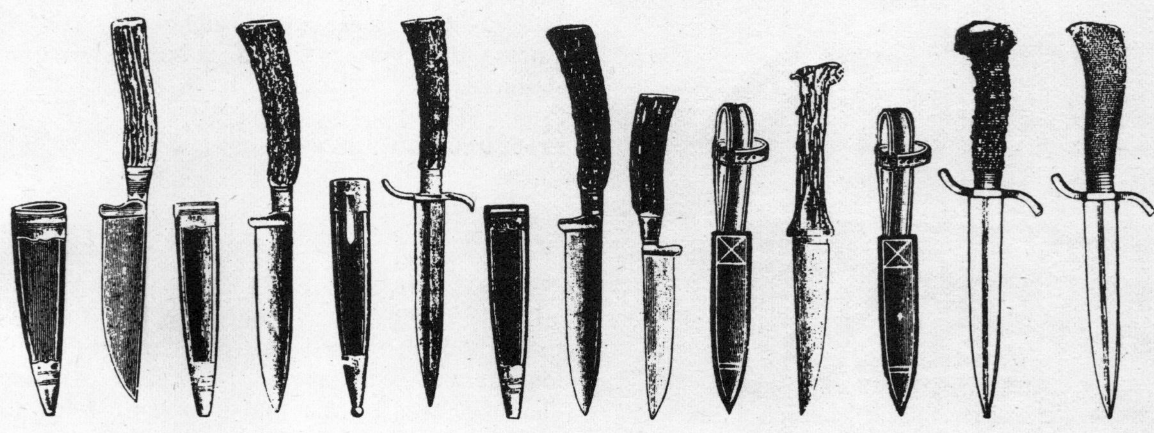

INTEREST IN fine knives has seen a manifold growth in recent years, and probably the greatest part of that growth has been from the gun owning and using fraternity. As a result, it seems only natural that we include a chapter on knives in the *Gun Digest Book of Gun Accessories & Services*.

A great many of the fine knives being produced today are hunting knives, though surely many of those are being acquired for their artistic and collector's value and not for use in the field. Custom knives, made on order to customer specifications, can be a very expensive proposition; a wide selection of first class hunting knives are also offered by commercial knife manufacturers at very reasonable prices.

In the following pages you will find, arranged alphabetically by maker, examples from most of this nation's top knife makers along with the less expensive but still high-quality products of the larger manufacturers. At the end of the section we've included a number of knife accessories, principally sharpening stones and tools.

Custom knives are, of course, offered only by the individual makers. When contacting them include a stamped, self-addressed envelope to facilitate a reply, and remember that some knife makers are currently facing a backlog of two to three *years* in their production. Most gun shops and sporting goods stores offer at least a modest selection of good quality factory made hunting knives.

FOLDING HUNTING KNIFE

When closed, the "Pony," has an overall length of 3 inches—handy for field use on small game. The blade is made of 440C stainless. The Pony comes with brass bolsters and ebony wood handles.

Price: $5.85

From Ballard Cutlery.

FOLDING HUNTING KNIFE

Ballard Cutlery calls this model the "Folding Sportsman." It features a 440C stainless blade, ebony wood handles surrounded by stainless steel and a positive lock. Comes in 3 sizes.

Price: Model 250 (4½ inches closed) $11.75; Model 200 (3¼ inches closed) $9.25; Model 180 (2¾ inches closed) $7.75; optional leather case $3.50.

From Ballard Cutlery.

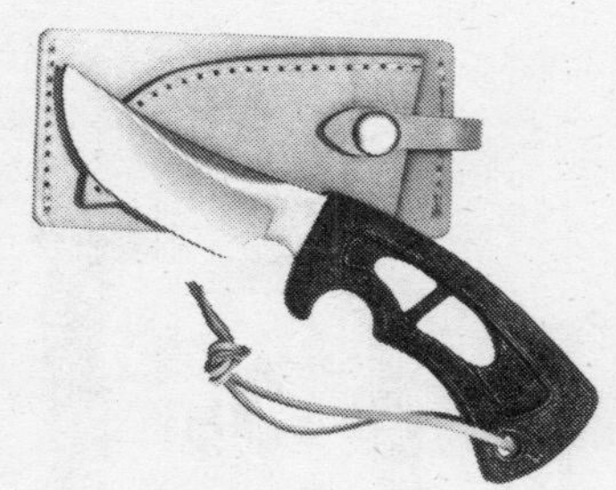

LIGHTWEIGHT SKINNER

Weighing only 8 ounces, this skinning knife features a 440C stainless steel blade 3¾ inches long. It comes with a heavy duty leather sheath. Handle is textured 440C stainless.

Price: $12

From Ballard Cutlery

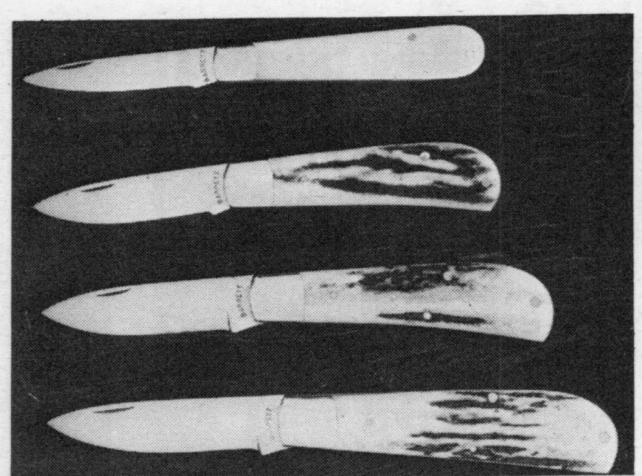

CUSTOM FOLDING KNIVES

In the photo nearby you'll see four folders handmade by Jack Barrett. As you can see, the style is consistent while the overall size of each folder changes. The steel used by this maker is 154CM for both the blade and spring. Hardwood handles are standard. Write maker direct for more information and delivery schedule.

Price: $150 (stag handles $25 extra).

From Jack Barrett.

CUSTOM KNIVES

Made by P.F. Beck, the knives shown are, from top to bottom: the Model No. 8, Model No. 3 and the Model No. 2. This maker favors full-tang knives with micarta handles as standard. The models shown here all have stag handles, available for $10 extra. Model No. 8 has a 2½-inch blade; the No. 3 comes with a 3¼-inch or 2¾-inch blade; the No. 2 has a 3½-inch blade. All blades are made of Crucible 154CM steel treated to Rockwell C61-62. Delivery time: about 12 months. Write for more information.

Price: No. 8 $60; No. 3 $60; No. 2 $70—Stag handles $10 extra.

From Beck Knives.

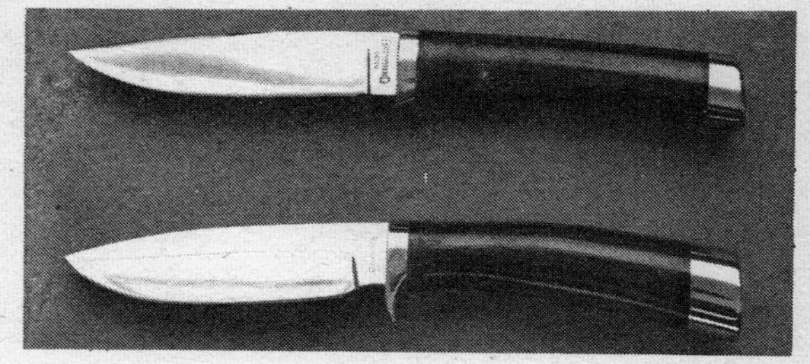

HUNTING KNIVES

The top knife is Browning's Drop Point Hunter II with a 3¾-inch stainless steel blade. Handle material is African ebony. The bottom knife is the Drop Point Hunter I. This knife is basically the same as the DPH II except for the blade shape and the handle (it's made of a wood/epoxy laminate). Both come with a custom-quality sheath.
Price: DPH-II $21.95; DPH-I $33.95.
From Browning Arms Company.

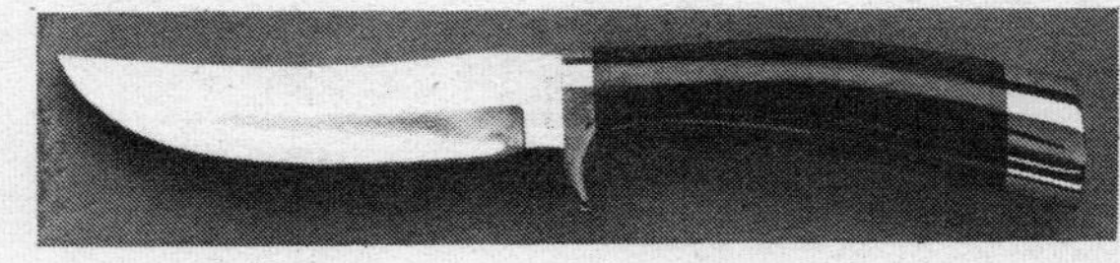

TRAILING POINT KNIFE

This Browning knife has a 4-inch stainless steel blade and comes with a wood/epoxy laminate handle. It's useful around the camp and in the field. Comes with a custom-quality sheath.
Price: $33.95
From Browning Arms Company.

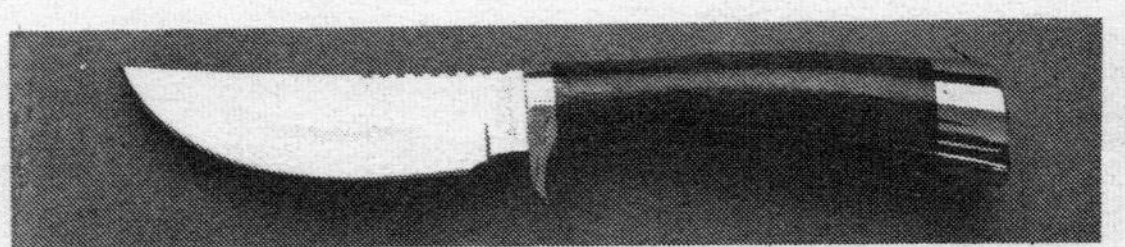

SKINNING KNIFE

Browning's Skinner II features a 3½-inch stainless steel blade complete with thumb grooves. Handle material is a combination of wood and epoxy—a laminate that won't absorb moisture. Comes with a custom-quality sheath.
Price: $33.95
From Browning Arms Company.

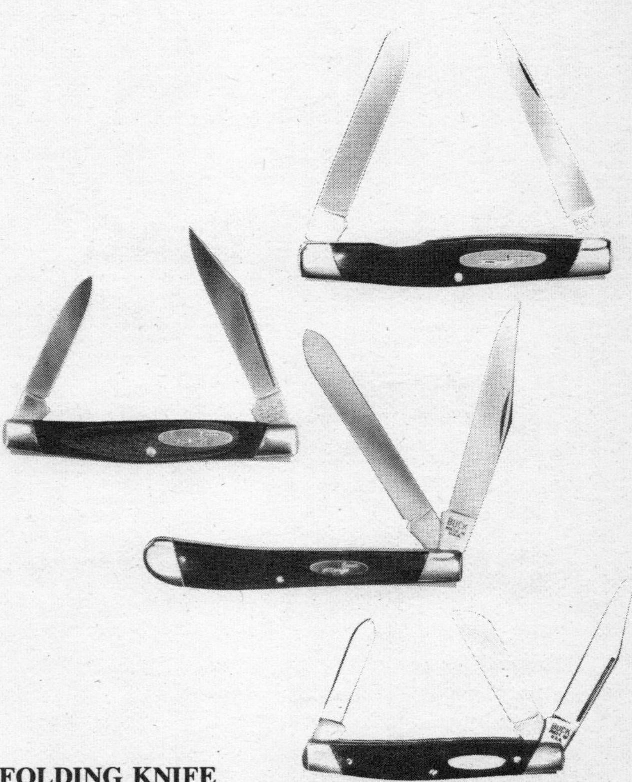

FOLDING KNIFE

This is Buck's Muskrat Model 313. Its overall length is 3⅞ inches and it comes with spey and slender skinning blades. Features stain-resistant steel blades.
Price: $14
From Buck Knives.

FOLDING KNIFE

This is Buck's Companion Model 309. It's a small, 3-inch long knife that comes with clip and pen blades. It features stain resistant steel blades.
Price: $13
From Buck Knives.

FOLDING KNIFE

This is Buck's Trapper Model 311. It comes with large clip and spey blades and is 4 inches long. It features stain resistant steel blades.
Price: $14
From Buck Knives.

FOLDING KNIFE

Buck's Stockman Model 301 is 3⅞ inches long and comes with clip, spey and sheepsfoot blades. Features stain-resistant steel blades.
Price: $17
From Buck Knives.

FOLDING KNIFE

Buck's Cadet Model 303 is slightly smaller than that firm's Stockman Model 301. It is 3¼ inches long and, like the Stockman, comes with clip, spey and sheepsfoot blades. Features stain-resistant steel blades.
Price: $15
From Buck Knives.

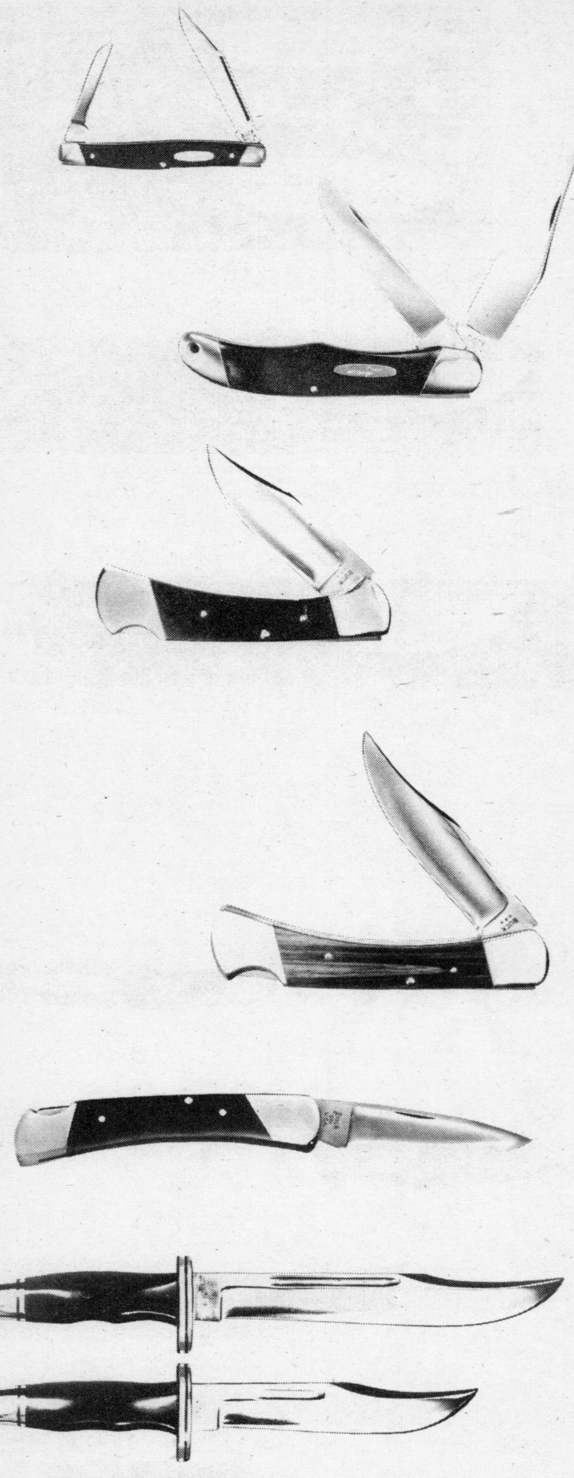

FOLDING KNIFE

Buck's Lancer Model 305 is a small knife with an overall length of 2⅝ inches. It has both clip and sheepsfoot blades. Features stain-resistant steel blades.

Price: $11

From Buck Knives.

FOLDING KNIFE

Buck's Trail Blazer Model 317 is a large working knife. This model is 5¼ inches long and comes with a sheath. Features stain-resistant steel blades.

Price: $26

From Buck Knives.

HEAVY-DUTY FOLDING KNIFE

Buck's Ranger Model 112 is a single-blade folder that's made for camp or field use. Like other Buck knives, the Ranger has a stain-resistant blade. Handle material is Macassar ebony, bolsters are *solid* brass and the knife has a positive-lock blade that's 4¼-inches long. Comes with sheath.

Price: $23

From Buck Knives.

DELUXE HEAVY-DUTY FOLDING KNIFE

This is the knife that paved the way for a lot of imitations. The Buck Folding Hunter Model 110 has earned an excellent, well-deserved reputation with hunters, military men and outdoorsmen in general. The 4⅞-inch stain-resistant blade is of the lock-open type. Features *solid* brass bolsters and Macassar ebony wood handles. Comes with sheath.

Price: $25

From Buck Knives.

SLIMLINE FOLDING KNIFE

This is Buck's Esquire Model 501 folder. Comes with stainless-steel liners and bolsters and features a lock-open blade and burgundy Buckarta handles. Overall length 3¾ inches; comes without sheath.

Price: $21

From Buck Knives.

CAMP/HUNTING KNIFE

This extra large Bowie-style knife is Buck's General Model 120. It comes with 7½-inch blade and is handy for medium to heavy-duty chores around the camp or in the field. Stain-resistant blade.

Price: $26

From Buck Knives.

CAMP/HUNTING KNIFE

Buck's Special Model 119 is a practical Bowie style knife with 6-inch blade and blood groove. Well balanced and shaped for general all-around use. Stain-resistant blade.

Price: $24

From Buck Knives.

CAMP/TRAIL KNIFE

Buck's Pathfinder Model 105 has a 5-inch stain-resistant blade. This knife is well suited for general outdoor use.

Price: $20

From Buck Knives.

Prices shown are subject to change.

HUNTING KNIFE

Buck's Personal Model 118 has a 4½-inch slender blade that's upswept for skinning use. (Good choice for field use on small game.) Features a stain-resistant blade.

Price: $18

From Buck Knives.

SMALL GAME KNIFE

Buck's Woodsman Model 102 has a 4-inch straight blade that's made out of stain-resistant steel. This little gem is a dandy for rabbits, squirrels and other small game. Has a stain-resistant steel blade.

Price: $17

From Buck Knives.

SKINNING KNIFE

Buck's Skinner Model 103 has a beefy 4-inch blade with a heavy, fine edge. Excellent for skinning out large game. Stain-resistant steel blade.

Price: $22

From Buck Knives.

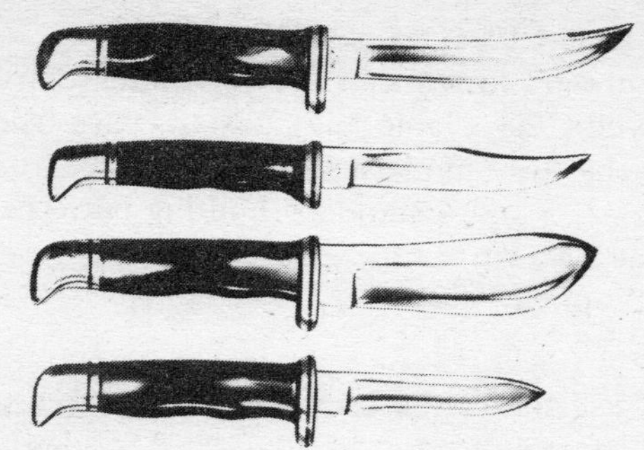

CAPING KNIFE

Buck's Caper Model 116 has a short 3¼-inch stain-resistant blade that's designed for working around the horns and ears of trophy game animals. It's also not a bad knife for upland game or small game in general. Popular knife.

Price: $18

From Buck Knives.

HUNTING KNIFE

This is Buck's top of the line hunting knife. It comes attractively packaged with a sheath. It features a slim 5-inch blade, brass guard and Buckarta handle. Well made, stain-resistant blade.

Price: $55

From Buck Knives.

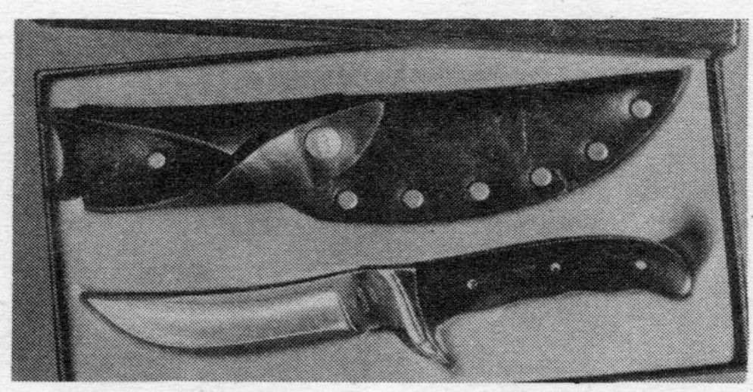

LOCK-BLADE FOLDER

This one's from Camillus Cutlery. It features a patented lock for the clip blade. In use it won't close on your fingers accidentally. Called the "Lok-Rancher," this folder comes with clip, spey and sheepsfoot blades—all made of stainless steel. Overall closed length is 4½ inches. It also has Indian stag handles.

Price: $19.25

From Camillus Cutlery.

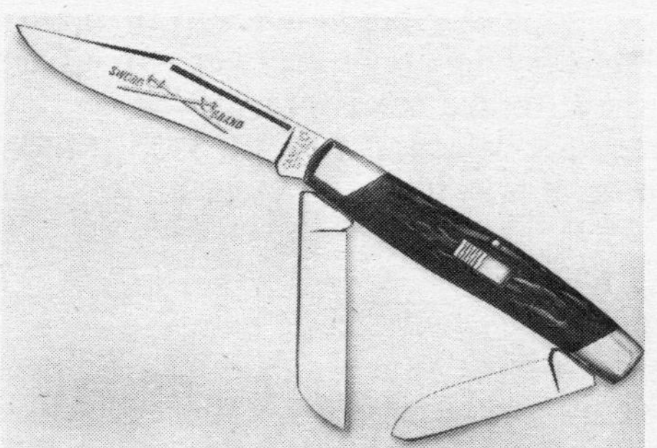

LOCK-BLADE FOLDER

This Camillus folder is called the "Cam-Lok." It has a single deluxe stainless blade that can be thumb-locked into safety when the blade is opened. It has Indian stag handles and nickel silver bolsters. Comes with a cowhide pouch. Closed length 4¾ inches.

Price: $21.25

From Camillus Cutlery.

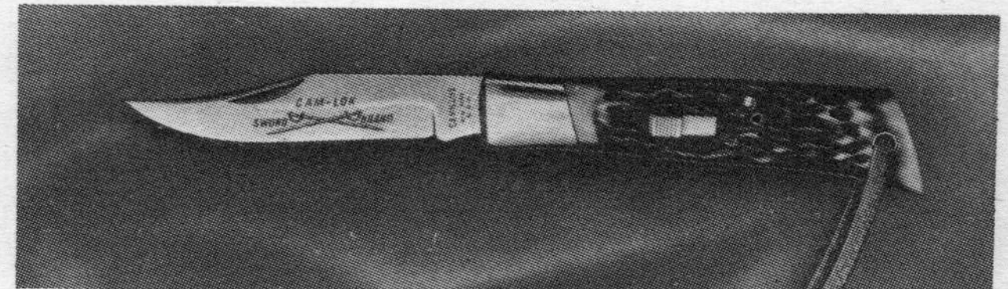

WATERFOWLER'S KNIFE

This knife is just one in a series of American Wildlife knives offered by Camillus Cutlery. While attractive to the collector, this knife is a *very* practical buy for the waterfowler. It comes with a stainless steel blade and gut hook, derlin handles and nickel silver bolsters.

Price: $16

From Camillus Cutlery

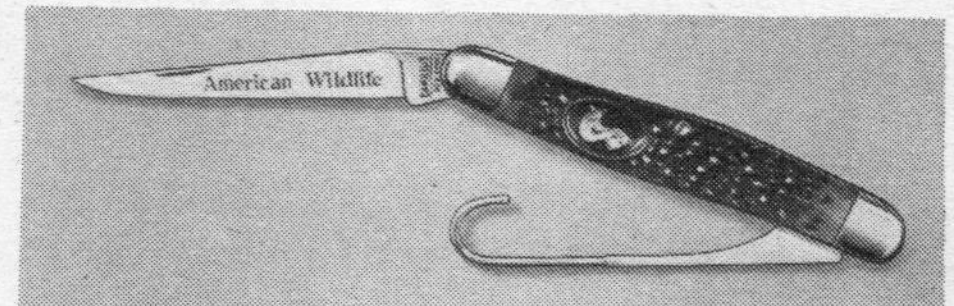

See the Directory for complete company addresses.

R. C. CAMPBELL CUSTOM KNIVES

This maker prefers to work in 440-C stainless hardened to Rockwell C-58. Campbell's designs vary from the antique to the fully modern. Shown nearby, from left, are his #1, 2, 3 and 4 standard hunting patterns.

Prices: Start at $90; write for details.

From R. C. Campbell.

FOLDER

This large Case folder features solid construction, nickel silver bolsters and wood handles. This particular model has a Case "Saber-Ground" 5¼" stainless steel blade.

Price: $29

From W. R. Case & Sons Cutlery Co.

FOLDER

This Case folder comes with its own sheath, has a 5-inch stainless steel blade and is called the "Shark Tooth." When fully opened the blade locks safely in place.

Price: $55

From W. R. Case & Sons Cutlery Co.

CUSTOM HUNTING KNIVES

These knives are made by Frank and Mark Centofante. From top to bottom: Models 1, 2 & 3. The steel preferred by the Centofantes is 154CM. Model No. 1 is available in 2¾- or 3-inch blade lengths. Model No. 2 comes in a 4-inch blade, while Model No. 3 has a 4¼- or 5-inch blade (your choice). Stag handles available for $15 additional. Delivery time is a little over 1 year from the date of order. Write for more information.

Price: Model No. 1 $135; Model No. 2 $135; Model No. 3 $140 for the 4-inch blade, $150 for the 4½-inch blade.

From Centofante Knives.

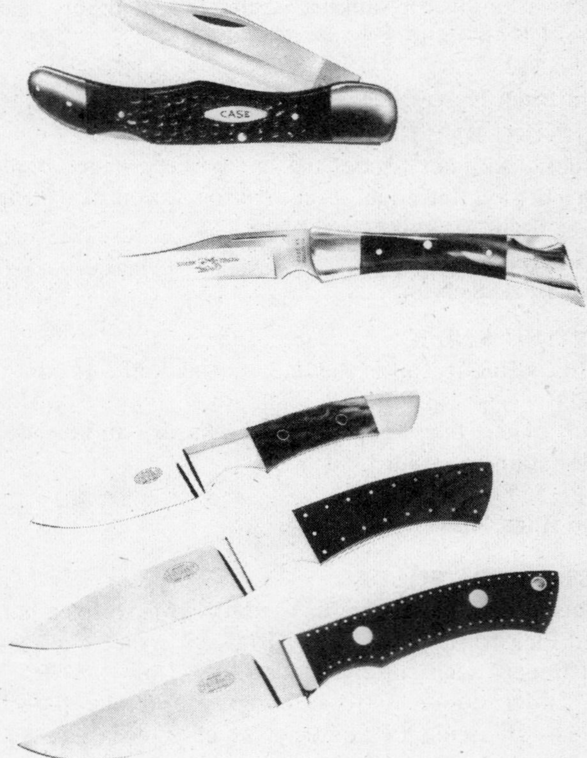

CUSTOM HUNTING KNIFE

Called the "Light Grizzly Hunter," this knife (not shown) is handmade by A. Corby. It features a 4 inch drop point with thumb notches on the spine. The steel 440C; guard and escutcheons are hand engraved silver. Handle material is micarta. Write direct for more information on other models and delivery time. (While we don't have a photo of the "Light Grizzly Hunter," we have provided a photo of Corby's "True Balance Fighting Knife" to show you an example of this maker's work.

Price: Light Grizzly Hunter $125; True Balance Fighting Knife $225.

From Knives By Corby.

CUSTOM INTEGRAL HILT AND CAP HUNTING KNIFE

The design is unique as the blade, hilt and cap are hand made from the same hunk of steel. Handle material on the knife shown is desert ironwood. Micarta and other handle materials—except stag—are available. Available steels 440-C or D-2. Comes with sheath. Write maker for more information as delivery time ranges from a few months to 4 years, depending on model ordered.

Price: $525

From T. M. Dowell.

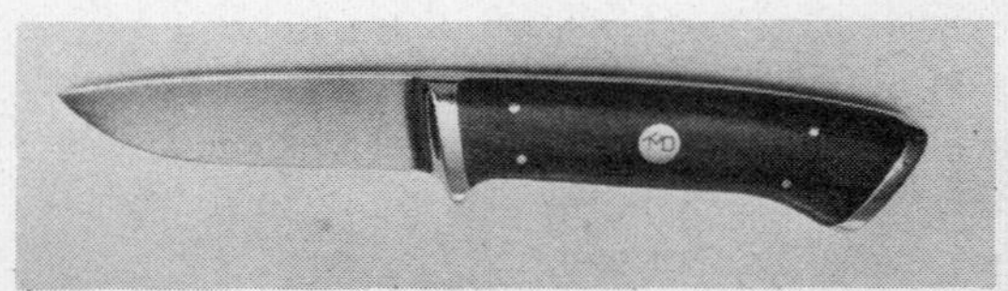

Prices shown are subject to change.

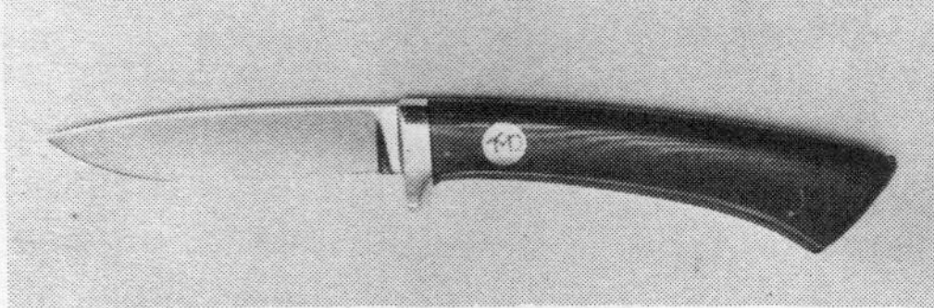

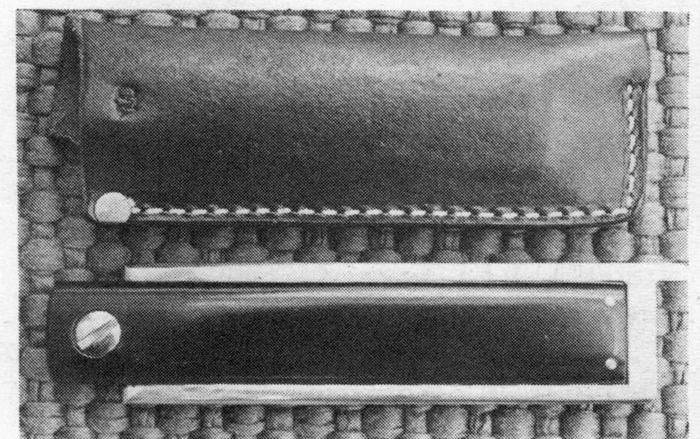

HUNTING KNIVES

Each Ensign Knife is made by hand. It's a one-piece knife; blade and handle are made of the same piece of stock. There are two basic models; The SSP (shown) and the SDP. The SSP is intended for small game use while the SDP is made for big game purposes. Both come with a leather sheath.

Price: $15 each; $30 for the pair.

From Ensign Knives.

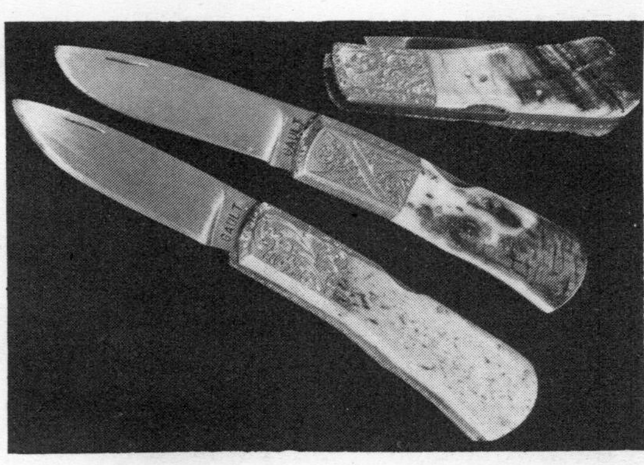

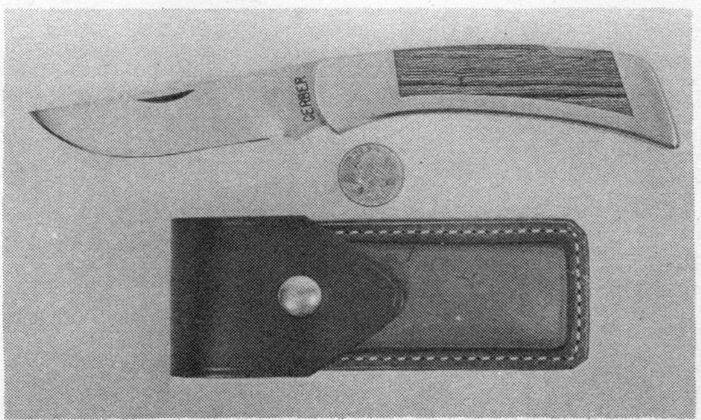

CUSTOM NARROW TANG HUNTING KNIFE

As shown, this handmade T. M. Dowell knife features a micarta handle and 4-inch blade made of 3/16 inch stock. D-2, 440-C or 154 CM steels are available; and, you can also get this model with an 1/8 inch thick blade when D-2 steel is ordered. Comes with its own sheath. Depending on model ordered, delivery time can run from a few months to 4 years.

Price: $170

From T. M. Dowell.

CUSTOM FOLDING HUNTING KNIFE

This hand-made Dowell knife is called the "Funny Folder II." It has a ⅞ inch wide blade that's 3¾ inches long. This knife is light, compact and rugged. Handle material is micarta and the knife comes with its own sheath. Delivery time a few months to 4 years, depending on model ordered. Write maker for more information.

Price: $160 for 154CM or D-2 steel; $225 for Vasco Wear steel.

From T. M. Dowell.

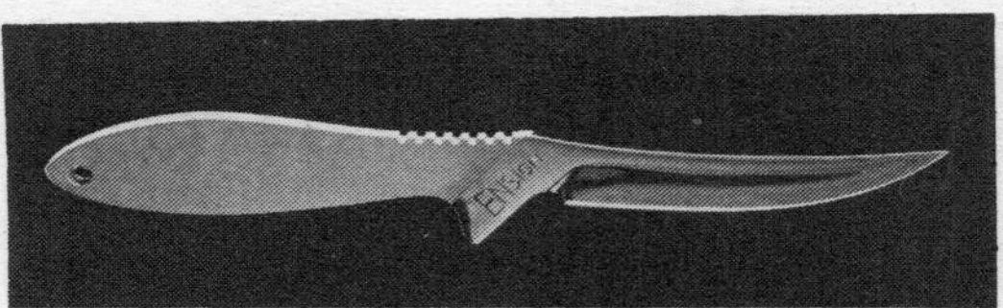

CUSTOM FOLDING KNIFE

This maker (Clay Gault) calls this knife the "Folding Lockback Hunter." The 2¾-inch blade is available in either D-2 or 154 CM steel, while the handle materials are all natural. The knives shown are custom engraved versions of the basic model and serve to show how far the maker will go in meeting customer requests.

Price: $125 for the basic Lockback Hunter.

From Clay Gault.

FOLDING KNIFE

Gerber's Folding Sportsman II has a single 3½ inch stainless steel blade that securely locks in place. The frame is all brass and the handles have tropical hardwood inlays. Comes complete with belt scabbard.

Price: $32.50

From Gerber Legendary Blades.

FOLDING HUNTING KNIFE

This is Gerber's "Folding Sportsman III;" it's a little larger than the FS-II. The FS-III comes with a brass frame and 4 inch stainless steel blade hardened to C57-59 on the Rockwell scale. When opened, this blade locks securely into place. Each knife comes with a leather belt scabbard.

Price: $42.50

From Gerber Legendary Blades.

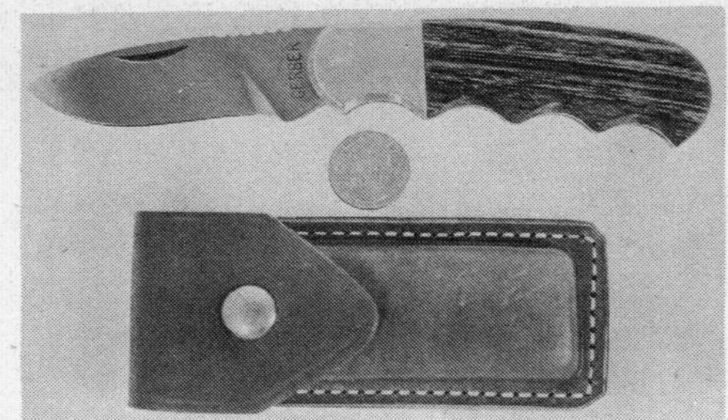

HEAVY DUTY FOLDER

Gerber's Magnum Folding Hunter is designed for the tougher field chores. It has a beefy 3¼ inch blade made of 440C surgical stainless steel complete with thumb grooves. Hardwood handles and frame are finger grooved for a sure hold. It comes complete with scabbard.

Price: $47.50

From Gerber Legendary Blades.

FOLDING KNIFE

Gerber's new "Paul Knife" comes in three models, each having an exclusive axial locking mechanism. It's offered with handles of brushed stainless steel, tropical hardwood or micarta. (Leather belt scabbard optional).

Price: Stainless handles $60; wood or ivory micarta handles $70; scabbard $7.

From Gerber Legendary Blades.

HUNTING KNIFE

Gerber's "Armorhide" knives feature a metal handle that's been textured to assure a non-slip grip. The blade is made of high-speed tool steel that's been chrome plated to prevent rusting. Blade lengths are available in 3¼ inch, 4 inch, 4¼ inch, 4½ inch and 4¾ inch sizes. Shown is the Model 450 with 4½ inch blade. Sheath comes with each knife.

Price: Model 450 $25.

From Gerber Legendary Blades.

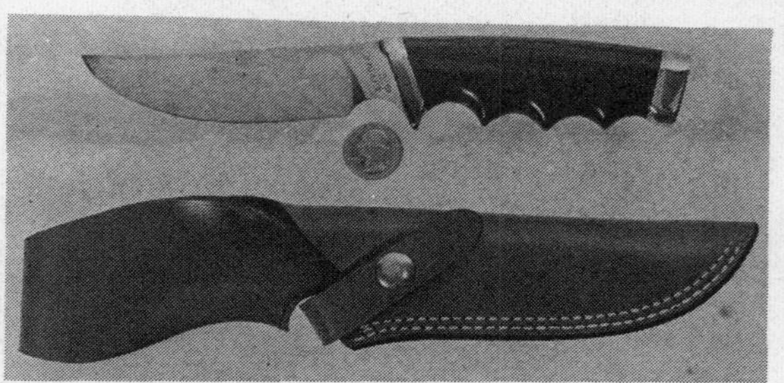

HUNTING KNIFE

Shown is Gerber's Model 4755, which is one of that firm's Presentation Series knives. The blade material 440C surgical stainless hardened to C58-60 on the Rockwell scale. The hilt and buttcap are also made of stainless steel while the handle is fashioned from tropical hardwood. A sheath comes with each knife.

Price: $79.50

From Gerber Legendary Blades.

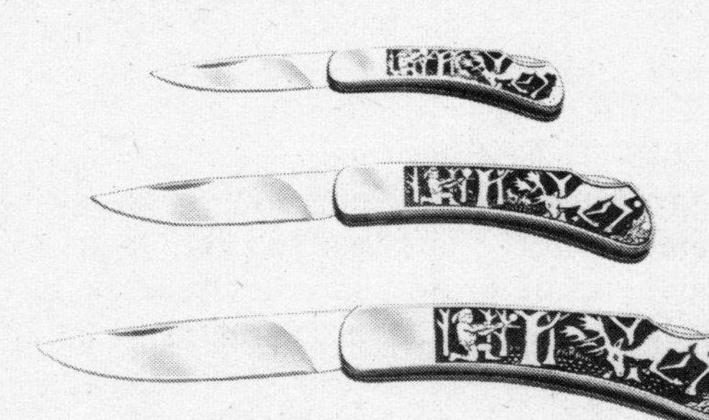

FOLDING HUNTING KNIVES

Available from Gutmann Cutlery, the three "Backwoodsman" knives shown come in 3-inch, 4-inch or 5-inch blade lengths. The blades lock safely into place and are made of 440C stainless. The handles are also stainless but have been etched with an outdoor hunting scene.

Price: From $18 to $24

From Gutmann Cutlery.

LADOW JOHNSTON CUSTOM KNIVES

"Bydoc" custom knives are individually made in four different styles. Johnston prefers to work with high carbon tool steel using sambar stag and 18% nickel silver as handle and furniture material. As an option (at extra cost) he will provide ivory handles or handles made from elk or moose antler.

Prices: Write maker direct.

From Ladow Johnston.

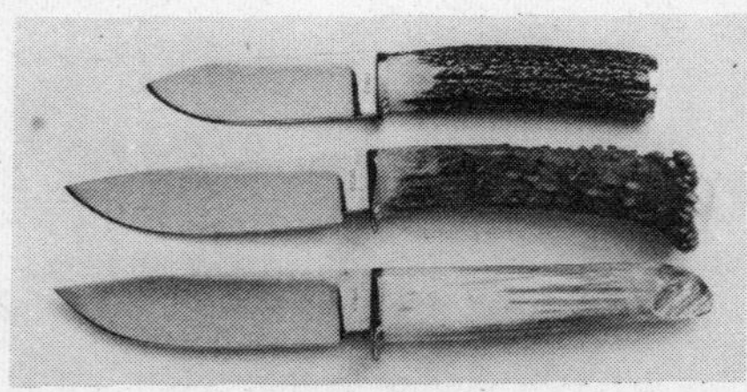

Prices shown are subject to change.

FOLDING KNIVES

Sid Jobs makes his own folders. He is fond of the Barlow patterns and it shows in his style. His steel of preference is 400C; however, he'll make blades out of 0-1 or D-2 if specified. Most handle material is natural; white bolsters are made of nickel silver. Write for more information.

Price: $120 for a basic 2-inch folder.

From S. R. Jobs.

CUSTOM FOLDING KNIFE

Shown nearby is an example of Lance Kelly's Model No. 7 folder. This knife is for the hunter/sportsman who wants something "more" when purchasing a custom folder. All of the engraving is done by the maker. D-2 steel is used for the blade while nickel silver and cocobolo wood are used for the bolsters and handles, respectively. Write the maker direct for more information on other models. Delivery time about 4 months.

Price: $350

From Lance Kelly.

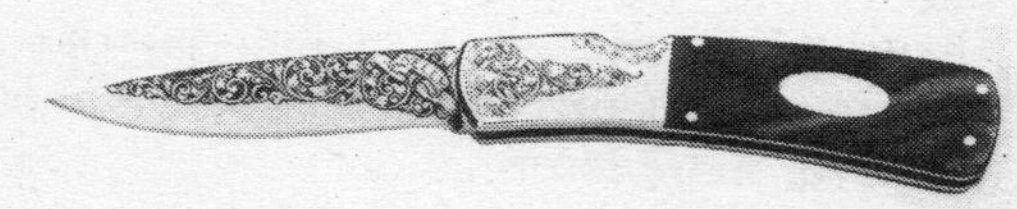

CUSTOM HAND MADE KNIVES

Reasonably priced, the knives offered by Jon Kirk are made from selected high carbon tool steel or high carbon chrome vanadium tool steel. Handle materials vary with customer wants. This maker offers everything from Bowies on down to small, practical hunting blades. Write maker direct for more information on models and delivery time.

Prices: Range from about $50 to $100.

From Jon Kirk.

CUSTOM HUNTING/SKINNING KNIFE

The knife shown is handmade by Tom Lee and is called the "Bobcat." The steel used in its construction is 154CM and the handle material is sambar stag. Blade length is about 3 inches—handy for field use. Write maker direct for more information on delivery time. Comes with sheath.

Price: $95

From Tom Lee.

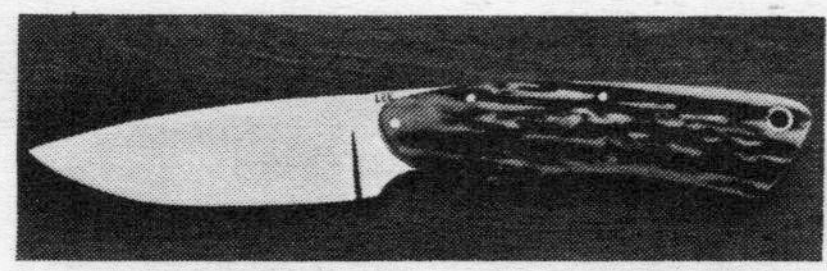

CUSTOM HUNTING KNIFE

This is Tom Lee's "Deerslayer" model. It's handmade out of 154CM steel and sambar stag. Blade length is 3¾ inches and it's 1-inch wide at the hilt. Comes with its own sheath.

Price: $120

From Tom Lee.

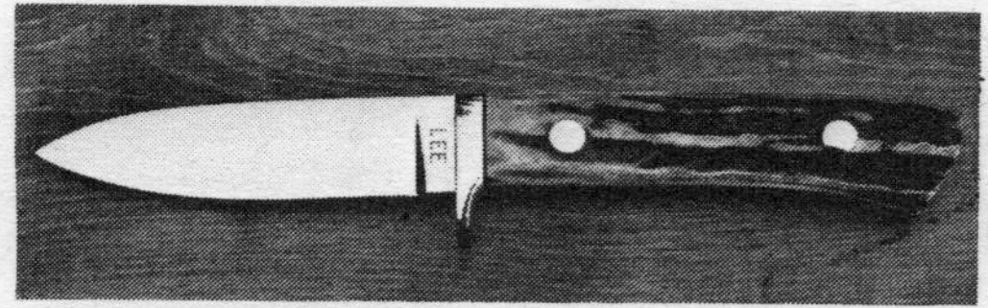

CUSTOM FOLDING KNIFE

The knife shown has a 3-inch blade made of 154CM steel and scrimshawed ivory handles. It's handmade. Write maker direct for more information on delivery time.

Price: $250

From Tom Lee.

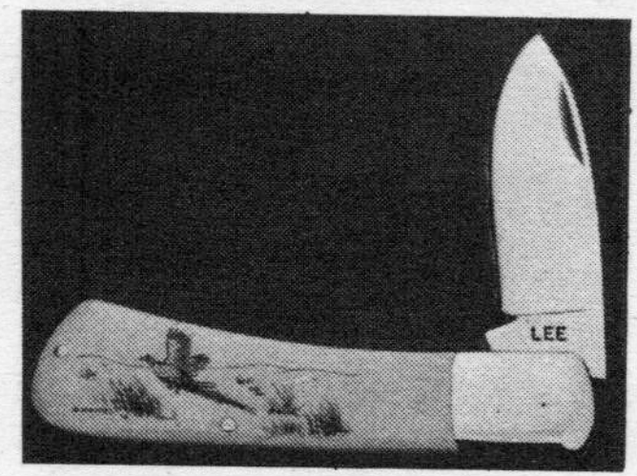

HARVEY McBURNETTE CUSTOM KNIVES

McBurnette's preferred steel is D-2 while his Bowies and "Show" knives are usually made from 440-C stain-resistant steel. In fact, D-2 steel, rosewood handles and brass trim are normal unless the customers want something special. His folders feature D-2 steel and nickel silver bolsters. Shown nearby is a custom folder based on McBurnette's "Folding Hunter" model. Delivery time is 8 months.

Price: $250 as shown; $140 for the plain model.

From Harvey McBurnette.

See the Directory for complete company addresses.

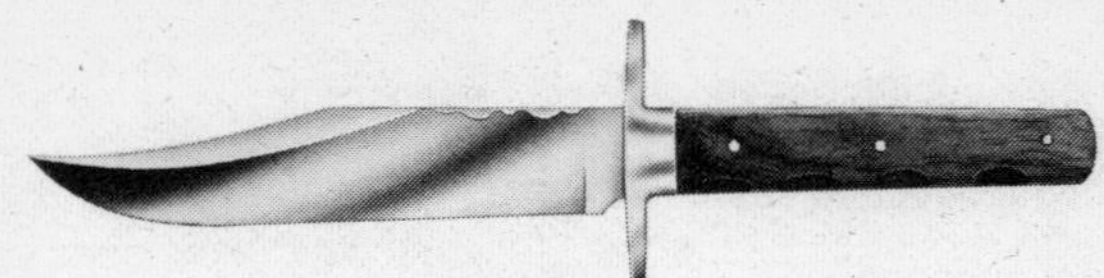

ROBERT OGG CUSTOM KNIVES

Each knife is made to order. The example shown was made by Ogg with the engraving done by Mel Wood and the scrimshaw by Glen Stearns. As far as materials go, Ogg will work to order. Current delivery time is about 6 months. Write for more information.

Price: $60 for a standard model folder.

From Robert Ogg.

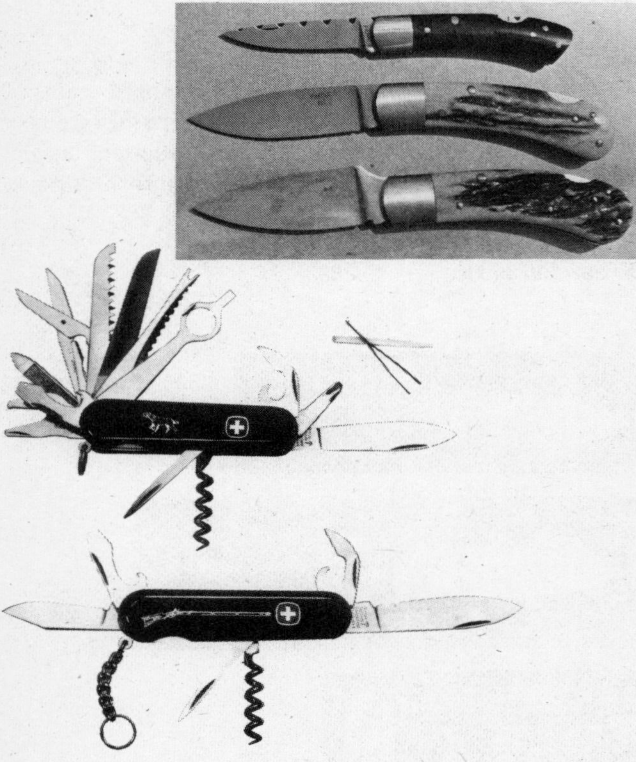

CUSTOM HUNTING KNIVES

Jim Pugh makes collectible custom knives; however, he also makes "using" knives as well. His choice of steel is 440C surgical stainless. Handles are either laminated rosewood with red and white spacers; or, laminated ebony wood with black and white spacers. Each knife comes with its own sheath. Write for more information.

Prices:

Model	Blade Length	With Yellow Bronze Pommel & Hilt
"The Cat"	3⅝″	$150
"The Grizzly"	3⅝″	$150
"The Falcon"	3⅝″	$150
"The Mako"	3⅝″	$150

From Pugh Made Knives.

J. R. HOPKINSON KNIFE

This Bowie style knife is imported and sold by Navy Arms. Blade is hand forged; knife has a wooden handle and a polished brass hilt.

Price: $24

From Navy Arms.

CUSTOM FOLDING HUNTING KNIVES

Melvin Pardue offers a line of folders that can be seen nearby. From top to bottom: Model No. 2; Model No. 4 and Model No. 5. Their respective blade lengths are 2½ inches, 3 inches and 3 inches. Pardue works in a good selection of steels and handle materials. Write maker direct for more information.

Price: Model No. 2 $90 (minus file work); Model No. 4 $90 (stag handles $15 extra); Model No. 5 $90 (stag handles $15 extra).

From Melvin M. Pardue.

SWISS ARMY KNIFE

Made by Wenger, and imported by Precise, this knife features a real selection of stainless steel blades. Handy around the camp. The model shown is the "Pointer."

Price: $45

From Precise.

SWISS ARMY KNIFE

This one's called the "Hunter" and comes with six handy blades or tools. It features solid construction and stainless steel blades.

Price: $14.95

From Precise.

FOLDING HUNTING KNIFE

Each Deerslayer folding knife has solid construction, thumb-rest blade and locking-blade features. Sheath not included.

Price: $21.95; sheath $4.

From Precise.

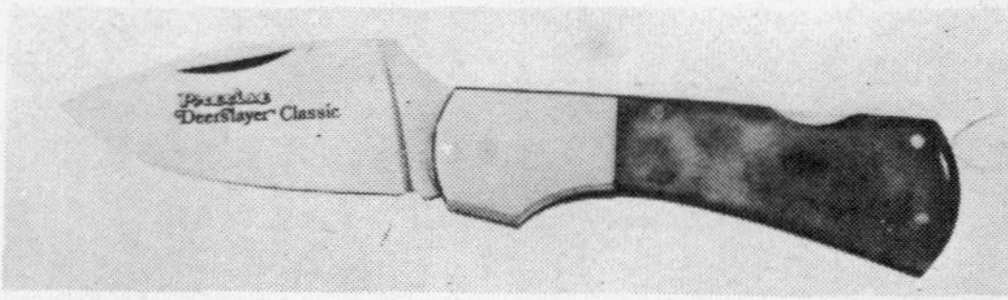

HUNTING KNIFE

Each "Deerslayer" knife has been designed to give the buyer the maximum amount of knife for the least amount of money. Available handle materials include derlin, ebony and micarta. Features a stainless steel blade and comes with a sturdy sheath.

Price: $44.95

From Precise.

Prices shown are subject to change.

HUNTING KNIFE

Randall's "Trout and Bird Knife" is well suited for general field use. It features a 4-inch blade complete with top cutting edge and hand-made sheath. Handle material is stag as shown; however, micarta handle also available. Purchaser has his choice of the best Swedish tool steel or special high-carbon stainless. Delivery time about 9 months. Write the maker direct for more information.

Price: $77

From Randall Made Knives.

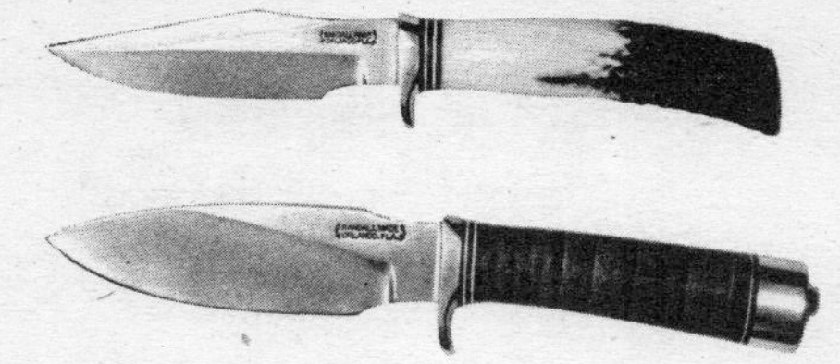

SURVIVAL FOLDING KNIFE

The RS-1 survival knife comes with sheath and built-in wire saw as shown. Handle material is rosewood—other natural and manmade handle materials also available.

Price: $50

From Remote Survival Company.

KNIFE KIT

This product is from Rigid Knives and is designed for the hunter who wants a hand in making his own blade. Each kit comes with a preshaped blade, hardwood slabs, bolsters and rivets. The blade is 3⅜ inches overall. Each kit comes with complete instructions.

Price: $22.50; sheath $6.50.

From Rigid Knives.

LARGE HUNTING KNIFE

This is the "Yukon" knife by Rigid. It features a 5½-inch blade with an overall length of 10⅝ inches.

Price: $54.50

From Rigid Knives.

SKINNING/GENERAL PURPOSE KNIFE

This is Rigid's R-4 "Ripper." The blade is a handy 4⅛ inches long. The first inch of the chamfer is sharpened to aid in opening large or small game prior to skinning.

Price: $44.50

From Rigid Knives.

SPORTSMAN'S KNIFE

With a 3⅝-inch blade, the Rigid "Rogue" is a simple, handy, field knife—good on the trail or in camp. Comes with a sleek finger guard.

Price: $27.50

From Rigid Knives.

SKINNING KNIFE

Randall's "Alaskan Skinner" has a 4-inch blade of 3/16-inch stock. (Optional blade lengths and thicknesses also available.) Comes with leather handle and brass hilt. Blade is thumb-notched just ahead of the brass hilt. (This design was done by Tommy Thompson, noted Alaskan guide.) The blade is made of Swedish tool steel; however, high-carbon stainless is available as an option. Delivery time about 9 months. Write maker direct for more information.

Price: $75

From Randall Made Knives.

FOLDERS

From left to right: The Navajo, The Apache and The Cherokee—all from Rigid Knives. The Navajo has brushed nickel silver bolsters and a locking 3⅛-inch blade. The Apache has oil-impregnated bearings, brass bolsters, positive locking and a 3¾-inch blade. Rigid's Cherokee model has a drop-point stainless blade that's primarily designed for skinning chores.

Price: Navajo $22.50; Apache $44.50; Cherokee $44.50.

From Rigid Knives.

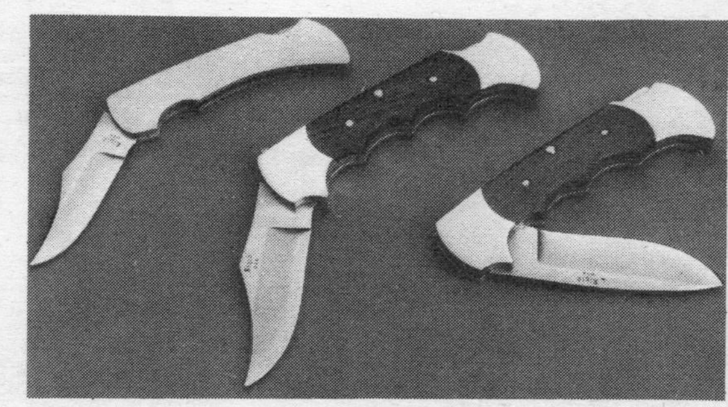

See the Directory for complete company addresses.

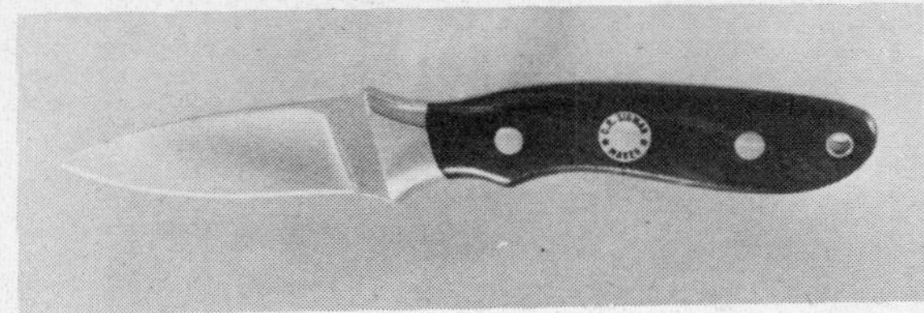

HUNTING CAPING KNIVES

The knives shown nearby are handmade by John T. Smith. Blades are available in A2 high carbon tool steel and 440C stainless steel. The knife shown with stag handles is the Model No. 19; the knife next to it is the Model No. 20 with bone micarta handle. The Model No. 19 has a 4 inch blade and is made for general hunting use. The No. 20 is a caping knife used for dressing out trophy game. Each knife comes with a custom fitted sheath. Delivery time is about one year.

Price: No. 19 (1/8-inch thick blade) $100, No. 19 3/16-inch thick blade) $110; No. 20 $80.

From John T. Smith Knives.

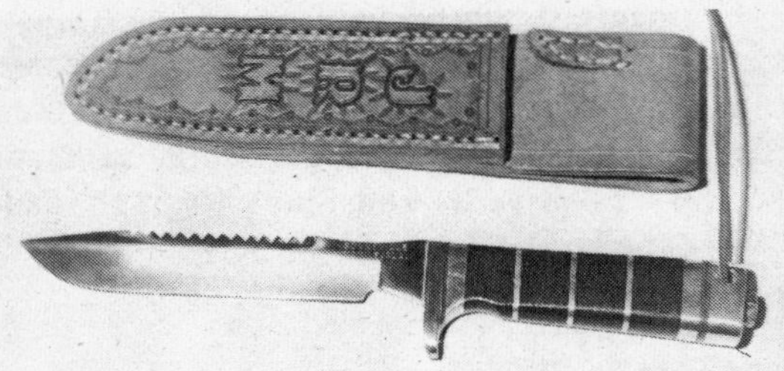

SKINNING KNIFE

Made by Bernard Sparks, this skinner is called the "Fox." It features a 400C stainless blade that's made out of 3/16-inch stock and measures 4 inches in length. It has a stainless steel hilt and rosewood handles. Write for more information.

Price: $125.

From Sparks Hand Made Knives.

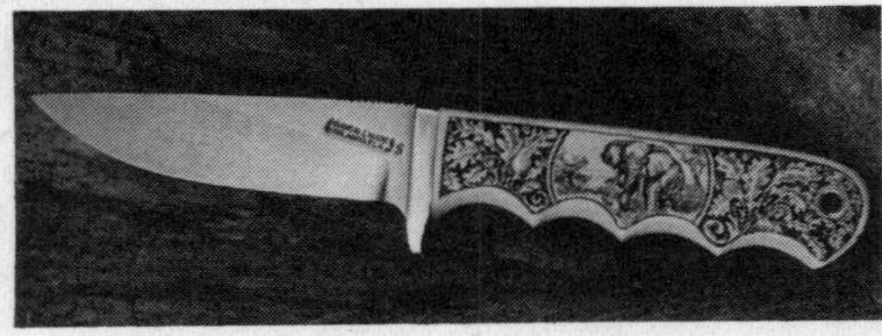

CORBET SIGMAN CUSTOM KNIVES

This custom maker's name is well known in both "collector" and "user" circles. Shown is Sigman's Model #2. It's available with 3½ or 4-inch blade. Delivery time, as of publication, is about 24 months. Sigman has worked with a good number of steels; however, he (and most of his customers) prefer stainless. Write for more information on other available models.

Price: $180; without metal bolsters $165.

From Corbet R. Sigman.

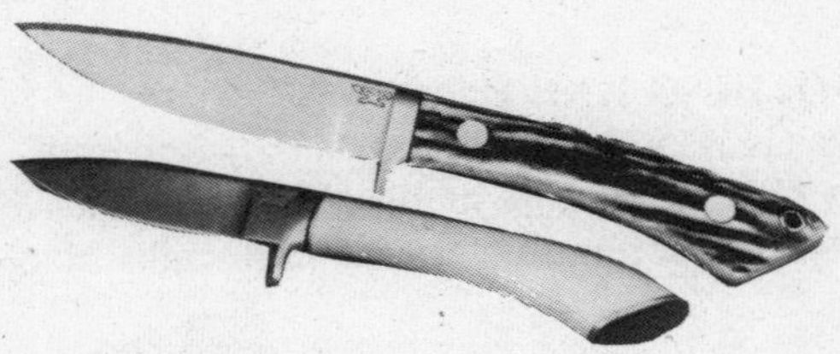

W. J. SONNEVILLE CUSTOM KNIVES

The Knife shown nearby is just one of 26 separate designs currently offered by the maker. The knife shown is called the "Bonita" and is designed for both the hunter and fisherman. Sonneville uses stag or micarta, plus aluminum and stainless steel for his handle construction. He works exclusively in Carpenter's 440C surgical stainless when it comes to blade material.

Price: $117 for the Bonita and Sheath as shown; write for more information on this and other Sonneville knives.

From W. J. Sonneville.

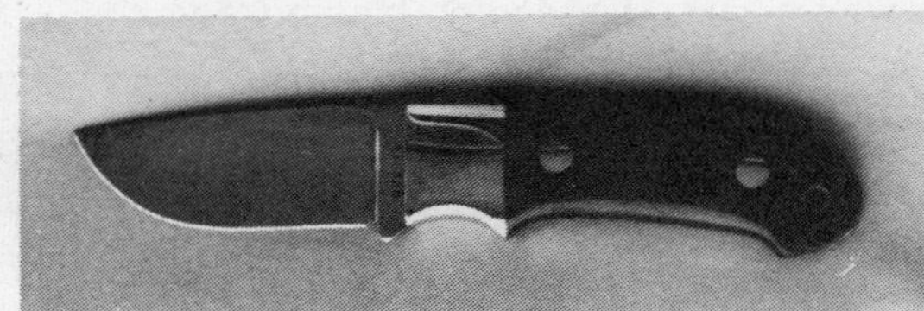

CUSTOM KNIFE SCRIMSHAW WORK

Available on a strictly custom basis, Glen Stearns will scrimshaw any antler, ivory or plastic knife handle. Shown nearby is an example of his work as done on a custom Randall knife. Custom designs are his specialty.

Prices: Write scrimshander direct.

From Glen E. Stearns.

VICTORINOX SWISS ARMY KNIVES

These well-made knives are always in demand. Shown nearby, from left to right: The Trooper, The Stag Hunter, The Executive and The Traveller. Each knife comes with a variety of blades, all made of stainless steel.

Price: Trooper $17.20; Stag Hunter $25.30; Executive $20.40; Traveller $21.30.

From Swiss Army Knives, Inc.

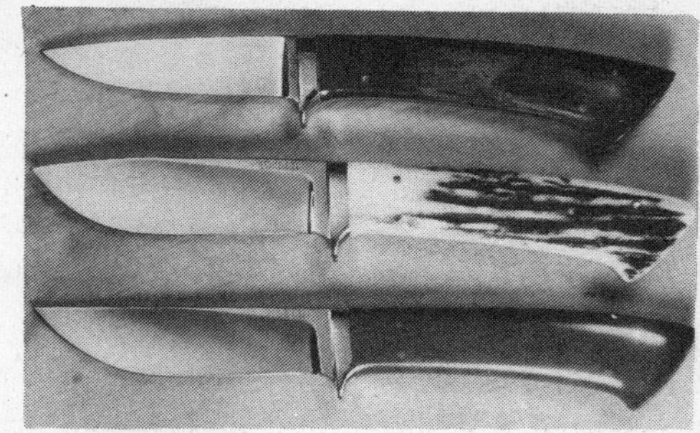

CUSTOM HUNTING KNIVES

These knives are handmade by Dwight Towell. The steel used is 154CM stainless and the handle materials range from stag to wood to micarta. In the nearby photo (from top to bottom) is a Model No. 9 with 3½ inch blade; Model No. 11 with a 4 inch blade and a Model No. 10, also with 4 inch blade. Write maker for more information as to delivery time, which, at time of publication, is about *6 years*.

Price: Models No. 9, 10 & 11 about $115.

From Dwight L. Towell.

HUNTING KNIFE

This handy field knife has a 3-inch blade, stag-pattern derlin handle and comes with a tooled leather sheath. Model No. 628.

Price: $9.65

From Western Cutlery Company.

HUNTING/SKINNING KNIFE

Comes with upswept 4½-inch blade. Can be used for skinning and other dressing-out chores. It also features solid hardwood handles and comes with molded leather sheath.

Price: $20.95

From Western Cutlery Company.

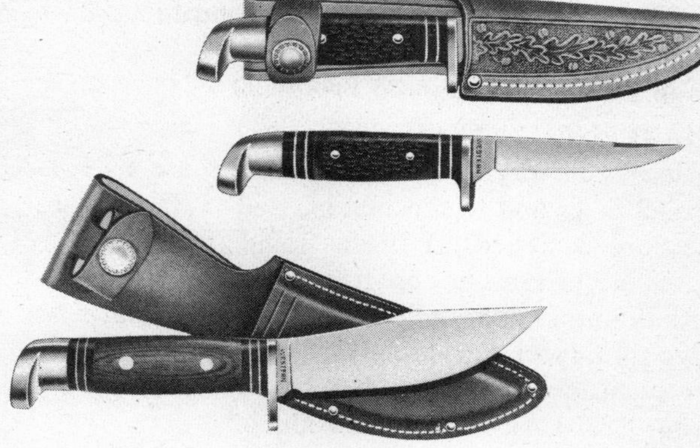

KNIFE SHARPENING STONES & OIL

In the nearby photo on the left is a Browning Arkansas Combination Sharpening Stone complete with cedar storage box. One side of the stone is soft novaculite, the other is hard Arkansas. In the center is a can of Browning Honing Oil which helps keep the pores of any sharpening stone free of build up. To the right is Browning's Pocket Stone. Its size (3⅞"x1¾"x⅝") makes it perfect for field use.

Price: Arkansas Combination Stone $16.95; Honing Oil $1.25; Pocket Sharpening Stone $4.95.

From Browning Arms Company.

SHARPENING KIT, STONES AND HONING OIL

Buck makes a good line of sharpening accessories for the hunter/sportsman. In the nearby photo, to the left is Buck's Model 133 Honing Kit; to the right is a can of Honing Oil; and, just below the oil is a Washita stone and a pocket-size hard Arkansas stone. All of these products have an excellent reputation for doing one thing—putting an edge on your knife.

Price: Honing Kit $8; Honing Oil $1; Washita Stone $3.50; Pocket Arkansas Stone $3.50.

From Buck Knives.

HONING DEVICE

Buck's Model 136 Honemaster is designed to be affixed to any knife blade that's more than ⅝-inch wide. It allows the user to maintain the same angle when sharpening his knife. It works.

Price: $7

From Buck Knives.

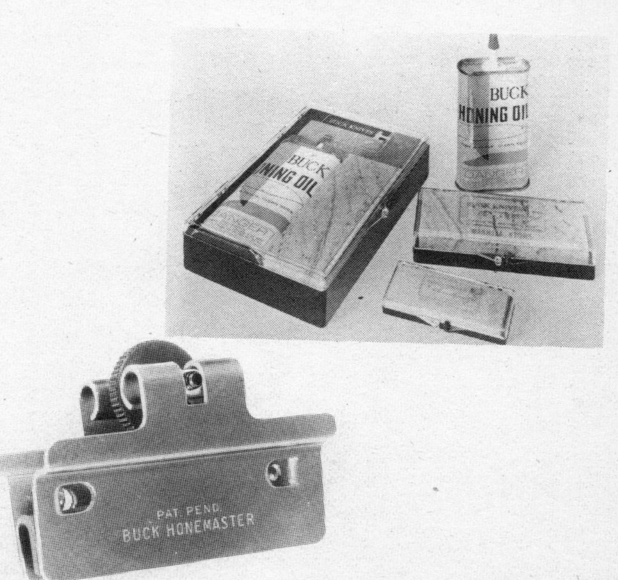

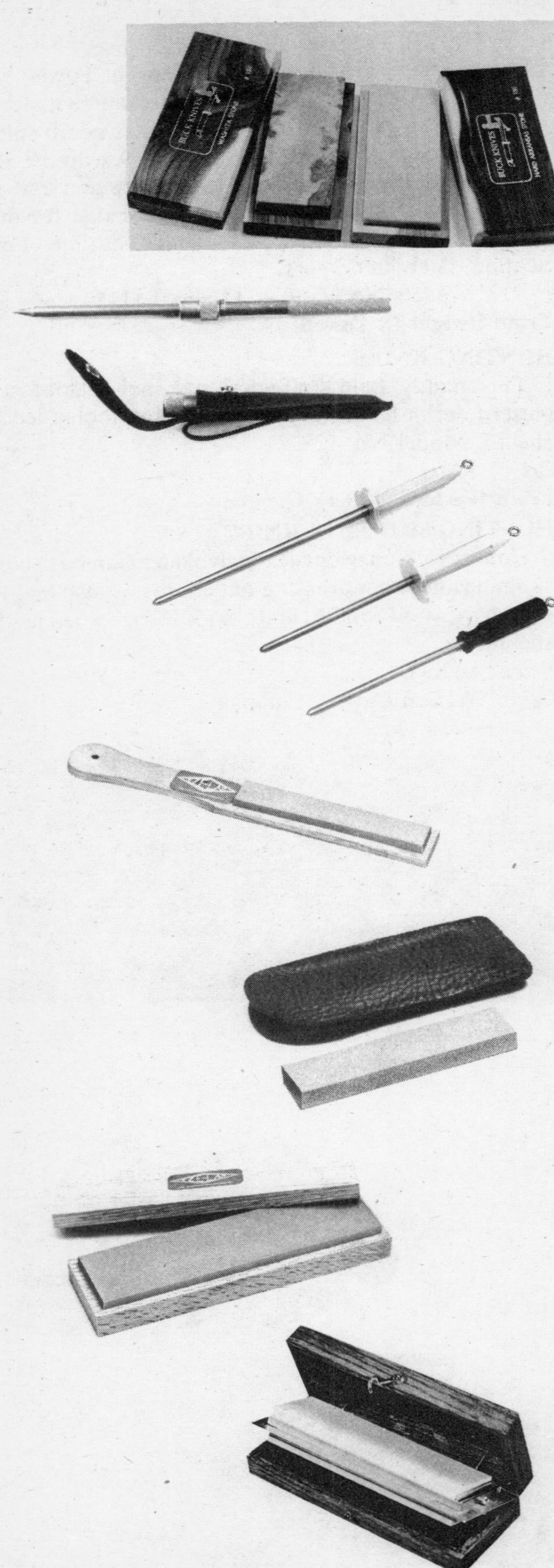

SHARPENING STONES

The boxed stone on the left is a Washita stone for putting a good initial edge on a dull blade. The boxed stone to the right is a hard Arkansas stone for putting an ultra sharp, final edge on the same blade. Boxes are made of cedar.

Price: Boxed Washita $7; Boxed Arkansas (hard) $10.

From Buck Knives.

POCKET KNIFE SHARPENER

EZE-LAP's diamond knife sharpener comes complete with a leather carrying pouch. The sharpening steel itself is impregnated with diamond dust—it works.

Price: $19.95

From EZE-LAP Diamond Products.

SHARPENING STEEL

Shown nearby, from top to bottom are EZE-LAPS Model P, G and K sharpening steels. As you can see, they are designed for professional or home use. The steels are of tubular construction and are impregnated with diamond dust. They are designed to put a perfect edge on any blade, quickly.

Price: Model P $48; Models G or K $31.

From EZE-LAP Diamond Products.

SHARPENING PADDLE

This EZE-LAP product actually features what that firm calls a ''Diamond Stone.'' The stone itself comes mounted on a sturdy hardwood handle. It's easy to control. Comes in fine, medium or coarse.

Price: 1-inch by 6-inch paddle: Fine $16.20; Med. $22.35; Coarse $32.80.

From EZE-LAP Diamond Products.

POCKET HONE

Like other EZE-LAP products, this pocket hone is impregnated with diamond dust to put a good sharp edge on the blade. The pocket hone comes with a handy leather pouch. Comes in fine, medium or coarse.

Price: 1-inch by 3-inch stone: Fine $7.15; Med. $9.85; Coarse $17.20.

From EZE-LAP Diamond Products.

DIAMOND SHARPENING STONE

Each stone comes in its own hardwood box. The stone is diamond impregnated and comes in a variety of sizes. It's available in fine, medium and coarse grits.

Price: 1-inch by 6-inch stone: Fine $16.45; Med. $22.60; Coarse $33.05.

From EZE-LAP Diamond Products.

SHARPENING STONES

Randall offers a well-made, hinged hardwood box that comes complete with soft Arkansas and medium India stones. The stones are mated together via screw locks; and, with the flip of your wrist you can select the stone you want to use.

Price: $45

From Randall Made Knives.

Prices shown are subject to change.

Ammunition & Components: Current, Obsolete & Surplus

Ammunition is obviously a necessary part of shooting, and while the more common calibers are readily available from practically every gun shop, there are a lot of first rate, shootable guns sitting idle because their owners can't locate proper ammunition for them. In this section we've succeeded in finding current sources for many of those less popular cartridges, both current and obsolete.

Current listings from most of the world's ammunition manufacturers whose products are available in the United States lead off the section. These listings, which are arranged alphabetically, are tabular; they deserve careful study, as there are some unusual listings whose current availability seems almost unknown. Next come the smaller makers and importers, some of whom offer only one or two calibers but who appear to be the only source for that particular cartridge. These are also arranged alphabetically. Surplus ammunition importers are the next grouping, also arranged in alphabetical order, and the section concludes with a very comprehensive listing of handloading component manufacturers.

Under the terms of the Gun Control Act of 1968, an unlicensed individual may purchase ammunition and ammunition components over-the-counter in any state but cannot order it shipped to him from out of state. This means that you must go through a local gunshop if you wish to order ammunition from one of the suppliers listed in this section. Expect local gunshops to stock only the more common calibers; most will be pleased to order special needs for a nominal handling and bookkeeping charge.

See the Directory for complete company addresses.

FEDERAL® AMMUNITION

Premium™

PREMIUM SHOTGUN SHELLS

PRICES INCLUDE 11% EXCISE TAX	GAUGE	LOAD NO.	SHELL LENGTH INCHES	POWDER DRAMS EQUIV.	OUNCES SHOT	SHOT SIZES	APPR. WEIGHT PER CASE	RETAIL PRICE PER BOX
PREMIUM MAGNUM LOADS	†10	P109	3½	4¼	2¼	BB24	49 lbs.	18.65
	†12	P158	3	4	1⅞	BB24	39 lbs.	13.20
	†12	P157	3	4	1⅝	46	36 lbs.	12.30
	†12	P156	2¾	4	1½	BB246	33 lbs.	11.40
	†20	P258	3	3	1¼	24	27 lbs.	10.30
PREMIUM HI-POWER LOADS	12	P154	2¾	3¾	1¼	2467½	57 lbs.	8.55
	20	P254	2¾	2¾	1	46	45 lbs.	7.55
PREMIUM FIELD LOADS	12	P153	2¾	3¼	1¼	7½ 8	56 lbs.	7.95
	12	P152	2¾	3¼	1⅛	7½ 8	52 lbs.	7.35
	20	P252	2¾	2½	1	7½ 8	45 lbs.	6.75

PREMIUM CENTERFIRE RIFLE CARTRIDGES

PRICES INCLUDE 11% EXCISE TAX	LOAD NO.	CARTRIDGE		BULLET WEIGHT GRAINS	APPR. WEIGHT PER CASE	RETAIL PRICE PER BOX
PREMIUM CENTERFIRE RIFLE CARTRIDGES	P22250B	22-250 Rem.	Boat Tail Hollow Point Bullet	55	22 lbs.	8.35
	P243C	243 Winchester	Boat Tail Soft Point Bullet	100	26 lbs.	10.30
	P243D	243 Winchester	Boat Tail Hollow Point Bullet	85	25 lbs.	10.30
	P2506C	25-06 Remington	Boat Tail Soft Point Bullet	117	30 lbs.	11.20
	P270C	270 Winchester	Boat Tail Soft Point Bullet	150	32 lbs.	11.20
	P270D	270 Winchester	Boat Tail Soft Point Bullet	130	31 lbs.	11.20
	P270E	270 Winchester	Nosler Partition Bullet	150	32 lbs.	13.75
	P7RD	7mm Rem. Mag.	Boat Tail Soft Point Bullet	150	37 lbs.	13.75
	P7RE	7mm Rem. Mag.	Boat Tail Soft Point Bullet	165	38 lbs.	13.75
	P3006D	30-06 Springfield	Boat Tail Soft Point Bullet	165	34 lbs.	11.20
	P3006E	30-06 Springfield	Boat Tail Soft Point Bullet	200	36 lbs.	11.20
	P3006F	30-06 Springfield	Nosler Partition Bullet	180	35 lbs.	13.75
	P300WC	300 Win. Mag.	Boat Tail Soft Point Bullet	200	41 lbs.	14.45
	P308C	308 Winchester	Boat Tail Soft Point Bullet	165	31 lbs.	11.20

†Premium Magnums are packed 25 rounds per box, 10 boxes per case. Other Premium Shotshells are packed 25 rounds per box, 20 boxes per case. Premium Centerfire cartridges are packed 20 rounds per box, 25 boxes per case.

Prices shown are subject to change.

FEDERAL CENTERFIRE RIFLE CARTRIDGES

Shown nearby is a complete run down on the metallic rifle cartridges that are available from Federal. The selection of both cartridge and bullet styles is extensive.
Price: See chart.
From Federal Cartridge Company.

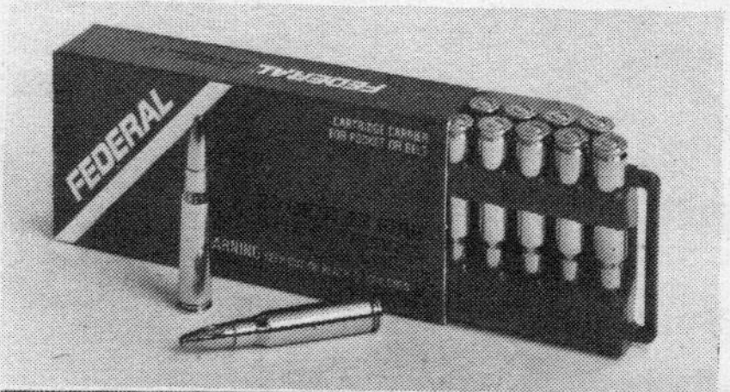

FEDERAL CENTERFIRE PISTOL CARTRIDGE

The selection shown nearby is sufficient to easily meet the needs of hunters, lawmen and competitive pistol shooters.
Prices: See chart.
From Federal Cartridge Company.

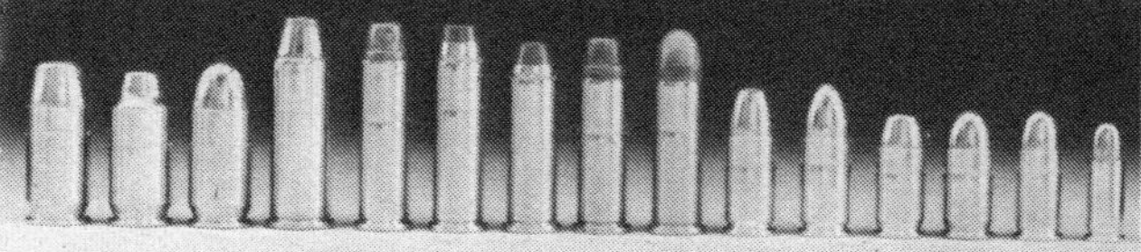

CENTERFIRE PISTOL CARTRIDGES

Load No.	Cartridge	Bullet	Bullet Weight Grains	Retail Price Per Box
25AP	25 Auto Pistol (6.35mm)	MC	50	10.20
32AP	32 Auto Pistol (7.65mm)	MC	71	11.60
380AP	380 Auto Pistol	MC	95	11.85
380BP	380 Auto Pistol	JHP	90	11.85
9AP	9mm Luger Auto Pistol	MC	123	14.45
9BP	9mm Luger Auto Pistol	JHP	115	14.45
38A	38 Special Match	Lead WC	148	11.45
38B	38 Special	Lead RN	158	11.00
38C	38 Special	Lead SWC	158	11.25
‡38D	38 Special (+P)	Lead RN	158	12.20
‡38E	38 Special (+P)	JHP	125	13.95
‡38F	38 Special (+P)	JHP	110	13.95

Load No.	Cartridge	Bullet	Bullet Weight Grains	Retail Price Per Box
‡38G	38 Special (+P)	Lead SWC HP	158	11.90
‡38H	38 Special (+P)	Lead SWC	158	11.25
‡38J	38 Special (+P)	JSP	125	13.95
357A	357 Magnum	JSP	158	15.30
357B	357 Magnum	JHP	125	15.30
357C	357 Magnum	Lead SWC	158	12.95
357D	357 Magnum	JHP	110	15.30
357E	357 Magnum	JHP	158	15.30
†44B	44 Remington Magnum	JHP	180	18.15
45LCA	45 Colt	Lead SWC HP	225	14.75
45A	45 Auto Match	MC	230	15.95
45B	45 Auto Match	MC SWC	185	16.45
45C	45 Auto	JHP	185	16.45

Retail sales records must be kept for all above items per Gun Control Act of 1968.
‡ This ammunition is loaded to a higher pressure, as indicated by the "+P" marking on the case headstamp, to achieve higher velocity. Use only in firearms especially designed for this cartridge and so recommended by the manufacturer.
† For Rifle or Pistol

CENTERFIRE RIFLE CARTRIDGES

Load No.	Cartridge	Bullet	Bullet Weight Grains	Retail Price Per Box
•222A	222 Remington	SP	50	7.05
22250A	22-250 Remington	SP	55	7.75
•223A	223 Rem. (5.56mm)	SP	55	7.75
•223B	223 Rem. (5.56mm)	MC	55	7.75
243A	243 Winchester	SP	80	9.65
243B	243 Winchester	HI-S SP	100	9.65
6A	6mm Remington	SP	80	9.65
6B	6mm Remington	HI-S SP	100	9.65
2506A	25-06 Remington	HP	90	10.50
2506B	25-06 Remington	HI-S SP	117	10.50
270A	270 Winchester	HI-S SP	130	10.50
270B	270 Winchester	HI-S SP	150	10.50
7A	7mm Mauser	HI-S SP	175	10.70
7B	7mm Mauser	HI-S SP	139	10.70
7RA	7mm Rem. Magnum	HI-S SP	150	13.00
7RB	7mm Rem. Magnum	HI-S SP	175	13.00
•30CA	30 Carbine	SP	110	6.75
•30CB	30 Carbine	MC	110	6.75

Load No.	Cartridge	Bullet	Bullet Weight Grains	Retail Price Per Box
•3030A	30-30 Winchester	HI-S SP	150	8.20
•3030B	30-30 Winchester	HI-S SP	170	8.20
•3030C	30-30 Winchester	HP	125	8.20
3006A	30-06 Springfield	HI-S SP	150	10.50
3006B	30-06 Springfield	HI-S SP	180	10.50
3006C	30-06 Springfield	SP	125	10.50
3006D	30-06 Springfield	BT SP	165	10.90
3006E	30-06 Springfield	BT SP	200	10.90
300A	300 Savage	HI-S SP	150	10.55
300B	300 Savage	HI-S SP	180	10.55
300WB	300 Win. Magnum	HI-S SP	180	13.70
308A	308 Winchester	HI-S SP	150	10.50
308B	308 Winchester	HI-S SP	180	10.50
8A	8mm Mauser	HI-S SP	170	10.80
32A	32 Win. Special	HI-S SP	170	8.75
35A	35 Remington	HI-S SP	200	9.70
†•44A	44 Rem. Magnum	HSP	240	8.00
4570A	45-70 Government	HSP	300	11.90

• Retail sales records must be kept for these items per the Gun Control Act of 1968.
MC — Metal Case, JHP — Jacketed Hollow Point, WC — Wadcutter, RN — Round Nose, SWC — Semi-Wadcutter,
HP — Hollow Point, JSP — Jacketed Soft Point, SP — Soft Point, HI-S — HI-Shok®, BT — Boat-Tail, HSP — Hollow Soft Point
† For Rifle or Pistol

Prices include the 11% Federal excise tax. Prices subject to change without notice.
Pistol cartridges packed 50 rounds per box, 20 boxes per case.
Rifle cartridges packed 20 rounds per box, 25 boxes per case.

See the Directory for complete company addresses.

RETAIL PRICE LIST

SHOTGUN SHELLS

Gauge	Load No.	Shell Length Inches	Powder Drams Equiv.	Ounces Shot	Shot Sizes	Retail Price Per Box
HI-POWER® MAGNUM LOADS						
▲10	F103	3½	4¼	2	BB 2 4	16.75
▲12	F131	3	4	1⅞	BB 2 4	12.35
▲12	F129	3	4	1⅝	2 4 6	11.45
▲12	F130	2¾	3¾	1½	BB 2 4 5 6	10.25
▲16	F165	2¾	3¼	1¼	2 4 6	9.70
▲20	F207	3	3	1¼	2 4 6 7½	9.30
▲20	F205	2¾	2¾	1⅛	4 6 7½	8.25
HI-POWER® LOADS						
12	F127	2¾	3¾	1¼	BB 2 4 5 6 7½ 8 9	7.90
16	F164	2¾	3¼	1⅛	4 5 6 7½ 9	7.55
20	F203	2¾	2¾	1	4 5 6 7½ 8 9	6.90
28	F283	2¾	2¼	⅞	6 7½ 8	7.05
410	F413	3	MAX.	11/16	4 5 6 7½ 8	6.55
410	F412	2½	MAX.	½	6 7½	5.55
STEEL SHOT LOADS						
▲12	W149	3	MAX.	1⅜	BB 1 2 4	14.10
▲12	W148	2¾	MAX.	1¼	1 2 4	12.65
12	W147	2¾	3¾	1⅛	1 2 4	10.55
FIELD LOADS						
12	F124	2¾	3¼	1¼	7½ 8 9	7.05
12	F123	2¾	3¼	1⅛	4 5 6 7½ 8 9	6.75
16	F162	2¾	2¾	1⅛	4 6 7½ 8	6.60
20	F202	2¾	2½	1	4 5 6 7½ 8 9	6.10
TARGET LOADS						
12	K117	2¾	2¾	1⅛	7½ 8 9	6.45
12	K118	2¾	3	1⅛	7½ 8 9	6.45
12	C117	2¾	2¾	1⅛	7½ 8 8½ 9	6.30
12	C118	2¾	3	1⅛	7½ 8 9	6.30
12	F119	2¾	2¾	1⅛	7½ 8 9	6.05
12	F122	2¾	3	1⅛	7½ 8 9	6.05
12	T122	2¾	3	1⅛	9	6.45
16	F167	2¾	2¾	1⅛	8	6.45
20	F206	2¾	2½	⅞	8 9	5.60
20	S206	2¾	2½	⅞	9	5.60
28	F280	2¾	2	¾	9	6.75
410	F412	2½	MAX.	½	9	5.55

Gauge	Load No.	Shell Length Inches	Powder Drams Equiv.	Shot Sizes	Retail Price Per Box
HI-POWER® BUCKSHOT LOADS					
☆10	G108	3½	Sup.Mag.	4 Buck — 54 Pellets	3.67
12	F131	3	Sup.Mag.	00 Buck — 15 Pellets	2.85
12	F131	3	Sup.Mag.	1 Buck — 24 Pellets	2.85
12	F131	3	Sup.Mag.	4 Buck — 41 Pellets	2.85
▲12	A131	3	Sup.Mag.	4 Buck — 41 Pellets	14.25
12	F130	2¾	Mag.	00 Buck — 12 Pellets	2.51
12	F130	2¾	Mag.	1 Buck — 20 Pellets	2.51
12	F130	2¾	Mag.	4 Buck — 34 Pellets	2.51
▲12	A130	2¾	Mag.	4 Buck — 34 Pellets	12.55
☆12	G127	2¾	Max.	00 Buck — 9 Pellets	2.24
12	F127	2¾	Max.	00 Buck — 9 Pellets	2.24
12	F127	2¾	Max.	0 Buck — 12 Pellets	2.24
12	F127	2¾	Max.	1 Buck — 16 Pellets	2.24
12	F127	2¾	Max.	4 Buck — 27 Pellets	2.24
▲12	A127	2¾	Max.	4 Buck — 27 Pellets	11.20
16	F164	2¾	Max.	1 Buck — 12 Pellets	2.24
20	F207	3	Max.	2 Buck — 18 Pellets	2.51
20	F203	2¾	Max.	3 Buck — 20 Pellets	2.21
HI-POWER® RIFLED SLUG LOADS					
12	F127	2¾	Max.	1 oz. Rifled Slug	2.59
16	F164	2¾	Max,	⅘ oz. Rifled Slug	2.59
20	F203	2¾	Max.	⅝ oz. Rifled Slug	2.37
410	F412	2½	Max.	⅕ oz. Rifled Slug	2.24

22 RIMFIRE CARTRIDGES

Load No.	50 rounds per box, 100 boxes per case except where noted	Bullet Weight Grains	Retail Price Per Box
HI-POWER® HIGH VELOCITY			
701	22 Short Copper Plated	29	1.55
703	22 Short Copper Plated Hollow Point	29	1.65
706	22 Long Copper Plated	29	1.65
710	22 Long Rifle Copper Plated	40	1.74
712	22 Long Rifle Copper Plated Hollow Point	38	1.92
716	22 Long Rifle #12 Shot	#12 Shot	3.60
*810	22 Long Rifle Copper Plated	40	3.48
*812	22 Long Rifle Copper Plated Hollow Point	38	3.84
CHAMPION™ STANDARD VELOCITY			
702	22 Short Lead Lubricated	29	1.55
711	22 Long Rifle Lead Lubricated	40	1.74
*811	22 Long Rifle Lead Lubricated	40	3.48

* 100 rounds per box, 50 boxes per case

Buckshot and Rifled Slugs packed 5 rounds per box, 50 boxes per case except ▲ 25 rounds per box, 10 boxes per case.
All other shotshells packed 25 rounds per box, 20 boxes per case.

☆ Granulated Filler between pellets.

Prices include 11% Federal excise tax.
Retail sales records must be kept for all 22 rimfire ammunition per Gun Control Act of 1968.

Prices shown are subject to change.

FEDERAL 10-, 12- and 20-GAUGE PREMIUM SHOTSHELL LOADS

This ammo has really caught on with hunters everywhere. All shot is copper plated for best possible patterns and maximum penetration on game. The quality control on these shotgun shells is *excellent*.

Price: Prices approximate at time of publication. See your dealer for exact prices; however, we've provided you with the price chart we received. We suggest you use it as a guide.

From Federal Cartridge Company.

EMPTY PRIMED PAPER 12-GAUGE SHOTSHELLS

These shells feature a low-cup design and a low inside basewad. If you're a hunter or competition shooter who's been looking for 2¾-inch paper hulls, here they are. Come packed 100 per box, 10 boxes per case of 1000.

Price: See your local dealer.

From Federal Cartridge Company.

FEDERAL PLASTIC SHOT CUPS

These slit shot cups are made to combine with fiber and card wads for wad column. Come packed 250 per bag, 10 bags per case of 2500.

Price: See your local dealer.

From Federal Cartridge Company.

FEDERAL PUSHIN'-CUSHION 12, 20 and 28-GAUGE WAD COLUMNS

These plastic wad columns provide extra gas sealing and no-tilt, controlled compression on loading and firing. Good over-powder sealing qualities. Come 250 per bag, 20 bags per case of 5000.

Price: See your local dealer.

From Federal Cartridge Company.

FEDERAL SHOTSHELL WADS IN 12 AND 20 GAUGE

These fiber cushion wads have waxed edges and are available in ¼-, ⅜- and ½-inch heights. Come in 12 or 20 gauge. Packed 500 per bag, 10 bags per case of 5000 except for ½-inch 12 gauge, which comes 250 wads per bag, 2500 wads per 10-bag case.

Price: See your local dealer.

From Federal Cartridge Company.

FEDERAL 12 AND 20 GAUGE CARD WADS

These card wads are available in .045, .080, .135 and .200. Packed 1000 per bag, 10 bags per case of 10,000.

Price: See your local dealer.

From Federal Cartridge Company.

FEDERAL'S NEW .357 MAGNUM LOAD

This new loading features a 110-grain, jacketed hollow point. It's a good defense/law enforcement cartridge. Expansion is rapid, providing plenty of knockdown power.

Price: $14.75 per 50.

From Federal Cartridge Company.

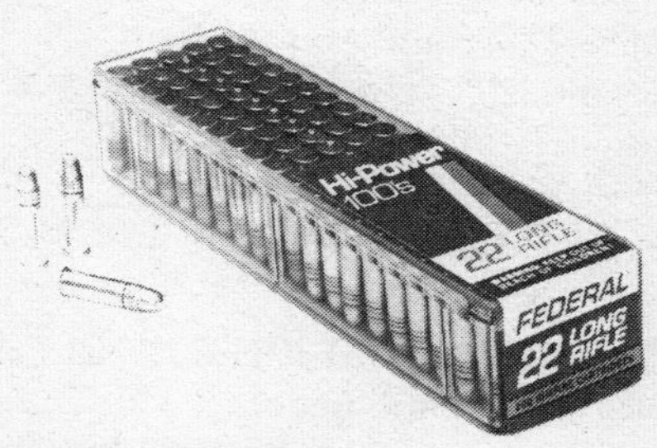

FEDERAL RIMFIRE AMMO

The nearby chart has just about everything a rimfire buff will want for his favorite .22. Both high- and standard-velocity loads are available in solid or hollow point styles. A birdshot loading is available as well.

Prices: See chart.

From Federal Cartridge Company.

FEDERAL 1-PIECE .410 WADS

This wad is of 1-piece construction and is segmented for easier loading. They come packed 250 per bag, 20 bags per 5000 case.

Price: See your local dealer.

From Federal Cartridge Company.

See the Directory for complete company addresses.

FEDERAL "PREMIUM" CENTERFIRE RIFLE AMMUNITION

This ammo has quickly earned an excellent reputation with shooters—it's *accurate*. Nothing but the finest components—including Nosler Partition bullets in some loadings—are used in manufacturing this ammo. The quality control is *extremely* high. See nearby chart for complete rundown on available calibers.

Price: From about $8.10 to about $14.05 per box of 20 rounds, depending upon caliber. (Magnums come 25 rounds per box.) See nearby chart.

From Federal Cartridge Company.

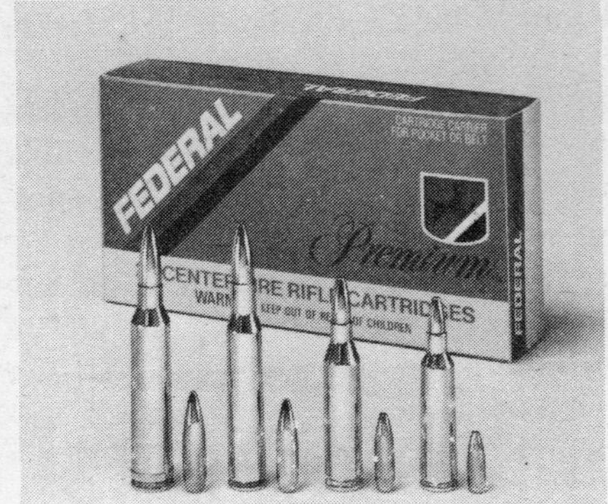

FEDERAL'S NEW .45 LONG COLT LOADING

This new load for the venerable .45 Long Colt features a new 225-grain semi-wadcutter, hollow point bullet. The muzzle velocity out of a 5½-inch barrel is approximately 900 feet per second.

Price: $14.20 per 50 rounds.

From Federal Cartridge Company.

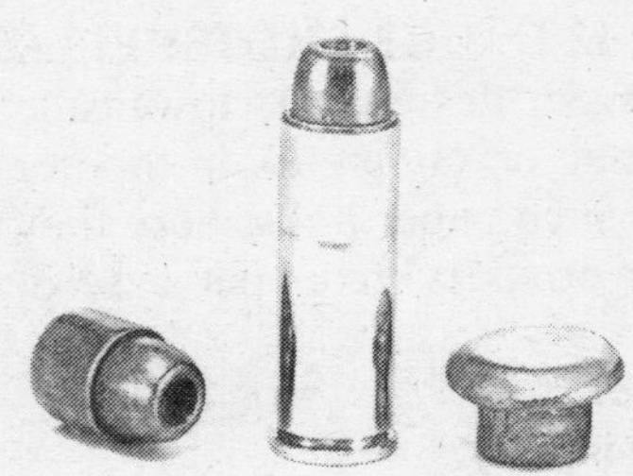

FEDERAL UNPRIMED RIFLE AND PISTOL BRASS

Federal offers handloaders a wide selection of brass. They are available in most popular calibers as can be seen in the nearby chart.

Price: See your local dealer.

From Federal Cartridge Company.

FEDERAL RIFLE, PISTOL, SHOTGUN PRIMERS

These primers have an excellent reputation for uniformity—they've won a lot of matches. They are available in all sizes and, where rifle primers are concerned, they are available in "match" version. See nearby chart.

Price: See your local dealer.

From Federal Cartridge Company.

PRIMERS

Federal Code Number	Type	Use	Nominal Diameter in Inches	Color Coding
100	Small Pistol	Standard velocity pistol and revolver loads.	.175	Green
150	Large Pistol	Standard velocity and magnum pistol and revolver loads.	.210	Green
200	Small Rifle	Rifle; high velocity and magnum pistol and revolver loads.	.175	Red
205	Small Rifle	Thick cup design especially for .17 Rem. and .22 centerfire loads.	.175	Purple
210	Large Rifle	Standard rifle loads.	.210	Red
215	Large Magnum Rifle	Magnum rifle loads.	.210	Purple
205M	Small Rifle Match	Match version of No. 205.	.175	Purple
210M	Large Rifle Match	Match version of No. 210.	.210	Red
209	Shotshell	Standard and magnum loads in 12, 16, and 20 gauge.	.243	
399	Shotshell	Alternate for 12 and 20 gauge target loads, especially Champion II hull.	.243	
410	Shotshell	For .410 and 28 gauge loads.	.243	

RIFLE—Unprimed

Federal Code Number	Caliber	Number Per Box	Recommended Federal Primer Number for Handloads
222UP	222 Remington	20	200 or 205
223UP	223 Remington	20	200 or 205
22250UP	22-250 Remington	20	210
243UP	243 Winchester	20	210
2506UP	25-06 Remington	20	210
270UP	270 Winchester	20	210
7UP	7mm Mauser	20	210
7RUP	7mm Rem. Magnum	20	215
30CUP	30 Carbine	20*	200
3030UP	30-30 Winchester	20	210
3006UP	30-06 Springfield	20	210
300WUP	300 Win. Magnum	20	215
308UP	308 Winchester	20	210
8UP	8mm Mauser	20	210
222MUP	222 Rem. Match†	20*	205M
308MUP	308 Win. Match†	20*	210M

*Packed in partitioned carton, without plastic "Cartridge Carrier" pack.
†Nickel-plated case.

PISTOL—Unprimed

Federal Code Number	Caliber	Number Per Box	Recommended Federal Primer Number for Handloading
380 UP	380 Auto Pistol	50	100
9 UP	9mm Luger Auto Pistol	50	200
38 UP	38 Special	50	100*
357 UP	357 Magnum	50	200
44 UP	44 Rem. Magnum	50	150
45 UP	45 Automatic	50	150

Packed 50 per box, 20 boxes per case of 1000.

*For standard velocity loads only. No. 200 recommended for high velocity loads.

Prices shown are subject to change.

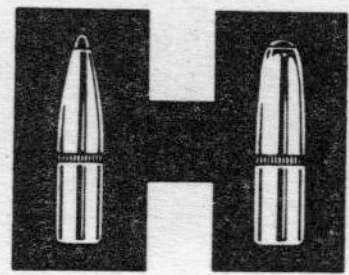

HORNADY MANUFACTURING COMPANY
P.O. Box 1848 • Grand Island, Nebraska 68801 • Phone 308-382-1390

Hornady FRONTIER CARTRIDGES for accurate game-stopping performance.

Brand-new brass cases loaded with famous Hornady bullets.

		Retail (PER BOX)	
■ 222 REM.			
50 gr. SX	#8010	$ 6.80	
55 gr. SX	#8015	$ 6.80	
■ 223 REM.			
55 gr. SP	#8025	$ 7.35	
55 gr. FMJ	#8027	$ 7.35	
■ 22-250 REM.			
53 gr. HP	#8030	$ 7.35	
55 gr. SP	#8035	$ 7.35	
55 gr. FMJ	#8037	$ 7.35	

LEGEND

BBWC—Bevel Base Wadcutter	HP—Hollow Point
BT—Boat Tail	RN—Round Nose
DEWC—Double End Wadcutter	SJ—Short Jacket
FMJ—Full Metal Jacket	SP—Spire Point
FP—Flat Point	SWC—Semi-Wadcutter
HBWC—Hollow Base Wadcutter	SX—Super Explosive

Prices effective January 1, 1979
(All prices subject to change without notice.)

***Packed 50 per box. All others packed 20 per box.**

		Retail (PER BOX)	
■ 243 WIN.			
75 gr. HP	#8040	$ 9.20	
80 gr. FMJ	#8043	$ 9.20	
100 gr. SP	#8045	$ 9.20	
■ 270 WIN.			
110 gr. HP	#8050	$ 9.50	
130 gr. SP	#8055	$ 9.50	
150 gr. SP	#8058	$ 9.50	
■ 7mm REM. MAG.			
154 gr. SP	#8060	$12.50	
175 gr. SP	#8065	$12.50	
■ 30 M1 CARBINE			
*110 gr. RN	#8070	$15.50	
*110 gr. FMJ	#8077	$15.50	
■ 30-30 WIN.			
150 gr. RN	#8080	$ 8.00	
170 gr. FP	#8085	$ 8.00	
■ 308 WIN.			
150 gr. SP	#8090	$ 9.85	
165 gr. SP	#8095	$ 9.85	
165 gr. BTSP	#8098	$10.25	
MATCH 168 gr. BTHP	#8097	$11.50	
■ 30-06 SPRINGFIELD			
150 gr. SP	#8110	$ 9.85	
165 gr. BTSP	#8115	$10.25	
MATCH 168 gr. BTHP	#8117	$11.50	
180 gr. SP	#8118	$ 9.85	

		Retail (PER BOX)	
■ 300 WIN. MAG.			
NEW 180 gr. SP	#8200	$13.25	
■ 380 AUTO			
*90 gr. JHP	#9010	$11.35	
*100 gr. FMJ	#9015	$11.35	
■ 9MM LUGER			
*90 gr. JHP	#9020	$13.80	
*100 gr. FMJ	#9023	$13.80	
*115 gr. JHP	#9025	$13.80	
■ 38 SPECIAL			
*110 gr. JHP	#9030	$12.90	
*125 gr. JHP	#9032	$12.90	
*125 gr. JFP	#9033	$12.90	
MATCH *148 gr. HBWC	#9043	$10.60	
*158 gr. JHP	#9036	$12.90	
*158 gr. LRN	#9045	$10.60	
*158 gr. SWC	#9046	$10.60	
■ 357 MAG.			
*125 gr. JHP	#9050	$14.40	
*125 gr. JFP	#9053	$14.40	
*158 gr. JHP	#9056	$14.40	
*158 gr. SWC	#9065	$12.40	
■ 44 REM. MAG.			
200 gr. JHP	#9080	$ 7.50	
240 gr. JHP	#9085	$ 7.50	
240 gr. SWC	#9087	$ 6.45	
■ 45 ACP			
185 gr. JHP	#9090	$ 6.40	
MATCH 185 gr. SWC	#9095	$ 6.50	
200 gr. SWC	#9110	$ 5.85	
230 gr. FMJ	#9097	$ 6.40	

ROUND LEAD BALLS

Here is an item for Black Powder shooters. Round Lead Balls in 12 sizes, from .350 through .570.

		Retail (Price Per 100)	
.350	#6010	$ 3.50	
.375	#6020	$ 3.50	
.433	#6030	$ 4.10	
.440	#6040	$ 4.10	
.445	#6050	$ 4.20	
.451	#6060	$ 4.30	
.454	#6070	$ 4.40	
.457	#6080	$ 4.40	
.490	#6090	$ 4.90	
.530	#6100	$ 5.25	
.535	#6110	$ 5.55	
.570	#6120	$ 5.70	

Hornady Crimp-on Gas Checks

Designed with open edges thicker than sidewalls. Size die crimp assures tight fit to the bullet. They're permanent.

Before sizing on bullets

After sizing on bullets

		Retail (Per 1000)	
22 cal.	#7010	$ 7.50	
6mm cal.	#7020	$ 7.50	
25 cal.	#7030	$ 7.50	
6.5mm cal.	#7040	$ 7.50	
270 cal.	#7050	$ 7.50	
7mm cal.	#7060	$ 7.50	
30 cal.	#7070	$ 7.50	

		Retail (Per 1000)	
32 cal. (8mm)	#7080	$ 7.50	
338 cal.	#7090	$ 8.75	
348 cal.	#7100	$ 8.75	
35 cal.	#7110	$ 7.50	
375 cal.	#7120	$ 8.75	
44 cal.	#7130	$ 8.75	
45 cal.	#7140	$ 8.75	

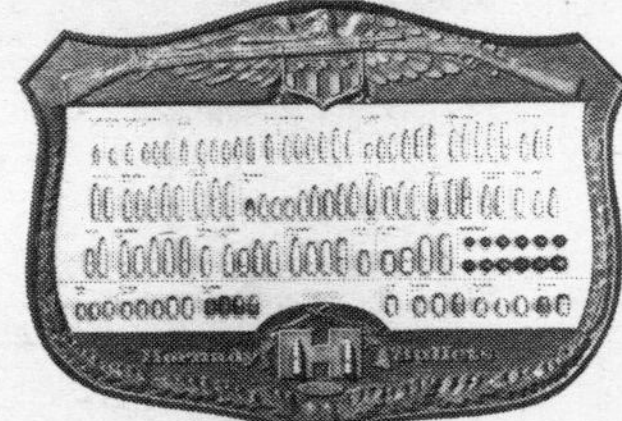

HORNADY BULLET BOARD

Simply put, this board comes with every projectile Hornady produces. It's a practical item (as well as decorative) when it comes time to select a bullet for use or explain projectile characteristics to friends.
Price: $45
From Hornady Manufacturing Company.

See the Directory for complete company addresses.

Hornady Bullets

...a complete selection for handloading

RIFLE BULLETS

17 CALIBER (.172)

Bullet	No.	Price Per 100 Retail
25 gr. HP	#1710	$ 5.90

22 CALIBER (.222)

Bullet	No.	Price Per 100 Retail
40 gr. Jet	#2210	$ 5.00

22 CALIBER (.223)

Bullet	No.	Price Per 100 Retail
45 gr. Hornet	#2220	$ 5.00

22 CALIBER (.224)

Bullet	No.	Price Per 100 Retail
45 gr. Hornet	#2230	$ 5.00
50 gr. SPSX	#2240	$ 5.10
50 gr. SP	#2245	$ 5.10

22 CALIBER MATCH

Bullet	No.	Price Per 100 Retail
53 gr. HP	#2250	$ 6.00

Bullet	No.	Price Per 100 Retail
55 gr. SPSX	#2260	$ 5.15
55 gr. SP	#2265	$ 5.15
55 gr. FMJ	#2267	$ 5.50
60 gr. SP	#2270	$ 5.50
60 gr. HP	#2275	$ 6.10

22 CALIBER (.227)

Bullet	No.	Price Per 100 Retail
70 gr. SP	#2280	$ 6.75

6MM CALIBER (.243)

Bullet	No.	Price Per 100 Retail
70 gr. SP	#2410	$ 6.55
75 gr. HP	#2420	$ 6.60
80 gr. FMJ	#2430	$ 7.15
87 gr. SP	#2440	$ 6.85
I 100 gr. SP	#2450	$ 7.15
100 gr. RN	#2455	$ 7.25

25 CALIBER (.257)

Bullet	No.	Price Per 100 Retail
60 gr. FP	#2510	$ 6.50
75 gr. HP	#2520	$ 6.80
87 gr. SP	#2530	$ 7.00
100 gr. SP	#2540	$ 7.25
117 gr. RN	#2550	$ 7.70
120 gr. HP	#2560	$ 7.85

6.5MM CALIBER (.264)

Bullet	No.	Price Per 100 Retail
100 gr. SP	#2610	$ 7.70
129 gr. SP	#2620	$ 8.30
I 140 gr. SP	#2630	$ 8.50
140 gr. RN	#2635	$ 8.65
I 160 gr. RN	#2640	$ 9.20

270 CALIBER (.277)

Bullet	No.	Price Per 100 Retail
100 gr. SP	#2710	$ 7.50
110 gr. HP	#2720	$ 7.65
I 130 gr. SP	#2730	$ 8.10
I 150 gr. SP	#2740	$ 8.50
I 150 gr. RN	#2745	$ 8.50

7MM CALIBER (.284)

Bullet	No.	Price Per 100 Retail
120 gr. SP	#2810	$ 7.75
120 gr. HP	#2815	$ 7.80
I 139 gr. SP	#2820	$ 8.10
I 154 gr. SP	#2830	$ 8.65
I 154 gr. RN	#2835	$ 8.80

7MM MATCH

Bullet	No.	Price Per 100 Retail
162 gr. BTHP	#2840	$10.15

Bullet	No.	Price Per 100 Retail
I 175 gr. SP	#2850	$ 8.95
I 175 gr. RN	#2855	$ 9.00

30 CALIBER (.308)

Bullet	No.	Price Per 100 Retail
100 gr. SJ	#3005	$ 5.00
110 gr. SP	#3010	$ 7.25
110 gr. RN	#3015	$ 6.20
110 gr. FMJ	#3017	$ 6.20
130 gr. SP	#3020	$ 7.85
I 150 gr. SP	#3031	$ 8.00
I 150 gr. RN (30-30)	#3035	$ 8.00
150 gr. FMJ-BT (NEW)	#3037	$ 9.00
I 165 gr. SP	#3040	$ 8.35
I 165 gr. BTSP	#3045	$ 8.65

30 CALIBER NEW NATIONAL MATCH

Bullet	No.	Price Per 100 Retail
168 gr. BTHP	#3050	$10.15

Bullet	No.	Price Per 100 Retail
I 170 gr. FP (30-30)	#3060	$ 8.35
I 180 gr. SP	#3070	$ 8.50
I 180 gr. RN	#3075	$ 8.50

30 CALIBER MATCH

Bullet	No.	Price Per 100 Retail
190 gr. BTHP	#3080	$11.00

Bullet	No.	Price Per 100 Retail
I 220 gr. RN	#3090	$ 9.50
220 gr. RN-FMJ	#3097	$24.85

303 CAL. and 7.7 JAP (.312)

Bullet	No.	Price Per 100 Retail
150 gr. SP	#3120	$ 8.50
174 gr. RN	#3130	$ 8.85

32 SPECIAL (.321)

Bullet	No.	Price Per 100 Retail
170 gr. FP	#3210	$ 8.50

"I" denotes Interlock bullets.

Prices shown are subject to change.

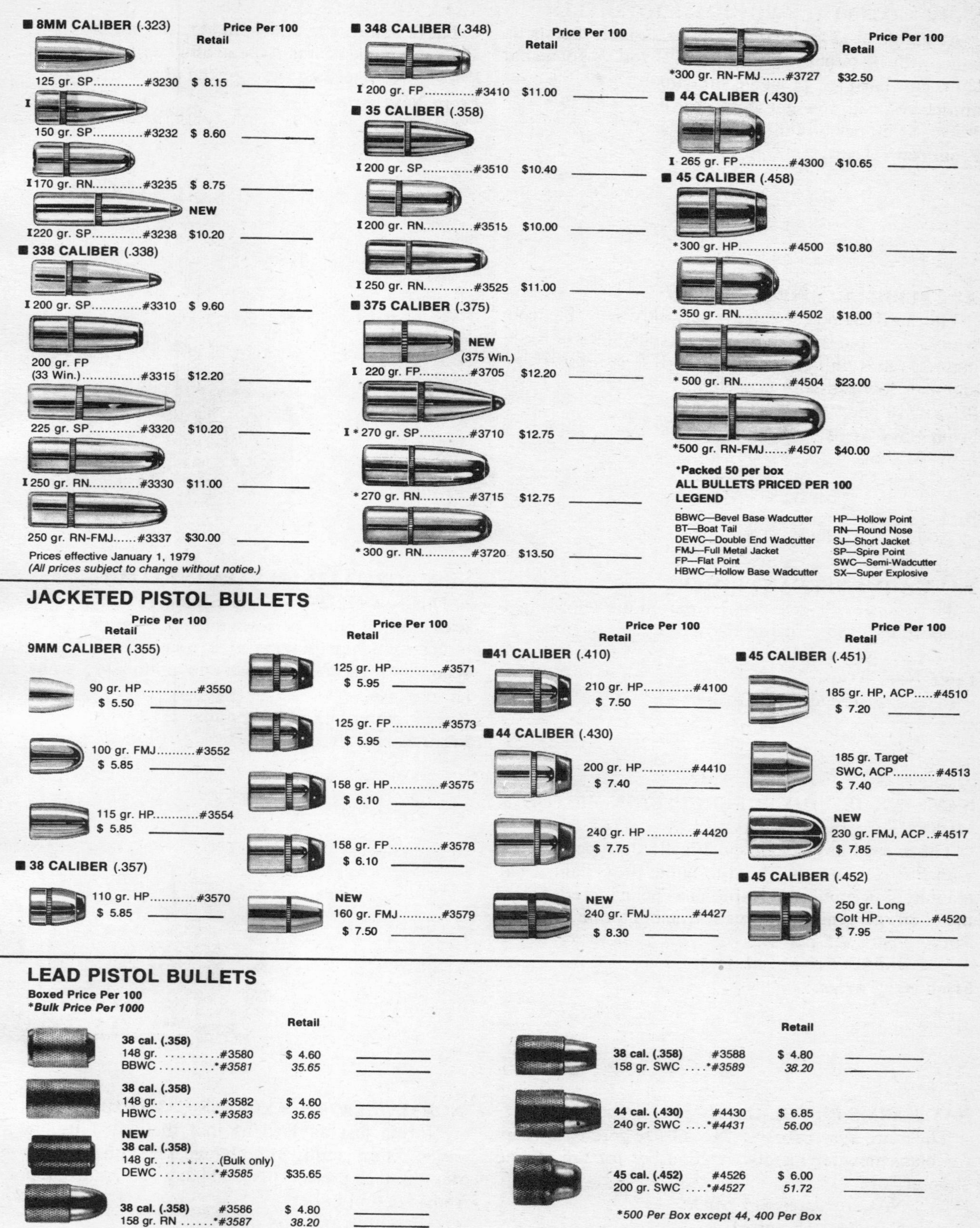

■ 8MM CALIBER (.323)

	Price Per 100 Retail	
125 gr. SP............#3230	$ 8.15	_______
I 150 gr. SP............#3232	$ 8.60	_______
I 170 gr. RN............#3235	$ 8.75	_______
I 220 gr. SP............#3238 (NEW)	$10.20	_______

■ 338 CALIBER (.338)

	Retail	
I 200 gr. SP............#3310	$ 9.60	_______
200 gr. FP (33 Win.)..............#3315	$12.20	_______
225 gr. SP............#3320	$10.20	_______
I 250 gr. RN............#3330	$11.00	_______
250 gr. RN-FMJ......#3337	$30.00	_______

Prices effective January 1, 1979
(All prices subject to change without notice.)

■ 348 CALIBER (.348)

	Price Per 100 Retail	
I 200 gr. FP............#3410	$11.00	_______

■ 35 CALIBER (.358)

	Retail	
I 200 gr. SP............#3510	$10.40	_______
I 200 gr. RN............#3515	$10.00	_______
I 250 gr. RN............#3525	$11.00	_______

■ 375 CALIBER (.375)

	Retail	
I 220 gr. FP............#3705 NEW (375 Win.)	$12.20	_______
I * 270 gr. SP............#3710	$12.75	_______
* 270 gr. RN............#3715	$12.75	_______
* 300 gr. RN............#3720	$13.50	_______

	Price Per 100 Retail	
*300 gr. RN-FMJ......#3727	$32.50	_______

■ 44 CALIBER (.430)

	Retail	
I 265 gr. FP............#4300	$10.65	_______

■ 45 CALIBER (.458)

	Retail	
*300 gr. HP............#4500	$10.80	_______
* 350 gr. RN............#4502	$18.00	_______
* 500 gr. RN............#4504	$23.00	_______
*500 gr. RN-FMJ......#4507	$40.00	_______

***Packed 50 per box**
ALL BULLETS PRICED PER 100
LEGEND

BBWC—Bevel Base Wadcutter
BT—Boat Tail
DEWC—Double End Wadcutter
FMJ—Full Metal Jacket
FP—Flat Point
HBWC—Hollow Base Wadcutter
HP—Hollow Point
RN—Round Nose
SJ—Short Jacket
SP—Spire Point
SWC—Semi-Wadcutter
SX—Super Explosive

JACKETED PISTOL BULLETS

9MM CALIBER (.355)

	Price Per 100 Retail	
90 gr. HP.............#3550	$ 5.50	_______
100 gr. FMJ..........#3552	$ 5.85	_______
115 gr. HP...........#3554	$ 5.85	_______

■ 38 CALIBER (.357)

	Price Per 100 Retail	
110 gr. HP...........#3570	$ 5.85	_______
125 gr. HP............#3571	$ 5.95	_______
125 gr. FP............#3573	$ 5.95	_______
158 gr. HP............#3575	$ 6.10	_______
158 gr. FP............#3578	$ 6.10	_______
NEW 160 gr. FMJ..........#3579	$ 7.50	_______

■ 41 CALIBER (.410)

	Price Per 100 Retail	
210 gr. HP............#4100	$ 7.50	_______

■ 44 CALIBER (.430)

	Retail	
200 gr. HP............#4410	$ 7.40	_______
240 gr. HP............#4420	$ 7.75	_______
NEW 240 gr. FMJ..........#4427	$ 8.30	_______

■ 45 CALIBER (.451)

	Price Per 100 Retail	
185 gr. HP, ACP.....#4510	$ 7.20	_______
185 gr. Target SWC, ACP..........#4513	$ 7.40	_______
NEW 230 gr. FMJ, ACP..#4517	$ 7.85	_______

■ 45 CALIBER (.452)

	Retail	
250 gr. Long Colt HP.............#4520	$ 7.95	_______

LEAD PISTOL BULLETS

Boxed Price Per 100
Bulk Price Per 1000

	Retail	
38 cal. (.358) 148 gr. ....#3580	$ 4.60	_______
BBWC..........*#3581	*35.65*	_______
38 cal. (.358) 148 gr. ....#3582	$ 4.60	_______
HBWC..........*#3583	*35.65*	_______
NEW 38 cal. (.358) 148 gr. ....(Bulk only) DEWC..........*#3585	$35.65	_______
38 cal. (.358) #3586	$ 4.80	_______
158 gr. RN......*#3587	*38.20*	_______
38 cal. (.358) #3588	$ 4.80	_______
158 gr. SWC....*#3589	*38.20*	_______
44 cal. (.430) #4430	$ 6.85	_______
240 gr. SWC....*#4431	*56.00*	_______
45 cal. (.452) #4526	$ 6.00	_______
200 gr. SWC....*#4527	*51.72*	_______

**500 Per Box except 44, 400 Per Box*

See the Directory for complete company addresses.

NAVY ARMS BLACK POWDER SHOTSHELLS

Available in 12 gauge only, these 2¾-inch shotshells come with 1⅛ ounces of No. 6 shot. If you've got an old damascus barreled 12-gauge shotgun in shootable condition, you can now get ammo for it.
Price: $3.50 per box of 10 shells.
From Navy Arms.

.41 CALIBER RIMFIRE AMMO

This hard to find cartridge is currently available from Navy Arms and is being made by a subsidiary of Remington, on Remington's tooling. It's non-corrosive and uses low-pressure propellant.
Price: $18 per 50 rounds.
From Navy Arms.

NAVY ARMS BERDAN PRIMERS

These large rifle-size primers permit the reloading of big-bore brass for English double rifles.
Price: See you local dealer.
From Navy Arms.

NAVY ARMS "HOT" PERCUSSION PISTOL & MUSKET CAPS

These caps have been specifically designed for use with Pyrodex or other hard-to-ignite propellants. The amount of priming composition has been increased and the shell thickened to prevent fragmentation.
Price: Pistol $15 per M.
Musket $18 per M.
From Navy Arms.

NAVY ARMS PISTOL CAPS

These are non-corrosive, No. 11 size percussion caps for black powder pistols. A good bet for the serious shooter.
Price: Non-corrosive $15 per M
Corrosive $8 per M.
From Navy Arms.

NAVY ARMS MINIE BALLS

These balls are available in .45, .50 and .58 calibers. They are made of quality lead alloy and are accurate.
Price: $3.50 per bag—any of the above calibers.
From Navy Arms.

NEW NORMA .22-250 VARMINT LOAD

This new .22-250 loading combines match accuracy with hunting-bullet performance. A 53-grain, soft point bullet exits the muzzle at a nominal 3710 feet per second—slightly flatter than conventional 55-grain bullet loadings.
Price: $9 per box of 20 rounds.
From Norma Precision.

NORMA .280/7mm EXPRESS CARTRIDGE

Norma just advised us that their .280 Remington ammunition is fully interchangeable with Remington's new 7mm Express. This load has a 150-grain soft point, semi boattail bullet.
Price: $10.50 per box of 20.
From Norma Precision.

Prices shown are subject to change.

NORMA CENTERFIRE RIFLE AND PISTOL AMMUNITION

Norma offers a wide selection of rifle and pistol ammo. Its reputation with shooters and hunters, for both accuracy and performance, is excellent. As you will see in the charts provided, Norma also offers a broad selection of hard to get rifle cartridges, both domestic and foreign. Their pistol ammo is also quite good; in fact, the Norma .44 Magnum load has a well established reputation as a real power house—perfect for deer-sized game.

Prices: See chart.

LOADED CENTERFIRE RIFLE AMMUNITION STANDARD CALIBERS

Stk. No.	Cartridge	Wt. Grs.	Bullet Style	No. Per Box	Retail Per Box
15711	.222 Rem.	50	SP	20	6.65
15712	.222 Rem.	50	FJ	20	6.65
15714	.222 Rem.	53	SpPSP	20	7.05
15733	.22-250 Rem.	53	SpPSP	20	9.00
16002	.243 Win.	100	FJ	20	9.05
16003	.243 Win.	100	SP	20	9.05
16902	.270 Win.	130	SPBT	20	9.85
16903	.270 Win.	150	SPBT	20	9.85
17002	7 mm Mauser	150	SPBT	20	10.05
17021	7 mm Rem.Mag.	150	SPBT	20	12.20
17050	.280 Rem.	150	SPBT	20	10.05
17621	.30 Carbine	110	SP	20	6.30
17623	.308 Win.	130	SPBT	20	9.85
17624	.308 Win.	150	SPBT	20	9.85
17628	.308 Win.	180	PPDC	20	9.85
17630	.30-30 Win.	150	SPFN	20	9.50
17631	.30-30 Win.	170	SPFN	20	9.50
17640	.30-06	130	SPBT	20	9.90
17643	.30-06	150	SPBT	20	9.90
17648	.30-06	180	SP	20	9.90
17653	.30-06	180	PPDC	20	9.90
17656	.30-06 (10 pack)	180	PPDC	10	5.20
17712	.303 British	150	SP	20	10.10
17713	.303 British	180	SPBT	20	10.10
17901	8x57 J(8 Mauser)	196	SP	20	10.15
18003	8x57 JS(8Mauser)	196	SP	20	10.15

BT-Boat Tail
DC-Dual Core
FJ-Full Jacket
FN-Flat Nose
FP-Flat Point
HP-Hollow Point
L-Lead
PP-Plastic Point
PC-Power Cavity
RN-Round Nose
SP-Soft Point
SpP-Spire Point
SW-Semi Wad Cutter
WC-Wad Cutter

LOADED CENTERFIRE PISTOL AMMUNITION

Stk. No.	Cartridge	Wt. Grs.	Bullet Style	No. Per Box	Retail Per Box
17612	.30 Luger	93	FJRN	50	19.25
17614	.32 ACP	77	FJRN	50	11.90
19021	9 mm Luger	115	HP	50	15.00
19022	9 mm Luger	116	FJRN	50	15.00
19026	9 mm Luger	116	SPFN	50	15.00
19110	.38 Special	148	LWC	50	12.25
19112	.38 Special	158	LRN	50	12.00
19114	.38 Special	158	FJSW	50	17.65
19119	.38 Special	110	HP	50	15.40
19124	.38 Special	158	SPFN	50	14.40
19125	.38 Special	158	HP	50	14.40
19101	.357 Magnum	158	HP	50	16.15
19106	.357 Magnum	158	FJSW	50	19.00
19107	.357 Magnum	158	SPFN	50	16.15
11103	.44 Magnum	240	PC	50	23.70
11103	.44 Magnum	240	PC	20	10.25
11105	.44 Auto Mag.	240	FP	50	32.65
11105	.44 Auto Mag.	240	FP	20	13.65

LOADED CENTERFIRE AMMUNITION UNIQUE (metric) CALIBERS

Stk. No.	Cartridge	Wt. Grs.	Bullet Style	No. Per Box	Retail Per Box
15604	.22 Sav.Hi Pwr	71	SP	20	16.15
15605	.22 Sav.Hi Pwr	71	FJ	20	16.15
15701	.220 Swift	50	SP	20	13.30
16531	6.5 Jap.	139	SPBT	20	14.80
16532	6.5 Jap.	156	SP	20	14.80
16535	6.5 Carcano	156	SP	20	14.80
16536	6.5 Carcano	139	PPDC	20	14.80
16550	6.5 Norma(6.5x55)	77	SP	20	14.80
16552	6.5 Norma(6.5x55)	156	SP	20	14.80
16557	6.5 Norma(6.5x55)	139	PPDC	20	14.80
17005	7 x 57 R	150	SPBT	20	16.25
17006	7 x 57 R	150	FJBT	20	16.25
17013	7 x 64	150	SPBT	20	16.20
17511	7.5 x 55 Swiss	180	SPBT	20	15.00
17634	7.62 Russian	180	SPBT	20	15.30
17638	.308 Norma Mag.	180	PPDC	20	19.85
17701	7.65 Arg. Mauser	150	SP	20	14.80
17721	7.7 Jap.	130	SP	20	15.05
17722	7.7 Jap.	180	SPBT	20	15.05
19001	.358 Norma Mag.	250	SP	20	19.85
19302	9.3 x 57	286	PPDC	20	19.00
19314	9.3 x 62	286	PPDC	20	19.00

From Norma Precision.

See the Directory for complete company addresses.

NORMA UNPRIMED RIFLE AND PISTOL CASES

As you can see from the chart shown, Norma offers an exceptionally good selection of U.S. and foreign rifle brass. While the pistol brass list, to some, may seem small, please note that Norma offers .44 Auto Mag brass. If you've been looking for Auto Mag cases, you have just come to the right spot! All Norma brass has a solid reputation for lasting through loading, after loading.

Price: See below.

UNPRIMED RIFLE CASES

Stk. No.	Caliber	No. Per Box	Sugg. Retail Price
25701	.220 Swift	20	5.60
25711	.222 Remington	20	3.95
25731	.22-250 Remington	20	5.50
26001	.243 Winchester	20	5.15
25604	.22 Sav. Hi Power	20	5.85
26531	6.5 Jap.	20	6.00
26535	6.5 Carcano	20	6.00
26551	6.5 Norma (6.5x55)	20	6.00
26901	.270 Winchester	20	5.45
27001	7 mm Mauser	20	5.45
27004	7 x 57 R	20	7.50
27012	7 x 64	20	7.90
27021	7 mm Rem. Mag.	20	7.35
27050	.280 Remington	20	5.90
27620	.30 U.S. Carbine	20	3.40
27623	.308 Winchester	20	5.45
27630	.30-.30 Winchester	20	5.30
27637	.308 Norma Mag.	20	7.90
27640	.30-06	20	5.45
27711	.303 British	20	5.45
27511	7.5 x 55 Swiss	20	6.45
27634	7.62 Russian	20	6.45
27701	7.65 Arg. Mauser	20	6.45
27721	7.7 Jap.	20	6.45
27901	8 x 57 J.318 Dia.	20	6.00
28001	8 mm Mauser	20	5.45
29001	.358 Norma Mag.	20	7.95
29301	9.3 x 57	20	7.95
29311	9.3 x 62	20	7.95

From Norma Precision.

NOSLER BULLETS

Nearby you'll see a full run down on Noslers complete line of Partition and Solid Base Bullets. For a complete run down on prices, see the chart below. (Prices subject to change.)

Price: See below.

Solid Base Bullets (100 per box)

CALIBER	GRAIN WT.	STYLE	PRICE PER BOX
	50	Spitzer	$ 5.65
	50	Hollow Point	5.70
	50	H.P. MATCH	7.35
.22	52	Hollow Point	6.75
	52	H.P. MATCH	7.90
	55	Spitzer	6.00
	60	Spitzer	6.20
	70	Hollow Point	7.70
	70	H.P. MATCH	10.00
6mm	85	Spitzer	7.90
	100	Spitzer	8.30
	100	Spitzer	8.45
.25	120	Spitzer	9.00
6.5mm	120	Spitzer	9.30
	100	Spitzer	8.55
.270	130	Spitzer	9.50
	150	Spitzer	9.90
	120	Spitzer	9.00
7mm	140	Spitzer	9.55
	150	Spitzer	9.85
	150	Flat Pt. (.30-30)	9.65
	150	Spitzer	9.65
	150	Hollow Point	9.65
	150	H.P. MATCH	12.10
.30	165	Spitzer	9.95
	168	Hollow Point	10.00
	168	H.P. MATCH	12.60
	170	Flat Pt. (.30-30)	9.95
	180	Spitzer	10.25

Partition Bullets (50 per box)

CALIBER	GRAIN WT.	STYLE	PRICE PER BOX
	85	Semi-Spitzer	$ 9.05
6mm	95	Spitzer	9.15
	100	Semi-Spitzer	9.30
	100	Spitzer	9.30
.25	115	Spitzer	9.65
	117	Semi-Spitzer	9.65
	125	Spitzer	9.95
6.5mm	140	Spitzer	10.35
	130	Spitzer	10.10
.270	150	Spitzer	10.55
	160	Semi-Spitzer	10.75
	140	Spitzer	10.35
	150	Spitzer	10.55
7mm	160	Spitzer	10.80
	175	Semi-Spitzer	11.10
	150	Spitzer	10.50
	150	Protected Point	10.50
	165	Spitzer	10.80
.30	165	Protected Point	10.80
	180	Spitzer	11.25
	180	Protected Point	11.25
	200	Round Nose	11.50
	210	Spitzer	14.50
.338	250	Round Nose	15.45

From Nosler.

Prices shown are subject to change.

NOSLER

Caliber	Diameter		Bullet Weight and Style
6mm	.243″		85 Gr. Semi Spitzer
	.243″		95 Gr. Spitzer
	.243″		100 Gr. Semi Spitzer
.25	.257″		100 Gr. Spitzer
	.257″		115 Gr. Spitzer
	.257″		117 Gr. Semi Spitzer
6.5mm	.264″		125 Gr. Spitzer
	.264″		140 Gr. Spitzer
.270	.277″		130 Gr. Spitzer
	.277″		150 Gr. Spitzer
	.277″		160 Gr. Semi Spitzer
7mm	.284″		140 Gr. Spitzer
	.284″		150 Gr. Spitzer
	.284″		160 Gr. Spitzer
	.284″		175 Gr. Semi Spitzer
.30	.308″		150 Gr. Spitzer
	.308″		150 Gr. Protected Point
	.308″		165 Gr. Spitzer
	.308″		165 Gr. Protected Point
	.308″		180 Gr. Spitzer
	.308″		180 Gr. Protected Point
	.308″		200 Gr. Round Nose
.338	.338″		210 Gr. Spitzer
	.338″		250 Gr. Round Nose

Caliber	Diameter		Bullet Weight and Style
.22	.224″		50 Gr. Spitzer
	.224″		50 Gr. Hollow Point
	.224″		50 Gr. Hollow Point Match
	.224″		52 Gr. Hollow Point
	.224″		52 Gr. Hollow Point Match
	.224″		55 Gr. Spitzer
	.224″		60 Gr. Spitzer
6mm	.243″		70 Gr. Hollow Point
	.243″		70 Gr. Hollow Point Match
	.243″		85 Gr. Spitzer
	.243″		100 Gr. Spitzer
.25	.257″		100 Gr. Spitzer
	.257″		120 Gr. Spitzer
6.5mm	.264″		120 Gr. Spitzer
.270	.277″		100 Gr. Spitzer
	.277″		130 Gr. Spitzer
	.277″		150 Gr. Spitzer
7mm	.284″		120 Gr. Spitzer
	.284″		140 Gr. Spitzer
	.284″		150 Gr. Spitzer
.30	.308″		150 Gr. Flat Point
	.308″		150 Gr. Spitzer
	.308″		150 Gr. Hollow Point
	.308″		150 Gr. Hollow Point Match
	.308″		165 Gr. Spitzer
	.308″		168 Gr. Hollow Point
	.308″		168 Gr. Hollow Point Match
	.308″		170 Gr. Flat Point
	.308″		180 Gr. Spitzer

See the Directory for complete company addresses.

CCI RIFLE, PISTOL AND SHOTSHELL PRIMERS

For metallic rifle cartridges, Standard Magnum and Benchrest primers are available in large or small sizes. Large or small sizes are available in Standard or Magnum for pistol ammo. In the shotshell line, CCI offers their 109, 209, and 157 primers to handle just about every make of popular shotshell.
Price: See your local dealer.
From CCI.

SPEER BIG GAME BULLETS

Shown nearby is a complete selection of Speer rifle bullets for big game. Calibers range from .224 through .458.
Price: See your local dealer.
From Speer Bullets.

SPEER PISTOL BULLETS

The Speer pistol bullets shown nearby are available in all popular calibers. Round lead balls for black powder shooters are also available.
Price: See your local dealer.
From Speer Bullets.

SPEER RIFLE BULLETS FOR VARMINTS

These light bullets are available in calibers ranging from .223 to .308. They've been engineered for maximum expansion and minimal core slippage.
Price: See your local dealer.
From Speer Bullets.

SPEER RIFLE BULLETS FOR VARMINTS

22 CALIBER (.223)

40 grain Spire Point, #1005

45 grain Spitzer, #1011

22 CALIBER (.224)

40 grain Spire Point, #1017

45 grain Spitzer, #1023

50 grain Spitzer, #1029

52 grain Hollow Point, #1035

52 grain Gold Match, #1039

55 grain Full Metal Jacket, #1045

55 grain Spitzer, #1047

6mm CALIBER (.243)

75 grain Hollow Point, #1205

80 grain Spitzer, #1211

90 grain Full Metal Jacket, #1215

90 grain Spitzer, #1217

25 CALIBER (.257)

87 grain Spitzer, #1241

100 grain Spitzer, #1405

100 grain Hollow Point, #1407

6.5mm CALIBER (.263)

120 grain Spitzer, #1435

270 CALIBER (.277)

100 grain Hollow Point, #1447

100 grain Spitzer, #1453

7mm CALIBER (.284)

115 grain Hollow Point, #1617

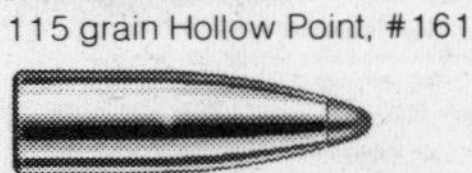

130 grain Spitzer, #1623

30 CALIBER (.308)

100 grain PLINKER®, #1805

110 grain HP VARMINTER, #1835

110 grain Round Nose, #1845

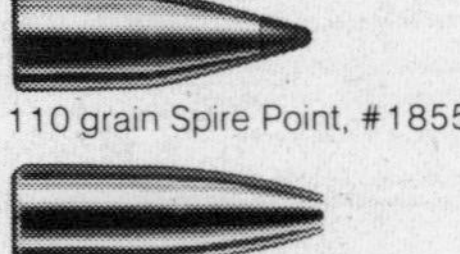

110 grain Spire Point, #1855

130 grain Hollow Point, #2005

Prices shown are subject to change.

SPEER HANDGUN BULLETS

Jacketed Pistol Bullets
100 per box

9mm CALIBER (.355)

88 grain Hollow Point, #4000

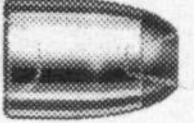

100 grain Hollow Point, #3983

125 grain Soft Point, #4005

38 CALIBER (.357)

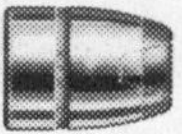

110 grain Hollow Point, #4007

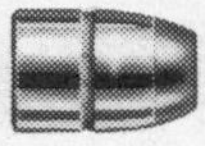

125 grain Soft Point, #4011

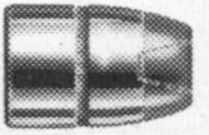

125 grain Hollow Point, #4013

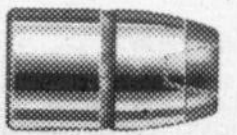

140 grain Hollow Point, #4203

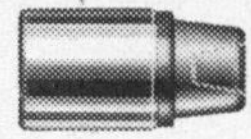

146 grain Hollow Point, #4205

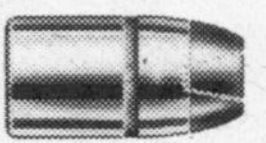

158 grain JHP, #4211

158 grain Soft Point, #4217

160 grain Soft Point, #4223

41 CALIBER (.410)

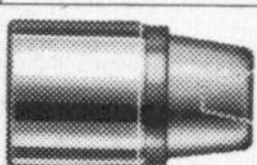

200 grain Hollow Point, #4405

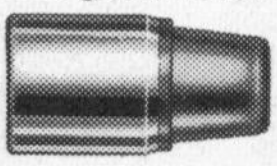

220 grain Soft Point, #4417

44 CALIBER (.429)

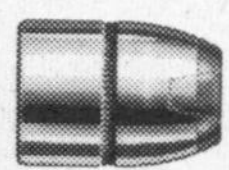

200 grain Magnum HP, #4425

225 grain Hollow Point, #4435

240 grain Soft Point, #4447

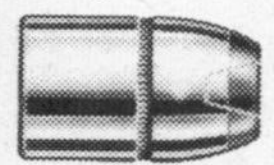

240 grain Magnum HP, #4453

240 Magnum SP, #4457

45 CALIBER (.451)

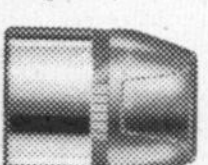

200 grain HP, #4477

225 grain Magnum HP, #4479

260 grain HP, #4481

Lead Pistol Bullets
100 per box

9mm CALIBER (.356)

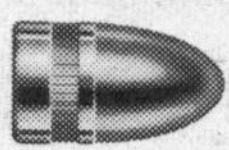

125 grain RN, #4601

38 CALIBER (.358)

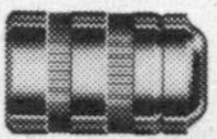

148 grain BBWC, #4605

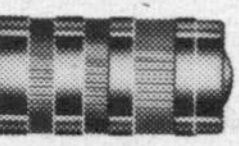

148 grain HBWC, #4617

158 grain SWC, #4623

158 grain Round Nose, #4647

44 CALIBER (.430)

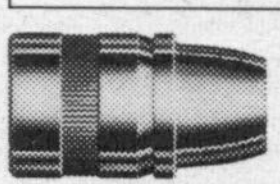

240 grain SWC, #4660

45 CALIBER (.452)

200 grain SWC, #4677

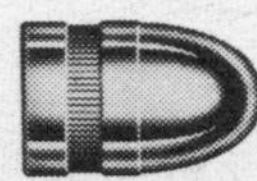

230 grain Round Nose, #4690

250 grain SWC, #4683

Round Lead Balls
100 per box

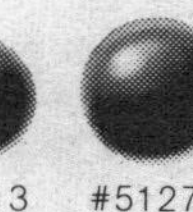
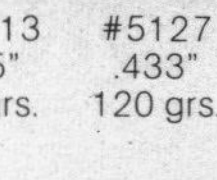

#5110 .350" 64 grs.

#5113 .375" 80 grs.

#5127 .433" 120 grs.

#5129 .440" 128 grs.

#5131 .445" 133 grs.

#5133 .451" 138 grs.

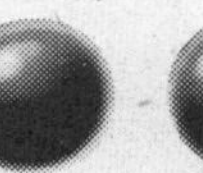

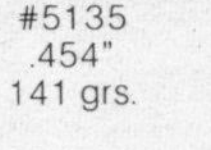

#5135 .454" 141 grs.

#5137 .457" 144 grs.

#5139 .490" 177 grs.

#5140 .495" 182 grs.

#5142 .530" 224 grs.

#5150 .535" 230 grs.

#5180 .570" 278 grs.

See the Directory for complete company addresses.

SPEER RIFLE BULLETS FOR BIG GAME

100 per box except as noted.

22 CALIBER (.224)

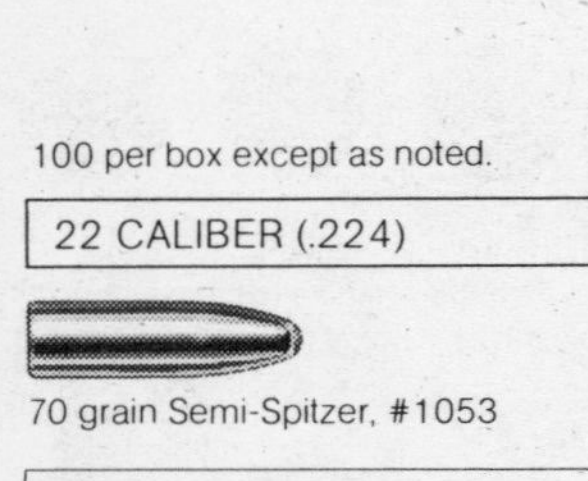

70 grain Semi-Spitzer, #1053

22 CALIBER (.228)

70 grain Semi-Spitzer, #1057

6mm CALIBER (.243)

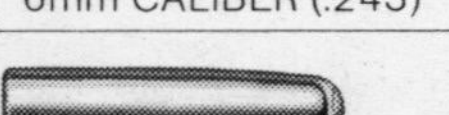

105 grain Round Nose, #1223

105 grain Spitzer, #1229

25 CALIBER (.257)

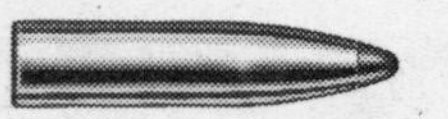

120 grain Spitzer, #1411

6.5mm CALIBER (.263)

140 grain Spitzer, #1441

270 CALIBER (.277)

130 grain Spitzer, #1459

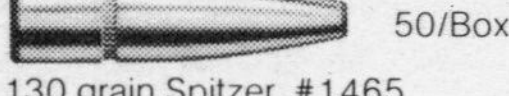

130 grain Spitzer, #1465 — 50/Box

150 grain Spitzer, #1605

150 grain Grand Slam, #1608 — 50/Box

7mm CALIBER (.284)

145 grain Spitzer, #1629

160 grain Spitzer, #1635

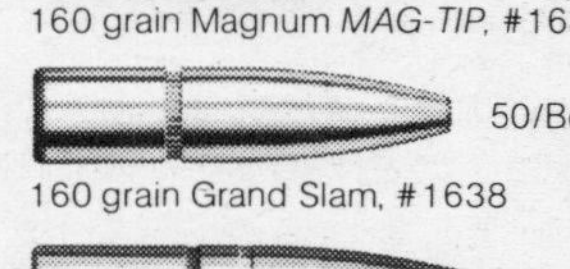

160 grain Magnum *MAG-TIP*, #1637

160 grain Grand Slam, #1638 — 50/Box

175 grain Magnum *MAG-TIP*, #1641

175 grain Grand Slam, #1643 — 50/Box

30 CALIBER (.308)

150 grain Flat Nose, #2011

150 grain Round Nose, #2017

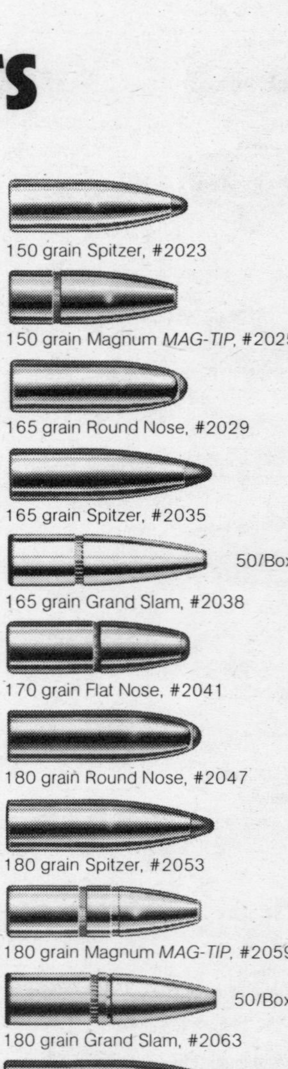

150 grain Spitzer, #2023

150 grain Magnum *MAG-TIP*, #2025

165 grain Round Nose, #2029

165 grain Spitzer, #2035

165 grain Grand Slam, #2038 — 50/Box

170 grain Flat Nose, #2041

180 grain Round Nose, #2047

180 grain Spitzer, #2053

180 grain Magnum *MAG-TIP*, #2059

180 grain Grand Slam, #2063 — 50/Box

200 grain Spitzer, #2211 — 50/Box

303 CALIBER (.311)

150 grain Spitzer, #2217

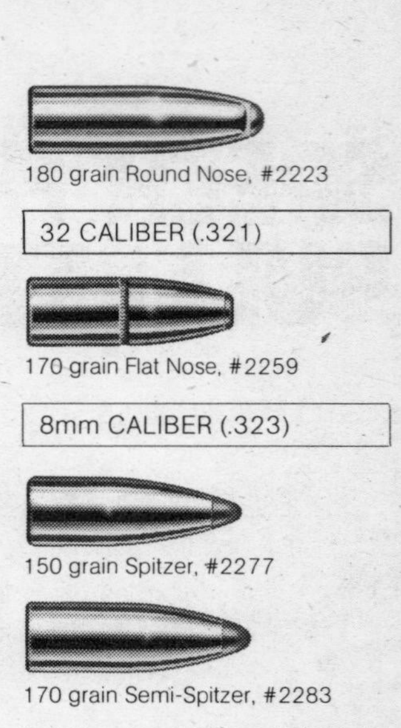

180 grain Round Nose, #2223

32 CALIBER (.321)

170 grain Flat Nose, #2259

8mm CALIBER (.323)

150 grain Spitzer, #2277

170 grain Semi-Spitzer, #2283

338 CALIBER (.338)

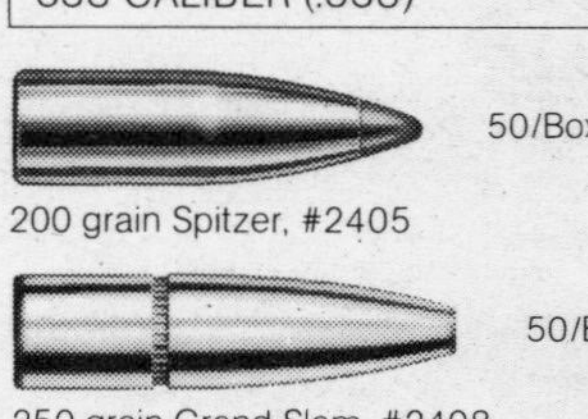

200 grain Spitzer, #2405 — 50/Box

250 grain Grand Slam, #2408 — 50/Box

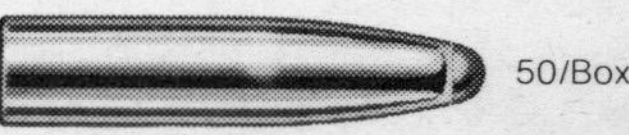

275 grain Semi-Spitzer, #2411 — 50/Box

35 CALIBER (.358)

180 grain Flat Nose, #2435

250 grain Spitzer, #2453 — 50/Box

375 CALIBER (.375)

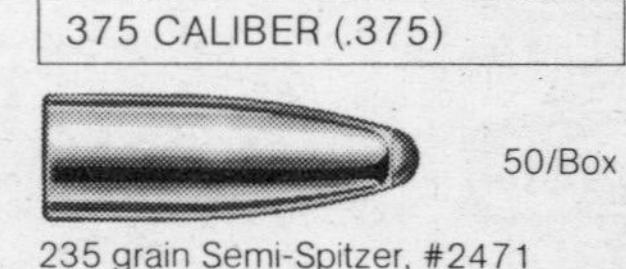

235 grain Semi-Spitzer, #2471 — 50/Box

285 grain Grand Slam, #2473 — 50/Box

45 CALIBER (.458)

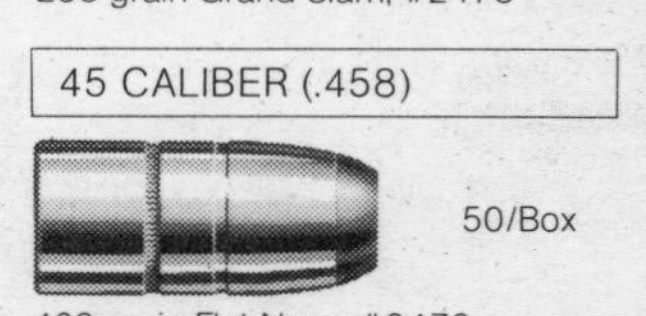

400 grain Flat Nose, #2479 — 50/Box

Prices shown are subject to change.

CCI AMMO

Packed 100 rds per plastic box except as noted.

22 RIMFIRE

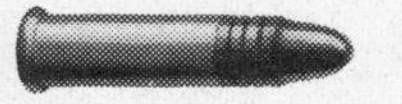
Mini-Mag Long Rifle, #0030

Mini-Mag Long Rifle, #0034
50 pack paper

Mini-Mag Long Rifle (HP), #0031

Mini-Group Long Rifle, #0032

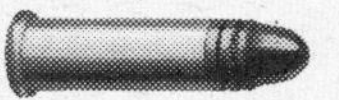
Mini-Mag Long, #0029

Mini-Mag Short, #0027

Mini-Mag Short (HP), #0028

Mini-Group Short Target, #0037

Mini-Mag CB Long, #0038

Mini-Cap CB, #0026

20/Box
Mini-Mag (Shotshell), #0039

50/Box
Stinger, Long Rifle (HP), #0050

50/Box
Maxi-Mag WMR (Solid), #0023

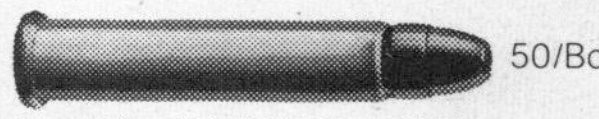
50/Box
Maxi-Mag WMR (HP), #0024

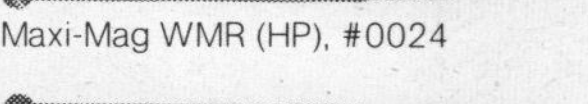
20/Box
Maxi-Mag WMR (Shotshell), #0025

Centerfire

Packed 50 per box except as noted.

380 AUTO

Reserve
380 88JHP, #3605
MV*1000 Ft/Sec., ME-195 Ft. Lbs.

9mm LUGER

Marshal
9mm Luger, 100 JHP, Brass, #3610
MV*-1315 Ft/Sec., ME-384 Ft. Lbs.

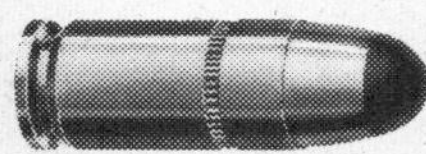
M-P
9mm Luger, 125 JSP, Brass, #3620
MV*-1120 Ft/Sec., ME-348 Ft. Lbs.

38 SPECIAL

Special Agent
38 Special, 110 JHP, Nickel, #3710
MV*-1245 Ft/Sec., ME-378 Ft. Lbs.

Detective
38 Special, 125 JHP, Nickel +P, #3720
MV*-1425 Ft/Sec., ME-563 Ft. Lbs.

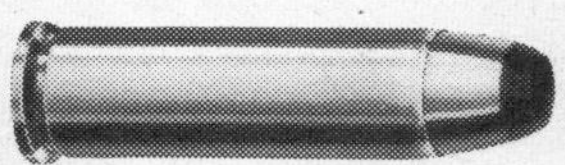
Patrolman
38 Special, 125 JSP, Nickel +P, #3725
MV*-1425 Ft/Sec., ME-563 Ft. Lbs.

Deputy
38 Special, 140 JHP, Nickel +P, #3740
MV*-1200 Ft/Sec., ME-447 Ft. Lbs.

Match
38 Special, 148 HBWC, Brass, #3748
MV*-825 Ft/Sec., ME-223 Ft. Lbs.

ABBREVIATION GUIDE:
JHP–Jacketed Hollow Point; JSP–Jacketed Soft Point;
HBWC–Hollow Base Wadcutter; SWC–Semi-Wadcutter; RN–Round Nose

Service
38 Special, 158 SWC, Nickel, #3752
MV*-975 Ft/Sec., ME-333 Ft. Lbs.

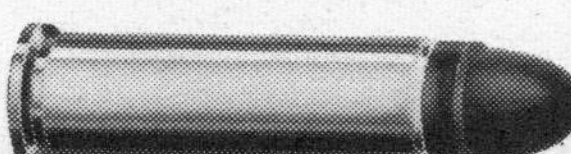
Service
38 Special, 158 RN, Nickel, #3758
MV*-975 Ft/Sec., ME-333 Ft. Lbs.

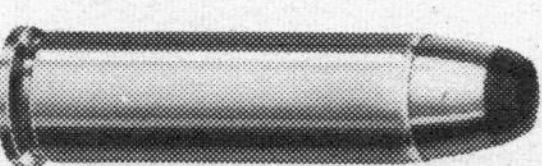
Trooper
38 Special, 158 JSP, Nickel +P, #3759
MV*-1025 Ft/Sec., ME-368 Ft. Lbs.

S.W.A.T.
38 Special, 158 JHP, Nickel +P, #3760
MV*-1025 Ft/Sec., ME-368 Ft. Lbs.

38/357 Shotshell, Nickel, #3708
#9 shot (box of 50)
38/357 Shotshell, Nickel, #3709
#9 shot (box of 10)
MV*-1150 Ft/Sec., ME-308 Ft. Lbs.

357 MAGNUM

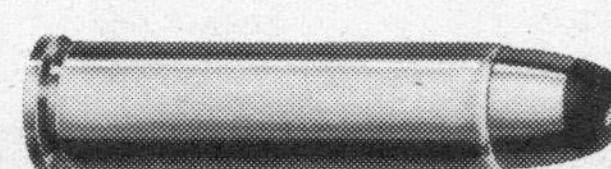
Special Agent
357 Magnum, 110 JHP, Nickel, #3910
MV*-1700 Ft/Sec., ME-705 Ft. Lbs.

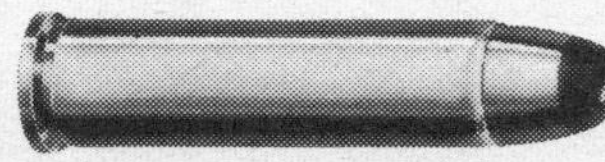
Detective
357 Magnum, 125 JHP, Nickel, #3920
MV*-1900 Ft/Sec., ME-1001 Ft. Lbs.

Patrolman
357 Magnum, 125 JSP, Nickel, #3925
MV*-1900 Ft/Sec., ME-1001 Ft. Lbs.

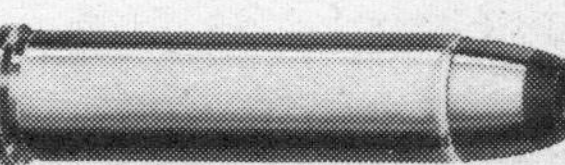
Deputy
357 Magnum, 140 JHP, Nickel, #3940
MV*-1780 Ft/Sec., ME-984 Ft. Lbs.

Trooper
357 Magnum, 158 JSP, Nickel, #3959
MV*-1625 Ft/Sec., ME-926 Ft. Lbs.

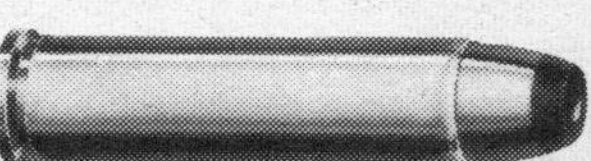
S.W.A.T.
357 Magnum, 158 gr. JHP, Nickel, #3960
MV*-1625 Ft/Sec., ME-926 Ft. Lbs.

44 MAGNUM

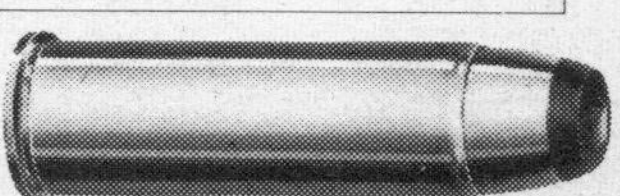
Sheriff
44 Magnum, 200 JHP, Brass, #3972
(box of 25)
MV*-1675 Ft/Sec., ME-1246 Ft. Lbs.

Sheriff
44 Magnum, 240 JSP, Brass, #3974
(box of 25)
MV*-1650 Ft/Sec., ME-1450 Ft. Lbs.

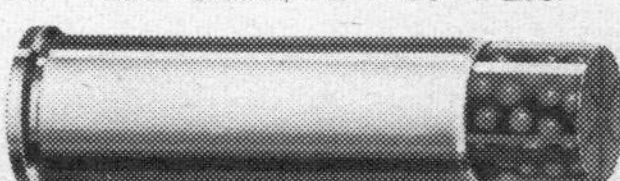
44 Magnum Shotshell, Brass, #3978
#9 shot (box of 25)
44 Magnum Shotshell, Brass, #3979
#9 shot (box of 10)
MV*-1200 Ft/Sec., ME-494 Ft. Lbs. (total)

45 AUTO

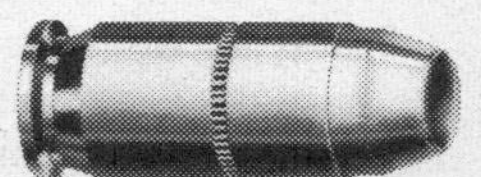
Inspector 45 Auto, 200 JHP, Brass, #3965 (box of 25)
MV*-1025 Ft/Sec., ME-466 Ft. Lbs.

RWS METRIC (AND U.S.) CENTERFIRE RIFLE CARTRIDGE

All of the ammunition listed below is Boxer primed and *fully reloadable*. Many *Gun Digest* readers write our offices in an attempt to locate this ammo. Look no further. RWS offers many bullet styles: "H"-Mantel (semi partition); "KS" (core soft point); "TIG" (Torpedo Shape); "TUG" (Torpedo Shape, again); "T"-Mantel (Regular S.P.) and the "V"-Mantel (FMJ). See nearby chart for a more detailed description of these bullet styles.

Price: See below.

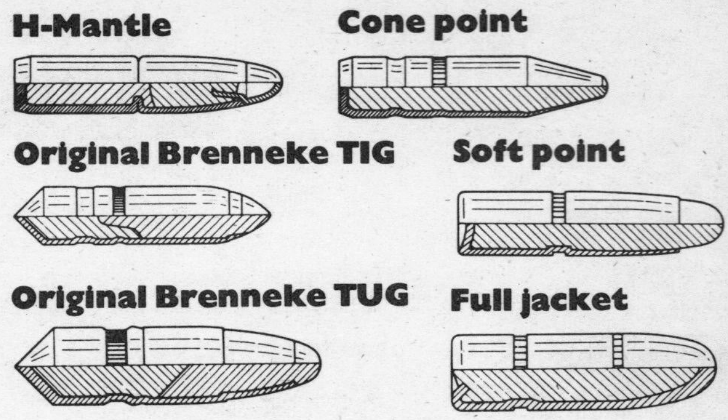

Stock Number	Description	Suggested List (Box of 20)
2116383	.22 Hornet 46gr Full Jacket	$14.35
2116375	.22 Hornet 46 gr Copper Soft Point	14.35
2116820	5.6x50 Mag. 50gr Soft Point	19.10
2116839	5.6x50 Mag. 50gr Full Jacket	19.10
2116847	5.6x50R Mag. 50gr Soft Point	19.10
2116855	5.6x50R Mag. 50gr. Full Jacket	19.10
2116863	5.6x52R .22 Sav HP 71gr Soft Point	28.00
2116707	5.6x52R .22 Sav HP 71gr Full Jacket	28.00
2116715	5.6x57 74gr Cone Point	25.50
2116723	5.6x57 74gr Full Jacket	25.50
2116731	5.6x57R 74gr Cone Point	25.50
2116758	5.6x57R 74gr Full Jacket	25.50
2116812	.243Win 96gr Cone Point	22.90
2117037	6.5x54 M.Sch. 159gr Soft Point RN	22.90
2117045	6.5x57 154gr H-Mantle Open Hollow Point	26.75
2117061	6.5x57 93 Soft Point Spitzer	21.65
2117096	6.5x57 127gr Cone Point	24.20
2117088	6.5x57 93gr Full Jacket	21.65
2117118	6.5x57R 154gr H-Mantle Open Hollow Point	26.75
2117134	6.5x57R 93gr Soft Point	21.65
2117150	6.5x57R 127gr Cone Point	24.20
2117142	6.5x57R 93gr Full Jacket	21.65
2117185	6.5x68 93gr Soft Point Spitzer	28.00
2117215	6.5x68 127gr Cone Point	30.60
2117207	6.5x68 93gr Full Jacket	28.00
2117223	6.5x68R 93gr Soft Point Spitzer	34.45
2117258	6.5x68R 127 Cone Point	37.00
2117320	7.57 173gr H-Mantle Copper HP	28.00
2117347	7x57 162gr Cone Point	25.50
2118521	7x57 162gr Original Brenneke-TIG	25.50
2118513	7x57 162gr Original Brenneke-TIG	28.00
2118556	7x57 177gr Original Brenneke-TIG	28.00
2117436	7x57R 173gr H-Mantle Copper HP	28.00
2117452	7x57R 116gr Cone Point	25.50
2118548	7x578R 162gr Cone Point	25.50
2118564	7x57R 162gr Original Brenneke-TIG	28.00
2118572	7x57R 177gr Original Brenneke-TIG	28.00
2117517	7x64 173gr H-Mantle Copper HP	28.00
2117541	7x64 173gr Soft Point Round Nose	22.90
2117576	7x64 116gr Cone Point	25.50
2118475	7x64 162gr Cone Point	25.50
2118580	7x64 162gr Original Brenneke-TIG	28.00
2118599	7x64gr Original Brenneke-TIG	28.00
2117592	7x65R 173gr H-Mantle Copper HP	28.00
2117622	7x65R 173gr Soft Point Round Nose	22.90
2117649	7x65R 116gr Cone Point	25.50
2118483	7x65R 162gr Cone Point	25.50
2118602	7x65R 162gr Original Brenneke-TIG	28.00
2118610	7x65R 177gr Original Brenneke-TIG	28.00
2117290	.270Win 130gr H-Mantle	28.00
2119188	.30M1 Carbine 110gr Soft Point	*20.35
2123436	.30M1 Carbine 110FJ	*20.35
2117738	30-06 181gr H-Mantle Copper HP	28.00
2119218	30-06 181gr Original Brenneke-TUG	28.00
2117665	.308Win 181gr H-Mantle Copper HP	28.00
2119196	.308Win 181gr Original Brenneke-TUG	28.00
2118408	.308Win 190gr Match Bullet	29.30
2129124	.308Win Plastic Training	*16.50
2117819	8x57J 196gr Soft Point RN	21.65
2117886	8x57JR 196g Soft Point RN	21.65
2117916	8x57JS 187gr H-Mantle Copper HP	28.00
2117932	8x57JS 196gr Soft Point	24.20
2119226	8x57JS 198gr Original Brenneke-TIG	28.00
2117983	8x57JRS 187gr H-Mantle Copper HP	28.00
2118009	8x57JRS 196gr Soft Point	24.20
2119234	8x57JRS 198gr Original Brenneke-TIG	28.00
2118106	8x60S 187gr H-Mantle Copper HP	29.30
2118114	8x68S 187gr H-Mantle Copper HP	31.90
2118122	8x68S 224gr Cone Point	29.30
2118130	8x68S 196gr Full Jacket	28.00
2118149	8x68S 181gr Cone Point	29.30
2118157	8.15x46R 151gr Soft Point	29.30
2118211	9.3x62 285gr Soft Point RN	28.00
2118238	9.3x62 293gr Full Jacket	28.00
2119242	9.3x62 293gr Original Brenneke-TUG	31.90
2119269	9.3x64 285gr Soft Point RN	28.00
2119285	9.3x64 293gr Full Jacket	28.00
2119250	9.3x64 293gr Original Brenneke-TUG	31.90
2118246	9.3x72R 193gr Soft Point	29.30
2118262	9.3x74R 258gr H-Mantle Copper HP	38.30
2118270	9.3x74R 285gr Soft Point RN	33.15
2118289	9.3x74R 293gr Full Jacket	34.45
2119277	9.3x74R 293gr Original Brenneke-TUG	38.30
2118459	.375 H&H Mag 300gr Cone Point	38.30
2118467	.375 H&H Mag 300gr Full Jacket	38.30
2118319	10.75x68 348gr Full Jacket	34.45
2119323	10.75x73 (.404) Jeffreys 400gr Full Jacket	38.30

*Box of 50.

From Eastern Sports International.

ROTTWEIL "SEMI-MAGNUM" 12-GAUGE SHOTSHELL

This 2¾-inch shell is made in 12 gauge only. Plastic hull and brass-plated head. Available loaded with No. 2, 4, 5 or 6 shot. Come 10 to the box. Extra hard shot.
Price: $4.99 per 10.
From Eastern Sports International.

ROTTWEIL "TIGER" 2½-INCH SHOTSHELLS

These shells are packed 10 to the box and are available in 12, 16 and 20 gauges. Hulls are of plastic construction. If you've been searching for this length of shell; well, here you are.
Price: $3.60 per box of 10 (all Field loads).
From Eastern Sports International.

ROTTWEIL "EXPRESS" BUCKSHOT LOADS

These shells come packed 10 to the box. They are 2⅝ inches long and come loaded with 00, No. 1 or No. 4 buck in 12 gauge; No. 1 buck in 16 gauge.
Price: $4.99 per box of 10.
From Eastern Sports International.

ROTTWEIL BRENNEKE SLUG LOADS

These shotshells have an excellent reputation for accuracy among deer hunters. The slug itself has a felt base. Comes in 12, 16 or 20 gauges. Packed 10 to the box.
Price: $6.50 per 10.
From Eastern Sports International.

.22 SHORT AND LONG RIFLE AMMO

This RWS ammo is available in match and regular loadings.
Price: See Below.

Stock Number	Description	Sug. List Box
2132451	.22 LR Match 39 gr. Lead	$3.25
2134187	.22 LR R50 39 gr. Lead	5.55
2134276	.22 Short R25 28 gr. Lead	3.80
2132443	.22 LR Pistol Match 39 gr. Lead	3.25

From Eastern Sports International.

FLOBERT CB CAPS

These low-powered caps come in .22, .32, .38 and .38 S&W Blank. With the exception of the blank—which is perfect for starting pistols—the above low-powered rounds are ideal for pest control or practice.
Price: See Below.

Stock Number	Description	Sug. List
2130327	.22 6mm Crimped Blank (Box of 100)	$2.40
213505	.22 6mm BB Caps (Box of 100)	4.50
2130521	.22 6mm CB Caps (Box of 100)	4.60
2134624	.32 7mm Centerfire Blank (Box of 50)	7.00
2134632	.38 9mm Centerfire Blank (Box of 50)	7.00
2134586	.38 S&W Blank (Box of 50)	7.00

From Eastern Sports International.

RWS METRIC (AND U.S.) UNPRIMED EMPTY BRASS

Many shooters around the country are constantly on the lookout for brass for their metric caliber rifles. Eastern Sports International has a good supply of the following brass.
Price: See Below.

Stock Number	Description	Suggested List (Box of 20)
2144603	5.6x50 Mag	$10.25
2144581	5.6x50R Mag	10.25
2144557	5.6x52R	11.50
2144573	5.6x57	14.10
2144565	5.6x57R	14.10
2144638	6.5x57	10.25
2144654	6.5x57R	10.25
2144611	6.5x54M.Sch.	11.50
2144689	6.5x68	14.10
2144492	7x57R	10.25
2144808	7x64	10.25
2143832	7x65R	10.25
2144751	.308 for MATCH	10.25
2144913	8x57JR	10.25
2144948	8x57JS	10.25
2144980	8x57JRS	10.25
2145030	8x68S	14.10
2145103	9.3x64	12.80
2145111	9.3x72R	11.50
2145146	9.3x74R	12.80
2145170	10.75x68	14.10
2145189	10.75x73 (.404) Jeffreys	15.40

From Eastern Sports International.

RWS BERDAN AND BOXER PRIMERS

For those shooters who need Berdan primers the following list will be helpful. Boxer primers are also available.
Price: See Below.

2104334	Berdan Primer No. 4506 Small Pistol	Bx/250	$3.70
2104350	Berdan Primer No. 4521 Large Pistol	Bx/250	3.70
2104385	Berdan Primer No. 5005 Large Pistol	Bx/250	3.70
2104342	Berdan Primer No. 4520 Small Rifle	Bx/250	3.70
2104423	Berdan Primer No. 5620 Large Rifle	Bx/250	4.35
2104415	Berdan Primer No. 5608 Large Rifle	Bx/250	4.35
2104458	Berdan Primer No. 6000 Large Rifle	Bx/150	3.85
2104466	Berdan Primer No. 6504 Large Rifle	Bx/150	3.85
2104512	Berdan Primer No. 6507 Large Rifle	Bx/150	4.25
2102250	Anvil Primer No. 4031 Small Pistol	Bx/250	5.75
2102285	Anvil Primer No. 5337 Large Pistol	Bx/250	5.75
2102315	Anvil Primer No. 4033 Small Rifle	Bx/250	6.40
2102358	Anvil Primer No. 5341 Large Rifle	Bx/250	6.40
2102382	Anvil Primer No. 5342 Large Rifle	Bx/250	6.40
2102501	Anvil Primer No. 8212	Bx/50	5.15

From Eastern Sports International.

RWS BULLETS FOR METRIC AND U.S. CARTRIDGES

The following list of bullets is currently available from Eastern Sports International. If you shoot metric cartridges, you'll know how hard it was, in the past, to find some of the below listed bullets.
Price: See Below.

Stock Number	Description	Unit Tin of	Sug. List
	5.6mm (.22)		
2145642	71gr soft point pointed (.228)	50	$16.00
2145790	71gr full jacket (.228)	50	16.00
2146231	74gr cone point (.224)	50	18.60
2146339	74gr full jacket (.224)	50	16.00
	6.5mm (.264)		
2146460	127gr cone point	25	10.90
2145952	154gr H-mantle open hollow point	25	13.45
	7mm (.284)		
2146452	116gr cone point	25	10.90
2145258	162gr cone point	25	10.90
2145529	162gr TIG	25	12.60
2145693	173gr soft point round nose	25	9.60
2146029	173gr H-mantle copper hollow point	25	14.75
2145537	177gr TIG	25	12.20
	.270 (.277)		
2145995	130gr H-mantle copper hollow point	25	13.45
	.30 (.308)		
2146010	181gr H-mantle copper hollow point	25	14.75
2145449	181gr TUG	25	12.20
2146363	190gr Match Bullet	25	14.75
	8mm		
2145715	196gr soft point (.318)	25	9.60
2146444	181gr cone point (.323)	25	10.90
2146053	187gr H-mantle copper hollow point (.323)	25	13.45
2145510	198gr TIG (.323)	25	12.20
2146312	224gr cone point (.323)	25	13.45
	9.3mm		
2146223	193 gr soft point flat nose (.364)	25	9.60
2146088	258gr H-mantle copper HP (.366)	25	14.75
2145774	285gr soft point round nose (.366)	25	9.60
2145901	285gr full jacket (.366)	25	9.60
2145502	293gr TUG (.366)	25	13.45
	10.75mm (.423)		
2145936	347gr full jacket	25	9.00
2145944	401gr full jacket (for .404) Jeffreys	20	9.60

From Eastern Sports International.

Prices shown are subject to change.

RWS PERCUSSION CAPS

These caps provide all the spark you'll need to get that black powder gun into action. Available in a good range of styles.
Prices: See below.

Stock Number	Description	Sug. List per 100
2105268	Percussion Cap No. 1075 #11	$1.50
2105195	Percussion Cap No. 1055 (Special for High Nipple)	2.45
2105276	Musket Cap No. 1081 (4-flange)	1.80
2103893	Musket Cap No. 1218 (6-flange cannon)	3.70

From Eastern Sports International.

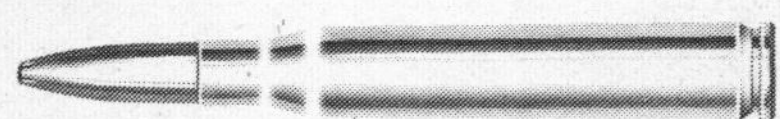

REMINGTON'S NEW 7mm "EXPRESS" RIFLE CARTRIDGE

If you're a western mule deer hunter or are simply looking for a flat-shooting cartridge, you should consider this new Remington offering. It's a flat shooting cartridge that sends a 150-grain "Core-Lokt" PSP bullet out the muzzle at just under 3,000 fps.
Price: $10.90 per 20 rounds.
From Remington Arms Company.

REMINGTON'S NEW .30-30 ACCELERATOR CARTRIDGE

This cartridge turns your favorite saddle carbine into an effective varmint gun. A nylon .30 caliber sabot holds a 55-grain .224 caliber soft-point slug firmly in the case; and, when fired, the sabot peels back after the bullet/sabot combo leaves the muzzle. According to the factory, the accuracy is quite good. It travels at an impressive 3,400 feet per second.
Price: $9.10 per 20 rounds.
From Remington Arms Company.

NEW REMINGTON .38 SUPER, .38 SPECIAL AND .357 MAGNUM CARTRIDGES

Quite simply, all of these new Remington offerings are designed to provide maximum power and punch. The .38 Super loading features a 115-grain JHP slug while the .38 Special has a 110-grain SJHP slug. The .357 loading has a projectile quite similar (identical) to the one used in the .38; however, it weighs 115 grains. All of these new offerings are "Plus-P" loads.
Price:

.38 Super	$13.10
.38 Special	13.95
.357 Magnum	15.30

All packed 50 rounds per box.
From Remington Arms Company.

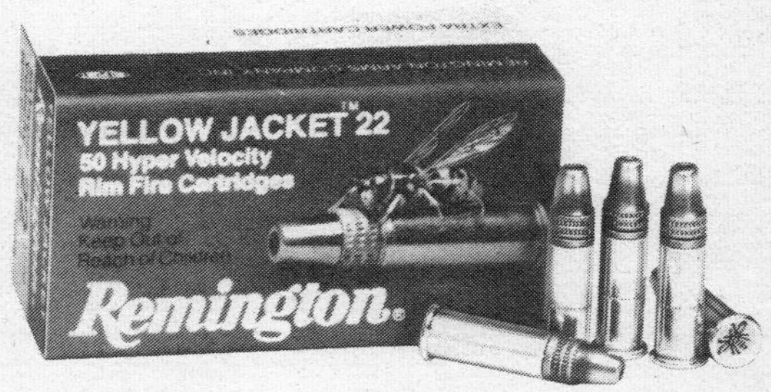

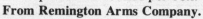

REMINGTON'S NEW "YELLOW JACKET" RIMFIRE

This .22 round travels at over 1500 fps. It has a 33-grain truncated hollow point bullet that has an explosive effect on small varmints. Feeds reliably.
Price: $2.10 per 50 rounds.
From Remington Arms Company.

DUPONT SMOKELESS POWDERS

Dupont rifle, pistol and shotgun propellants have been popular with shooters for years. Most of the powders in the nearby photo are available in ½- or 1-pound cannisters, 4- 5- or 8-pound caddies or 12- and 20-pound kegs.
Price: See your local dealer.
From Du Pont Explosives Products.

REVISED Remington® AMMUNITION RETAIL PRICE LIST

11% FEDERAL TAX INCLUDED. PRICES SUBJECT TO CHANGE WITHOUT NOTICE.

REMINGTON "EXPRESS" PLASTIC SHOTGUN SHELLS *with "KLEANBORE" priming*

Index No.	Gauge	Length Shell Inches	Powder Equiv. Drams	Ozs. of Shot	Shot Size	Suggested Retail Price Per Box
"EXPRESS" EXTRA LONG RANGE LOADS						
SP10	10 Ga.	2⅞	4¾	1⅝	4	$10.85
SP12	12 Ga.	2¾	3¾	1¼	BB, 2, 4, 5, 6, 7½, 9	7.90
SP16	16 Ga.	2¾	3¼	1⅛	4, 5, 6, 7½, 9	7.55
SP20	20 Ga.	2¾	2¾	1	4, 5, 6, 7½, 9	6.90
SP28	28 Ga.	2¾	2¼	¾	6, 7½	7.05
SP410	410 Ga.	2½	Max.	½	4, 6, 7½	5.55
SP4103	410 Ga.	3	Max.	11/16	4, 5, 6, 7½, 9	6.55
"NITRO MAG" HIGH-PERFORMANCE LOADS						
SP12SNM	12 Ga.	2¾	Max.	1½	2,4	10.85
SP12NM	12 Ga.	3	4	1⅝	2,4	11.85
"EXPRESS" MAGNUM LOADS						
SP10Mag	10 Ga.	3½	Max.	2	BB, 2, 4	18.40
SP12SMag	12 Ga.	2¾	Max.	1½	2, 4, 5, 6	10.25
SP12Mag	12 Ga.	3	4	1⅝	2, 4, 6	11.45
SP12HMag	12 Ga.	3	Max.	1⅞	BB, 2, 4	12.35
SP16CMag	16 Ga.	2¾	Max.	1¼	2, 4, 6	9.70
SP20SMag	20 Ga.	2¾	Max.	1⅛	4, 6, 7½	8.25
SP20HMag	20 Ga.	3	Max.	1¼	2, 4, 6, 7½	9.30
STEEL SHOT WATERFOWL LOADS						
STL12	12 Ga.	2¾	Max.	1⅛	1, 2, 4	10.55
NEW STL12Mag	12 Ga.	3	Max.	1¼	1, 2, 4	13.20
"EXPRESS" RIFLED SLUG						
SP12RS-25PK	12 Ga.	2¾	3¾	⅞	Rifled Slug	12.95
†SP12RS-5PK	12 Ga.	2¾	3¾	⅞	Rifled Slug	2.59
†SP16RS-5PK	16 Ga.	2¾	3	⅘	Rifled Slug	2.59
†SP20RS-5PK	20 Ga.	2¾	2¾	⅝	Rifled Slug	2.37
†SP410RS-5PK	410 Ga.	2½	Max.	⅕	Rifled Slug	2.24
"EXPRESS" BUCKSHOT LOADS — "POWER-PAKT"						
SP12BK	12 Ga.	2¾	3¾	...	00 Buck — 9 Pellets	11.20
SP12BK	12 Ga.	2¾	3¾	...	0 Buck — 12 Pellets	
SP12BK	12 Ga.	2¾	3¾	...	1 Buck — 16 Pellets	
SP12BK	12 Ga.	2¾	3¾	...	4 Buck — 27 Pellets	
NEW SP12BK-5PK	12 Ga.	2¾	3¾	...	000 Buck — 8 Pellets	2.24
†SP12BK-5PK	12 Ga.	2¾	3¾	...	00 Buck — 9 Pellets	
†SP12BK-5PK	12 Ga.	2¾	3¾	...	0 Buck — 12 Pellets	
†SP12BK-5PK	12 Ga.	2¾	3¾	...	1 Buck — 16 Pellets	
†SP12BK-5PK	12 Ga.	2¾	3¾	...	4 Buck — 27 Pellets	
†SP16BK-5PK	16 Ga.	2¾	3	...	1 Buck — 12 Pellets	2.24
†SP20BK-5PK	20 Ga.	2¾	2¾	...	3 Buck — 20 Pellets	2.21

Index No.	Gauge	Length Shell Inches	Powder Equiv. Drams	Ozs. of Shot	Shot Size	Suggested Retail Price Per Box
"EXPRESS" MAGNUM BUCKSHOT LOADS — "POWER-PAKT"						
SP12SMag BK	12 Ga.	2¾	4	...	00 Buck — 12 Pellets	$12.55
SP12SMag BK	12 Ga.	2¾	4	...	1 Buck — 20 Pellets	
†SP12SMag BK-5PK	12 Ga.	2¾	4	...	00 Buck — 12 Pellets	2.51
†SP12SMag BK-5PK	12 Ga.	2¾	4	...	1 Buck — 20 Pellets	
SP12HMag BK	12 Ga.	3	4½	...	00 Buck — 15 Pellets	14.25
SP12HMag BK	12 Ga.	3	4½	...	1 Buck — 24 Pellets	
SP12HMag BK	12 Ga.	3	4½	...	4 Buck — 41 Pellets	
†SP12HMag BK-5PK	12 Ga.	3	4½	...	00 Buck — 15 Pellets	2.85
†SP12HMag BK-5PK	12 Ga.	3	4½	...	1 Buck — 24 Pellets	
†SP12HMag BK-5PK	12 Ga.	3	4½	...	4 Buck — 41 Pellets	
"SHUR SHOT" PLASTIC SHOTGUN SHELLS						
*R12L	12 Ga.	2¾	3¼	1	4, 5, 6, 8	6.30
R12H	12 Ga.	2¾	3¼	1⅛	4, 5, 6, 7½, 8, 9	6.75
RP12H	12 Ga.	2¾	3¼	1¼	7½, 8	7.05
*R16	16 Ga.	2¾	2½	1	6, 8	6.30
R16H	16 Ga.	2¾	2¾	1⅛	4, 5, 6, 7½, 8, 9	6.75
*R20	20 Ga.	2¾	2½	⅞	6, 8	5.65
R20M	20 Ga.	2¾	2½	1	4, 5, 6, 7½, 8, 9	6.10
"SHUR SHOT" PLASTIC SCATTER LOADS						
RSL12	12 Ga.	2¾	3	1⅛	8	7.16
"RXP" PLASTIC TARGET LOADS						
XR12M	12 Ga.	2¾	3	1⅛	7½, 8, 9	6.45
XR12L	12 Ga.	2¾	2¾	1⅛	7½, 8, 8½, 9	
XR20	20 Ga.	2¾	2½	⅞	9	5.60
PLASTIC TARGET LOADS						
SP28	28 Ga.	2¾	2	¾	9	6.75
SP410	410 Ga.	2½	Max.	½	9	5.55
PLASTIC INTERNATIONAL TARGET LOADS						
NSP12H	12 Ga.	2¾	3¼	1⅛	7½, 8 (Nickel)	8.20
SP12H	12 Ga.	2¾	3¼	1⅛	7½, 8	7.00

All shells packed 25 per box, 500 per case (except where noted). † = Packed 5 per box, 250 per case

REMINGTON RIM FIRE CARTRIDGES *with "KLEANBORE" priming*

Index No.	Description	Bullet Weight Grains	Style	Suggested Retail Price Per Box
"HIGH VELOCITY" 22 CARTRIDGES				
•1022	22 Short, High Velocity	29	Lead	$ 1.55
•1122	22 Short, High Velocity, Hollow Point	27	Lead	1.65
•1322	22 Long, High Velocity	29	Lead	1.65
•1522	22 Long Rifle, High Velocity	40	Lead	1.74
•1500	22 Long Rifle, High Velocity (100 Pack)	40	Lead	3.48
•1622	22 Long Rifle, High Velocity Hollow Point	36	Lead	1.92
•1600	22 Long Rifle, High Velocity, Hollow Point (100 pack)	36	Lead	3.84
NEW •1722	Yellow Jacket-22LR Hyper Velocity	33	T.C.H.P.	2.10
•1822	22 W.R.F. (Remington Special), High Velocity	45	Lead	5.06
•1050	5 mm Remington Rim Fire Magnum High Velocity	38	P.L.H.P.	8.67
SPECIAL MATCH CARTRIDGES				
•6600	22 Long Rifle, Match — for Rifles, (100 pack)	40	Lead	5.54
•6800	22 Long Rifle, Match — for Pistols (100 pack)	40	Lead	
SHOT CARTRIDGE				
•9322	22 Long Rifle, High Velocity, Rim Fire		Dust	3.60

Index No.	Description	Bullet Weight Grains	Style	Suggested Retail Price Per Box
STANDARD VELOCITY 22 CARTRIDGES				
•5522	22 Short, Target	29	Lead	$ 1.55
•5722	22 Short, Gallery Special (250 in box)	29	Lead	7.28
•*NP57	Same as 5722 except Nickel Plated	29	Lead	7.75
•6722	22 Short, New and Improved Spatter-Less (250 in box)	15	Spec. Comp.	7.28
•*NP67	Same as 6722 except Nickel Plated	15	Spec. Comp.	7.75
•6122	22 Long Rifle, Target	40	Lead	1.74
•6100	22 Long Rifle, Target (100 pack)	40	Lead	3.48
7522	22 Win. Automatic	45	Lead	5.54
BLANK CARTRIDGES				
9022	22 Short, Rim Fire (250 in box)		—	10.00
32 BLNK	32 S. & W., Center Fire		—	9.45
38 SWBL	38 S. & W., Center Fire		—	11.45
38 BLNK	38 Special, Center Fire		—	11.50

P.L.H.P. = Power-Lokt, Hollow Point.
T.C.H.P. = Truncated Cone Hollow Point.

*Subject to stock on hand. All cartridges packed 50 per box except where otherwise noted.
•Retail recordkeeping required for these items under the Gun Control Act of 1968.

Remington, Shur Shot, Power Piston, Fire Ball, Power-Lokt, Kleanbore, Accelerator, Targetmaster, Core-Lokt, Jet, Power-Pakt, Nitro Mag, RXP are trademarks registered in the U.S. Pat. and Tm. Off. High Velocity, Express, Spatter-Less, Yellow Jacket, Target are trademarks of Remington Arms Company, Inc.

DU PONT

Remington Arms Company, Inc., Bridgeport, Connecticut 06602

Prices shown are subject to change.

CENTER FIRE RIFLE CARTRIDGES

Index No.	Cartridge	Wgt. Grs.	Bullet Style	No. In Box	Suggested Retail Price Per Box
	17 Remington				
R17REM	Power-Lokt	25	H.P.	20	$ 8.96
	22 Hornet				
•R22HN1		45	Ptd. S.P.	50	16.55
•R22HN2		45	H.P.	50	
	222 Remington				
•R222R1		50	Ptd. S.P.	20	7.05
•R222R2		50	M.C.	20	7.05
•R222R3	Power-Lokt	50	H.P.	20	7.70
	222 Remington Magnum				
R222M1		55	Ptd. S.P.	20	7.98
R222M2	Power-Lokt	55	H.P.	20	8.55
	223 Remington				
R223R1		55	Ptd. S.P.	20	7.75
R223R2	Power-Lokt	55	H.P.	20	8.30
	22-250 Remington				
R22501		55	Ptd. S.P.	20	7.75
R22502	Power-Lokt	55	H.P.	20	8.30
	6mm Remington				
R6MM1		80	Ptd. S.P.	20	9.65
R6MM2	Power-Lokt	80	H.P.	20	10.25
R6MM3	Core-Lokt	90	Ptd. S.P.	20	9.65
R6MM4	Core-Lokt	100	Ptd. S.P.	20	9.65
	243 Win.				
R243W1		80	Ptd. S.P.	20	9.65
R243W2	Power-Lokt	80	H.P.	20	10.25
R243W3	Core-Lokt	100	Ptd. S.P.	20	9.65
	25-06 Remington				
R25061	Power-Lokt	87	H.P.	20	10.50
R25062	Core-Lokt	100	Ptd. S.P.	20	
R25063	Core-Lokt	120	Ptd. S.P.	20	
	25-20 Win.				
R25202		86	S.P.	50	15.65
	25-35 Win.				
•R2535W	Core-Lokt	117	S.P.	20	10.70
	250 Savage				
R250SV		100	Ptd. S.P.	20	9.80
	257 Roberts				
R257	Core-Lokt	117	S.P.	20	10.80
	6.5mm Remington Magnum				
R65MM2	Core-Lokt	120	Ptd. S.P.	20	15.65
	264 Win. Magnum				
R264W1	Core-Lokt	100	Ptd. S.P.	20	13.50
R264W2	Core-Lokt	140	Ptd. S.P.	20	13.50
	270 Win.				
R270W1		100	Ptd. S.P.	20	10.50
R270W2	Core-Lokt	130	Ptd. S.P.	20	10.50
R270W3		130	Br. Pt.	20	11.05
R270W4	Core-Lokt	150	S.P.	20	10.50
	280 Remington				
R280R1	Core-Lokt	150	Ptd. S.P.	20	10.90
R280R2	Core-Lokt	165	S.P.	20	
	7mm Express Remington				
NEW R7M061	Core-Lokt	150	Ptd. S.P.	20	10.90
	7mm Remington Magnum				
R7MM1	Core-Lokt	125	Ptd. S.P.	20	13.00
R7MM2	Core-Lokt	150	Ptd. S.P.	20	
R7MM3	Core-Lokt	175	Ptd. S.P.	20	
	7mm Mauser				
R7MSR		175	S.P.	20	10.70
	30 Carbine				
•R30CAR		110	S.P.	50	16.80
	30 Remington				
R30REM	Core-Lokt	170	S.P.	20	10.55
	30-30 Win.				
•R30301	Core-Lokt	150	S.P.	20	8.20
•R30302	Core-Lokt	170	S.P.	20	8.20
•R30303	Core-Lokt	170	H.P.	20	8.20
NEW •R3030A	Accelerator	55	S.P.	20	9.10
	30-40 Krag				
R30401	Core-Lokt	180	S.P.	20	11.05
R30402	Core-Lokt	180	Ptd. S.P.	20	
	30-06 Springfield				
R30061		125	Ptd. S.P.	20	10.50
R30062	Core-Lokt	150	Ptd. S.P.	20	10.50
R30063		150	Br. Pt.	20	11.10
R30064	Core-Lokt	180	S.P.	20	10.50
R30065	Core-Lokt	180	Ptd. S.P.	20	10.50
R30066		180	Br. Pt.	20	11.10
R30067	Core-Lokt	220	S.P.	20	10.50
NEW R3006B	Core-Lokt	165	Ptd. S.P.	20	10.50
R30069	Accelerator	55	Ptd. S.P.	20	11.65
	300 Savage				
R30SV1	Core-Lokt	150	S.P.	20	10.55
R30SV2	Core-Lokt	150	Ptd. S.P.	20	
R30SV3	Core-Lokt	180	S.P.	20	
R30SV4	Core-Lokt	180	Ptd. S.P.	20	
	300 H. & H. Magnum				
R300HH	Core-Lokt	180	Ptd. S.P.	20	14.05
	300 Win. Magnum				
R300W1	Core-Lokt	150	Ptd. S.P.	20	13.70
R300W2	Core-Lokt	180	Ptd. S.P.	20	
	303 British				
R303B1	Core-Lokt	180	S.P.	20	10.75
	308 Win.				
R308W1	Core-Lokt	150	Ptd. S.P.	20	10.50
R308W2	Core-Lokt	180	S.P.	20	
R308W3	Core-Lokt	180	Ptd. S.P.	20	
	8mm Mauser				
R8MSR	Core-Lokt	170	S.P.	20	10.80
	8mm Remington Magnum				
R8MM1	Core-Lokt	185	Ptd. S.P.	20	15.35
R8MM2	Core-Lokt	220	Ptd. S.P.	20	

Index No.	Cartridge	Wgt. Grs.	Bullet Style	No. In Box	Suggested Retail Price Per Box
	32-20 Win.				
•R32201		100	Lead	50	$12.75
•R32202		100	S.P.	50	15.75
	32 Win. Special				
R32WS2	Core-Lokt	170	S.P.	20	8.75
	35 Remington				
•R35R1	Core-Lokt	150	Ptd. S.P.	20	9.70
•R35R2	Core-Lokt	200	S.P.	20	
	350 Remington Magnum				
R350M1	Core-Lokt	200	Ptd. S.P.	20	15.10
	375 H. & H. Magnum				
R375M1		270	S.P.	20	16.25
R375M2		300	M.C.	20	
	38-40 Win.				
•R3840W		180	S.P.	50	20.00
	444 Marlin				
R444M		240	S.P.	20	11.30
	44-40 Win.				
•R4440W		200	S.P.	50	21.10
	45-70 Government				
R4570G		405	S.P.	20	11.90
	458 Win. Magnum				
R458W1		500	M.C.	20	33.30
R458W2		510	S.P.	20	21.95

CENTER FIRE PISTOL AND REVOLVER CARTRIDGES

Retail record keeping required for all below items under the Gun Control Act of 1968.

Index No.	Cartridge	Wgt. Grs.	Bullet Style	No. In Box	Suggested Retail Price Per Box
	22 Remington "Jet"				
R22JET		40	S.P.	50	17.50
	221 Remington "Fire Ball"				
R221F		50	Ptd. S.P.	20	7.95
	25 (6.5mm) Auto.				
R25AP		50	M.C.	50	10.20
	30 (7.65mm) Luger				
R30LUG		93	M.C.	50	16.35
	32 S. & W.				
R32SW		88	Lead	50	9.55
	32 S. & W. Long				
R32SWL		98	Lead	50	9.85
	32 Short Colt				
R32SC		80	Lead	50	9.45
	32 Long Colt				
R32LC		82	Lead	50	9.85
	32 (7.65mm) Auto.				
R32AP		71	M.C.	50	11.60
	357 Magnum				
R357M1		125	S.J.H.P.	50	15.30
R357M2		158	S.J.H.P.	50	15.30
R357M3		158	S.P.	50	15.30
R357M4		158	M.P.	50	15.10
R357M5		158	Lead	50	12.95
R357M6	(Brass Case)	158	Lead	50	12.95
NEW R357M7		110	S.J.H.P.	50	15.30
	9mm Luger				
R9MM1		115	J.H.P.	50	14.45
R9MM2		124	M.C.	50	
	380 Automatic				
R380A1		88	J.H.P.	50	11.85
R380AP		95	M.C.	50	
	38 Auto. Colt Pistol (A)				
R38ACP		130	M.C.	50	12.80
	38 Super Auto. Colt Pistol (B)				
R38SUP	(+P)	130	M.C.	50	12.60
NEW R38SU1	(+P)	115	J.H.P.	50	13.10
	38 S. & W.				
R38SW		146	Lead	50	10.95
	38 Special				
R38S1	(+P)	95	S.J.H.P.	50	13.95
R38S2	(+P)	125	S.J.H.P.	50	13.95
R38S3	Targetmaster, Wadcutter	148	Lead	50	11.45
R38S4	Targetmaster, Round Nose	158	Lead	50	11.25
R38S5		158	Lead	50	11.00
R38S6	Semi-Wadcutter	158	Lead	50	11.25
R38S7		158	M.P.	50	13.95
R38S8	(+P)	158	Lead	50	12.20
R38S9		200	Lead	50	11.75
NEW R38S10	(+P)	110	S.J.H.P.	50	13.95
NEW R38S12	(+P)	158	L.H.P.	50	13.70
	38 Short Colt				
R38SC		125	Lead	50	10.75
	41 Remington Magnum				
R41MG1		210	S.P.	50	20.10
R41MG2		210	Lead	50	17.20
	44 Remington Magnum				
R44MG1	Gas-Check	240	Lead	50	19.50
R44MG2		240	S.P.	20	8.00
R44MG3		240	S.J.H.P.	20	8.00
R44MG4		240	Lead	50	16.66
	44 S. & W. Special				
R44SW		246	Lead	50	15.40
	45 Colt				
R45C		250	Lead	50	15.65
	45 Automatic				
R45AP1	Targetmaster, Wadcutter	185	M.C.	50	16.45
R45AP2		185	J.H.P.	50	16.45
R45AP3	Targetmaster	230	M.C.	50	16.45
R45AP4		230	M.C.	50	15.95
	45 Auto. Rim				
R45AR		230	Lead	50	17.00

Ammunition with (+P) on the case head stamp is loaded to higher pressure. Use only in firearms designated for this cartridge and so recommended by the gun manufacturer.

Br.Pt. = Bronze Point
M.C. = Metal Case
S.P. = Soft Point
C.L. = Core-Lokt
M.P. = Metal Point
T.M. = Targetmaster
S.J. = Semi-Jacketed
R.N. = Round Nose
S.W.C. = Semi Wadcutter
W.C. = Wadcutter
Ptd. S.P. = Pointed Soft Point
Spec. = Special
S.L. = Self Loading
P.L. = Power-Lokt
H.P. = Hollow Point
A.P. = Automatic Pistol
L.H.P. = Lead Hollow Point

(A) = Adapted for Colt Military and Pocket Model Automatic Arms. (B) = Adapted for Colt Super Automatic Arms.

•Retail recordkeeping required for these items under the Gun Control Act of 1968.

Form No. SR 79R (Rev.) Printed in U.S.A.

SIERRA RIFLE AND HANDGUN BULLETS

Sierra has a superb reputation with shooters for providing highly accurate bullets that perform as advertised. They offer a wide variety of calibers and styles—match and hunting.

Price: See nearby chart.

From Sierra Bullets.

Sierra Bullets
"The Bulletsmiths"

PRICE LIST

JACKETED RIFLE BULLETS

INV.	STOCK NO.	DESCRIPTION	RETAIL PRICE	ORDER QTY.
		.22 CALIBER .223 Diameter Hornet		
	1100	40 gr. Hornet	5.10	
	1110	45 gr. Hornet	5.10	
		.22 CALIBER .224 Diameter Hornet		
	1200	40 gr. Hornet	5.10	
	1210	45 gr. Hornet	5.10	
		.22 CALIBER .224 Diameter High Velocity		
	1300	45 gr. Semi-pointed	5.35	
	1310	45 gr. Spitzer	5.35	
	1320	50 gr. Semi-pointed	5.35	
	1330	50 gr. Spitzer	5.35	
	1340	50 gr. Blitz	5.35	
	1350	55 gr. Semi-pointed	5.45	
	1360	55 gr. Spitzer	5.45	
	1370	63 gr. Semi-pointed	5.55	
		.22 CALIBER .224 Diameter Bench Rest		
	1400	53 gr. Hollow Point	6.60	
	1410	52 gr. Hollow Point B.T.	6.75	
		6MM .243 Diameter		
	1500	60 gr. Hollow Point	6.65	
	1505	70 gr. Hollow Point B.T.	7.45	
	1510	75 gr. Hollow Point	7.05	
	1520	85 gr. Spitzer	7.20	
	1530	85 gr. Hollow Point B.T.	7.40	
	1540	100 gr. Spitzer	7.65	
	1550	100 gr. Semi-pointed	7.65	
	1560	100 gr. Spitzer B.T.	7.90	
		.25 CALIBER .257 Diameter		
	1600	75 gr. Hollow Point	7.15	
	1610	87 gr. Spitzer	7.45	
	1615	90 gr. Hollow Point B.T.	7.55	
	1620	100 gr. Spitzer	7.75	
	1630	117 gr. Spitzer Boat Tail	8.30	
	1640	117 gr. Spitzer Flat Base	8.25	

INV.	STOCK NO.	DESCRIPTION	RETAIL PRICE	ORDER QTY.
	1650	120 gr. Hollow Point B.T.	8.30	
		6.5MM .264 Diameter		
	1700	85 gr. Hollow Point	7.45	
	1710	100 gr. Hollow Point	7.95	
	1720	120 gr. Spitzer	8.30	
	1730	140 gr. Spitzer Boat Tail	8.90	
	1740	140 gr. Matchking H.P.	9.65	
		.270 CALIBER .277 Diameter		
	1800	90 gr. Hollow Point	7.95	
	1810	110 gr. Spitzer	8.15	
	1820	130 gr. Spitzer Boat Tail	8.95	
	1830	130 gr. Spitzer Flat Base	8.55	
	1840	150 gr. Spitzer Boat Tail	9.30	
	1850	150 gr. Round Nose	8.65	
		7MM .284 Diameter		
	1900	120 gr. Spitzer	8.10	
	1910	140 gr. Spitzer	8.65	
	1920	160 gr. Spitzer Boat Tail	9.45	
	1930	168 gr. Matchking H.P.	10.10	
	1940	175 gr. Spitzer Boat Tail	10.05	
	1950	170 gr. Round Nose	9.20	
		.30 CALIBER .307 Diameter		
	2000	150 gr. Flat Nose 30-30	8.60	
	2010	170 gr. Flat Nose 30-30	8.90	
	2020	125 gr. Hollow Point Flat Nose 30-30	8.35	
		.30 CALIBER .308 Diameter		
	2100	110 gr. Rd. Nose Carbine	6.35	
	2110	110 gr. Hollow Point	7.80	
	2120	125 gr. Spitzer	8.25	
NEW	2125	150 gr. Spitzer Boat Tail	8.70	
	2130	150 gr. Spitzer	8.50	
	2135	150 gr. Round Nose	8.50	
	2140	165 gr. Hollow Point B.T.	9.30	
	2145	165 gr. Spitzer Boat Tail	9.30	

Prices shown are subject to change.

INV.	STOCK NO.	DESCRIPTION	RETAIL PRICE	ORDER QTY.
____	2150	180 gr. Spitzer Flat Base	9.40	____
____	2160	180 gr. Spitzer Boat Tail	9.60	____
____	2165	200 gr. Spitzer Boat Tail	10.70	____
____	2170	180 gr. Round Nose	9.10	____
____	2180	220 gr. Round Nose	10.00	____

.30 CALIBER Competition

INV.	STOCK NO.	DESCRIPTION	RETAIL PRICE	ORDER QTY.
____	2200	168 gr. International H.P.	10.95	____
____	2210	190 gr. Matchking H.P.	11.30	____
____	2220	180 gr. Matchking H.P.	11.05	____
____	2230	200 gr. Matchking H.P.	11.50	____
____	2240	220 gr. Matchking H.P.	12.95	____

JACKETED RIFLE BULLETS

.303 CALIBER .311 Diameter

INV.	STOCK NO.	DESCRIPTION	RETAIL PRICE	ORDER QTY.
____	2300	150 gr. Spitzer	9.00	____
____	2310	180 gr. Spitzer	9.30	____

8MM .323 Diameter

INV.	STOCK NO.	DESCRIPTION	RETAIL PRICE	ORDER QTY.
____	2400	150 gr. Spitzer	9.10	____
____	2410	175 gr. Spitzer	9.40	____
____	2420	220 gr. Spitzer B.T.	6.40*	____

.338 CALIBER

INV.	STOCK NO.	DESCRIPTION	RETAIL PRICE	ORDER QTY.
____	2600	250 gr. Spitzer Boat Tail	6.75*	____

.35 CALIBER

INV.	STOCK NO.	DESCRIPTION	RETAIL PRICE	ORDER QTY.
____	2800	200 gr. Round Nose	5.15*	____

.375 CALIBER

INV.	STOCK NO.	DESCRIPTION	RETAIL PRICE	ORDER QTY.
____	3000	300 gr. Spitzer Boat Tail	8.70*	____

.45-70 CALIBER

INV.	STOCK NO.	DESCRIPTION	RETAIL PRICE	ORDER QTY.
____	8900	.45-70 Gov't 300 gr. Flat Nose	5.65*	____

JACKETED PISTOL BULLETS

.38 CALIBER .357 Diameter

INV.	STOCK NO.	DESCRIPTION	RETAIL PRICE	ORDER QTY.
____	8300	110 gr. Jacketed Hollow Cavity	6.20	____
____	8310	125 gr. Jacketed Soft Point	6.30	____
____	8320	125 gr. Jacketed Hollow Cavity	6.30	____
____	8330	150 gr. Jacketed Hollow Cavity	6.40	____
____	8340	158 gr. Jacketed Soft Point	6.40	____
____	8350	170 gr. Silhouette F.M.J.	7.75	____

JACKETED PISTOL BULLETS

9MM .355 Diameter

INV.	STOCK NO.	DESCRIPTION	RETAIL PRICE	ORDER QTY.
____	8100	90 gr. Jacketed Hollow Point	6.20	____
____	8110	115 gr. Jacketed Hollow Point	6.30	____

.41 CALIBER .410 Diameter

INV.	STOCK NO.	DESCRIPTION	RETAIL PRICE	ORDER QTY.
____	8500	170 gr. Jacketed Hollow Cavity	7.95	____
____	8520	210 gr. Jacketed Hollow Cavity	8.10	____

44 MAGNUM .4295 Diameter

INV.	STOCK NO.	DESCRIPTION	RETAIL PRICE	ORDER QTY.
____	8600	180 gr. Jacketed Hollow Cavity	8.00	____
____	8610	240 gr. Jacketed Hollow Cavity	8.20	____

.45 CALIBER .4515 Diameter

INV.	STOCK NO.	DESCRIPTION	RETAIL PRICE	ORDER QTY.
____	8800	185 gr. ACP Jacketed Hollow Point	8.05	____
NEW	8810	185 gr. Match	8.25	____
____	8820	240 gr. Jacketed Hollow Cavity Long Colt	8.20	____

WINCHESTER-WESTERN STAYNLESS PRIMERS

These primers are uniformly made to provide the best possible ignition under all hunting and shooting conditions. They are available for rifle, pistol and shotgun use. See nearby chart for more info.

Price: See nearby chart.

Packed 100 per box

New Symbol	Old Symbol	Primer	Type	Case Contains	Case Wt. Lbs. (Approx.)	Suggested Retail Price Per 100
W209	K4005P	#209	Shotgun Shells	5,000	15	$18.80
WLR	K4009P	#8½-120	Large Rifle	5,000	7	10.50
WSR	K4002P	#6½-116	Small Rifle	5,000	5	10.50
WSP	K4001P	#1½-108	Small (Regular) Pistol	5,000	5	10.50
WLP	K4003P	#7-111	Large (Regular) Pistol	5,000	7	10.50
WSPM	KM401P	#1½M-108	Small (Magnum) Pistol	5,000	5	12.15
WLPM	KM403P	#7M-11F	Large (Magnum) Pistol	5,000	7	12.15

From Winchester-Western.

WINCHESTER-WESTERN UNPRIMED EMPTY RIFLE BRASS

Winchester-Western brass has an excellent reputation with handloaders. The selection of brass, as can be seen in the chart nearby, is extensive.
Price: See nearby chart.
From Winchester-Western.

New Symbol	Old Symbol	Caliber	Wt. Lbs.† Per Case	Suggested Retail Price Per 100
U218B	U218B	*218 Bee	6	$14.05
U22H	U22H	*22 Hornet	4	14.05
U22250	U22250	22-250 Remington	14	24.10
U220S	U220S	220 Swift	13	25.55
U222R	U222R	222 Remington	8	16.80
U223R	U223R	223 Remington	8	19.80
U225	U225	225 Winchester	12	20.60
U243	U243	243 Winchester	14	24.10
U6mmR	U6mmR	6mm Remington	15	24.10
U2520	U2520	*25-20 Winchester	6	16.30
U256	U256P	*256 Winchester Magnum	6	17.35
U250	U250	250 Savage	13	25.95
U2506	U2506	25-06 Remington	16	25.40
U257	U257	257 Roberts	14	25.95
U264	U264	264 Winchester Magnum	19	31.60
U270	U270	270 Winchester	16	25.40
U284	U284	284 Winchester	17	29.30
U7mm	U7mm	7mm Mauser	14	27.35
U7MAG	U7mmR	7mm Remington Magnum	19	31.60
U30C	UW30M1	*30 Carbine	6	14.60
U3030	U3030	30-30 Winchester	12	21.85
U3006	U3006	30-06 Springfield	16	25.40
U3040	U3040	30-40 Krag	15	27.35
U300WM	U30WM	300 Winchester Magnum	21	31.60
U300H	U300H	300 H & H Magnum	21	34.80
U300	U300	300 Savage	13	25.95
U308	U308	308 Winchester	14	24.10
U303	UW303B	303 British	14	27.35
U32W	U32WS	32 Winchester Special	12	23.50
U3220	U3220	*32-20 Winchester	5	16.25
U8mm	UW8mm	8mm Mauser	15	27.35
U338	U338	338 Winchester Magnum	20	31.60
U348	UW348	348 Winchester	19	37.05
U35R	U35R	35 Remington	14	25.95
U358	U358	358 Winchester	15	26.45
U375H	U375H	375 H & H Magnum	20	37.20
U375W	U375W	375 Winchester	20	32.65
U3840	U3840	*38-40 Winchester	9	16.30
U3855	U3855	38-55 Winchester	12	30.75
U4440	U4440	*44-40 Winchester	9	16.30
U44M	U44MP	*44 Remington Magnum	9	14.90
U4570	UW4570	45-70 Government	15	23.40
U458	UW458	458 Winchester Magnum	19	37.20

*Packed 50 to the box—all others 20 per box.
†Weights to nearest lb.

WINCHESTER-WESTERN PRIMER CHART

The nearby chart will be of help in determining just what type of primer is best suited for the cartridges you reload. It's included as a guide and aid for handloaders.
Price: N/A
From Winchester-Western.

WINCHESTER-WESTERN UNPRIMED. PISTOL BRASS

Winchester's pistol brass is available in calibers ranging from .25 ACP through .45 ACP. Has a good reputation with handloaders.
Price: See nearby chart.
From Winchester-Western.

New Symbol	Old Symbol	Caliber	Wt. Lbs.† Per Case	Suggested Retail Price Per 100
U25A	U25AP	25 Automatic	2	$ 9.80
U256	U256P	256 Winchester Magnum	6	17.35
U32A	U32AP	32 Automatic (7.65mm Browning)	3	9.60
U32SW	U32SWP	32 S & W	3	8.55
U32SWL	U32SWLP	32 S & W Long (32 Colt New Police)	4	8.55
U357	U357P	357 Magnum (Nickel Plated)	6	11.00
U9mm	UW9LP	9mm Luger (9mm Parabellum)	4	14.05
U38SW	U38SWP	38 S & W (38 Colt New Police)	6	9.60
U38SP	U38SP	38 Special	5	9.95
U38A	U38AP	38 Automatic (and .38 Super)	5	11.55
U380A	U380AP	380 Automatic (9mm Short - 9mm Corto)	4	9.60
U41	U41M	41 Remington Magnum	9	14.50
U44S	UW44SP	44 S & W Special	9	12.40
U44M	U44MP	44 Remington Magnum	9	14.90
U45C	U45CP	45 Colt	9	14.90
U45A	U45AP	45 Automatic	7	14.05

†Weights to nearest lb. Pistol & Revolver Cases (Packed 50 per box)

Center fire primers are recommended for use as follows:

Large Rifle
220 Swift
22-250
225 Winchester
243 Winchester
6mm Remington
25-35 Winchester
250 Savage
25-06
257 Roberts
6.5 Remington Magnum
264 Win. Mag.
270 Winchester
284 Winchester
7mm Mauser
280 Remington
7mm Rem. Mag.
30-30 Winchester
30 Remington
30-06 Springfield
30-40 Krag
300 Win. Mag.
300 H & H Magnum
300 Savage
303 Savage
303 British
308 Winchester
32 Win. Special
32 Remington
32-40 Winchester
8mm Mauser
338 Win. Mag.
348 Winchester
35 Remington
358 Winchester
350 Remington Magnum
375 H – H Magnum
38-55 Winchester
444 Marlin
45-70 Government
458 Win. Mag.

Small Rifle
218 Bee
22 Hornet
222 Remington
222 Remington Magnum
223 Remington
25-20 Winchester
256 Win. Mag.
30 Carbine
32-20 Winchester

Small (Reg.) Pistol
25 Automatic
30 Luger
32 Automatic
32 S & W
32 S & W Long
32 Short Colt
32 Long Colt
32 Colt New Police
9mm Luger
38 S & W
38 Special
38 Short Colt
38 Long Colt
38 Colt New Police
38 Super-Auto
38 Automatic
380 Automatic

Large (Reg.) Pistol
38-40 Winchester
44 S & W Special
44-40 Winchester
45 Colt
45 Automatic

Small (Mag.) Pistol
357 Magnum

Large (Mag.) Pistol
41 Rem. Magnum
44 Rem. Magnum

Prices shown are subject to change.

WINCHESTER-WESTERN BALL POWDER

Winchester-Western's lineup of ball powders covers all of your rifle, pistol and shotgun needs. Ball powder has an excellent reputation for providing both low pressures and long barrel life.

Price: See nearby chart.

From Winchester-Western.

Symbol	Type	Unit	Units Per Case	Case Wt. lbs.	Suggested Retail Price Per Unit	Suggested Retail Price Per Case
231						
2311	Pistol	1 lb.	10	14	$ 9.05	$ 90.50
2313	Pistol	3 lbs.	6	24	24.75	148.50
2318	Pistol	8 lbs.	4	38	59.70	238.80
23112	Pistol	12 lbs.	1	14	84.90	84.90
296						
2961	Mag. Pistol & Shot Shell	1 lb.	10	14	7.90	79.00
2963	Mag. Pistol & Shot Shell	3 lbs.	6	24	21.35	128.10
2968	Mag. Pistol & Shot Shell	8 lbs.	4	38	54.00	216.00
452AA						
452AA1	Shot Shell	1 lb.	10	14	8.65	86.50
452AA3	Shot Shell	3 lbs.	6	24	23.60	141.60
452AA6	Shot Shell	6 lbs.	4	30	42.75	171.00
452AA10	Shot Shell	10 lbs.	1	12	67.40	67.40
473AA						
473AA1	Shot Shell	1 lb.	10	14	7.90	79.00
473AA3	Shot Shell	3 lbs.	6	24	21.35	128.10
473AA6	Shot Shell	6 lbs.	4	30	40.45	161.80
473AA10	Shot Shell	10 lbs.	1	12	64.20	64.20
540						
5401	Shot Shell	1 lb.	10	14	8.25	82.50
5403	Shot Shell	3 lbs.	6	24	22.40	134.40
5408	Shot Shell	8 lbs.	4	30	56.60	226.40
54012	Shot Shell	12 lbs.	1	14	80.20	80.20
571						
5711	Shot Shell	1 lb.	10	14	8.65	86.50
5713	Shot Shell	3 lbs.	6	24	23.45	140.70
5718	Shot Shell	8 lbs.	4	38	59.25	237.00
57112	Shot Shell	12 lbs.	1	14	84.00	84.00
630						
6301	Pistol & Rifle	1 lb.	10	14	7.90	79.00
6308	Pistol & Rifle	8 lbs.	4	38	53.95	215.80
680						
6801	Rifle	1 lb.	10	14	8.90	89.00
748						
7481	Rifle	1 lb.	10	14	8.90	89.00
7488	Rifle	8 lbs.	4	38	60.80	243.20
760						
7601	Rifle	1 lb.	10	14	8.90	89.00
7608	Rifle	8 lbs.	4	38	60.80	243.20
785						
7851	Rifle	1 lb.	10	14	8.90	89.00
7858	Rifle	8 lbs.	4	38	60.80	243.20

Western®

SUPER-X MARK 5 LONG RANGE LOADS

Symbol No.	Gauge	Length of Shell Inches	Powder Dram Equiv.	Oz. Shot	Shot Sizes	Suggested Retail Per Box
SX10	10	2⅞	Max.	1⅝	4	$10.20
SX12P	12	2¾	Max.	1¼	BB, 2, 4, 5, 6, 7½, 9	7.40
SX16PH	16	2¾	Max.	1⅛	4, 5, 6, 7½, 9	7.10
SX20P	20	2¾	Max.	1	4, 5, 6, 7½, 9	6.50
SX28	28	2¾	Max.	¾	6, 7½	6.60
SX41	410	2½	Max.	½	4, 6, 7½	5.25
SX413	410	3	Max.	1 1/16	4, 5, 6, 7½, 9	6.15

SUPER-X MARK 5 LONG RANGE MAGNUM LOADS

Symbol No.	Gauge	Length of Shell Inches	Powder Dram Equiv.	Oz. Shot	Shot Sizes	Suggested Retail Per Box
SX10M	10	3½ Mag.	Max.	2	2	17.30
SX12PH	12	2¾ Mag.	Max.	1½	2, 4, 5, 6	9.65
§WSX12PJ	12	3 Mag.	Max.	1⅜	2	8.95
SX12PM	12	3 Mag.	Max.	1⅝	2, 4, 6	10.75
SX123P	12	3 Mag.	Max.	1⅞	BB, 2, 4	11.60
SX16PM	16	2¾ Mag.	Max.	1¼	2, 4, 6	9.10
SX20PH	20	2¾ Mag.	Max.	1⅛	4, 6, 7½	7.75
SX20PM	20	3 Mag.	Max.	1¼	4, 6, 7½	8.75

SUPER DOUBLE X FIELD LOADS

Symbol No.	Gauge	Length of Shell Inches	Powder Dram Equiv.	Oz. Shot	Shot Sizes	Suggested Retail Per Box
SX103X	10	3½ Mag.	Max.	2¼	BB, 2, 4	18.40
XG12X	12	2¾	Max.	1¼	2, 4, 6	8.10
SX12X	12	2¾ Mag.	Max.	1½	2, 4, 6	10.20
SX123X	12	3 Mag.	Max.	1⅞	BB, 2, 4	12.00
XG20X	20	2¾	Max.	1	4, 6	7.10
SX203X	20	3 Mag.	Max.	1¼	2, 4, 6	9.65

STEEL SHOT — SUPER-X

Symbol No.	Gauge	Length of Shell Inches	Powder Dram Equiv.	Oz. Shot	Shot Sizes	Suggested Retail Per Box
SX12SSF	12	2¾	Max.	1¼	1, 2, 4	12.65
SX12SSM	12	3	Max.	1½	1, 2, 4	15.50

SUPER-X WITH LUBALOY (COPPERIZED) SHOT

Symbol No.	Gauge	Length of Shell Inches	Powder Dram Equiv.	Oz. Shot	Shot Sizes	Suggested Retail Per Box
§L12P	12	2¾	Max.	1¼	2, 5, 6	7.60

SUPER-X WITH LUBALOY (COPPERIZED) SHOT MAGNUM LOADS

Symbol No.	Gauge	Length of Shell Inches	Powder Dram Equiv.	Oz. Shot	Shot Sizes	Suggested Retail Per Box
§L12PM	12	3 Mag.	Max.	1⅝	4, 6	10.75

SUPER-X MARK 5 SUPER BUCKSHOT LOADS

Symbol No.	Gauge	Length of Shell Inches	Powder Dram Equiv.	Oz. Shot	Shot Sizes	Suggested Retail Per Box
SX12PRB	12	2¾	—	—	00 Buck— 9 Pellets	10.55
■SX12P0B	12	2¾	—	—	0 Buck—12 Pellets	10.55
SX12P4B	12	2¾	—	—	4 Buck—27 Pellets	10.55
■SX16PB	16	2¾	—	—	1 Buck—12 Pellets	10.55

SUPER-X MARK 5 SUPER BUCKSHOT LOADS—5 ROUND PACK

Symbol No.	Gauge	Length of Shell Inches	Powder Dram Equiv.	Oz. Shot	Shot Sizes	Suggested Retail Per Box
SX12RB5PK	12	2¾	—	—	00 Buck— 9 Pellets	2.11
SX120B5PK	12	2¾	—	—	0 Buck—12 Pellets	2.11
SX121B5PK	12	2¾	—	—	1 Buck—16 Pellets	2.11
SX124B5PK	12	2¾	—	—	4 Buck—27 Pellets	2.11
SX16B5PK	16	2¾	—	—	1 Buck—12 Pellets	2.11
SX20B5PK	20	2¾	—	—	3 Buck—20 Pellets	2.08

SUPER-X MAGNUM MARK 5 SUPER BUCKSHOT LOADS

Symbol No.	Gauge	Length of Shell Inches	Powder Dram Equiv.	Oz. Shot	Shot Sizes	Suggested Retail Per Box
■SX12PB	12	2¾ Mag.	—	—	00 Buck—12 Pellets	11.75
■SX123PB	12	3 Mag.	—	—	00 Buck—15 Pellets	13.40
■SX12MB	12	2¾ Mag.	—	—	1 Buck—20 Pellets	11.75
SX1231B	12	3 Mag.	—	—	1 Buck—24 Pellets	13.40
SX12PMB	12	3 Mag.	—	—	4 Buck—41 Pellets	13.40

SUPER-X MAGNUM MARK 5 SUPER BUCKSHOT LOADS — 5 ROUND PACK

Symbol No.	Gauge	Length of Shell Inches	Powder Dram Equiv.	Oz. Shot	Shot Sizes	Suggested Retail Per Box
X104B5	10	3½ Mag.	—	—	4 Buck—54 Pellets	3.45
SX12B5PK	12	2¾ Mag.	—	—	00 Buck—12 Pellets	2.35
SX123B5PK	12	3 Mag.	—	—	00 Buck—15 Pellets	2.68
SX12M1B5PK	12	2¾ Mag.	—	—	1 Buck—20 Pellets	2.35
SX1231B5PK	12	3 Mag.	—	—	1 Buck—24 Pellets	2.68
SX12MB5PK	12	3 Mag.	—	—	4 Buck—41 Pellets	2.68

SUPER-X RIFLED SLUG LOADS

Symbol No.	Gauge	Length of Shell Inches	Powder Dram Equiv.	Oz. Shot	Shot Sizes	Suggested Retail Per Box
■SX16PRS	16	2¾	Max.	⅘	Rifled Slug	12.20
■SX20PRS	20	2¾	Max.	⅝	Rifled Slug	11.05
■SX41RS	410	2½	Max.	⅕	Rifled Slug	10.55

SUPER-X RIFLED SLUG LOADS — 5 ROUND PACK

Symbol No.	Gauge	Length of Shell Inches	Powder Dram Equiv.	Oz. Shot	Shot Sizes	Suggested Retail Per Box
SX12RS5PK	12	2¾	Max.	⅞	Rifled Slug	2.44
SX16RS5PK	16	2¾	Max.	⅘	Rifled Slug	2.44
SX20RS5PK	20	2¾	Max.	⅝	Rifled Slug	2.21
SX41RS5PK	410	2½	Max.	⅕	Rifled Slug	2.11

■25 Round Box Discontinued — will supply in 5 Round Boxes when 25 round stock is depleted.
£U16H, 16Ga. and U20H, 20 Ga. with 7½ or 8 shot, recommended for trapshooting.
†Packed 250 per box.

UPLAND MARK 5 FIELD LOADS

Symbol No.	Gauge	Length of Shell Inches	Powder Dram Equiv.	Oz. Shot	Shot Sizes	Suggested Retail Per Box
WU10BL	10	2⅞	8	—	Blank (Black Powder)	$12.30
U12	12	2¾	3¼	1	4, 5, 6, 8	5.90
U12H	12	2¾	3¼	1⅛	4, 5, 6, 7½, 8, 9	6.30
U12P	12	2¾	3¼	1¼	6, 7½, 8	6.60
WU12BL	12	2¾	6	—	Blank (Black Powder)	9.40
U16	16	2¾	2½	1	6, 8	5.90
‡£U16H	16	2¾	2¾	1⅛	4, 5, 6, 7½, 8, 9	6.30
U20	20	2¾	2½	⅞	6, 8	5.30
£U20H	20	2¾	2½	1	4, 5, 6, 7½, 8, 9	5.70

WESTERN FIELD TRIAL POPPER-LOAD

Symbol No.	Gauge	Length of Shell Inches	Powder Dram Equiv.	Oz. Shot	Shot Sizes	Suggested Retail Per Box
XP12FBL	12	2¾	—	—	Blank	4.70

DOUBLE A PLUS TRAP LOADS

Symbol No.	Gauge	Length of Shell Inches	Powder Dram Equiv.	Oz. Shot	Shot Sizes	Suggested Retail Per Box
WW12AAP	12	2¾	2¾	1⅛	7½, 8	6.25
WW12MAAP	12	2¾	3	1⅛	7½, 8	6.25

DOUBLE A INTERNATIONAL TRAP LOADS

Symbol No.	Gauge	Length of Shell Inches	Powder Dram Equiv.	Oz. Shot	Shot Sizes	Suggested Retail Per Box
WWIN12AH	12	2¾	3¼	1⅛	7½, 8 (Nic. Pl. Shot)	8.00
WWIN12A	12	2¾	3¼	1⅛	7½, 8	6.80

DOUBLE A PLUS HANDICAP TRAP LOAD

Symbol No.	Gauge	Length of Shell Inches	Powder Dram Equiv.	Oz. Shot	Shot Sizes	Suggested Retail Per Box
WW12AAXP	12	2¾	3	1⅛	7½, 8	6.25

DOUBLE A PLUS SKEET LOADS

Symbol No.	Gauge	Length of Shell Inches	Powder Dram Equiv.	Oz. Shot	Shot Sizes	Suggested Retail Per Box
WW12AAP	12	2¾	2¾	1⅛	9	6.25
WW12MAAP	12	2¾	3	1⅛	9	6.25

DOUBLE A SKEET LOADS

Symbol No.	Gauge	Length of Shell Inches	Powder Dram Equiv.	Oz. Shot	Shot Sizes	Suggested Retail Per Box
WW20AA	20	2¾	2½	⅞	9	5.45
WW28AA	28	2¾	2	¾	9	6.55
WW41AA	410	2½	Max.	½	9	5.35

DOUBLE A INTERNATIONAL SKEET LOAD (No shot protectors)

Symbol No.	Gauge	Length of Shell Inches	Powder Dram Equiv.	Oz. Shot	Shot Sizes	Suggested Retail Per Box
WWAA12IS	12	2¾	3½	1⅛	9	6.80

DOUBLE A SPECIAL SKEET LOAD (No shot protectors)

Symbol No.	Gauge	Length of Shell Inches	Powder Dram Equiv.	Oz. Shot	Shot Sizes	Suggested Retail Per Box
§WW12MAAS	12	2¾	3	1⅛	9	5.30

SUPER TARGET LOADS (Paper not plastic)

Symbol No.	Gauge	Length of Shell Inches	Powder Dram Equiv.	Oz. Shot	Shot Sizes	Suggested Retail Per Box
WW12	12	2¾	2¾	1⅛	7½, 8, 9	6.25
WW12M	12	2¾	3	1⅛	7½, 8, 9	6.25

SUPER PIGEON TARGET LOAD

Symbol No.	Gauge	Length of Shell Inches	Powder Dram Equiv.	Oz. Shot	Shot Sizes	Suggested Retail Per Box
WW12SP	12	2¾	3¼	1¼	7½, 8	7.60

SUPER-X 22 RIMFIRE CARTRIDGES (HIGH VELOCITY)

Symbol No.	Cartridge	Bullet or Shot Wt. Grs.	Type of Bullet	Suggested Retail Per Box
SX22S	22 Short SUPER-X	29	Lubaloy	$1.47
SX22SH	22 Short H.P. SUPER-X	27	Lubaloy	1.57
SX22L	22 Long SUPER-X	29	Lubaloy	1.57
WWSX22X	22 L.R. SUPER-X Xpediter	29	Lubaloy H.P.	2.27
SX22LR	22 L.R. SUPER-X	40	Lubaloy	1.66
SX22LR1*	22 L.R. SUPER-X	40	Lubaloy	3.31
SX22LRD	22 L.R. DYNAPOINT SUPER-X	40	(Semi H.P.)	1.81
SX22LRH	22 L.R. H.P. SUPER-X	37	Lubaloy	1.82
SX22LRH1*	22 L.R. H.P. SUPER-X	37	Lubaloy	3.64
SX22RS	22 L.R. Shot SUPER-X	25	No. 12 Shot	3.41
SX22WMR	22 Win. Magnum SUPER-X	40	Jacketed H.P.	4.52
SX22MR1	22 Win. Magnum SUPER-X	40	Full Metal Case	4.52

H.P.—Hollow Point L.R.—Long Rifle *Packed 100 per box—all others 50

T-22 RIMFIRE CARTRIDGES (STANDARD VELOCITY)

Symbol No.	Cartridge	Bullet or Shot Wt. Grs.	Type of Bullet	Suggested Retail Per Box
T22S	22 Short	29	Lead, Lub.	1.47
T22LR	22 L.R.	40	Lead, Lub.	1.65

T22 Long Rifle cartridges are designed to give a high degree of accuracy and are especially recommended for all-around shooting and target practice with rifles and pistols.
L.R.—Long Rifle Lub.—Lubricated

SUPER-MATCH RIMFIRE CARTRIDGES

Symbol No.	Cartridge	Bullet or Shot Wt. Grs.	Type of Bullet	Suggested Retail Per Box
SM22LR	22 L.R. SUPER-MATCH Mark III	40	Lead, Lub.	3.33
SM22G	22 L.R. SUPER-MATCH Gold	40	Lead, Lub.	4.45
SM22LR4	22 L.R. SUPER-MATCH Mark IV Pistol	40	Lead, Lub.	3.59

Super-Match cartridges are especially recommended for the highest degree of accuracy in all match shooting with rifles and pistols.
L.R.—Long Rifle Lub.—Lubricated

OTHER RIMFIRE CARTRIDGES

Symbol No.	Cartridge	Bullet or Shot Wt. Grs.	Type of Bullet	Suggested Retail Per Box
W22BL	22 Short Blank (Blk. Powder)	—	—	1.91
†WW22CBS2	22 Short C.B.	29	Lead	7.31

‡9 Shot recommended for Skeet.
§Discontinued Stock — Offered subject to prior sale.

Prices shown are subject to change.

CENTERFIRE RIFLE

Symbol No.	Cartridge	Wt. Grs.	Type of Bullet	Suggested Retail Per Box
•218B	218 Bee	46	HP	$23.30
•22H1	22 Hornet	45	SP	16.05
•22H2	22 Hornet	46	HP	16.05
222501	22-250 Remington	55	PSP	7.50
222R	222 Remington	50	PSP	6.85
222R1	222 Remington	55	FMC	6.85
223R	223 Remington	55	PSP	7.50
223R1	223 Remington	55	FMC	7.50
2251	225 Winchester	55	PSP	8.05
2431	243 Win. (6 mm)	80	PSP	9.35
2432	243 Win. (6 mm)	100	PP (SP)	9.35
6MMR1	6 mm Remington	80	PSP	9.35
6MMR2	6 mm Remington	100	PSP	9.35
25061	25-06 Remington	90	PEP	10.20
25062	25-06 Remington	120	PEP	10.20
•25201	25-20 Winchester	86	L	15.20
•25202	25-20 Winchester	86	SP	15.20
2535	25-35 Winchester	117	SP	10.40
2501	250 Savage	87	PSP	9.50
2503	250 Savage	100	ST Exp	10.00
•2561P	256 Win. Magnum	60	HP	18.65
**2571	257 Roberts	87	PSP	10.50
2572	257 Roberts	100	ST Exp	11.05
2573	257 Roberts	117	PP (SP)	10.50
W2641	264 Win. Magnum	100	PSP	13.10
W2642	264 Win. Magnum	140	PP (SP)	13.10
2701	270 Winchester	100	PSP	10.20
2705	270 Winchester	130	PP (SP)	10.20
2703	270 Winchester	130	ST Exp	10.75
2704	270 Winchester	150	PP (SP)	10.20
W2841	284 Winchester	125	PP (SP)	11.55
W2842	284 Winchester	150	PP (SP)	11.55
7MM	7 mm Maus. (7x57)	175	SP	10.35
7MMR1	7 mm Rem. Mag.	150	PP (SP)	12.60
7MMR2	7 mm Rem. Mag.	175	PP (SP)	12.60
7MMR3	7 mm Rem. Mag.	125	PP (SP)	12.60
•W30M1	30 Carbine	110	HSP	16.35
•W30M2	30 Carbine	110	FMC	16.35
30301	30-30 Winchester	150	HP	8.00
30306	30-30 Winchester	150	PP (SP)	8.00
30302	30-30 Winchester	150	ST Exp	8.40
30303	30-30 Winchester	170	PP (SP)	8.00
30304	30-30 Winchester	170	ST Exp	8.40
30060	30-06 Springfield	110	PSP	10.20
30062	30-06 Springfield	125	PSP	10.20
30061	30-06 Springfield	150	PP (SP)	10.20
30063	30-06 Springfield	150	ST Exp	10.75
30064	30-06 Springfield	180	PP (SP)	10.20
30066	30-06 Springfield	180	ST Exp	10.75
30068	30-06 Springfield	220	PP (SP)	10.20
30069	30-06 Springfield	220	ST Exp	10.75
30401	30-40 Krag	180	PP (SP)	10.70
30403	30-40 Krag	180	ST Exp	11.30
30WM1	300 Win. Magnum	150	PP (SP)	13.30
30WM2	300 Win. Magnum	180	PP (SP)	13.30
30WM3	300 Win. Magnum	220	ST Exp	14.00

CENTERFIRE RIFLE (Continued)

Symbol No.	Cartridge	Wt. Grs.	Type of Bullet	Suggested Retail Per Box
W300H2	300 H & H Mag.	180	ST Exp	$13.65
W300H3	300 H & H Mag.	220	ST Exp	14.35
3001	300 Savage	150	PP (SP)	10.25
3003	300 Savage	150	ST Exp	10.80
3004	300 Savage	180	PP (SP)	10.25
3005	300 Savage	180	ST Exp	10.80
3032	303 Savage	190	ST Exp	11.90
W303B1	303 British	180	PP (SP)	10.45
W3081	308 Winchester	110	PSP	10.20
W3087	308 Winchester	125	PSP	10.20
3085	308 Winchester	150	PP (SP)	10.20
3082	308 Winchester	150	ST Exp	10.75
3086	308 Winchester	180	PP (SP)	10.20
3083	308 Winchester	180	ST Exp	10.75
W3084	308 Winchester	200	ST Exp	10.75
32WS2	32 Win. Special	170	PP (SP)	8.50
W32WS3	32 Win. Special	170	ST Exp	9.00
•32201	32-20 Winchester	100	L	12.30
•32202	32-20 Winchester	100	SP	15.20
W8MM	8mm Mauser (8x57; 7.9)	170	PP (SP)	10.50
W3381	338 Win. Magnum	200	PP (SP)	15.95
W3382	338 Win. Magnum	250	ST Exp	16.80
W3482	348 Winchester	200	ST Exp	19.00
35R1	35 Remington	200	PP (SP)	9.40
35R3	35 Remington	200	ST Exp	10.25
•W351SL2	351 Win. SL	180	SP	25.55
W3581	358 Win. (8.8mm)	200	ST Exp	14.85
W375W	375 Winchester	200	PP	11.90
W375W1	375 Winchester	250	PP	11.90
375H1	375 H & H Mag.	270	PP (SP)	15.80
W375H2	375 H & H Mag.	300	ST Exp	16.65
W375H3	375 H & H Mag.	300	FMC	15.80
•W3840	38-40 Win.	180	SP	19.25
W3855LF	38-55 Winchester Legendary Frontiersmen	255	SP	12.50
•44MP	44 Rem. Mag. SX	240	L (GC)	18.80
44MHSP	44 Rem. Mag. SX	240	HSP	7.70
•4440	44-40 Winchester	200	SP	20.35
W4570	45-70 Govt.	405	SP	11.55
W4580	458 Win. Magnum	500	FMC	32.35
W4581	458 Win. Magnum	510	SP	21.30

CENTERFIRE PISTOL & REVOLVER

Symbol No.	Cartridge	Wt. Grs.	Type of Bullet	Suggested Retail Per Box
•25AP	25 Auto (6.35 mm)	50	FMC	9.80
•2561P	256 Win. Magnum	60	HP	18.65
•W30LP	30 Luger (7.65 mm)	93	FMC	15.75
•32AP	32 Automatic	71	FMC	11.20
•32SWP	32 S & W	85	L	9.20
•32SWLP	32 Smith & Wesson (Colt New Police) Long	98	L	9.50
•32SCP	32 Short Colt	80	L	9.10
•32LCP	32 Long Colt	82	L	9.50
	32 Colt New Police	See 32 S & W Long		
•32201	32-20 Winchester	100	L	12.30

CENTERFIRE PISTOL & REVOLVER (Continued)

Symbol No.	Cartridge	Wt. Grs.	Type of Bullet	Suggested Retail Per Box
•32202	32-20 Winchester	100	SP	$15.20
•3573P	357 Magnum SX	110	JHP	14.75
•3576P	357 Magnum SX	125	JHP	14.75
•3571P	357 Magnum SX	158	L	12.50
•3572P	357 Magnum SX	158	Met. Pierc.	14.55
•3574P	357 Magnum SX	158	JHP	14.75
•3575P	357 Magnum SX	158	JSP	14.75
•W9MMJSP	9mm Luger (Par)	95	JSP	13.95
•W9LP	9mm Luger (Par)	115	FMC	13.95
**•W9MMJHP	9mm Luger (Par)	100	JHP	13.95
•X9MMSHP	9 mm Luger (Par)	115	STHP	14.65
•X9MMWM	9 mm Win. Mag.	115	FMC	14.65
•38SWP	38 S & W	145	L	10.55
•38S1P	38 Special	158	L	10.60
•38S2P	38 Special	158	MP	13.45
•38S3P	38 Special	200	L	11.35
•38S6PH	38 Spec. SX +P	110	JHP	13.45
•W38S7PH	38 Spec. SX +P	125	JHP	13.45
•38S8P	38 Spec. SX +P	130	FMC	13.95
•W38SPD	38 Spec. SX +P	158	HP	13.15
•W38WCP	38 Spec. SX +P	158	SWC	10.85
•38S4P	38 Spec. SX +P	150	L	11.50
•38S5P	38 Spec. SX +P	150	Met. Pierc.	13.45
•38SMRP	38 Special SM Mid-range	148	L Wad Cutter	11.05
•38SMP	38 Special SM	158	Lead	10.85
•38SCP	38 Short Colt	130	L	10.35
•38LCP	38 Long Colt	150	L	15.25
•38A3P	38 Automatic SX (For use only in 38 Colt Super and Colt Commander Automatic Pistols) +P	125	JHP	12.60
•38A1P	38 Automatic SX (For use only in 38 Colt Super and Colt Commander Automatic Pistols) +P	130	FMC	12.15
•38A2P	38 Automatic (For all 38 Colt Automatic Pistols)	130	FMC	12.35
•380AP	380 Automatic	95	FMC	11.45
•W3840	38-40 Winchester	180	SP	19.25
•W41MP	41 Rem. Mag. SX	210	L	16.55
•W41MJSP	41 Rem. Mag. SX	210	JSP	19.40
•W44SP	44 S & W Special	246	L	14.85
•44MP	44 Rem. Mag. SX	240	L(GC)	18.80
44MHSP	44 Rem. Mag. SX	240	HSP	7.70
•4440	44-40 Winchester	200	SP	20.35
•45CP	45 Colt	255	L	15.05
•45A1P	45 Automatic	230	FMC	15.35
X45ASHP	45 Automatic	185	STHP	6.45
•45AWCP	45 Automatic SM Clean Cutting	185	FMC	15.85
•X45WM	45 Win. Mag.	230	FMC	16.15

CENTERFIRE BLANK CARTRIDGES

Symbol No.	Cartridge	Suggested Retail Per Box
•W32BL1P	32 S & W (No Bullet) Smokeless	9.10
•W32BL2P	32 S & W (No Bullet) Black Powder	9.10
•W38BLP	38 S & W (No Bullet) Smokeless	11.05
•W38SBLP	38 Special (No Bullet) Smokeless	11.10

+P=Ammunition with a (+P) on the case head stamp is loaded to higher pressure. Use only in firearms designated for this cartridge and so recommended by the gun manufacturer.
•Packed 50 in a box—others 20 in a box.
**Discontinued — Stock offered subject to prior sale.

BT—Boat Tail
FMC—Full Metal Case
GC—Gas Check
HV—High Velocity
HP—Hollow Point
HSP—Hollow Soft Point
JSP—Jacketed Soft Point
JHP—Jacketed Hollow Point
L—Lead
Mag.—Magnum
Met. Pierc.—Metal Piercing
MP—Metal Point
MR—Mid-Range
OPE—Open Point Expanding
PEP—Positive Expanding Point
PP—Power-Point
Rem.—Remington
SL—Self-Loading
ST Exp—Silvertip Expanding
SP—Soft Point
PSP—Pointed Soft Point
Spgfld.—Springfield
SM—Super-Match
STHP—Silvertip Hollow Point
SWC—Semi-Wad Cutter
SX—Super-X
Win.—Winchester

275 WINCHESTER AVENUE, NEW HAVEN, CONNECTICUT 06511

BARNES BULLETS

These jacketed hunting bullets come in 30 different calibers in a number of different weights and shapes. (Calibers range from .17 through .600.) These bullets have a good reputation with shooters and hunters. *Price:* See nearby chart.

PRICE LIST

CALIBER	Jacket Thickness	Retail
17 Caliber		**PER 50**
.172 25 Gr. Semi-Spitzer S.P.	030"	$6.50
22 Caliber		
.224 60 Gr. Semi-Spitzer S.P.	030"	$6.25
.224 60 Gr. Semi-Spitzer F.M.J.	030"	6.35
.224 70 Gr. Semi Spitzer S.P.	030"	6.35
.224 83 Gr. Semi Spitzer S.P.	030"	6.50
.228/.230 diameter $1.00 extra		
6 mm. Caliber		
.243 90 Gr. Semi-Spitzer S.P.	030"	$6.60
.243 110 Gr. Semi-Spitzer S.P.	030"	6.80
.243 120 Gr. Round Nose S.P.	030"	6.90
25 Caliber		
.257 90 Gr. Semi-Spitzer S.P.	032"	$6.60
.257 90 Gr. Semi-Spitzer F.M.J.	032"	6.75
.257 125 Gr. Semi-Spitzer S.P.	032"	6.90
6.5 mm. Caliber		
.264 130 Gr. Semi-Spitzer S.P.	032"	$6.95
.264 150 Gr. Semi-Spitzer S.P.	032"	7.10
.264 165 Gr. Semi-Spitzer S.P.	032"	7.45
270 Caliber		
.277 130 Gr. Semi-Spitzer S.P.	032"	$7.00
.277 130 Gr. Semi-Spitzer F.M.J.	032"	7.20
.277 150 Gr. Semi-Spitzer S.P.	032"	7.25
.277 160 Gr. Semi-Spitzer S.P.	032"	7.35
.277 180 Gr. Round Nose S.P.	032"	7.70
.277 180 Gr. Round Nose F.M.J.	032"	8.90
7 mm. Caliber		
.284 125 Gr. Semi-Spitzer S.P.	032"	$7.00
.284 140 Gr. Semi-Spitzer S.P.	032"	7.35
.284 160 Gr. Semi-Spitzer S.P.	032"	7.50
.284 180 Gr. Semi-Spitzer S.P.	032"	7.70
.284 195 Gr. Semi-Spitzer S.P.	032"	7.85
.284 200 Gr. Round Nose F.M.J.	035"	9.20
.288 diameter $1.00 extra		
30 Caliber		
.308 150 Gr. Semi-Spitzer S.P.	032"	$7.45
.308 180 Gr. Semi-Spitzer S.P.	032"	7.55
.308 200 Gr. Semi-Spitzer S.P.	032"	7.75
.308 225 Gr. Semi-Spitzer S.P.	032"	7.90
.308 250 Gr. Round Nose S.P.	032"	8.10
.308 250 Gr. Round Nose F.M.J.	035"	9.80
8 mm. Caliber		
.323 150 Gr. Semi-Spitzer S.P.	032"	$7.50
.323 180 Gr. Semi-Spitzer S.P.	032"	7.60
.323 200 Gr. Semi-Spitzer S.P.	032"	7.95
.323 225 Gr. Semi-Spitzer S.P.	049"	11.70
.323 250 Gr. Semi-Spitzer S.P.	032"	8.30
.318 diameter $1.00 extra		
338 Caliber		**PER 50**
.338 200 Gr. Semi-Spitzer S.P.	032"	$7.40
.338 250 Gr. Semi-Spitzer S.P.	032"	7.95
.338 250 Gr. Semi-Spitzer S.P.	.049"	11.30
.338 300 Gr. Round Nose S.P.	049"	12.00
.338 300 Gr. Round Nose F.M.J.	032"	13.40
.333/.330 diameter $1.00 extra		
348 Winchester		
.348 250 Gr. Flat Nose S.P. Cannelured	032"	$7.90
35 Caliber		
.358 200 Gr. Semi-Spitzer S.P.	032"	$7.40
.358 250 Gr. Semi-Spitzer S.P.	032"	7.95
.358 275 Gr. Semi-Spitzer S.P.	049"	11.70
.358 300 Gr. Round Nose S.P.	032"	8.60
.358 300 Gr. Round Nose S.P.	049"	12.10
.358 300 Gr. Round Nose F.M.J.	049"	13.50
9.3 Caliber		
.366 250 Gr. Semi-Spitzer S.P.	032"	$7.95
.366 300 Gr. Semi-Spitzer S.P.	032"	8.60
38/55 Winchester		
.375 255 Gr. Flat Nose S.P.	032"	$7.95
.377 255 Gr. Flat Nose S.P.	032"	7.95
375 Caliber		
.375 250 Gr. Semi-Spitzer S.P.	032"	$7.95
.375 300 Gr. Semi-Spitzer S.P.	032"	8.60
.375 300 Gr. Semi-Spitzer S.P.	049"	12.10
.375 350 Gr. Round Nose S.P.	032"	11.30
.375 350 Gr. Round Nose S.P.	049"	13.50
.375 350 Gr. Round Nose F.M.J.	049"	13.60
401 Winchester S.L.		
.406 250 Gr. Round Nose S.P.	032"	$8.05
411 Caliber		
.411 300 Gr. Semi-Spitzer S.P.	032"	$8.75
.411 400 Gr. Round Nose S.P.	032"	11.30
.411 400 Gr. Round Nose S.P.	049"	14.50
.411 400 Gr. Round Nose F.M.J.	049"	15.90
.408 diameter $1.00 extra		
416 Caliber		
.416 300 Gr. Semi-Spitzer S.P.	032"	$8.85
.416 400 Gr. Round Nose S.P.	032"	11.40
.416 400 Gr. Round Nose S.P.	049"	14.60
.416 400 Gr. Round Nose F.M.J.	049"	16.00
404 Jeffrey		
.423 400 Gr. Round Nose S.P.	032"	$9.00
.423 400 Gr. Round Nose S.P.	049"	14.80
.423 400 Gr. Round Nose F.M.J.	049"	16.20
444 Marlin		
.430 250 Gr. Flat Nose S.P.	032"	$8.10
.430 300 Gr. Flat Nose S.P.	032"	8.70
425 Westley Richards		**PER 50**
.435 410 Gr. Round Nose S.P.	049"	$15.30
.435 410 Gr. Round Nose F.M.J.	049"	16.80
45/70 Caliber		
.458 300 Gr. Semi-Spitzer S.P.	032"	$8.25
.458 300 Gr. Round Nose S.P.	032"	8.25
.458 400 Gr. Semi-Spitzer S.P.	032"	10.80
.458 400 Gr. Round Nose S.P.	032"	10.80
.458 500 Gr. Semi-Spitzer S.P.	032"	12.75
.458 500 Gr. Round Nose S.P.	032"	12.75
458 Magnum Caliber		
.458 400 Gr. Semi-Spitzer S.P.	049"	$14.75
.458 400 Gr. Round Nose S.P.	049"	14.75
.458 500 Gr. Semi-Spitzer S.P.	049"	16.20
.458 500 Gr. Round Nose S.P.	049"	16.20
.458 500 Gr. Round Nose F.M.J.	049"	17.50
.458 600 Gr. Semi-Spitzer S.P.	049"	18.80
.458 600 Gr. Round Nose S.P.	049"	18.80
.458 600 Gr. Round Nose F.M.J.	049"	19.90
.455 diameter $1.00 extra		
465 Nitro		
.468 500 Gr. Round Nose S.P.	049"	$16.40
.468 500 Gr. Round Nose F.M.J.	049"	17.80
470 Nitro - 475 A&M		
.475 500 Gr. Round Nose S.P.	049"	$16.40
.475 500 Gr. Round Nose F.M.J.	049"	17.80
.475 600 Gr. Round Nose S.P.	049"	19.20
.475 600 Gr. Round Nose F.M.J.	049"	19.90
475 No. 2 Jeffrey		
.488 500 Gr. Round Nose S.P.	049"	$18.30
.488 500 Gr. Round Nose F.M.J.	049"	19.60
.483 diameter $1.00 extra		
505 Gibbs		
.505 600 Gr. Round Nose S.P.	049"	$22.90
.505 600 Gr. Round Nose F.M.J.	049"	25.90
.505 700 Gr. Round Nose S.P.	049"	29.20
.505 700 Gr. Round Nose F.M.J.	049"	32.20
.510 diameter $1.00 extra		
50/110 Winchester		
.510 300 Gr. Flat Nose S.P.	032"	$8.70
.510 450 Gr. Flat Nose S.P.	032"	11.00
577 Nitro		**PER 20**
.585 750 Gr. Round Nose S.P.	049"	$15.00
.585 750 Gr. Round Nose F.M.J.	049"	18.00
600 Nitro		
.620 900 Gr. Round Nose S.P.	049"	$20.00
.620 900 Gr. Round Nose F.M.J.	049"	24.00

A current F.F.L. is required with bullet purchases. If not a license holder order through your local dealer.
Dealer prices available. (Outside United States license not required).
Special calibers/weights not listed made to order. Call or write for price quote. Small orders welcome.

From Barnes Bullets.

Prices shown are subject to change.

10-GAUGE HUNTING WAD

Holding up to 2½ ounces of shot, these wads for 3-inch, 10-gauge shells provide top long range performance. Maker advises us they will hold killing patterns right up to the 80-yard mark.

Price: $4 per 100.

From Ballistics Products, Inc.

PLASTIC SHOTCUP WADS

Available for 12 gauge 3-inch shells, these wads help improve patterns and extend the range of magnum loads. Holds 1⅝ ounces of shot.

Price: 12 gauge $4 per 100.

From Ballistics Products, Inc.

BARBER'S OBSOLETE AMMUNITION

Barber's remanufactured offerings will gladden the hearts of more than one shooter. They are currently offering *loaded* .32-40, .33 Winchester, .38-55 Winchester (with lead or jacketed bullets) .38-56 and .40-82 Winchester ammo. (The last 2 cartridges available in late '79.)

Price: See below.	per 20
.32-40	$13.50
.33 Win.	16.50
.38-55 Win. (Lead)	13.50
.38-55 Win. (Jacketed)	15.50
.38-56 Win.	Price not available
.40-82 Win.	Price not available

From Barber's Ammunition Company.

AUTO MAG AMMUNITION

Beal's supplies a wide variety of .357, .41 and .44 AMP (Auto Mag Pistol) ammo. Break-in, hunting and metallic silhouette loadings are available. This outfit can also supply brass as well as loaded ammo.

Price: Loaded ammo $34.50 to $45 per 50 rounds depending on caliber and loading. Unprimed brass per 100 is $42.50 for .357 or .41 AMP, $41.50 for .44 AMP. (They will also reload your brass for $17.50 per box of standard loads.)

From Beal's Bullets.

LONG RANGE RIFLE BULLETS

These jacketed ballistically efficient bullets feature a rebated boat-tail, two-diameter design with bonded core. They are available in .375, .416 and .458 calibers. Weight from 270 grains (.375) to 525 grains (.458).

Price: Write maker direct.

From Beal's Bullets.

BITTERROOT BULLET COMPANY

Bitterroot bullets have an *excellent* reputation with both hunters and shooters. These jacketed/bonded rifle bullets are available in calibers ranging from .277 through .375. They come 10 bullets to the pack. This is a custom shop and only 3 or 4 calibers are on hand at any one time. You may send a SASE and 35¢ for an illustrated brochure.

Prices: See below.

Caliber & Weight	1-Bullet Sample	20-Bullet Packet
.277-130	$1.00	$12.00
.277-150	1.00	12.00
7mm-140	1.00	12.00
7mm-160	1.00	13.00
7mm-175	1.00	13.00
.308-165	1.00	13.00
.308-180	1.00	13.00
.308-200	1.00	14.00
.338-200	1.00	14.00
.338-225	1.25	15.00
.338-250	1.25	16.00
.358-250	1.25	16.00
.358-275	1.25	16.00
*.358-300	1.25	17.00
.375-275	1.25	16.00
.375-300	1.25	17.00
*.375-325	1.25	18.00

*By special order only.

From Bitterroot Bullet Company

AQUILLA NICKEL PLATED LEAD SHOT

This nickel plated shot is designed to give maximum penetration and superior patterns. Imported from Italy by Diana, it certainly isn't cheap; however, for maximum performance on waterfowl and other game, you just might want to give it a try. It's available in BB, No. 1, No. 2, No. 3, No. 4, No. 5 and No. 6.

Price: Approximately $16 per 11-pound bag—price includes shipping.

From Diana Import Co.

See the Directory for complete company addresses.

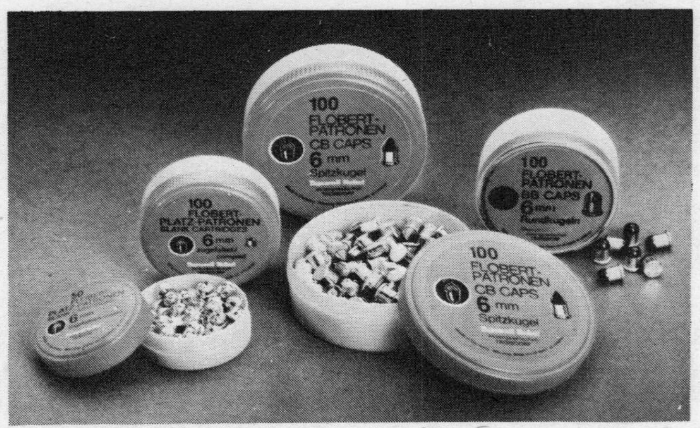

FLOBERT CB CAPS

These low-powered caps come in .22, .32, .38 and .38 S&W Blank. With the exception of the blank—which is perfect for starting pistols—the above low-powered rounds are ideal for pest control or practice.

From Eastern Sports International.

CUSTOM HANDLOADS FROM GONZALEZ

With the price of new ammo climbing higher every year, many shooters and hunters have turned to custom handloading shops. Ramon Gonzalez offers both rifle and pistol ammo loaded to factory specs (using a customer's brass) for a cost that's $2.00 below the normal retail price per box. He will also load in "quantity" and work up special loads on request (write for a price or quotation). See the list below to see if your favorite cartridge is listed:

Rifle and Pistol Calibers

.22 Jet	.32 S. & W.	.357 S.&W. Mag.
.22 Hornet	.32 Colt	.25 Rem.
.222 Rem.	.30 Rem	.358 Win.
.22-250 Varmint	.30-30 Win.	.38-55 Win.
.220 Swift	.300 Sav.	.375 H. & H.
.243 Win.	.30-40 Krag.	.41 Rem. Mag.
.244/6mm Rem.	.30-06 Govt.	.44 Russian
.25-35 Win.	.300 H. & H.	.44 S.&W. Spec.
.25-36 Marlin	.308 Norma	.44-40 Win.
.250-3000 Sav.	.300 Win. Mag.	.44 Rem. Mag.
.257 Roberts	.300 Wby.	.45 ACP
6.5 mm Carcano	.303 British	.45 Long Colt
6.5 mm Jap.	7.7 mm Jap.	.45-70 Govt.
6.5x54 mm M.S.	.32 Win. Spl.	.458 Win. Mag.
.264 Win. Mag.	8 mm Nambu	
.270 Win.	7x57 mm Mauser	
7x57 mm Mauser	8 mm-06	
.284 Win.	.338 Win. Mag.	
7 mm Rem. Mag.	.380 ACP	
.30 M1 Carbine	9 mm Para.	
.32 Long	.38 S.&W.	
.32 Short	.38 Special	

From Ramon B. Gonzalez

LEAD RIFLE AND PISTOL BULLETS

A wide range of bullets from 45-grain .22 caliber to 505-grain 50/70 caliber is available. Also available are lead bullets for 7.35mm Carcano, 8mm Nambu and .40/82. Bullets are precision sized and lubed and come in boxes of 50 or 100.

Prices: Write maker direct for more information.

From Green Bay Bullets.

FEDERAL ORDNANCE SURPLUS AMMO

Case lots of hard to find ammunition are usually available from Federal Ordnance. They tend to pride themselves on having a little bit of everything for everyone. Best bet is to write Federal Ordnance direct for current prices and availability of certain calibers. All ammo *must be shipped* to licensed FFL Dealers. The following list is representative of this outfit's usual offerings.

Prices: Write company direct.

Rifle (NC= Non-corrosive/C= Corrosive)

.223 (5.56mm)N.C.
7mm (7x57mm)C
7.5mm (For French Model 1936 Rifle) N.C.
7.35mm (Terni) C
7.62 x 39mm (Made by Lapua) N.C.
7.62 x 45 (SH M-52 Czech.)C
7.62mm (NATO)N.C.
7.62mm (NATO "Dummy" Ctgs.)
7.62 x 54mm (Moisin Nagant/Tokarev)C
.30 (M-1 Carbine)N.C.
.30-06 (Springfield)N.C.
7.65 (Argentine)C
.303 (British)C
8mm (Kropatschek)C
8mm (Mauser)C

Pistol (NC= Non-corrosive/C= Corrosive)

.30 (Mauser)C
.32 (ACP) N.C.
9mm (Bergmann)C
9mm (Luger)C
.38 (S&W)N.C.
.44 (Auto Mag)N.C.
.45 (ACP) N.C.

From Federal Ordnance.

.30 MAUSER/TOKAREV BRASS

This is once fired boxer primed surplus military brass that's been fully resized. The primer crimp has been removed. Hard to find.

Price: $7.50 per 100 pieces.

From Hardin Specialty Distributors.

HI-PER HANDGUN AMMUNITION

This ammo is strictly high performance. It's loaded in .38 Special, .357 Magnum, 9mm Luger, .45 ACP, .41 Magnum and .44 Magnum calibers. (.380 and .38 Super to be available shortly.) Brass is also available.

Price: See below.

LOADED AMMO

Cartridges	Bullet Weight Grains	List Price Per Box
38 Special + P	110 JHP	$11.10
38 Special + P	125 JHP	11.10
38 Special + P	158 JHP	11.10
38 Special	148 LWC	8.75
38 Special	158 LSWC	9.40
38 Special + P	158 LSWCHP	10.30
38 Special	158 LRN	9.40
357 Magnum	110 JHP	11.95
357 Magnum	125 JHP	11.95
357 Magnum	158 JHP	11.95
357 Magnum	158 JSP	11.95
357 Magnum	158 LSWC	10.20
357 Magnum	160 FMJ	13.00
9mm Luger	115 FMJ	11.60
9mm Luger	90 JHP	11.60
9mm Luger	115 JHP	11.60
45 Automatic	185 JHP	12.75
45 Automatic	185 JSWC	12.75
45 Automatic	230 FMJ	12.75
44 Magnum	240 JHP	15.25
44 Magnum	240 FMJ	15.25
44 Magnum	240 LSWC	13.40
41 Magnum	210 JHP	15.25

BRASS
(per 50 cases)

38 Special	Brass	$4.00
357 Magnum	Brass	4.30
9mm Luger	Nickel	6.05
41 Magnum	Nickel	6.70
44 Magnum	Nickel	6.70
45 Automatic	Brass	6.05
380 Automatic	Nickel	6.05
38 Super Automatic	Nickel	6.05

From Hi-Per Cartridge Corp.

INDOOR PRACTICE KIT FOR .38 SPECIAL OR .45 CALIBER HANDGUNS

The projectiles themselves are made of aluminum and have rubber 0-rings in two grooves. These projectiles are loaded (as per included directions) with W-W 630 and placed in a primed, empty case. When fired, the primer ignites the 630 powder which in turn sends the bullet on its way down the bore. Six projectiles, a bullet trap and a handy little reloading press is sold as a complete kit.

Price: $27.75 per Kit; projectiles $8 per 6. Specify .38 or .45 when ordering either.

From Hoffman Products.

ZINC WASHERS IN .38, .44 AND .45 CALIBERS

Zinc washers, when used as bases for cast lead bullets, have a reputation for eliminating leading. They are a little hard to find at times; that's why we've included them here.

Price: .38, $4.25 per M; .44 or .45, $4.75 per M.

From N. E. House Company.

KTW METAL PIERCING AMMO

This product is available to law enforcement personnel *only*. The ammo utilizes Teflon-coated projectiles that have remarkable penetration characteristics. It's currently available in .357 Magnum, .38 Special, .38 Super Colt, 9mm Luger, .380 ACP, .45 ACP, .44 Special, .25 ACP, .32 ACP and .30 carbine. Delivered to FFL holders or police departments *only*.

Price: All ammo sells for $3.50 per 5, 6 or 7 round box except for .30 Carbine which sells for $4.50 per 7 rounds.

From KTW, Inc.

RELIANCE CAST BULLETS

These cast bullets are available in a number of different styles in .38; 9mm; .38 ACP; .41 Mag.; .44 Mag.; 45 ACP and .45 Long Colt. All bullets come sized and lubed in quantities of 1000 and up.

Prices: Write maker direct.

From Reliance Bullets.

See the Directory for complete company addresses.

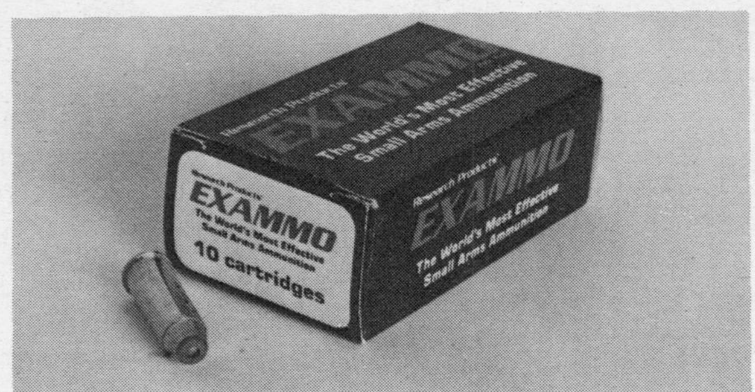

EXAMMO PISTOL AMMUNITION

Available in .380 ACP, 9mm Luger, .38 Special, .357 Magnum, .44 Magnum and .45 ACP, this ammo has greater stopping power but reduced danger for bystanders and property. Exammo states their bullets expand via gas. (Powder in the projectile ignites on impact generating the gas mentioned above.) Internal shock impact is stated to be 4 times that of a conventional projectile. Bullet will, however, break up when it impacts with a hard surface minimizing ricochets. Recommended for law enforcement and home protection use. Come 12 rounds to the box.

Price: .380 $10.30; 9mm Luger $11.70; .38 Sp. $10.45; .357 Mag. $11.15; .44 Mag. $13; .45 ACP $12.30.

From Research Products Distributing.

3-D .38 SPECIAL PRACTICE AMMO

This ammo is *very* reasonably priced. Each round features a hollow base 100-grain bullet. Recoil is very low while accuracy is high. Come packed 500 to the box.

Price: Loaded in your cases $18 per 500; Loaded in 3-D fired cases $40 per 500; Loaded in new 3-D cases $45 per 500—3-D pays freight both ways.

From The 3-D Co., Inc.

VITT-AERODYNAMIC SHOTGUN SLUG

These 12-gauge slugs have a superb reputation for accuracy and knock-down power. Velocity retention at 100 yards is superior to most other slugs.

Price: $8.50 per 25 slugs. $102 per 300 slugs.

From George N. Vitt.

OBSOLETE FOREIGN AND DOMESTIC AMMO

Tony Sailer offers an extremely wide selection of obsolete (or hard to find) ammunition for both rifle and pistol calibers. Where possible the cases used in the loading of this ammo are made from new, formed brass. Because of the growing demand for obsolete ammo, we've included this information for your perusal.

Price: See below—all ammo is per 20 rounds unless otherwise stated.

22 Hornet	55 gr.	(50)	$12.00	8mm Lebel	170 gr		$10.50
220 Swift	55 gr		9.50	8 x 72R	170 gr.		14.50
219 Zipper	55 gr.		9.50	8 x 60	180 gr.		11.50
22 M1 Carbine		(50)	15.00	8 x 60R	180 gr.		12.50
223 Rem			4.50	8mm Nambu	100 gr.	(50)	10.00
22 Hi-Power			10.50	8 x 57 Mauser	180 gr.		7.50
240 Apex			13.50	8 x 57J	170 gr.		9.50
25-20 SS		each	1.00	8 x 57 JR	170 gr.		12.50
25-20 Rep.	86 gr.	(50)	9.50	32-40	170 gr.		12.00
25 Remington	117 gr.		10.50	33 Win.	200 gr		11.00
25-36 Marlin			11.00	35 Win. M-95	250 gr.		14.50
6mm Lee Navy			13.50	35 Rem.	200 gr.		7.00
25-06 Rem.			7.50	35 Whelen	200-250 gr.		10.50
6.5 Jap	130 gr.		9.50	35 WSL	180 gr.	(50)	18.00
6.5 x 58R			13.50	38-40	180 gr.		12.50
256 Newton			10.50	38-55	255 gr.		12.00
6.5 Carcano	150 gr.		9.00	38-56	255 gr.		12.50
6.5 x 55	150 gr.		9.00	38-72	260 gr.		14.50
6.5 x 54 Mauser			12.50	9mm Steyr		(50)	11.00
6.5 x 57	150 gr.		10.00	9 x 56	250 gr.		10.50
6.5 x 57R	150 gr.		12.50	9 x.57	250 gr.		10.50
6.5 x 53R Dutch			9.00	9 x 57R	250 gr.		13.50
6.5 x 54 M. S.			9.50	9.3 x 57	250 gr.		12.50
6.5 x 58	130 gr.		12.50	9.3 x 62	250 gr.		12.00
270 Win.	130 gr.		7.50	9.3 x 72R	255 gr.		13.50
275 H&H	150 gr.		14.00	9.3 x 74R	250 gr.		14.00
7 x 64	140 gr.		12.50	9.5 x 57	270 gr.		11.50
7 x 65 R	140 gr.		12.50	401 WSL	230 gr.		13.50
7 x 57R	140 gr.		12.00	41 Long Colt		(50)	18.00
7 x 57 Mauser	140 gr.		7.50	405 Win.	300 gr.		14.50
7 x 72R	180 gr.		14.50	40-60 Win.	260 gr.		11.50
30 Mauser	100 gr	(50)	9.50	40-65 Win.	260 gr.		11.50
30 M1 Carbine	110 gr.	(50)	9.00	40-60 Marlin	260 gr.		11.50
7.5 MAS French			9.00	40-72	260 gr.		13.00
7.65 Mauser	180 gr.		9.50	43 Spanish	380 gr.		13.50
7.62 Russian	180 gr.		11.00	44-40	200 gr.	(50)	13.50
7.62 x 39	125 gr.		9.00	44 Russian	250 gr.	(50)	13.50
308 Win.	180 gr.		7.50	45 S&W	240 gr.	(50)	13.50
30-06	150-180 gr.		7.50	10.75 x 68	350 gr.		14.00
7.5 Swiss	180 gr.		10.50	45 Colt	250 gr.	(50)	10.50
300 Sav.	180 gr.		7.50	45-60	260 gr.		12.50
300 Win. Mag.	180 gr.		9.75	45-70	300 gr.		8.00
7.7 Jap	180 gr.		10.50	45-70 Hi Speed	300 gr.		10.00
32-20	100 gr.		8.50	12 ga. Black Powder		(25)	6.50
32 Rem.	170 gr.		10.00	38 Sp. (In your brass)		(25)	37.50/M
8 x 50R Siamese	170 gr.		10.50	38 Sp. (In his brass)		(50)	65.00/M
8 x 52R Type 66	170 gr.		10.50	45 ACP (In his brass)		(50)	75.00/M
7.35 Carcano	130 gr.		10.00	45 ACP (In your brass)		(50)	57.50/M
8 x 50R	170 gr.		10.00	9mm Shot		(50)	7.50
8 x 56 M.S.	170 gr.		10.50	9mm Luger (In his brass)		(50)	85.00/M
8 x 51 Mauser	170 gr.		11.00	9mm Luger (In your brass)		(50)	47.50/M
8 x 56R	170 gr.		10.50				

From Anthony F. Sailer.

.38, 9mm AND .45 LEAD BULLETS

The prices are reasonable. Available in quantities of 1000 and up. Come sized, lubed and ready to reload.

Price: $19.32 per 1000.

From Zero Bullet Company.

Prices shown are subject to change.

Handloading Equipment & Supplies

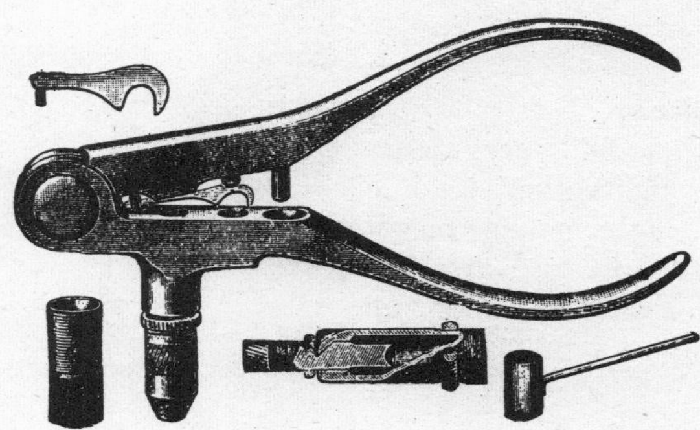

Handloading has had its enthusiasts from the earliest days of self-contained cartridges, but it has never been more popular than it is today. A good part of that increase in popularity is economic, with the price of most factory loaded ammo more than doubling in the past 10 years. However, a great deal of the credit for the increased enthusiasm for "rolling your own" has to be given to the makers of handloading equipment, who continue to bring out easier-to-use loading tools at reasonable prices. Also not to be overlooked is the satisfaction—and flexibility—of do-it-yourself ammunition loading. Not only is there a feeling of satisfaction when the bird drops or the X-ring is neatly punched out by ammunition you've assembled yourself, but there's the added ability to "tune" loads to optimum performance in a given arm.

As the handloading section is one of the longer parts of the book the following "table of contents" should prove helpful in locating specific types of reloading equipment. In order of appearance you'll find:

Cartridge Presses
Shotshell Presses
Dies
Powder Measures
Scales
Case cleaners, Gauges, Trimmers
Cartridge and Bullet Trays, Labels
Primer Feeders, Seaters
Furnaces
Dippers
Bullet Molds
Bullet Sizers, Lubricators, Lubricants
Bullet Swaging Dies, Core Making Tools
Chronographs

In addition, other items of value to the handloader will be found throughout the section.

As handloading has grown in popularity so have the larger gunshops added reloading equipment and supplies to their product lines. Often such shops have a handloading enthusiast on their staff, and when such is the case such a shop can be of priceless assistance to the beginning (and often experienced, as well) handloader.

For reloading components, see the preceding section, *Ammunition & Components: Current, Obsolete & Surplus*.

HIGH-PRODUCTION RIFLE/PISTOL/SHOTSHELL PRESS

With a per-hour production rate of 1,500 rounds, it's easy to see why this Hollywood press is called the "Automatic." Ideal for custom shops, clubs or the shooter who needs a lot of ammo for competitive shooting events.

Price: $1,650 (25% deposit with order).

From Whitney Sales.

PROGRESSIVE METALLIC CARTRIDGE PRESS

Available in handgun calibers only, the Camdex JS-63 features automatic case, primer, projectile and powder feeding. Production rate can approach 1,000 rounds per hour. Any standard ⅞x14 die can be used, and the press is made to handle any centerfire pistol cartridge.

Price: $1,100; conversion unit for a different caliber, $300; Electronic Alert System, $170.

From Camdex.

PROGRESSIVE RELOADING PRESS

The Star Progressive Reloader has a 40-year reputation for being one of the fastest, high volume loading presses ever made. With each pull of the handle you get a finished round of ammo. All tools and dies are mounted in a tool head, performing their operations on the shells in their respective positions simultaneously.

Price: $585.

From Star Machine Works.

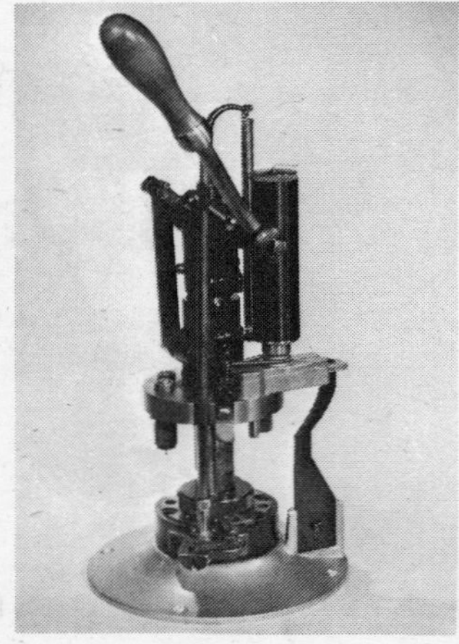

PROGRESSIVE METALLIC CARTRIDGE RELOADING PRESS

With an output of 500 rounds an hour, the Auto-Champion press is designed for the shooter who needs a lot of ammo, fast. It's designed for pistol cartridges only and is currently offered in .38/.357 or .45 ACP (9mm Luger to follow). Each press comes with your choice of powder bushing and seating stem (RN, WC or SWC), one primer tube and two case-feed tubes, tube coupling plus instructions and service manuals.

Price: $579.50

From C-H Tool and Die Corp.

METALLIC STRAIGHT-WALL CASE LOADER

The Ponsness-Warren Metal-Matic P-200 is made for straight wall metallic cases and can hold two different sets of ⅞x14 dies at once (conversion takes under 5 minutes). This unit is primarily designed for pistol cases and has a production rate of about 200 rounds per hour. The press has a total of 10 stations and will easily accommodate the above mentioned two sets of dies and a powder measure.

Price: $225; large or small primer pocket swaging tool, $15.

From Ponsness-Warren, Inc.

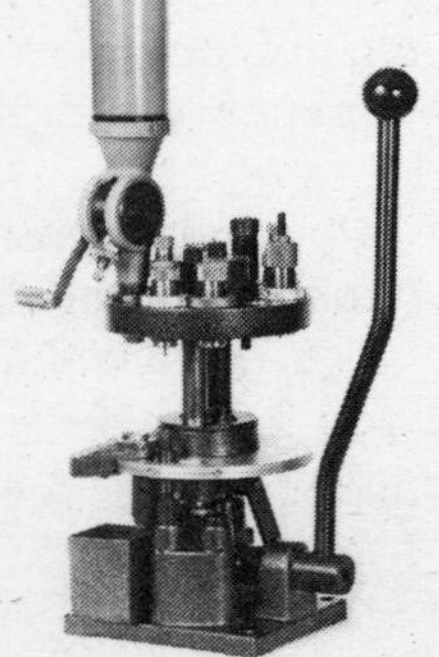

LYMAN All-American Turret Press

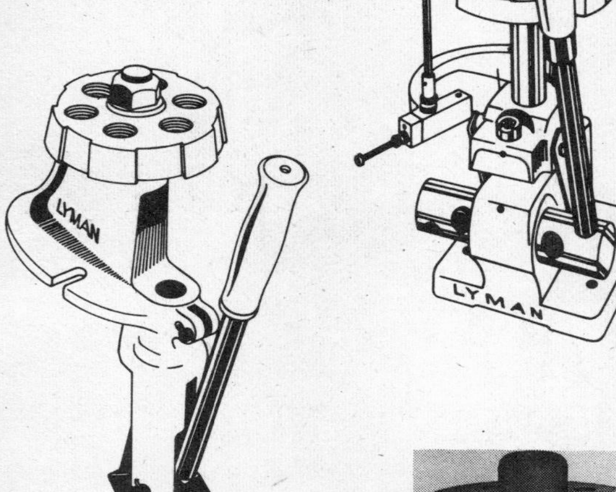

LYMAN Spar-T Press

TURRET-TYPE METALLIC CARTRIDGE PRESS

Lyman's All-American turret press combines both speed and precision. Holds one 3-die set and a powder measure, if so desired. Utilizes standard ⅞x14 dies—rifle or pistol. Auto primer feed available and shown mounted on the All-American press nearby.
Price: $129.95; auto primer feed, $24.95.
From Lyman Products Company.

TURRET-TYPE METALLIC CARTRIDGE PRESS

The Lyman Spar-T turret press has 6 stations and handles standard ⅞x14 rifle or pistol dies. Each station audibly locks into place. Speeds up the reloader's job.
Price: $82.95 complete with one set of dies; $67.95 for the press alone (as shown).
From Lyman Products Company.

GENERAL PURPOSE RELOADING PRESS

Called the Hollywood "Senior Turret," this press may be set up for rifle, pistol or shotshell reloading; even bullet swaging. Comes with turret indexing handle, one 1/2" die shell holder bushing, one 5/8" tie-down rod for swaging, one primer rod and one shell holder.
Price: $199.50
From Whitney Sales.

METALLIC CARTRIDGE RELOADING PRESS

The Bonanza Co-Ax press was designed to make the loading operation faster and more efficient. Dies simply snap in and out of the press frame. This allows you to go from, say, sizer to seater in 2-3 seconds. The Co-Ax provides up to three times the mechanical advantage of a common C-type press.
Price: $89.95.
From Bonanza Sports Mfg. Co.

METALLIC CARTRIDGE RELOADING PRESS

Handles all popular rifle and pistol dies. This C-H press is of the "H-type" design and holds one complete 2- or 3-die set. Comes complete with 3 shell holders (your choice) and will easily perform every loading operation.
Price: $79.50; $93.50 with one set of dies (your choice).
From C-H Tool and Die Corp.

METALLIC CARTRIDGE RELOADING PRESS

The RCBS Rockchucker Press is that firm's top-of-the-line loading tool. The O-Frame design is identical to the RS model except for the fact that the Rockchucker is much beefier and has a patented compound leverage action. The result is a press that's almost effortless to operate.
Price: $77.
From RCBS.

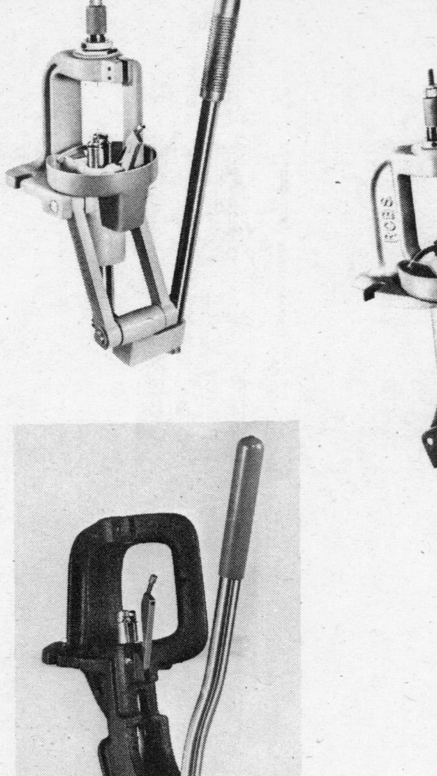

METALLIC CARTRIDGE RELOADING PRESS

The RCBS "RS" reloading press is about the same as the old "JR" variety. This particular press has been the favorite of handloaders for years. It features a beefy O-Frame that resists stress and warpage and is suitable for the reloading of most any metallic rifle or pistol case.
Price: $49.
From RCBS.

METALLIC CARTRIDGE RELOADING PRESS

The C-H Champion reloading press uses the O-Frame design for one of the beefiest reloading presses to be found. The massive ram is drilled to allow spent primers to fall completely through into a waste basket. Comes with an installed ⅞x14 bushing that can be removed so you can use swaging or shotgun dies.
Price: $99.50;$115.50 with one set of dies.
From C-H Tool and Die Corp.

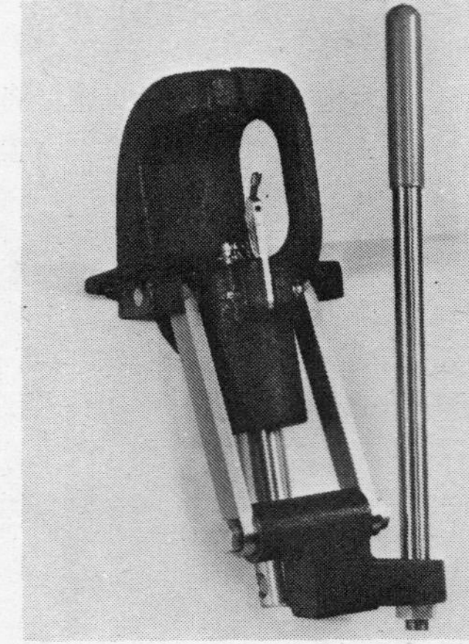

METALLIC CARTRIDGE RELOADING PRESS

Called the Jr. Champ, this C-H offering features an offset, 210-degree opening for easier access. The sturdy O-Frame design provides plenty of strength—it won't spring. Handles all popular rifle and pistol cartridges.
Price: $52.50 (includes your choice of shell holder); $68.50, with one set of dies, your choice.
From C-H Tool and Die Corp.

METALLIC CARTRIDGE PRESS

The Lyman O-Mag Press has a large press opening that will accommodate extra long cartridges and bullets without the usual fumbling created by standard length presses. Wide-open easy viewing of both bullet and case during reloading make standard length cases easier to reload. The O-Mag Press has maximum strength with a mounting base that features three holes rather than the usual two. The third hole is at the back of the press to provide maximum leverage, stability and security.
Price: $49.95
From Lyman Products Company

RELOADING PRESS

A good basic tool for the beginner or pistol/rifle shooter with a low-volume need for ammo. Reloads everything—even 50 caliber and 20mm cartridges. Swages all calibers of bullets be they lead, alloy or jacketed.
Price: $149.50.
From Whitney Sales.

C-TYPE RELOADING PRESS

Develops leverage at a ratio of over 40 to 1. This Redding Model No. 7 C-press is a good basic tool for the man who isn't concerned about high volume output.

Price: $48; with one set of dies and shell holder, $64.95

From Redding Reloading Equipment.

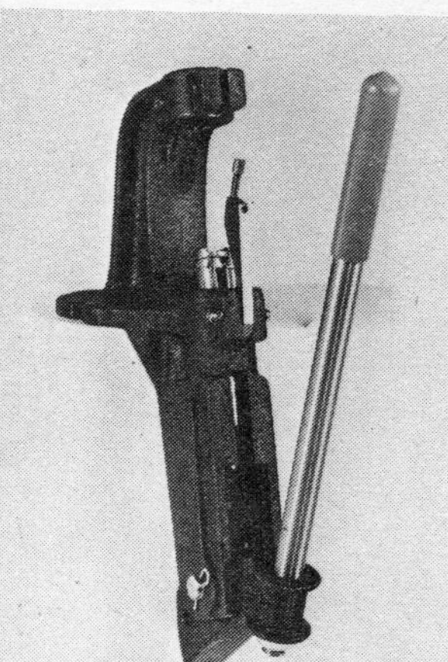

METALLIC CARTRIDGE RELOADING PRESS

Handles all popular rifle and pistol dies. Featuring an extra wide bowed mouth, the C-H "C-Press" is ribbed and gusseted for rigidity. Accepts standard ⅞x14 dies and shell holders.

Price: $49.95 (and your choice of shell holder); $69.95 (with one set of dies, your choice).

From C-H Tool and Die Corp.

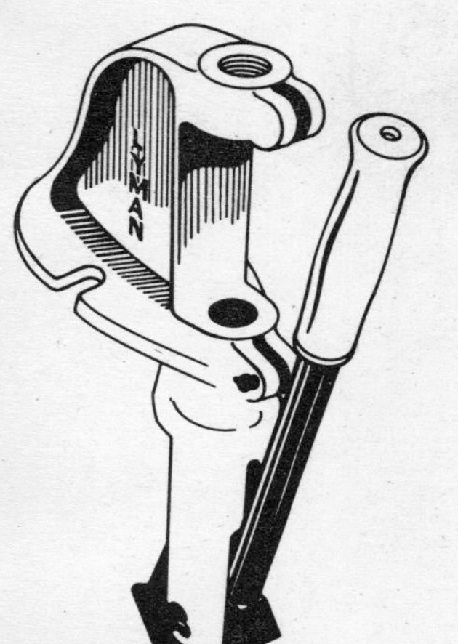

LYMAN Spartan Press

METALLIC CARTRIDGE PRESS

Lyman's C-Type Spartan press features an 11-pound iron frame and is rugged enough for swaging work. Handles rifle and pistol cartridges with ease. Comes with everything you'll need. Uses standard ⅞x14 dies.

Price: $59.95 complete with a set of dies; $49.95 for the press alone.

From Lyman Products Company.

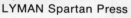

METALLIC CARTRIDGE PRESS

The Pacific Power "C" reloading press handles metallic rifle and pistol cases with ease. Features a universal primer arm and removable head shell holder ram. Uses standard ⅞x14 dies.

Price: $77.25 with one set of dies.

From Pacific Tool Company.

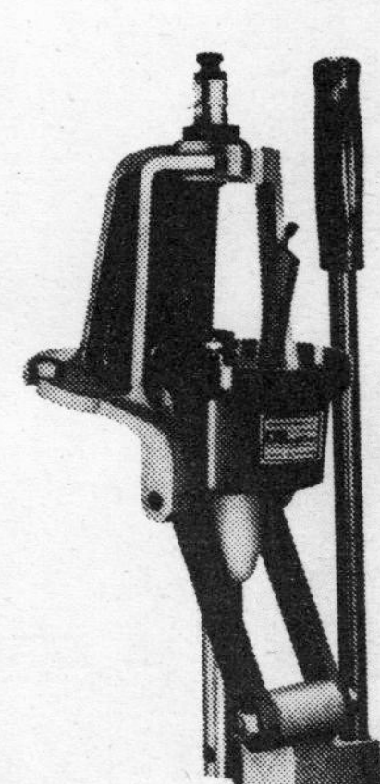

METALLIC CARTRIDGE PRESS

Pacific's Multi-Power "C" press is rugged. It will handle just about any reloading chore you may have, to include bullet swaging. Handles standard ⅞x14 dies.

Price: $99.50 with one set of dies.

From Pacific Tool Company.

TONG-TYPE RELOADING TOOL

This is the tool that started it all in the field of reloading. Available for both rifle and pistol calibers. Great for the reloader who has limited space.

Price: $35 with one set of dies.

From Lyman Products Company.

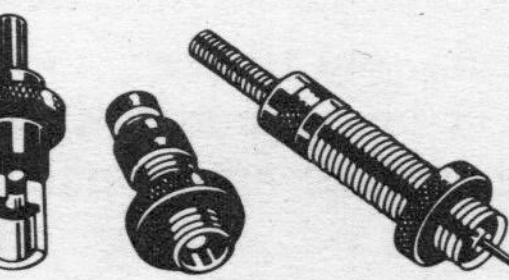
LYMAN 310 Tool Set

See the Directory for complete company addresses.

PORTABLE LOADING TOOL

Available in a wide variety of rifle and pistol calibers, the Pak-Tool is handy for the man who is limited in space or is heading into the wilderness. This sturdy tool comes complete with everything but the brass, bullets, powder and primers.
Price: $39.50 complete for one rifle caliber; $44.50 complete for one pistol caliber.
From Pak-Tool Company.

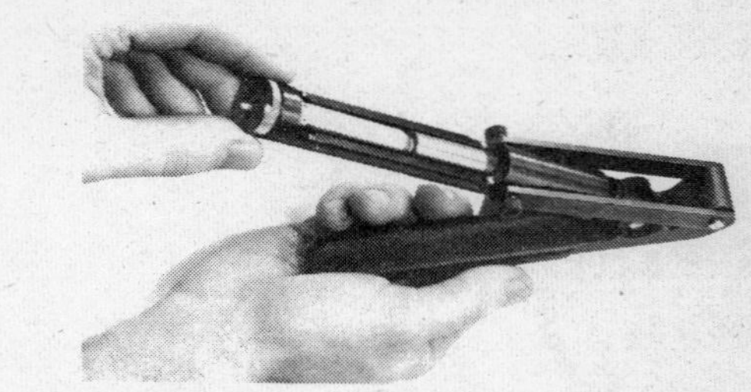

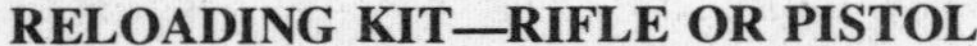

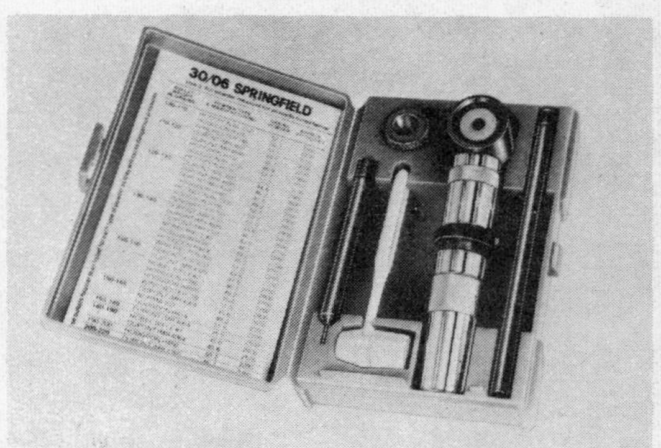

RELOADING KIT—RIFLE OR PISTOL

The Lee improved reloading kit is made in calibers (rifle and pistol) ranging from .22 Hornet through .45 Long Colt. Each kit comes with a charge cup, load chart, primer decapper and base, plus sizing tools. Complete instructions come with each kit. The entire kit is packed in a polypropylene box that features a lifetime hinge.
Price: $13.98.
From Lee Precision.

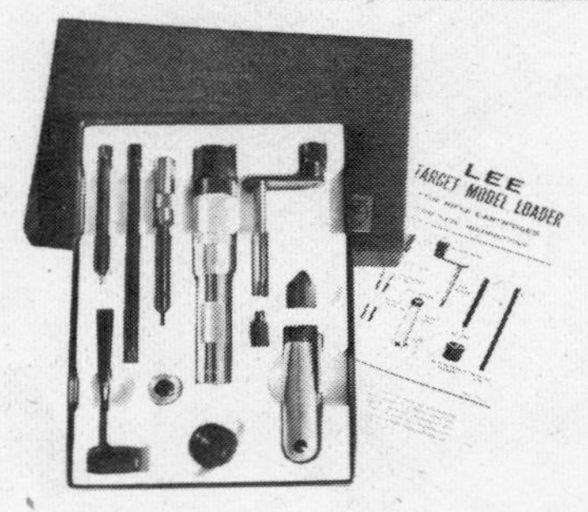

METALLIC CARTRIDGE LOADING KIT

Lee Custom's Target Model Loader Kit provides all of the equipment necessary to reload ammo suitable for competitive target shooting. Comes with an 8-page, illustrated, instruction booklet.
Price: $49.98.
From Lee Custom Engineering, Inc.

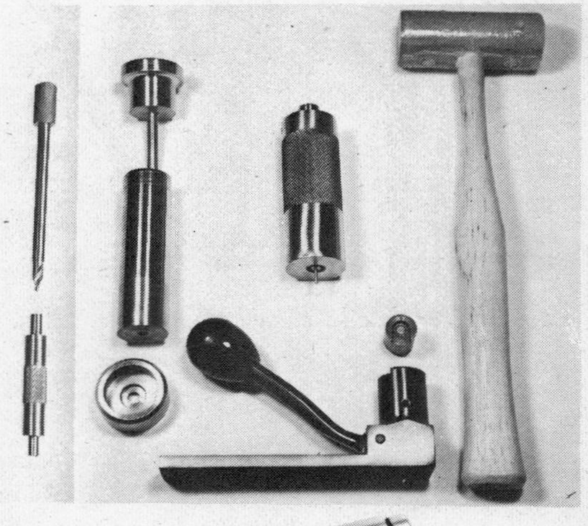

RELOADING TOOL SET (METALLICS)

Made for .222 Rem.; .222 Rem. Mag.; 6 x 47; .308 Win.; 25-06 Rem. and 6mm Rem. This reloading tool set is made to your rifle's specs; so, before buying, you must send the maker 6 fired cartridge cases (fired in *your* rifle). The kit's precision-made. It includes a straight-line bullet seater; sizing die; primer seater and rawhide mallet.
Price: $138.95 complete.
From Hart Products.

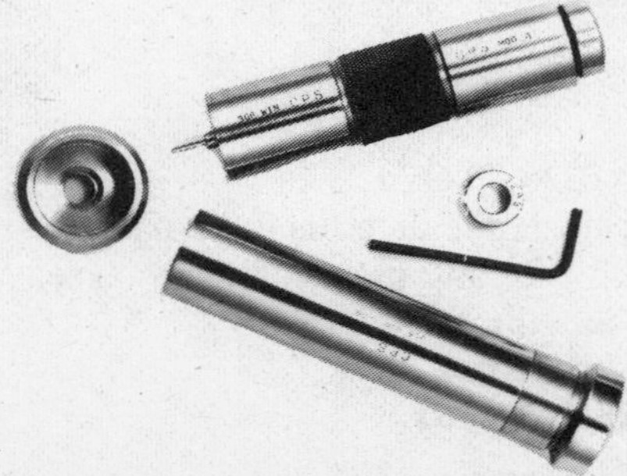

PRECISION LOADING TOOL

For rifle calibers only. The neck sizing die and de-primer consist of a body assembly, de-priming rod, sizing chamber and sizing ring. If you load for more than one caliber, you only need to purchase additional sizing chambers and rings.
Price: Neck sizing die and de-Primer, $35; straight line bullet seater, $25; additional sizing chambers and rings, $15.
From Central Products for Shooters.

Prices shown are subject to change.

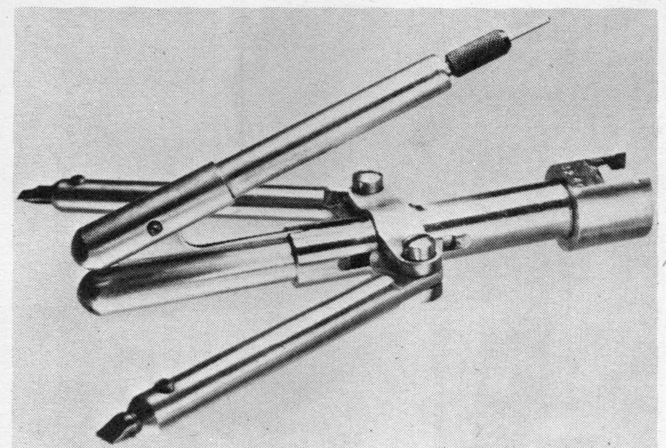

PORTABLE LOADING TOOL

Made of top materials. Designed for the shooter/hunter who's on the move. For available calibers see the following list:

.22 Hornet	.41 Mag	.45-70
.22-15-60	.45 COLT	.50-70
.222 Rimmed	9.3 x 72R.	11.7mm
.224 Wea.Mag.	.577-450	.32-35
.225 Win.	.50-110	.40-70 P.M.
.222 Rem.	7mm Rem.Mag.	.40-70 Bal.
.25-20 S.S.	.348 W.	.45-100
.28-30	.38-72	.32-20W.
.30-06	.40-70 S.S.	.300 H&H
.32 Ideal	.38 Exp.	.30 Rem.
.32-40	.43 Mau.	.32-30 Rem.
.38-40 Rem.	9.3 x 74R.	.44-77

Price: Complete tool $40; heads $5; decapping rods $3.50.

From Jerry Simmons.

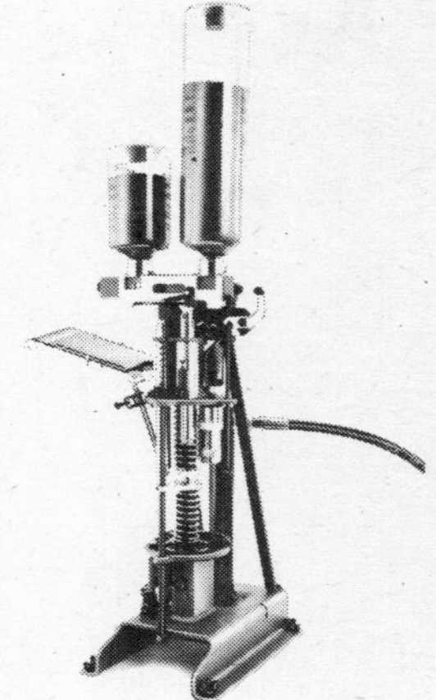

HYDRAULIC PRESS FOR SHOTSHELLS

The MEC Hustler is designed to turn out a high volume of loaded shotshells in a small amount of time. Simply put, the Hustler loads a full box of shells in less than two minutes. Its got everything. Available in most gauges.

Price: $679.80.

From Mayville Engineering Company.

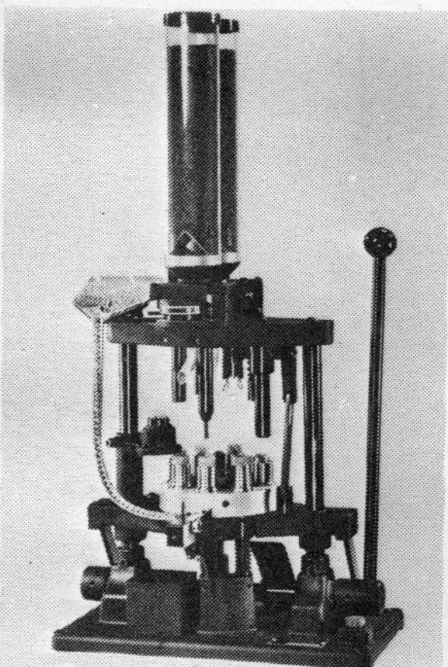

SHOTSHELL LOADING PRESS

The Ponsness-Warren Size-O-Matic (800B) shotshell press has an amazing production rate of 1,800 shells per hour with three operators; 1,200 shells per hour with two operators, and 700 shells per hour with one operator. All tooling is ground to exacting specs and the press is available in 12, 20, 28 or .410. The Size-O-Matic press will handle paper or plastic, high or low base shells with ease.

Price: $649.50.

From Ponsness-Warren, Inc.

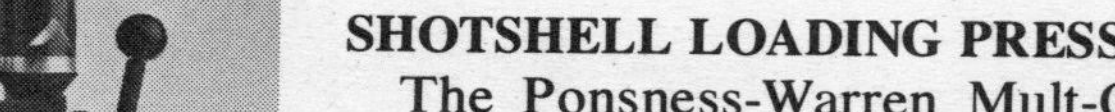

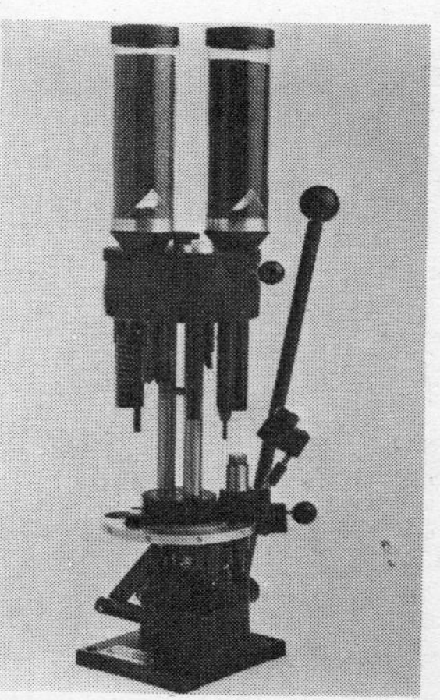

SHOTSHELL LOADING PRESS

The Ponsness-Warren Mult-O-Matic (600B) shotshell press is a high-production unit that can turn out 500 loaded shells—one case—in one hour's time. Features automatic primer feed, 6- and 8-point crimp starters and multiple-gauge capability. Completed shells are gravity fed down a handy shell chute. Available in 12, 16, 20, 28 or .410.

Price: $389.50; extra-gauge tooling set, $129.50; 3″ conversion kit for 12 or 20 gauge, $124.50.

From Ponsness-Warren, Inc.

SHOTSHELL PRESS

Available in 12, 16, 20 and 28 gauges, the Pacific 366-Auto shotshell loader is a progressive press that kicks out a loaded shell with each pull of the handle. Handles all 2¾″ shotshells; conversion kit to 3-inch 12 or 20 gauge shells available. The DL-360 allows the user to select right- or left-hand operation at will.
Price: $373; conversion kit to 12 or 20 gauge 3″ shells, $18.50.
From Pacific Tool Company.

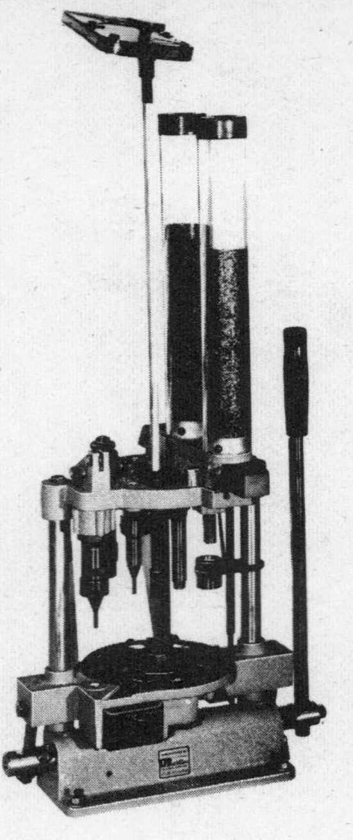

SHOTSHELL PRESS

The Pacific 266 press is a single-stage shotshell reloading press that has auto priming, right- or left-hand operation and is available in 12, 16, 20, 28 and .410. Handles all 2¾″ shells and, as an option, you can get a 3″ shell conversion kit in 12 or 20 gauge.
Price: $189, 12 and 20 gauge; $195 for 16, 28 and .410.
From Pacific Tool Company.

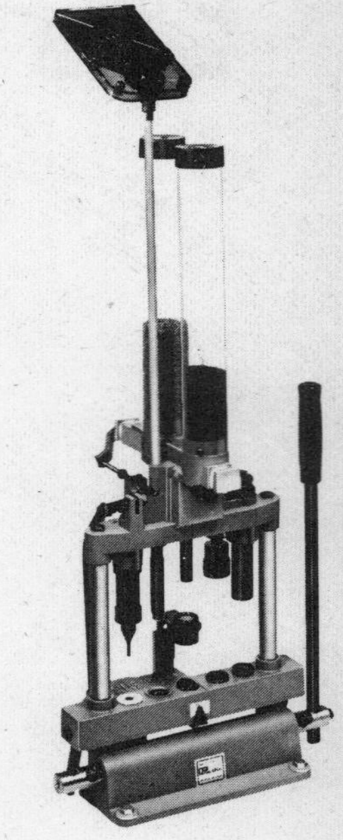

PROGRESSIVE SHOTSHELL PRESS

Twelve different operations at all six stations combine to produce a finished shell with each pull of the handle on the MEC Grabber. Primer feed, charging and crimping are all automatic. Available in most popular gauges.
Price: $253.
From Mayville Engineering Company.

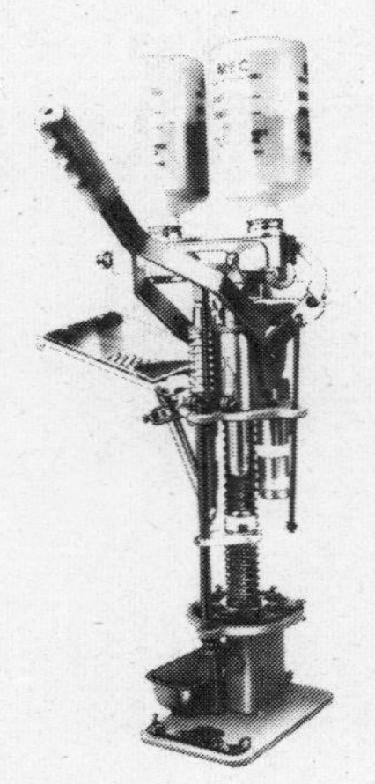

SHOTSHELL PRESS

The MEC Super 650 shotshell press is available in 12, 16, 20, 28 or .410 gauge. This is a progressive press—you get a finished shell with each pull of the handle. The Super 650 accommodates 6 shells at once. Comes with an auto-primer feed and "Auto-Cycle" charging. It also features an adjustable rammer tube to let you set wad pressure.
Price: $184.64.
From Mayville Engineering Company.

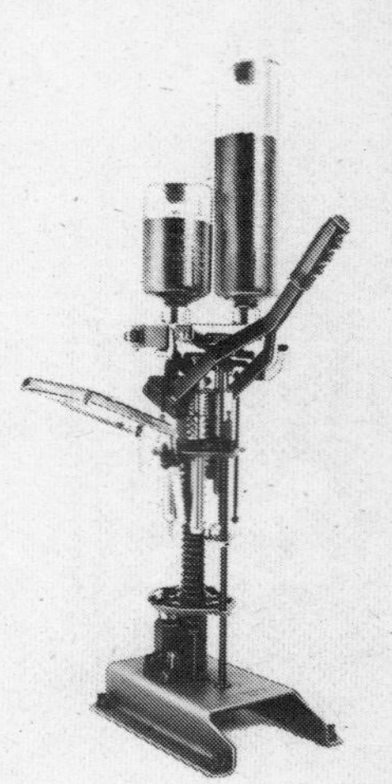

10-GAUGE SHOTSHELL PRESS

The Ponsness-Warren Magn-O-Matic 10 has been made for the water fowl crowd. No separate case sizer or conditioner is needed. This press has all the features of the P-W Du-O-Matic press with the exception it is not convertible to other gauges. Specifically made to load 3½-inch shells, this press will turn out 4 to 6 boxes of ammo in an hour.
Price: $215.
From Ponsness-Warren, Inc.

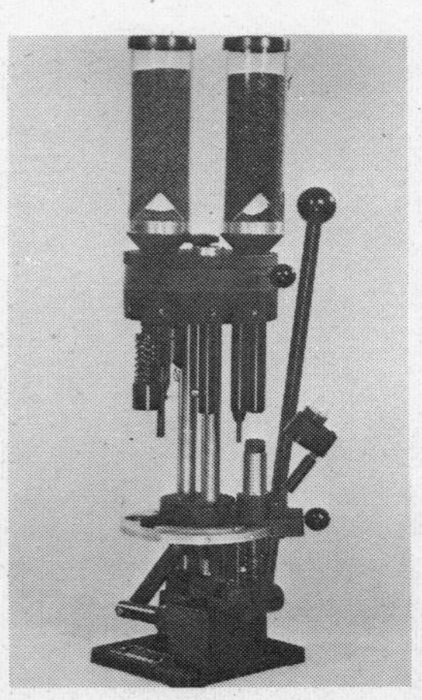

Prices shown are subject to change.

SHOTSHELL PRESS

The Versamec 700 features an exclusive MEC platform cam for a long ejection stroke at the resizing station. Pro-check feature prevents accidental spillage of powder and shot. Quick change crimp spinners allow for the selection of 6- or 8-point (or smooth cone for paper shells) in seconds. Comes in 12, 16, 20, 28 and .410.

Price: $100.43; spare die set, $33.88.

From Mayville Engineering Company.

SHOTSHELL PRESS

The MEC Sizemaster shotshell press comes in either 12, 16, 20, 28 or .410. Comes with E-Z Prime auto primer feed. This single-stage shotshell press also features a Spindex Star Crimp. This press will handle high or low base shells of either brass or steel head composition.

Price: $140; spare die sets, $50.60, for all gauges except 10 which sells for $59.40.

From Mayville Engineering Company.

SHOTSHELL PRESS

The Lyman 100SL shotshell press is available in 12 or 20 gauge and full-length sizes high or low brass, 2¾- or 3-inch shells. The 100SL also comes with an automatic primer feed and other time-saving features.

Price: $94.50; conversion kit to 12 or 20 gauge, $20; extra crimp starter heads, 6 or 8 folds, $7.

From Lyman Products Company.

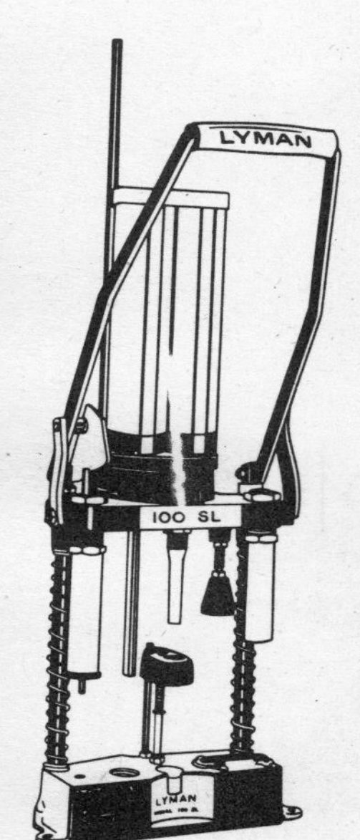

100 SL Shotshell Press

SHOTSHELL PRESS

The MEC 600JR Press gives rapid, single-stage operation. Features a Spindex Crimp Starter and a shellholder that positions and holds each shell firmly at every station. Available in 12, 16, 20, 28 and .410.

Price: $87.73; spare die set, $30.25.

From Mayville Engineering Company.

SHOTSHELL PRESS

Pacific's 105 shotshell press is low in price, but offers the user a lot more quality and performance than he might get elsewhere. Available in 12, 16 and 20 gauge and handles all 2¾" shells. Conversion kit available (as an option) for 3" 12 and 20 gauge shells.

Price: $75; conversion kit to 3" 12 or 20 gauge, $15.

From Pacific Tool Company.

SHOTSHELL PRESS

Pacific's 155 shotshell press is designed for the average shooter. It comes with a fool proof charge bar; and auto priming system (as an option), and is available in 10, 12, 16, 28 and .410. Handles all 2¾" shells and an optional conversion kit to 3" 12 or 20 gauge is also available.

Price: 10-gauge, $139.50; 12 or 20 gauge, $123.50; 16, 28 and .410, $128.50. With auto priming, $135 for 12 and 20 gauge; $139 for 16, 28 and .410.

From Pacific Tool Company.

See the Directory for complete company addresses.

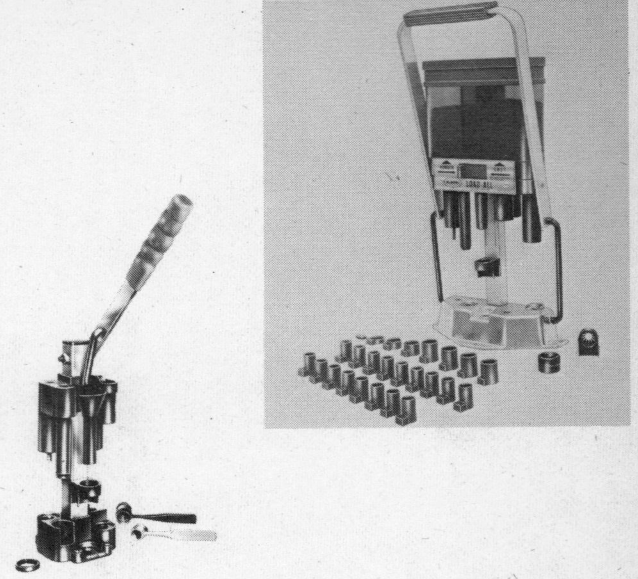

SHOTSHELL LOADING PRESS

The Lee Load-All is available in 12, 16 and 20 gauges and will handle both 2¾- and 3-inch shells in 12 and 20 gauges. An extremely simple press to use and you can get a production rate of about 100 or more shells per hour. Comes with 24 shot and powder bushings to meet your specific shooting needs.
Price: $33.98.
From Lee Precision.

SHOTSHELL LOADING TOOL

The Lee Load-All Junior is available in 12-gauge only, 2¼- or 3-inch shells. Full length sizes each shell, loads trap, field or magnum ammo and comes with one powder measure and an adjustable shot measure.
Price: $14.98.
From Lee Precision.

SHOTSHELL RESIZER

Called the Super-Sizer, this handy unit full-length sizes the brass head right back to factory specs. A super-sized shell will work freely in any magazine tube and will chamber perfectly. Available in 12, 16, 20, 28 or .410 gauges.
Price: $52.80.
From Mayville Engineering Company.

DIE STORAGE BOX

This one's made of strong, heavy-duty plastic that really offers your set of pet dies solid protection. Lid is a separate piece and can be used as a handy primer tray.
Price: $2.
From Pacific Tool Company.

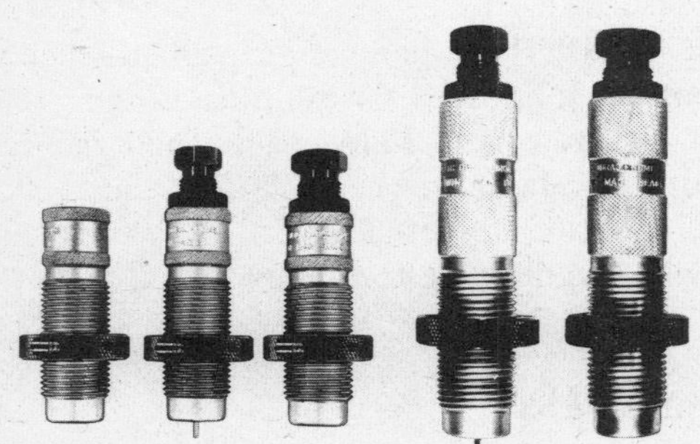

RELOADING DIES

Pacific reloading dies are precision made of the best materials and feature Durachrome finish. Available in all popular rifle and pistol calibers. Tungsten carbide dies available in several pistol calibers. Two- and 3-die sets available; full or neck sizing.
Price: $18.50, 2-die rifle set; $19.50, 3-die pistol set; $45 for 3-die T/C set.
From Pacific Tool Company.

WEATHERBY RELOADING DIES

These custom dies are available in 2- and 3-die sets for all of the Weatherby Magnum cartridges plus .30-06, and .270 Winchester. Comes with a hard-chrome finish. Precision made.
Price: 2-die set $29.95; 3-die set (includes neck-sizing sleeve) $32.95.
From Weatherby, Inc.

Prices shown are subject to change.

RELOADING DIES

Available in all popular calibers. Each die is precision hardened, honed and polished to a mirror finish on the inside. Standard ⅞"x14 threads fit all popular presses. C-H dies feature a lock ring that has a special nylon ball lock-up that's set-screw controlled.

See below for prices:

Series "A" Full Length Sizer and Seater Die	$17.95
Series "B" Sizer, Expander-Decapper and Seater Die	17.95
Series "C" Sizer-Decapper, Expander and Seater Die	17.95
Series "D" Neck Sizer and Seater Die	17.95
Series "E" Full Length Sizer, Neck Sizer and Seater Die	23.50
Series "F" Sizer, Expander-Decapper and Speed Seater Die	19.50
Series "G" Carbide Sizer, Expander-Decapper and Seater Die	34.50
Series "H" Carbide Sizer, Expander-Decapper and Speed Seater Die	35.50
Taper Crimp Dies Available in .38/.357 9mm Luger, .45 ACP	10.00

From C-H Tool and Die Corp.

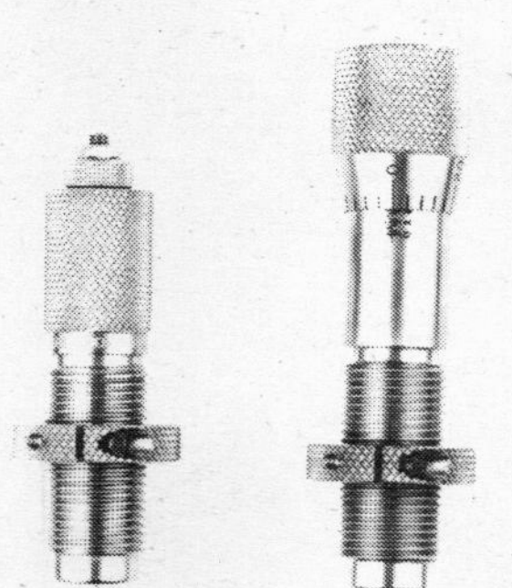

BENCH RIFLE DIE SET

The two-die set combines the proven concept of neck sizing with truly precise bullet seating. The Neck Sizing Die allows the cartridge to retain its fire-formed shape for best accuracy. The heart of the set is the Lyman Micro Seat Die featuring a large micrometer adjustable head. This die provides bullet seating precision not normally associated with ⅞x14 threaded dies. These new dies also feature Lyman's unique split-ring steel lock ring that can be tightened firmly without damaging screw threads. These die sets are available for .22 PPC, .22-250, .220 Swift, .222 Remington, .222 Remington Magnum, .223 Remington, .243 Winchester, 6mm Remington, 6mm PPC, 6x47mm, .25-06, .270 Winchester, 7mm Remington Magnum, 7mm Mauser, .30-06, .300 Winchester Magnum and .308 Winchester.

Price: $29.95

From Lyman Products Company.

DELUXE HANDGUN DIE SETS

The Lyman Multi-Deluxe die sets will appeal to the handgunner who uses more than one bullet style. Bullet seating screws for these new dies can be changed by simply screwing out the top of the die. Each set features 3 dies; a T-C sizing die, neck-expanding die and bullet seating die with either 2 or 3 seating screws, depending on available bullet styles. Available in .38 S&W, .38 Spl., .41 Mag., .44 Spl., .44 Mag., .45 ACP and .45 Long Colt.

Price: $37.95

From Lyman Products Company.

See the Directory for complete company addresses.

DIE LOCK RING

Screw-lock, not the old lead-ball variety. Easy to lock and unlock. Available as a separate unit.

Price: $1.10 each.

From Bonanza Sports Mfg. Co.

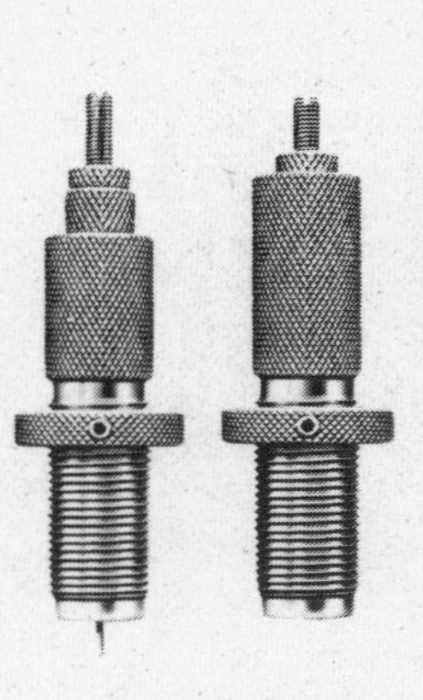

TWO-DIE RIFLE SET

Each RCBS 2-die rifle set comes with a sizing/decapping die and a seating die. They feature standard ⅞x14 threading and are available in all popular calibers and some wildcat cartridges on special order.

Price: From $20 to $25 depending on caliber.

From RCBS.

RIFLE AND PISTOL DIES

Bonanza rifle and pistol dies are manufactured with special attention to diameters, tapers, headspace and concentricity. They come with standard ⅞x14 threads that allow them to be used on various makes of presses.

Price: $18.95 for a 2-die rifle set; $19.50 for a 3-die pistol set.

From Bonanza Sports Mfg. Co.

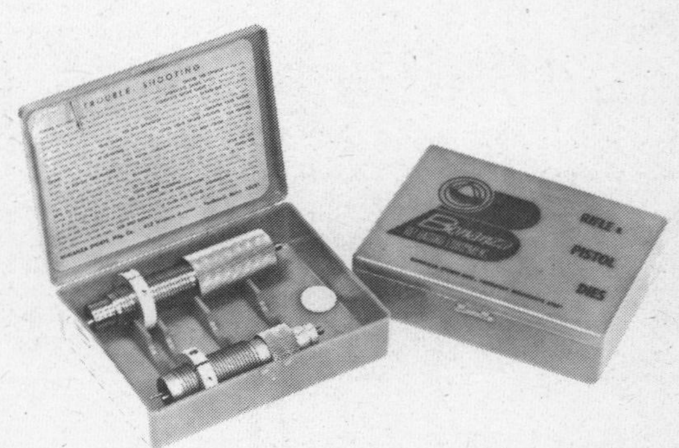

RELOADING DIES

Available for all popular calibers, rifle and pistol. Also, titanium carbide pistol 3-die sets are available. Each die box features a shell-holder top and bottom.

Price: 2-die rifle set, $19.50; 3-die pistol sets, $22.95; 3-die pistol set in titanium carbide—all calibers except 9mm Luger—$42.50 (9mm Luger, $52). Titanium sizing die only, $32.50 ($42 for 9mm Luger).

From Redding Reloading Equipment.

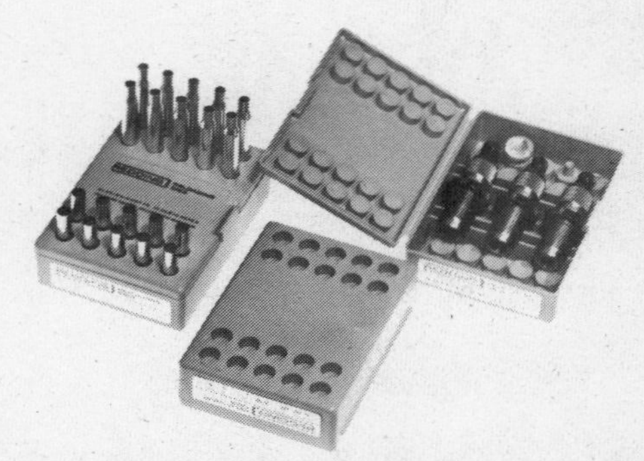

FLOATING SIZER DIE

Because of its design, the sizer bushing can be custom fitted to your cases fired in your gun. Since the bushing floats from side to side in the die, it is impossible for the die to distort the case during sizing. Assembled die is to the upper left of the nearby photo, knockout pin to the far right.

Prices: As follows:

Jones Floating Sizer die complete with knockout	$19.50
Jones hardened steel sizer bushings	3.00
Base of Jones Floating Sizer Die	3.95
Extra knockout pin for another caliber	3.00
Extra charge for non-benchrest caliber	3.00

(This charge applies to all cases over 2.235 inches in length and/or belted magnums.)

From Neil A. Jones.

REMOVABLE SHELL HOLDERS

These shell holders are made from quality tool steel with centers properly located for accurate priming and decapping. As you will see in the nearby photo, the Bonanza Shell Holder has a tapered entrance making case insertion and removal quite easy.

Price: $3.55 (Specify cartridge).

From Bonanza Sports Mfg. Co.

UNIVERSAL SHELL HOLDER

Available for all popular reloading presses. It enables the handloader to switch from cartridge to cartridge without having to switch from shell holder to shell holder.

Price: $7.95.

From Quinetics Corp.

Prices shown are subject to change.

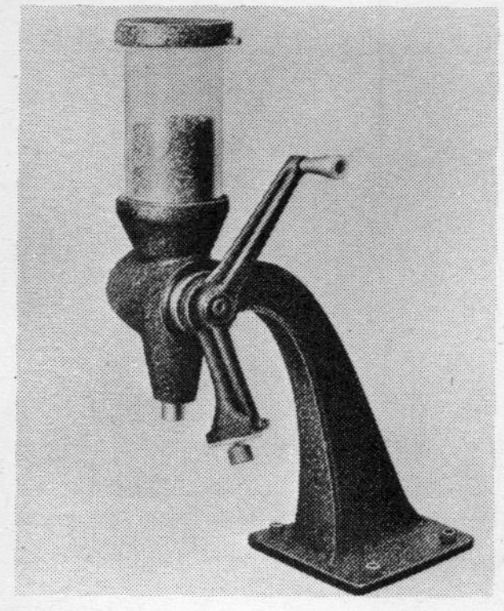

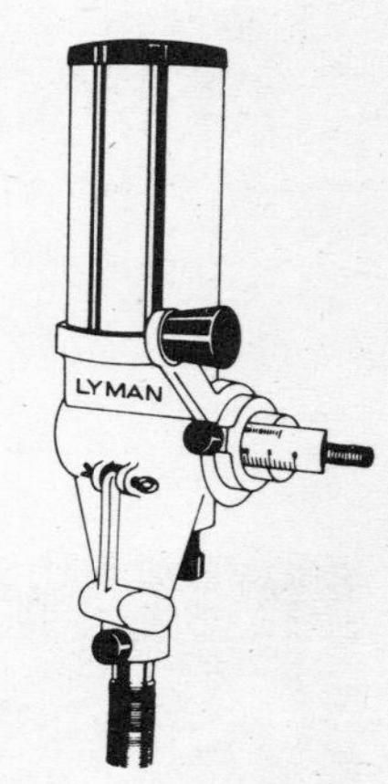

POWDER MEASURE

SAECO's precision powder measure is fully adjustable from 2-grains of Bullseye to 95-grains of 4350. Features a clear plastic hopper and is available with a bench stand. Drop tubes are furnished for both .22 and .30 caliber. Micro-Setting drums are precision ground and measure body is honed to a mirror finish.

Price: $49 with bench stand; $39.50, without.

From SAECO Reloading, Inc.

POWDER MEASURE

The Lyman No. 55 powder measure dispenses propellant to within a fraction of a grain with its precision micrometer bar. The clear plastic reservoir holds a generous 2,400 grains of powder.

Price: $36.95; optional 7,000 grain reservoir, $6.

From Lyman Products Company.

POWDER MEASURE

The RCBS Du-O-Measure powder dispenser is made to throw a precise amount of powder with each throw of the handle. The Du-O-Measure has a carefully bored and honed main casting, a large-capacity powder hopper, a built-in powder baffle and a unique drum that changes from large to small measuring cavity in seconds. Micrometer adjustable.

Price: $59.50.

From RCBS.

POWDER MEASURE

The Uniflo measure has a transparent powder hopper, micrometer adjustment and separate small and large measuring cylinders. (Optional .17 caliber drop tube available.)

Price: $32.50 with either large or small measuring cylinder.

From RCBS.

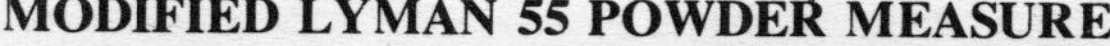

MODIFIED LYMAN 55 POWDER MEASURE

Comes with a micro measuring drum, long drop tube (clear plastic), pill bottle adaptor and Jones powder baffle.

See below for prices:

Lyman No. 55 with Micro Measuring Drum	$72.00
Your Lyman No. 55 Converted with Micro Measuring Drum	49.00
Pill Bottle Adaptor/Baffle for Lyman No. 55	10.50
Threaded Bottle Adaptor for Lyman No. 55	12.50
Pill Bottle Adaptor/Baffle for Belding & Mull Powder Measure	10.50
Clear Plastic Drop Tube	2.50

From Neil A. Jones

POWDER OR SHOT MEASURE

Micrometer adjustable and comes with one drop tube, an 8″ transparent cylinder, cylinder cover and disc.

Price for Either style: $49.

From Whitney Sales.

See the Directory for complete company addresses.

POWDER MEASURE STAND

Comes with standard ⅞x14 thread and is pre-drilled for bench mounting. Holds most common powder measures.
Price: $4.50.
From C-H Tool and Die Corp.

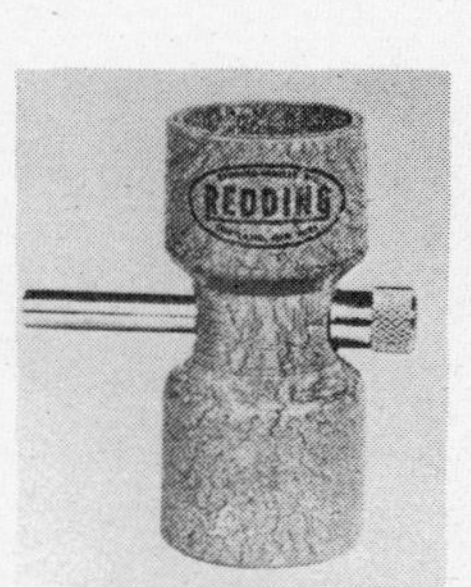

POWDER TRICKLER

Made for the exacting handloader who may need to measure out powder by the granule, not the grain.
Price: $7.95
From Redding Reloading Equipment.

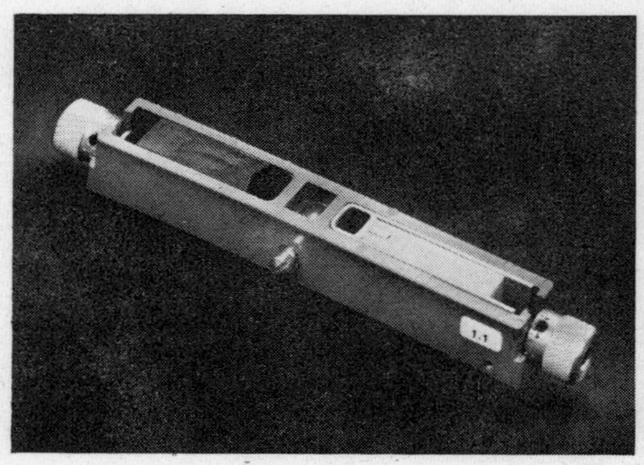

UNIVERSAL SHOTSHELL CHARGE BAR

This one bar does it all, no need to buy several. Micrometer adjustable to suit your loading needs. Comes with 5-year guarantee. Fits MEC 400, 600, 600 Jr., 700 Versamec, 250, 250 Super, Texan Lt, Gt and FW models.
Price: $17.95.
From Multi-Scale Charge LTD.

POWDER MEASURE STAND

The stand features the standard ⅞x14 threaded station and, when fitted with the optional adapter, will raise the Lyman No. 55 Powder Measure high enough to easily position cases in the new Lyman Double Sixty Loading Block beneath the powder drop tube.
Price: $11.95
From Lyman Products Company.

POWDER TRICKLER

A single twist of the knob dispenses one kernel of powder at a time. (Base may be weighted with shot for bench-top stability.)
Price: $4.50.
From C-H Tool and Die Corp.

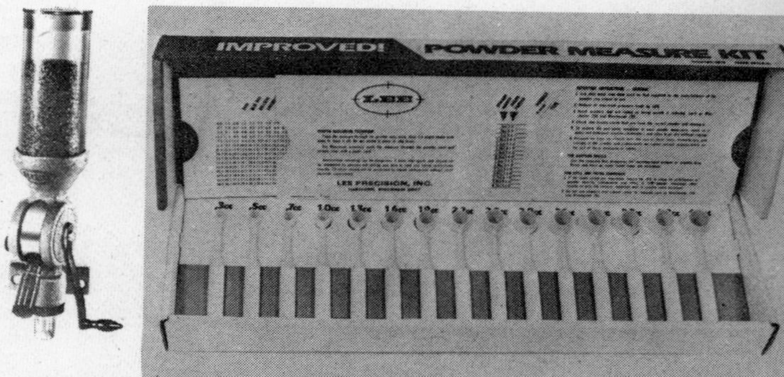

POWDER MEASURE

Comes with a transparent reservoir and top cap. Micrometer adjustment assures uniformity. See-through drop tube accepts all calibers from .22 through .600.
Price: Model No. 3, $39.95
From Redding Reloading Equipment.

POWDER TRICKLER

The Lyman Powder Dribbler features a large powder reservoir, good powder-pan height and a tip-free oversize base. Allows the handloader to dole out his powder one granule-at-a-time.
Price: $5.45
From Lyman Products Company

POWDER MEASURE KIT

Contains 15 separate charge cups and slide-rule chart for proper powder charges with all types of propellants for your particular cartridge.
Price: $4.98.
From Lee Precision.

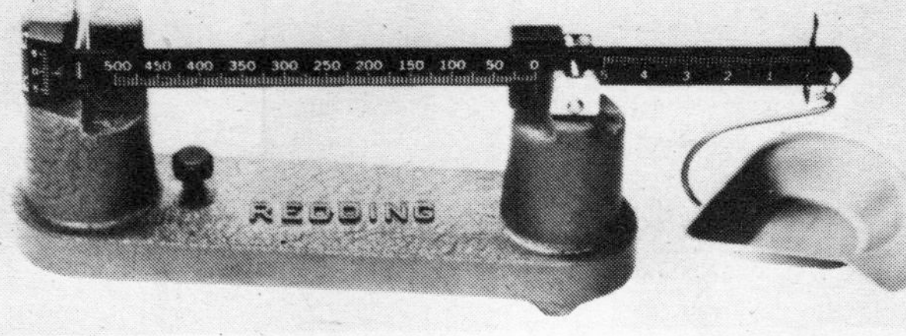

RELOADING SCALE

This Redding Model No. 2 scale has a 505-grain capacity, precision-milled V-groove beam, magnetic dampening and a 1/10-grain graduated over/under scale at the far left of the beam.
Price: $32.95
From Redding Reloading Equipment.

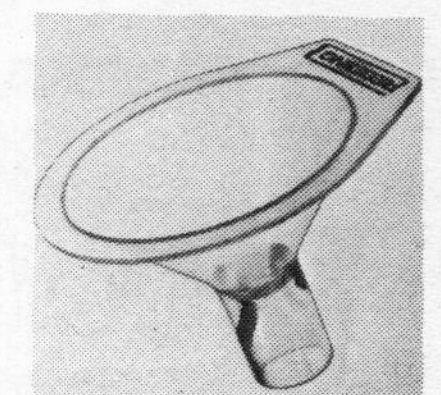

POWDER FUNNEL

Made for the dropping of individual charges or the transfer of powder.
Price: $1.50.
From Redding Reloading Equipment.

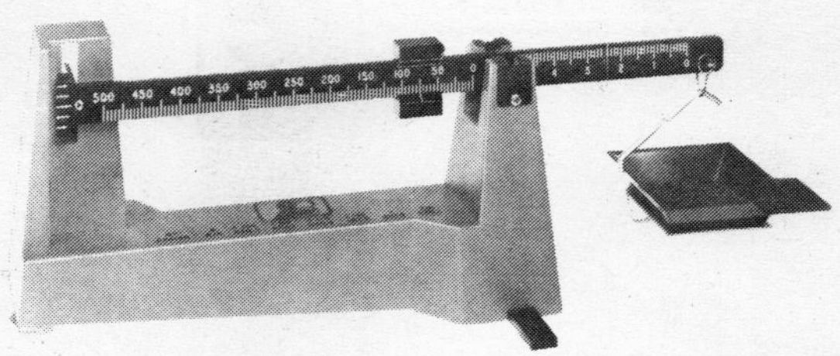

BULLET/POWDER SCALE

Pacific's Model-M has a 510-grain capacity, magnetic dampening and provides readout down to one-tenth of a grain.
Price: $37.50.
From Pacific Tool Company.

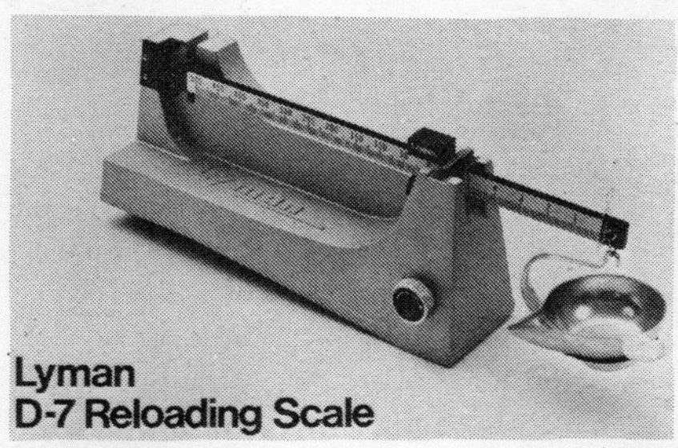
Lyman
D-7 Reloading Scale

POWDER SCALE

Lyman's D-7 powder scale has a 505-grain capacity, black on white beam markings, magnetic dampening, accuracy to one-tenth of a grain and other features. Ideal for weighing out charges and other components.
Price: $32.95
From Lyman Products Company.

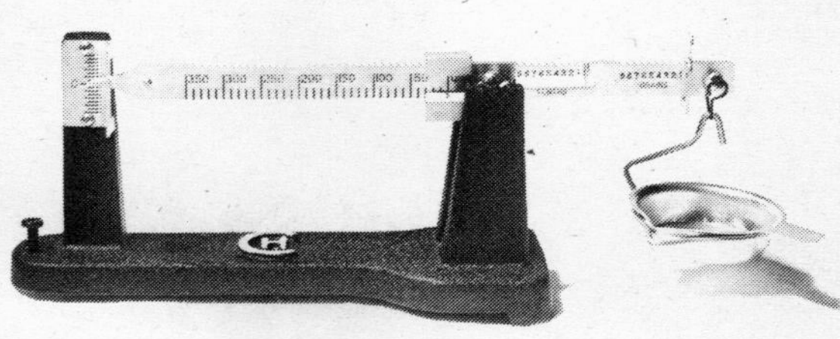

POWDER/BULLET SCALE

Comes with a chrome-plated brass beam, is graduated in 10-grain and 1/10-grain increments and has a leveling screw on the base. All metal construction, 360-grain capacity.
Price: $19.95.
From C-H Tool and Die Corp.

POWDER FUNNEL

Has all-aluminum construction and eliminates static electricity and clinging powder. Comes in 3 sizes.
Price: .17 cal, $2.50; .22 to .270 and 7mm to .45, $2.
From Pacific Tool Company.

POWDER/BULLET SCALE

The Bonanza Model "M" scale has a 505-grain capacity, tempered stainless steel right hand poise plus a pan and beam made of Lexan. Guaranteed accurate to one-tenth of a grain.
Price: $28.75.
From Bonanza Sports Mfg. Co.

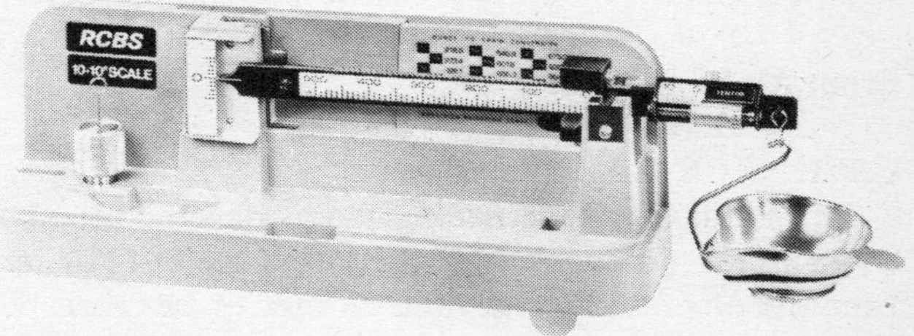

POWDER SCALE

The RCBS 10-10 scale is a precision instrument that helps the reloader accurately determine the weight of a particular powder charge, case or bullet. The scale has a 500-grain capacity, magnetic dampener and other features.
Price: $54.
From RCBS.

See the Directory for complete company addresses.

CARTRIDGE CASE CLEANER

Like-Nu case cleaner turns dirty brass clean without etching. One bottle cleans up to 200 .30-06 sized cases. Non-flammable.
Price: $3.50.
From Pacific Tool Company.

CASE CLEANER

Restores finish on metallic cases to original condition. This product is a liquid concentrate from which you can make 2 quarts of cleaning solution. The solution you make up is reusable. Won't weaken brass.
Price: $1.98 per 4-ounce bottle.
From Birchwood Casey.

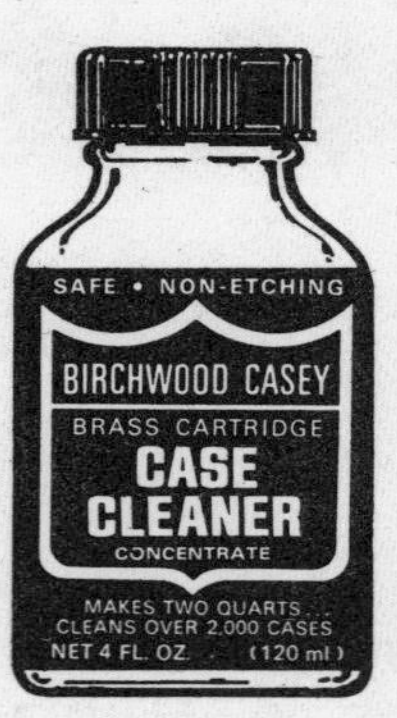

CASE CLEANER

Cleans handgun or rifle brass without etching, is non-corrosive.
Price: $8.25 per quart.
From Hodgdon Powder Company.

CASE LUBE

Hodgdon's miracle sizing lube is a pure, non-toxic, non-sticky resizing and case-forming lubricant. Resists oxidation and has cleaning effect on brass.
Price: $1.95 per 2-ounce bottle.
From Hodgdon Powder Company.

CASE SIZING LUBE

Comes in a handy screw-top, 2-ounce plastic bottle. Contains a high-pressure lube that prevents case from adhering to die walls during sizing.
Price: 95¢.
From Bonanza Sports Mfg. Co.

MECHANICAL CASE CLEANER

This tool consists of a special insert for your favorite electric drill. Simply insert the head into your drill, key it tight, insert your own shell holder and start polishing with a handful of steel wool. Lifetime guarantee.
Price: $18.95.
From Alpha Centauri, Inc.

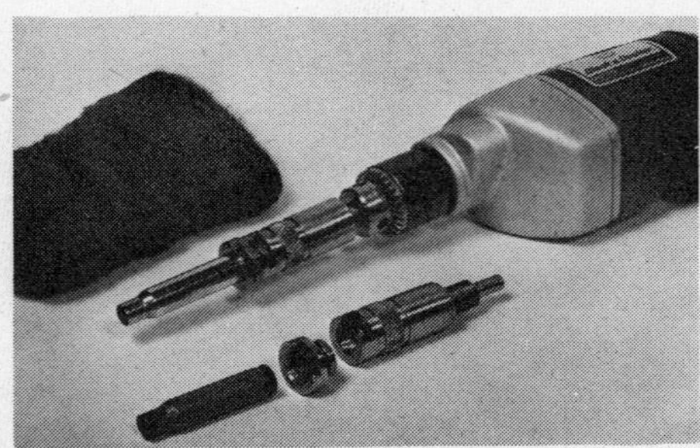

CASE NECK GAUGE

The Plum City case neck gauge is designed to show any variation of neck wall thickness to .001" or less. Ideal for the serious varmint shooter or benchrester.
Price: $42.50, including dial indicator.
From Plum City Ballistics Range.

CASE LENGTH GAUGE

Used to determine proper or improper overall case length. Tells the reloader when it's time to start trimming. Covers widest range of pistol and rifle calibers.
Price: $6.50.
From McKillen & Heyer, Inc.

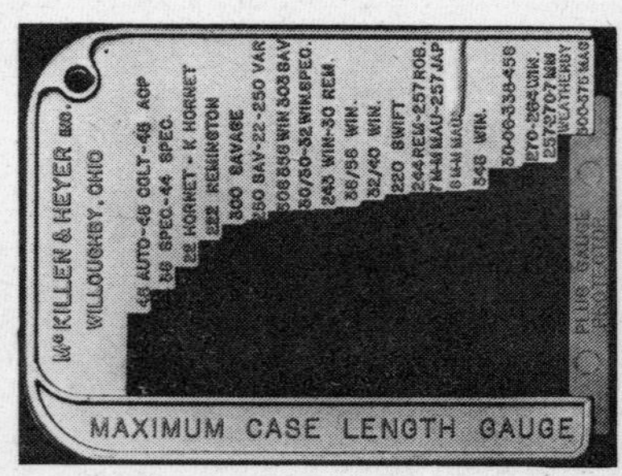

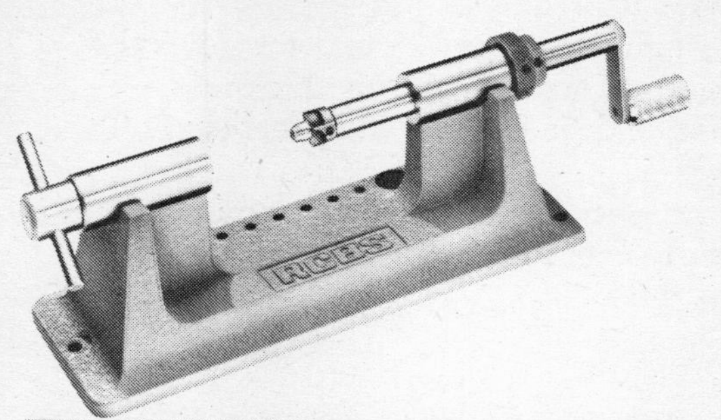

CASE TRIMMER

This trimmer features interchangeable collets for all popular calibers from .17 through .45. Each locks into the cutter head via set screw. The case holder is of the universal type and the trimmer body itself is drilled to hold spare collets.

Price: $27.

From RCBS.

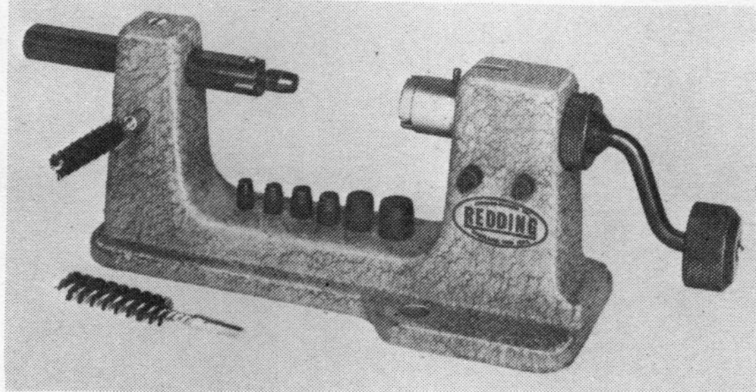

CASE TRIMMER

The Redding Model 14K case trimmer chamfers and deburrs the case neck while it's being trimmed. It also features a universal shell collett, recessed storage area for extra pilots, two (large and small) primer pocket cleaners and two neck cleaning brushes (.22 through .30 caliber).

Price: $34.50

From Redding Reloading Equipment.

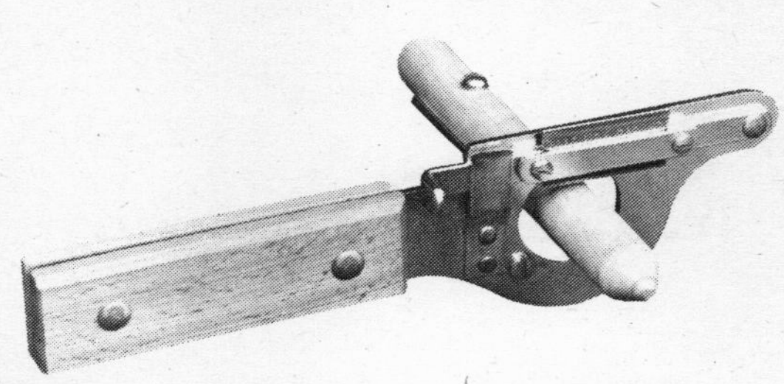

SHOTSHELL CASE TRIMMER

Quickly trims paper or plastic cases to desired length. Utilizes single-edge razor blade. Each trimmer comes with one dowel of proper gauge size; 10, 12, 16, 20 and .410 available.

Price: $13.50, postpaid; extra dowels in 10, 12 or 16 ga., $1.60 each; 20 and .410 dowels, $2, plus 75¢ postage.

From Anderson Mfg. Co.

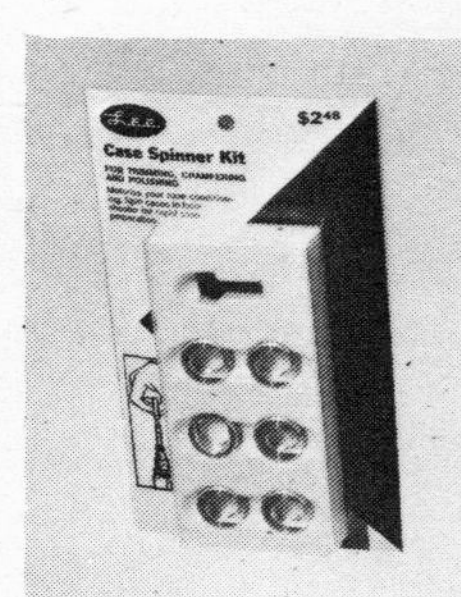

CASE SPINNER KIT

Contains ¼″ shank, plus six shell holders which can be used with approximately 80 different cartridges. Allows shooter to do his trimming and chamfering on a ¼″ drill, not by hand.

Price: $4.98.

From Lee Custom Engineering, Inc.

CASE TRIMMER

Trims case necks fast and easily; plus, clamping feature insures absolute trim uniformity. Finger adjustable. Specify case to be trimmed before buying or ordering.

Price: $17.95

From C-H Tool and Die Corp.

CASE SPINNER

Designed to be used with any ¼″ electric drill or drill press, and utilizes the shell holder from the Lee Custom Trimmer. Enables the user to "motorize" case trimming and chamfering operations.

Price: 98¢.

From Lee Custom Engineering, Inc.

TRIM DIES
The Pacific trim die has standard ⅞x14 threads, has a Durachrome finish and fits in any standard reloading press. Die comes in all popular calibers and is used to trim case necks to proper overall length.
Price: $10.75.
From Pacific Tool Company.

TRIM DIE
Each trim die comes for a specific cartridge. Trimming is extremely fast. You simply run the case up into the die and file off the protruding neck. Die is fully hardened, you can't damage it with a file. Available in .222, .22-250, .225 Win., .243 Win., 6mm Rem., .257 Roberts, .25-06 Rem., .257 Wea., 6.5x55, .270 Win., 7x57 Mauser, 7mm Rem. Mag, 7mm Wea., .308 Win., .30-06, .300 Win. Mag., .300 Wea. and 8x57.
Price: $9
From C-H Tool and Die Corp.

CHAMFERING/DEBURRING TOOL
Prepares the inside and outside of case necks. Removes burrs after trimming and bevels case mouth for easy bullet seating. Made from hardened tool steel, deep blue finish.
Price: $6.
From Pacific Tool Company.

DEBURRING TOOL
The Bonanza "Cricket" can also serve as a large or small primer pocket cleaner. After trimming, you can easily deburr your metallic case necks; it will handle any metallic case from .22 to .45.
Price: $2.25.
From Bonanza Sports Mfg. Co.

NECK CLEANING TOOL
Handle and brushes may be purchased separately. Ideal for cleaning inside metallic case necks.
Price: $2.25 with one brush; specify caliber.
From Bonanza Sports Mfg. Co.

NECK TURNING TOOL
This tool is designed to turn the outside of the case neck to any desired wall thickness. Available for most popular rifle calibers. Precision made.
Price: $36.95 for one caliber; handle $5.25; extra mandrel and button for different calibers $8.75.
From Hart Products.

CASE TRIMMER
Lyman's Universal Trimmer handles all metallic cartridges regardless of rim thickness. Also features coarse and fine cutter adjustments. Full selection of pilots.
Price: $34.95 with one pilot; extra pilot, $1.50.
From Lyman Products Company.

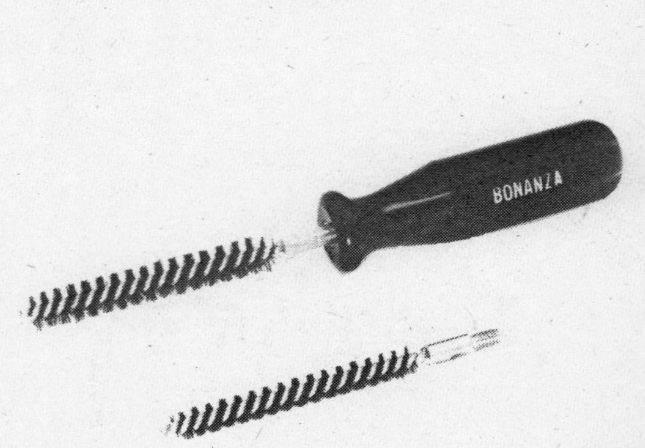

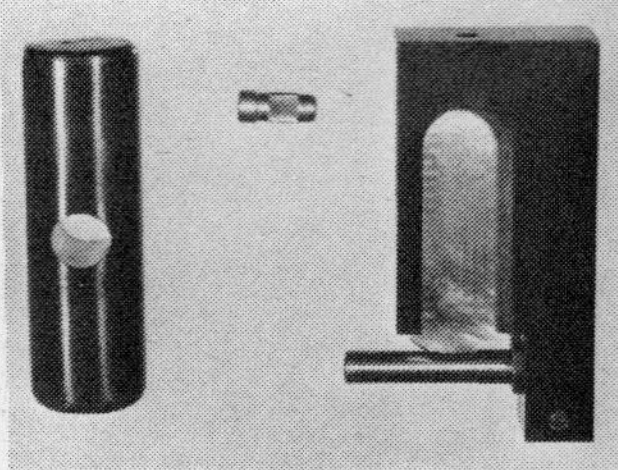

Prices shown are subject to change.

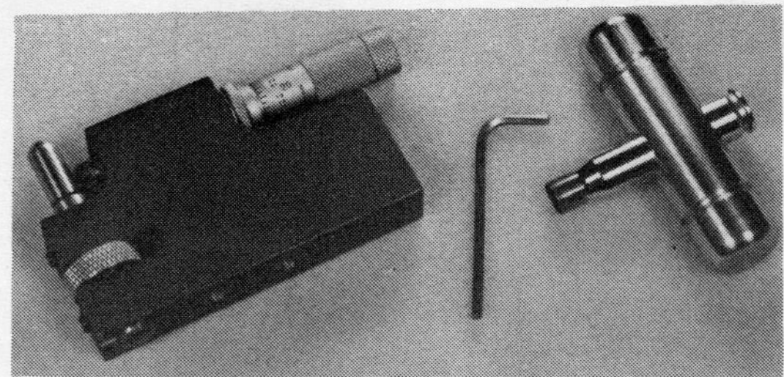

CASE NECK TURNING TOOL

For the accuracy-minded shooter. Micrometer adjustable cutting edge, accurate to .0001-inch. Mandrel, once locked into place, prevents operator from removing more brass than he planned on.

Price: Neck turner, integral micrometer and shell holder, $55; fully adjustable shellholder, $10; additional mandrels, $5.75.

From Central Products for Shooters.

NECK TURNING TOOL

Designed for the benchrester and varmint shooter who looks for precision in his reloads. The Marquart Neck Turning Tool allows case necks to be turned uniform within .0001". Comes complete with one pilot and appropriate case holder. Holders are available in .222 through .378 Weatherby Magnum.

Price: Complete tool, $36.50; extra pilots or holders, $6 each.

From Marquart Precision Company.

NECK TURNING TOOL

Features an extra wide cutter for a full width cut. Complete uniformity to .0001" is achieved through the use of precision ground cutters and pilots. Comes complete with the basic tool, one pilot, shell holder and allen wrenches. Extra pilots and shell holders available.

Price: $42; extra pilots to .30 caliber $6.50; over .30 caliber $10; extra shell holder $4.

From H-S Precision.

PRIMER POCKET REAMER

Made of solid steel with a knurled handle for a firm grip. Removes military crimp from the primer pockets of G.I. brass. Comes in large and small sizes.

Price: Small or large, $6.

From Pacific Tool Company.

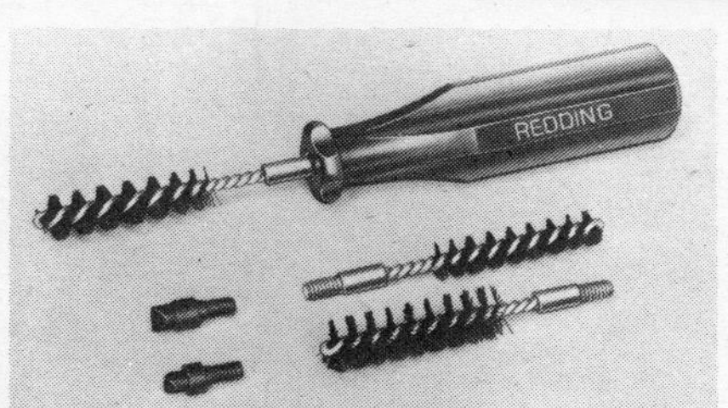

CASE PREPARATION KIT

Consists of handle threaded for two all-caliber brushes for cleaning case necks; and, large and small primer pocket cleaning studs.

Price: $5.95; extra brush or primer pocket cleaner, $1 each.

From Redding Reloading Equipment.

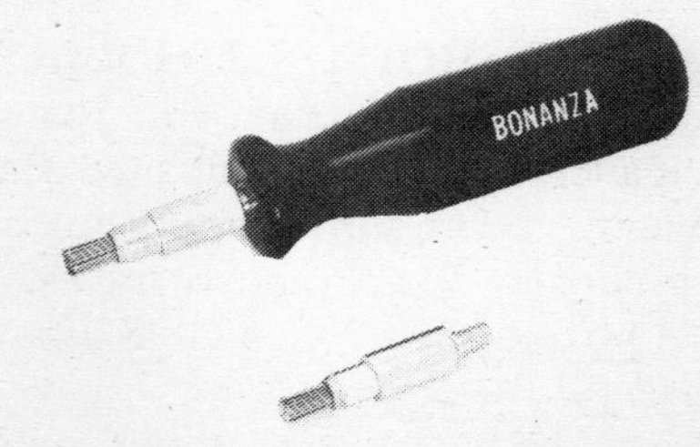

PRIMER POCKET CLEANING TOOL

Bonanza's primer pocket brush is designed to thoroughly clean out large or small primer pockets.

Price: $5.25 for handle, large and small brushes.

From Bonanza Sports Mfg. Co.

See the Directory for complete company addresses.

PRIMER POCKET CLEANER

Works like a Yankee Screwdriver to quickly remove primer residue. Comes in either large or small sizes.
Price: $2.48.
From Lee Custom Engineering, Inc.

PRIMER POCKET REAMER

Removes all crimp from military brass with just a couple of turns. Comes in either large or small primer pocket size.
Price: $3.45 each.
From C-H Tool and Die Corp.

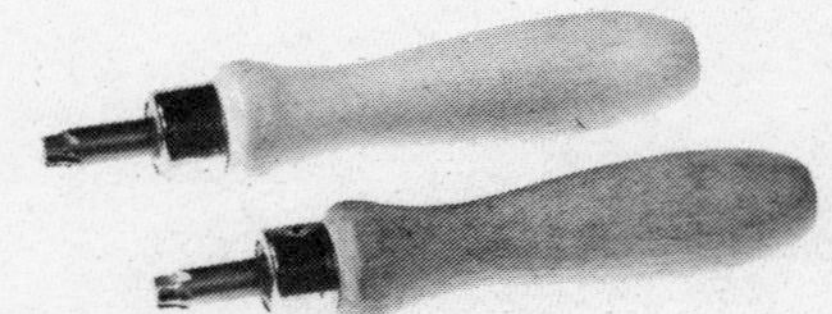

CASE BLOCK

Made of solid hardwood and holds 50 cases/cartridges. Available in six different sizes to accommodate most rifle or pistol cases.
Price: $1.95.
From Shassere.

CASE CADDY

Made of select solid hardwood and holds any number of case blocks. Container is varnished in satin. Holds up to 300 cases with six-case blocks. Unit comes complete with 3 blocks.
Price: $18.75; extra blocks, $1.95 each.
From Shassere.

PRIMER POCKET CLEANERS

One quick turn removes accuracy destroying primer residue. Large and small tools come singly, or as a combo tool.
Price: 98¢ for the combo; 78¢ for a large or small cleaner.
From Lee Custom Engineering, Inc.

CASE LUBE

Smooths out the loading process and helps prevent cases from getting stuck in sizing dies. Tested by Pacific on over 30,000 reloads under lab conditions.
Price: $2.35.
From Pacific Tool Company.

SHOOTING AND LOADING BLOCKS

Made from oil and solvent resistant elastomers. Loading block holds 84 pieces of brass; shooting block holds 10 rounds of loaded ammo.
Price: $6.95 for the shooting block; $10.95 for the loading block.
From H-S Precision.

LOADED SHOTSHELL HOLDER

Called the E-Z Pak, this item allows the shotshell reloader to stack his finished shells in proper order. When full, you slip an empty box over the whole works, tip it upside down, remove the E-Z Pak and you've got a full box of shells. Available in all gauges.
Price: $2.66.
From Mayville Engineering Company.

Prices shown are subject to change.

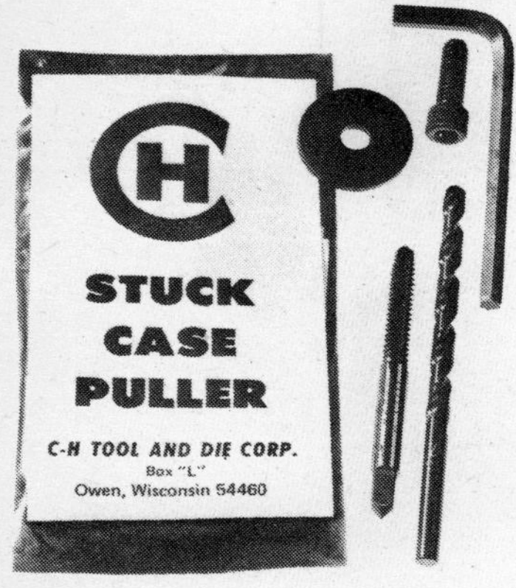

STUCK CASE PULLER

Easily removes stuck cases from sizing dies. To use, simply drill and tap the primer hole, screw the die part way into the press. Place the washer over the hole and insert the screw into the case. Turn the screw with the wrench and pull the case free.

Price: $3.95.

From C-H Tool & Die Corp.

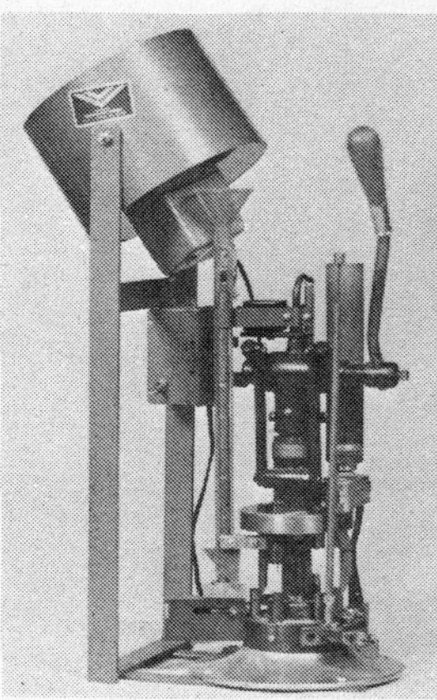

AUTOMATIC CASE FEEDER

The Chevron Case Master is designed to be used on Star, Phelps, C-H and other progressive pistol presses. It handles .38 Special, .357 Mag., .44 Spl., .44 Mag., .45 ACP, .45 AR and .45 Long Colt cases. The Case Master can also be set up for .38 Super, 9mm and other smaller cartridges if so desired and specified at the time of order. Electrically operated, the Case Master is designed to feed a large volume of cases to a number of progressive presses—it eliminates loading tubes entirely and simplifies (speeds up) the overall loading process.

Price: $159. (Shown nearby is a Case Master mounted on a Star press.)

From Chevron Case Master.

SHELL TRAY

Perfect for the shotshell reloader. Helps organize the bench. Each high-impact plastic carrier holds 50 shells in any gauge from 10 through 28.

Price: $1.98.

From Jasco (J. A. Somers Co.)

LOAD I.D. LABELS

These self-sticking labels are designed to be placed on a box of reloaded ammo; at a glance the shooter will be able to see the date the cartridges were loaded, the caliber, case, bullet, propellant, powder and other comments he entered on the label at the time of loading.

Price: $8 per roll of 500 labels.

From Milton Brynin.

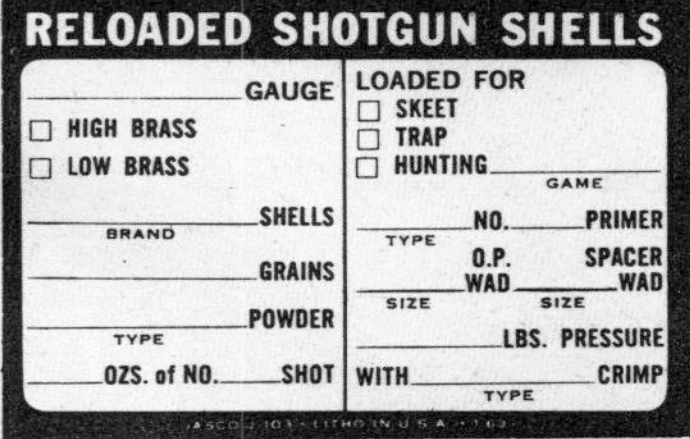

SHOTSHELL RELOADING LABELS

Identifies the purpose for which a particular load is to be used, i.e. for Skeet, trap or hunting. Also helps the reloader record the components used in the re-making of shotshells.

Price: 99¢ for 40 labels.

From Jasco (J. A. Somers Co.)

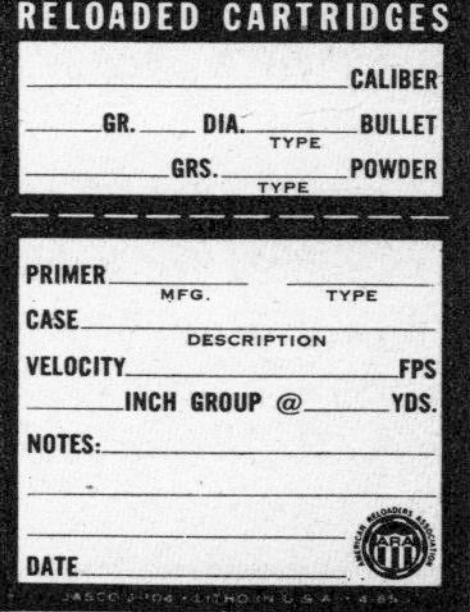

METALLIC CARTRIDGE RELOADING LABELS

Helps identify the load, date of loading and other vital information. Each label is gummed. Designed for metallic cartridges.

Price: $1.25 per pack of 27.

From Jasco (J. A. Somers Co.)

See the Directory for complete company addresses.

DURABLE AMMO BOX (PISTOL)

Perfect for the handloader. These sturdy nylon boxes come in two sizes. The #3 size holds 50 cartridges ranging in caliber from .30 Carbine through .357 Magnum. The #4 size holds 50 rounds ranging in caliber from .38-40 through .45 Long Colt.
Price: $1.50.
From Fitz.

PISTOL CARTRIDGE CARRIER

Box is made of indestructible material that does not warp, crack, chip or peel, expand or contract. Comes in green or brown and holds 50 rounds. Perfect for the handloader.
Prices are as follows:

50-9	9mm	$1.25
PS-3	.38 to .357 Mag.	$1.25
PL-4	45, .41, and .44 Mag.	$1.25

From MTM Molded Products Company.

DURABLE AMMO BOX (RIFLE)

Perfect for the handloader. Each box holds 20 centerfire cartridges ranging from .222 through .475 H & H. Specify the cartridge you intend to use when purchasing.
Price: $1.50.
From Fitz.

RIFLE AMMO CARRYING CASE

Holds a whopping 100 rounds. Perfect for the reloader who chases varmints or elusive M.O.A. groups. Comes with load information card. Snap closure and sturdy integral hinge guaranteed to hold up for one million openings and closings.
Price: $4.19.
From MTM Molded Products Company.

RIFLE CARTRIDGE CARRIER

Ideal for the reloader who turns out ammo in large quantities of one particular load. Load information card comes with each box. Box holds 50 rounds and does not warp, chip, peel, expand or contract. Integral hinge designed to last for over a million openings and closings. Comes in either brown or green.
Price as follows:

RS-50	.22 to .22 Mag.	$2.50
RS-S-50	.22 Hornet, PPC's, Rem. BR's, and 7.62 x 39	$2.50
RM-50	.22-250 to .308 Win.	$2.50
RL-50	.220 Swift to .458 Win.	$2.50

From MTM Molded Products Company.

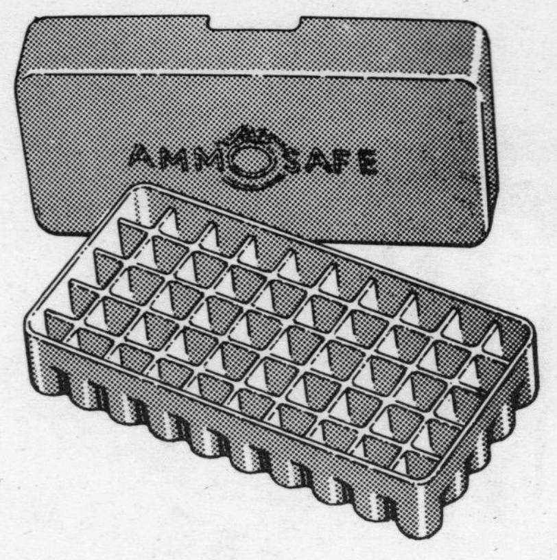

CASE LUBE KIT

Contains case lube and applicator tongs—no greasy fingers.
Price: $5.95.
From Redding Reloading Equipment.

RELOADING ACCESSORY KIT

Each RCBS Ammo-Crafter II Kit contains a burring tool, case lube kit, a 5-10 scale, a uniflow powder measure, powder funnel, an RCBS Reloading Guide and a Speer Reloading Manual—everything but the press and dies. By purchasing the entire kit, you will save the better part of a ten-dollar bill when compared to buying the items separately.
Price: $99.
From RCBS.

DECAPPER UNIT

Helps eliminate some of the muss and fuss. The shell holder head is reversible to take either the .222 family or .308 family (.243, 6mm, .22-250, .257, .25-06 and .30-06) size case heads. When set properly and locked with the Allen head set screw it is impossible to attempt decapping unless the decapping pin is in the flash hole.
Prices: See below (be sure to include postage as this is a direct sale item).

Jones de-capping tool complete for one caliber	$15.95
Extra decapping mandrels in .222, 6mm and .30 cals	3.50
Mandrels for other calibers on request (add)	1.00

From Neil A. Jones.

PLASTIC AMMO BOXES

Available for both rifle and pistol and come in high-visibility orange color. Good for storage of reloaded ammo or field use.
Price: Rifle (universal), .38 & .357, .44 & .45—all $1.10 per box.
From Hodgdon Powder Company.

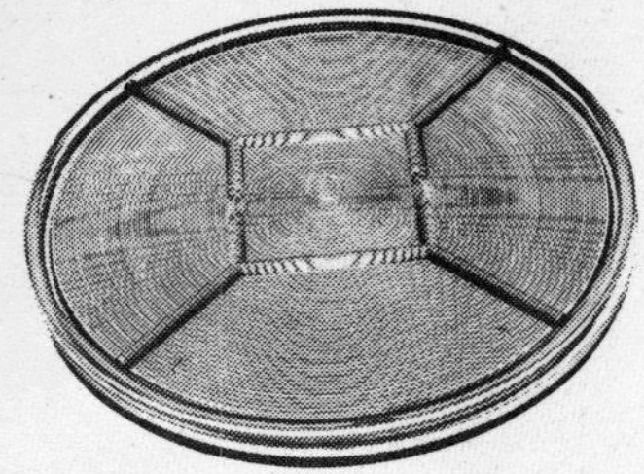

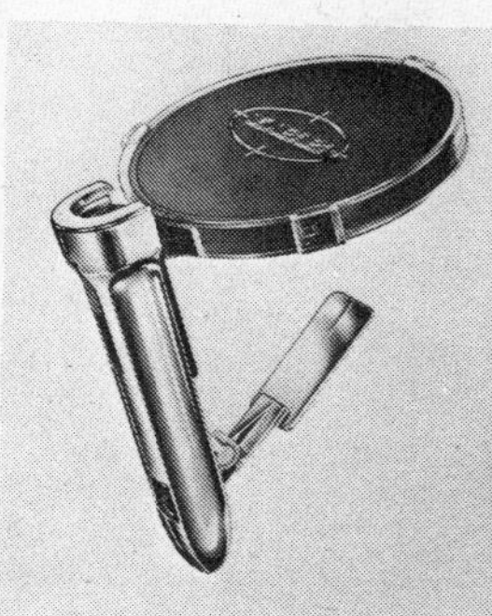

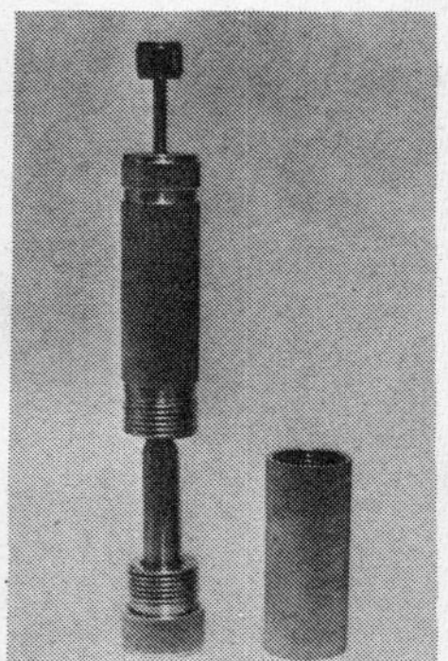

PRIMER TURNING TRAY

Dump in a box of primers and move the tray in a slight oscillating motion, and, all the primers will be oriented with the same side up.

Price: $1.75.

From Pacific Tool Company.

AUTOMATIC PRIMER

The Lee Auto Prime features a plastic tray that holds 100 primers which are gravity-fed into proper position by the user. Comes with both large and small primer trays and one shell holder. Eleven shell holder sizes take care of all popular calibers.

Price: $11.98; spare shell holder, $1.98.

From Lee Precision.

PRIMER SEATING TOOL

The Bonanza Primer Seater is made so that primers are seated in line with the primer pocket. Mechanical leverage allows primers to be seated without crushing. With the addition of one extra set of disc shell holders and one extra primer unit, you can prime rimmed or rimless cartridges from .222 up to .458 Win. Mag.

Price: $26.50; primer tube, $2.10.

From Bonanza Sports Mfg. Co.

PRIMER SEATER

Features removable shell holder, and a large and small primer ram. Shell holders available for all popular metallic cartridges.

Price: $4.98; $2.48 for shell holder of your choice.

From Lee Custom Engineering, Inc.

PRIMER SEATER

Allows the user to hand seat and "feel" the primer in to exact position. Features an integral shell holder.

Price: $3.98.

From Lee Custom Engineering, Inc.

PRIMING TOOL

The improved priming tool is hand operated, like the auto prime; however, you'll have to put 'em in one-at-a-time. Perfect for the benchrester or man who has a low volume of reloading.

Price: $4.98 with one shell holder; spare shell holders, $1.98.

From Lee Precision.

DECAPPER AND BASE

Perfect for removing crimped-in military primers. Guaranteed unbreakable. If it ever "lets go," return it to the factory for a free replacement. Available in .223 and .30 government.

Price: $2.48.

From Lee Precision.

BERDAN PRIMER DECAPPER

Called the "Power-Punch" this Berdan primer decapper uses a live primer to decap a dead one. When the Power-Punch is loaded and fired it literally drives the old primer right out of the case. The Power-Punch with anti-recoil sleeve is also ideal for removing crimped-in military primers.

Price: Single caliber, rifle or pistol $18.95; dual caliber (rifle/rifle or rifle/pistol), $23.95; single caliber with anti-recoil sleeve (magnum) $24.95.

From Efemes Enterprises.

See the Directory for complete company addresses.

LEAD POT

The Lee Lead Pot is made of drawn steel and has a 4-pound capacity. Designed for stove or hot-plate use.

Price: $1.98

From Lee Precision.

CASTING FURNACE

The Lee Bullet caster holds over 4-pounds of lead and maintains adequate heat for all bullet alloys. Has a 275-watt tubular heater. Comes with a 2-year guarantee.

Price: $17.98.

From Lee Precision.

CONTROLLED-HEAT CASTING FURNACE

The Lee Precision Melter has hand-adjustable heat control, holds 4 pounds of lead and comes with a 2-year guarantee. You can melt up a whole pot of alloy in 15 minutes with this model.

Price: $22.98.

From Lee Precision.

LEAD MELTING FURNACE

SAECO's Model 32 Melting Furnace has a pot capacity of 20 pounds of lead, and has a thermostat temperature range of 450°F. to 850°F. Ideal for heavy production work.

Price: $59.50 with ingot mold; $47.50 without thermostat.

From SAECO Reloading, Inc.

LEAD MELTING FURNACE

The SAECO Melting Furnace (Model 24) has a thermostat temperature range of 450°F. to 850°F. and a pot capacity of 11 pounds. Bottom-flow pour spout eliminates dipping. Each furnace is serial numbered and comes with a one-year guarantee.

Price: $74.50, complete with ingot mold.

From SAECO Reloading, Inc.

LEAD MELTING FURNACE

The Merit Melting Pot holds about 20 pounds of lead with an average heating time (from solid to melt) of about one-half hour. Features bottom pour spout. The Merit Melting Pot is designed to be used on a stove top or hotplate for its heat source.

Price: $52.50

From Merit Gunsight Co.

PRODUCTION LEAD MELTER

The Lee Production Pot holds a generous 10-pounds of alloy and features a draw spout at the front/bottom of the pot. It also has hand-adjustable heat control. Perfect for the man who has a lot of slugs to make up—ideal for gang-mold use. Comes with a 2-year guarantee.

Price: $38.98.

From Lee Precision.

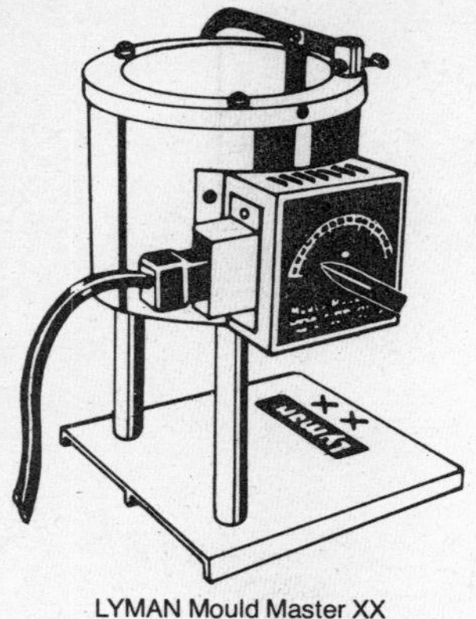

LYMAN Mould Master XX

LEAD MELTING FURNACE

Lyman's new, redesigned, Mould Master Furnace now has a steel crucible for greater strength. Features a side mount thermostat and 20-pound capacity.
Price: $89.95; $92.95 with mold-guide attachment.
From Lyman Products Company.

FLUXING COMPOUND

Marvelux is noncorrosive, nonfuming and greatly reduces dross formation when alloying lead for casting purposes. It also increases an alloy's fluidity, thereby assuring a well filled-out slug. Superior to beeswax and other common fluxes.
Price: $2.25 per ½-pound can; $4.25 per 1-pound can; $10 for a 4-pound can, and $16 for an 8-pound can.
From Marmel Products.

LEAD POT THERMOMETER

Constructed of stainless steel, this thermometer provides a read-out temperature range of 200° to 1000° F. Once you've determined what specific casting temperature works best, this thermometer helps you attain it accurately. Three-inch dial is easy to read and the 9-inch stem is long enough for any pot.
Price: $34.
From Marmel Products.

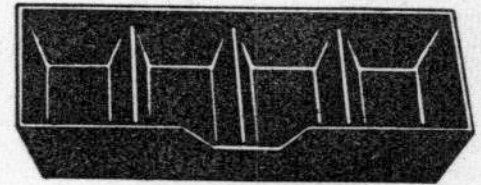

LYMAN Ingot Mould

INGOT MOLD

The Lyman ingot mold enables the bullet caster to store his desired alloy in handy ingot form. Made of cast iron.
Price: $5.
From Lyman Products Company.

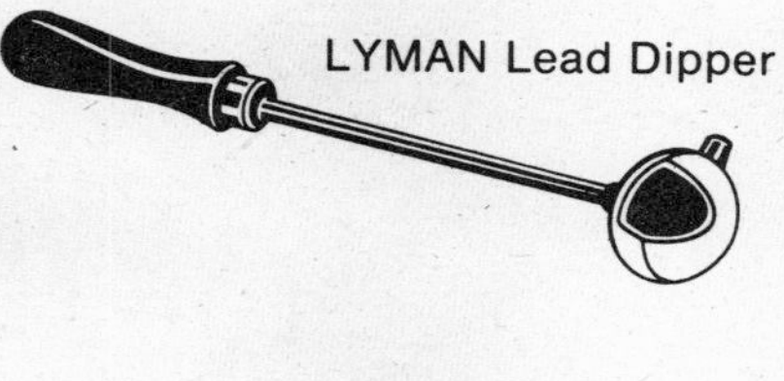

LYMAN Lead Dipper

LEAD DIPPER

The Lyman lead-dipper has a cast iron head, steel shaft and wooden handle. Shaped for easy pouring.
Price: $5.
From Lyman Products Company.

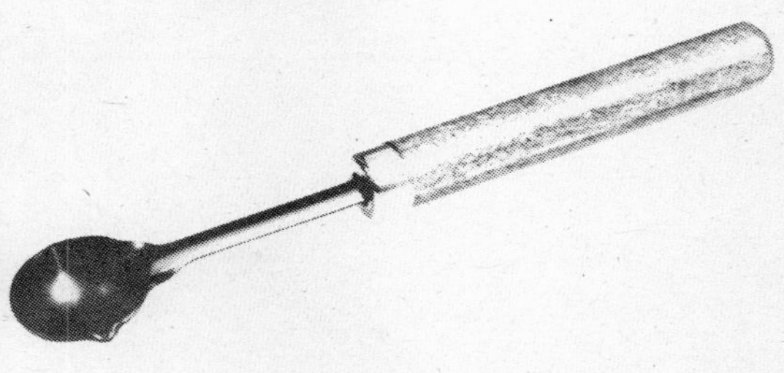

LEAD DIPPER

This is a good accessory for any lead casting operation. The Lee lead ladle has a sturdy hardwood handle and is well suited for either pouring lead or removing dross after fluxing.
Price: $1.98.
From Lee Precision.

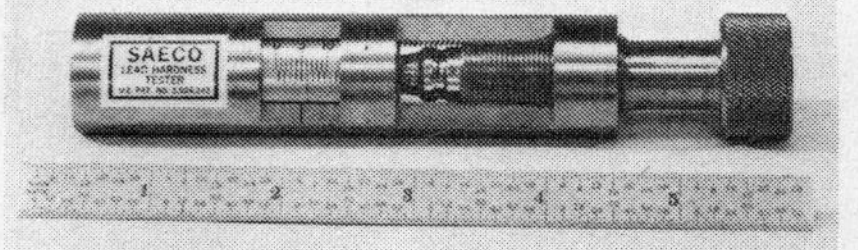

LEAD HARDNESS TESTER

The SAECO Lead Hardness Tester really fills a gap on the reloader's workbench. Permits the user to tell in a matter of seconds just how hard (or soft) his alloy is. Helps stop leading before it starts. Precision made.
Price: $44.50
From SAECO Reloading, Inc.

SINGLE CAVITY MOLD

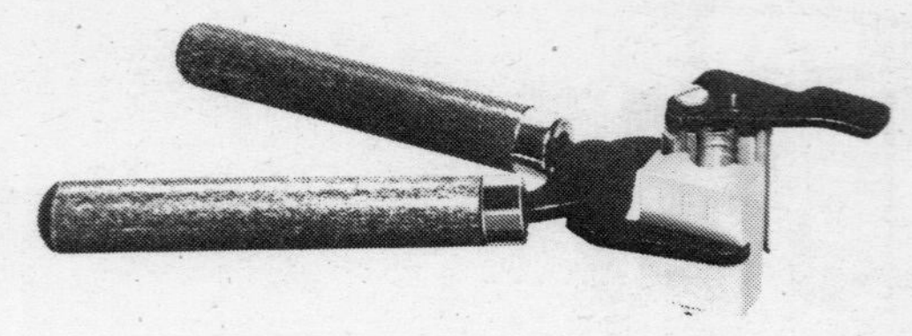

The Lee aluminum single cavity mold is available in a wide variety of bullet shapes, weights and calibers. Hollow point molds are available in the single cavity series.

Price: $11.98 with handles; $16.98 for hollowpoint.

From Lee Precision.

DOUBLE CAVITY MOLDS

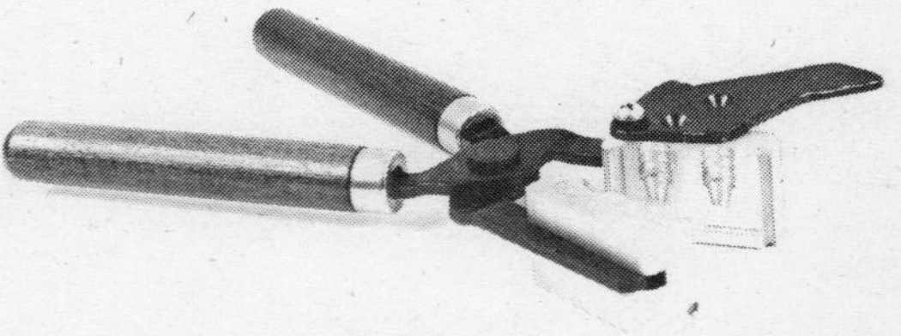

Lee's aluminum double cavity molds allow the caster to turn out more than 500 slugs an hour. Lee has a wide variety of bullet shapes, weights and calibers to choose from. Mold shown is the 140-grain SWC for .38 caliber handguns.

Price: $16.98 complete with handles. (Hollow point molds not available in double cavity.)

From Lee Precision.

BULLET MOULD

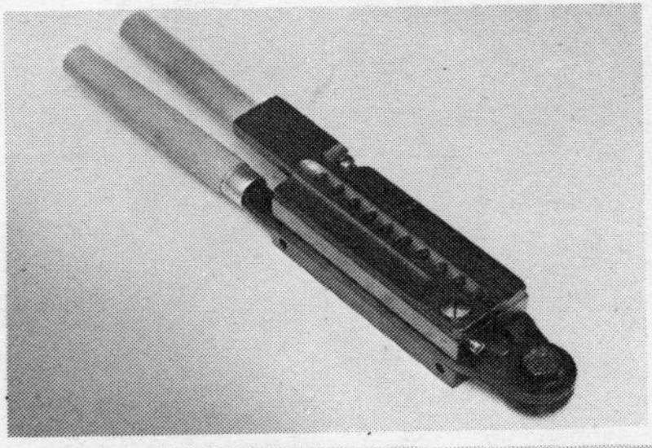

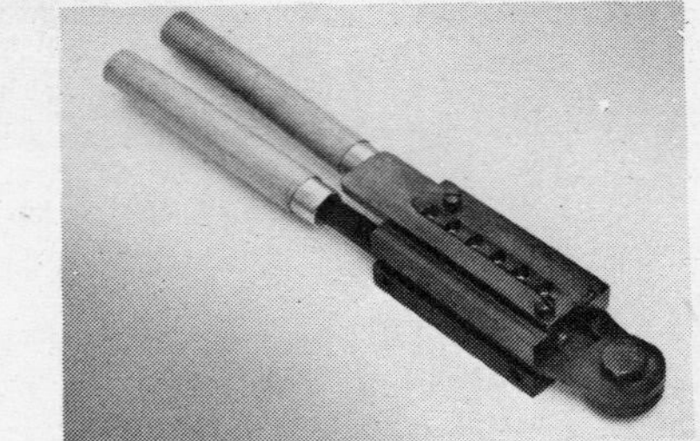

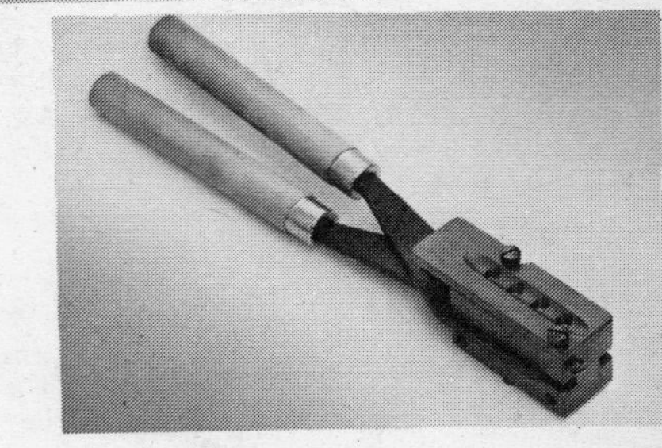

Hensley & Gibbs bullet moulds have gained much respect from handloaders over the years; and, from the outset we should advise that the demand for their product is such that there is a 6-month wait to get one. The Hensley & Gibbs moulds come in 4, 6 and 10-cavity styles and come in plain, bevel or gas check base shape. Before purchasing, be sure to specify what alloy you will use, what gun you will be shooting, sizing diameter and make of sizer. A fairly wide range of pistol calibers are available, however, the list of rifle calibers is limited. Pictured nearby from top to bottom are 10, 6 and 4 cavity molds.

Price: $69.50, 4-cavity; $104.50, 6-cavity; $174.50, 10-cavity. (When cut for larger than .38 cal. you get an 8-cavity mold). All prices include handles. Direct sales only.

From Hensley & Gibbs.

MATCH-PRECISION MOLD BLOCKS

SAECO's line of bullet mold blocks is well known among shooters who strive for accuracy. Available calibers and bullet shapes for both rifle and pistol are extensive—from 6mm up through .45-70.

Prices:		
Without Handles:	1 - Cavity mold	$24.50
	2 - Cavity mold	30.50
	3 - Cavity mold	37.50
	4 - Cavity mold	42.50
With Walnut Handles:	1 - Cavity mold	29.50
	2 - Cavity mold	35.50
	3 - Cavity mold	42.50
	4 - Cavity mold	47.50

From SAECO Reloading, Inc.

Prices shown are subject to change.

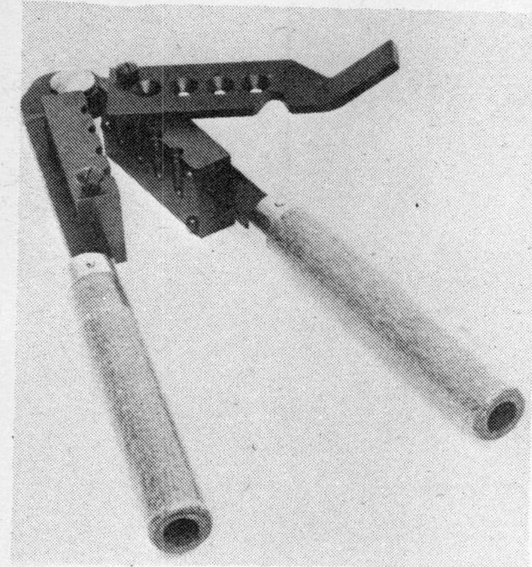

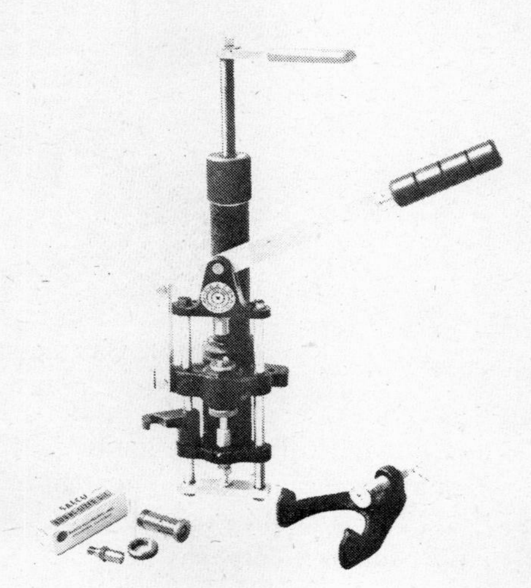

BULLET MOULDS

Lyman has one of the broadest selections of bullet moulds in the field of reloading. Pistol moulds are available in single, double and 4-cavity configuration. Rifle moulds are available in single or double cavity while shotgun slug moulds (12 or 20 gauge only) feature a single cavity. Calibers available range from .22 to .50. (Chart follows.) Four cavity mould shown nearby.

Price:

Pistol, single or double cavity (less handles)	$19.95
Pistol, 4-cavity (less handles)	42.95
Pistol, H.P., single cavity (less handles)	26.95
Rifle, single or double cavity (less handles)	19.95
Rifle, H.P., single cavity (less handles)	26.95
Shotgun Slug, 12 or 20 gauge, single cavity (less handles)	24.95
Handles, single or double cavity	7.00
Handles, 4-cavity	11.00

From Lyman Products Company.

CAST BULLET LUBRICATOR/SIZER

The SAECO Lubri-Sizer has been a standard with reloaders for years and is valued for its ability to turn out precisely-sized and lubed cast bullets. Uses solid stick lube. Also has a gas-check seating attachment.

.2240	.2800	.3120	.3240	.3575	.4275	.4500
.2265	.2870	.3130	.3260	.3580	.4285	.4515
.2440	.3080	.3140	.3380	.3760	.4290	.4520
.2575	.3090	.3160	.3490	.4010	.4300	.4540
.2660	.3100	.3190	.3540	.4100	.4310	.4575
.2680	.3105	.3210	.3555	.4265	.4320	.4580
.2780	.3110	.3230	.3565			

Price: $58.50; C-clamp, $8.50; sizing dies, $9; top punch, $4.

From SAECO Reloading, Inc.

CAST BULLET SIZER/LUBRICATOR

One setting of the pressure screw greases from 100 to 200 bullets. The bullets are forced through the lube/sizer, not down and back up, therefore, the Star has a reputation for being the fastest lubricator/sizer on the market. Comes complete with one die and bullet punch.

Price: $90; extra sizing die, $15; extra bullet punch, $7.50.

From Star Machine Works.

SIZER/PUNCH

Used for the hand resizing of bullets after they've been lubed. Shape and design permits resizing without lead shaving. Available in a broad range of bullet diameters.

Price: $4.98.

From Lee Precision.

BULLET SIZER/LUBRICATOR

The Lyman 450 Sizer/Lubricator is designed to precision size and lube cast rifle and pistol bullets. To change bullet diameters, you simply change an inexpensive die set. Die sets are available in all popular calibers.

Price: $49.50 less dies; $60.95 with one die and top punch.

From Lyman Products Company

AUTO FEED FOR LYMAN AND RCBS BULLET SIZERS

The Sugar Creek automatic bullet feeder keeps a continual flow of .38, .44 or .45 caliber slugs moving into the Lyman or RCBS sizer. The unit not only feeds, it ejects the completed bullet as well. With this unit one person can size and lube over 1,000 bullets an hour.

Price: $69.50

From Sugar Creek Gun Company.

LUBE CUTTER

The Lee lube cutter is made of aluminum and neatly wedges the lubricant away from the bullets. Designed for economical hand use. Available in a broad range of bullet diameters.

Price: $2.48.

From Lee Precision.

LUBING AND SIZING KIT

This handy Lee kit is the economical way to go when it comes to lubing and sizing rifle or pistol bullets. Contains lube pan, Hodgdon lube, lube cutter and sizer. Comes in a broad variety of bullet diameters.

Price: $8.98.

From Lee Precision.

BULLET LUBE

Micro-Lube comes in either solid or hollow cylindrical sticks. Helps prevent barrel leading, is heat and cold resistant, comes in two grades, regular and super-refined X-500.

Price: Regular $1; X-500, $1.50.

From Micro Ammunition.

BULLET LUBE

Marvelube is designed for the cast bullet shooter who's out to eliminate leading problems. Comes in hollow or solid sticks.

Price: $7 per 4 sticks.

From Marmel Products.

BULLET LUBE

Consists of pure beeswax and Alox—prevents barrel leading. Comes in hollow sticks only.

Price: $1.95

From Hodgdon Powder Company.

LYMAN Gas Checks

GAS CHECKS

Lyman's gas checks come in all popular calibers for both rifle and handgun. Prevents leading. They come 1,000 to a box and are made of the best gilding metal.

Price: $10; $12 for .45 caliber checks.

From Lyman Products Company.

BULLET LUBE

Tamarack bullet lube contains 50% Alox 2138-F and 50% commercial A-1 beeswax. Formulation identical to NRA's. For either rifle or pistol. Comes in flip-top plastic tube; available in either hollow or solid stick.

Price: $1.50

From Tamarack Products, Inc.

BULLET LUBE

Mirror-Lube eliminates bullet leading, and its lubricating qualities are not affected by weather conditions. Works equally well with rifle or pistol bullets and may be stored indefinitely without separation of ingredients. Available in solid or hollow sticks.

Price: $1.25

From Mirror-Lube.

BULLET LUBE

Cooper-Woodward's perfect bullet lube withstands heat, cold and prevents leading in hot loads. Comes in either solid or hollow sticks.

Price: $1 per stick.

From Cooper-Woodward.

MATCH SWAGING DIE/PRESS SET

Corbin's Hi-Power rifle match special bullet making set up is for the long range rifleman who wants complete control over his bullets. The following system comes complete for making rebated boattail bullets of high ballistic coefficient in 7mm, .270, .308 or .309 and 8mm. Includes enough supplies to make 2,000 bullets. Comes with four presses individually built for each of the dies plus lead wire, jackets, micrometer core cutter, lube and full instructions.

Price: $1,200. (Orders taken with deposit on waiting list.)

From Corbin Manufacturing & Supply, Inc.

BULLET SWAGING PRESS

The Corbin Mity Mite swaging press is designed for bullet swaging only. It's a horizontal ram press with half the stroke and twice the power of the largest reloading press. Dies are available for virtually every small arms caliber.

Price: From $183.50 up to about $390, depending on style of bullet to be swaged.

From Corbin Manufacturing & Supply Inc.

BULLET JACKET INDICATOR

The unit is motorized and serves to check out projectile uniformity in the area of wall thickness prior to the bullet being made.

Price: $115 with arbor for one caliber without the dial indicator; indicator sells for $35.50; arbors are available in .22, 6mm and .30 caliber at $5 each.

From J. H. Eaton.

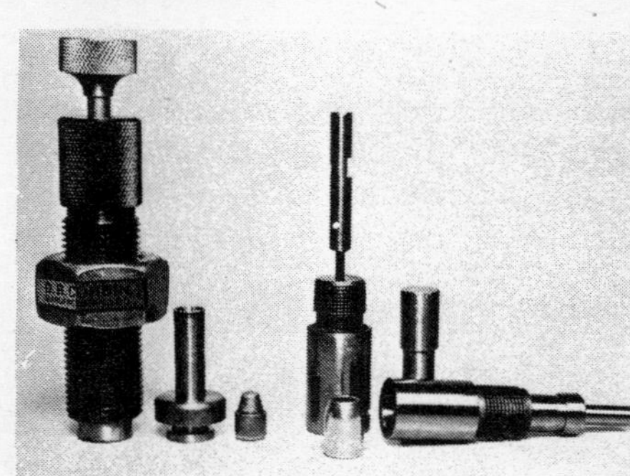

BULLET SWAGING DIES

Corbin's Swaging Dies allow the handloader to make up his own lead or jacketed bullets quickly and economically. Shown nearby is a set of Corbin handgun dies. The die set on the left features standard ⅞x14 threads and can be used on any modern reloading press; the die set on the right is specifically designed for the Mity Mite press. Available in all calibers for rifle or handgun.

Price:

Reloading Press Dies		Mity Mite Dies	
Rifle	$69	Rifle	$149.50
Handgun	39	Handgun	39 and up

From Corbin Manufacturing & Supply, Inc.

BULLET SWAGING DIES (RIFLE)

Made of the best quality of steel for longest possible life. Designed to be used exclusively with the RCBS Rockchucker press.

Price: For Rockchucker press ejection frame, one body die, with all dies and punches for one caliber, your choice of .22 or 6mm, $460.

From Pindell's Precision Tooling.

HALF-JACKET SWAGING DIE

Available in .308, .355, .357, .429 and .451 diameters. Comes with standard ⅞x14 threads for mounting on any C-H or other popular reloading press. One die forms and swages the lead bullet and bleeds off the excess. One tap on the ejector ejects the finished half-jacket slug.

Price: $14.95; nose punch (specify caliber), $4.50.

From C-H Tool and Die Corp.

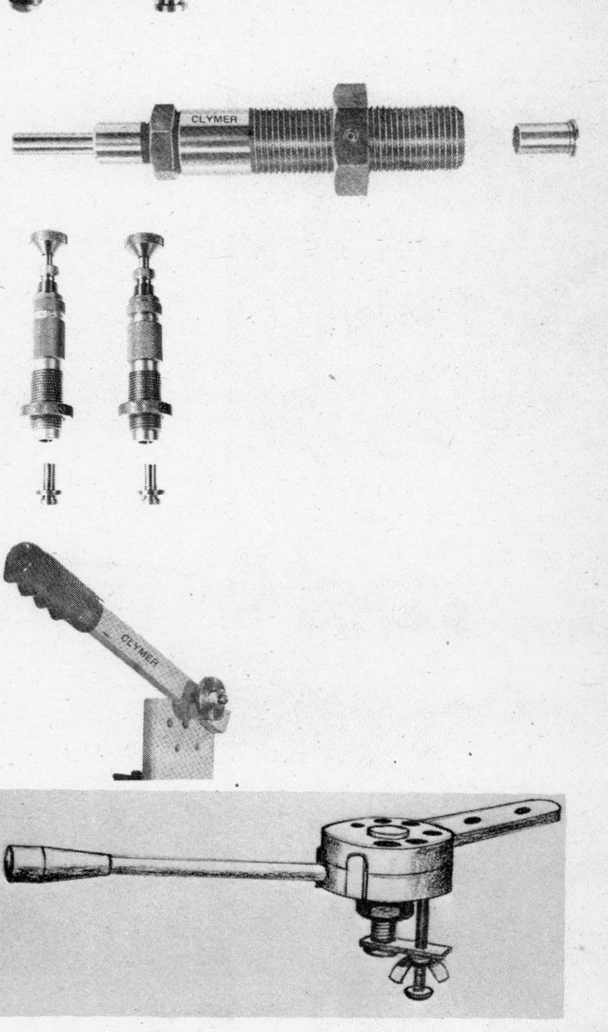

SWAGING DIE

Available for .30, .38, .44 and .45 calibers. Fits your own sizing press.

Price: $39.50.

From Clymer Manufacturing Co.

PISTOL BULLET SWAGING DIES

Available for making either jacketed hollow point or jacketed soft point bullets. Comes in .38-.357, .41 S&W, .44 Mag or .45 ACP. Handles any bullet weight from 110 to 250 grains, and comes with standard ⅞x14 threads.

Price: $29.95 (solid nose), $30.45 (hollow point). Comes complete, no extras to buy.

From C-H Tool and Die Corp.

LEAD CORE CUTTER

Capable of cutting lead wire in most popular calibers to desired length for your own swaging activities.

Price: $25

From Clymer Manufacturing Co.

LEAD WIRE CORE CUTTER

This unit was designed to cut cores for bullet swaging. It features six apertures which have been carefully reamed to close tolerances to accept wire normally used in swaging bullets. All cutting faces have been machined. Each aperture is fully adjustable as to weight of core.

Price: About $22.

From Lester Coats.

CORE MOLD

No need to cut wire for swaging purposes, you can cast the core you want. The Corbin Core Mold is available in single- or 4-cavity configuration, in all popular calibers.

Price: $29.50, 1-cavity; $39.50, 4-cavity.

From Corbin Manufacturing & Supply, Inc.

Prices shown are subject to change.

CORE CUTTER

Used to trim lead core wire to proper length for swaging. Handles all lead wire up to ⅜". Simply adjust to correct core weight and lock in place. Shearing action is quick and uniform.
Price: $16.95.
From C-H Tool and Die Corp.

SWAGING LUBE

Formulated especially for the swaging process.
Price: $1.50 per 2-ounce jar; $3.98 per pint.
From Corbin Manufacturing & Supply, Inc.

BULLET ALIGNMENT GAUGE

Accurately measures the concentricity of completed cartridges. Designed to be used with the Plum City Case Neck Gauge indicator.
Price: $37.50 with indicator; $24 without.
From Plum City Ballistics Range.

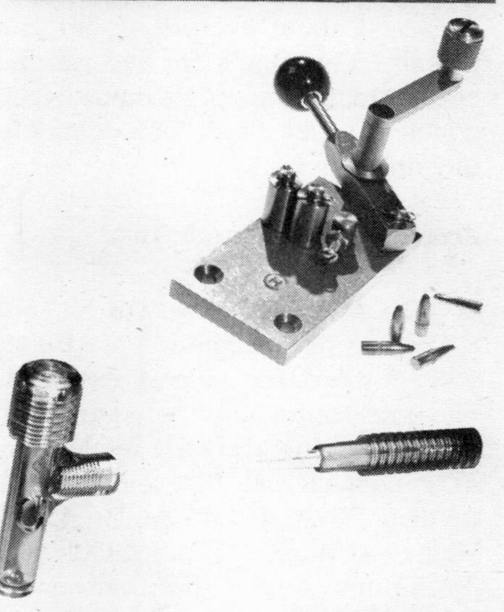

CANNELURE TOOL

Rolls grooves into bullets prior to crimping operation. Also rolls in a case cannelure on straight walled cases. Perfect for heavy magnum loads as the cannelure keeps the slug from setting back in the case. Fully adjustable, precision made.
Price: $21.95.
From C-H Tool and Die Corp.

BULLET PULLER

The Magnum Model kinetic bullet puller is designed so that the extracted slug, powder and case can be removed from the tool (and reused) without having to remove the cap. (Not for rimfire cartridges.)
Price: $12.95, postpaid.
From Quinetics Corp.

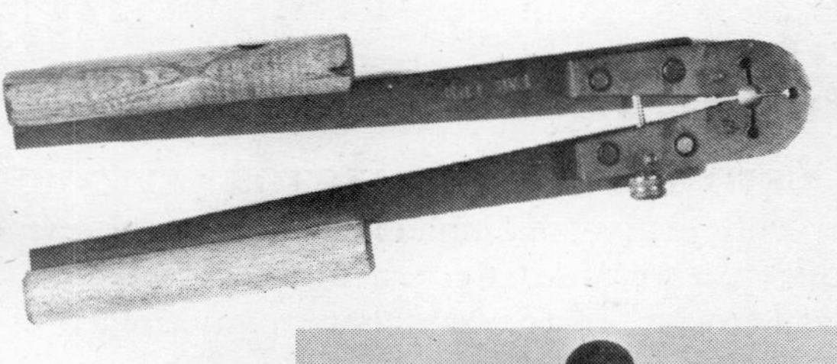

BULLET PULLER

The Lac-Cum Bullet Puller aids in tearing down old ammo or loads that may be dangerous or unwanted by the handloader.
Price: $8.49
From Pepplers Small Arms.

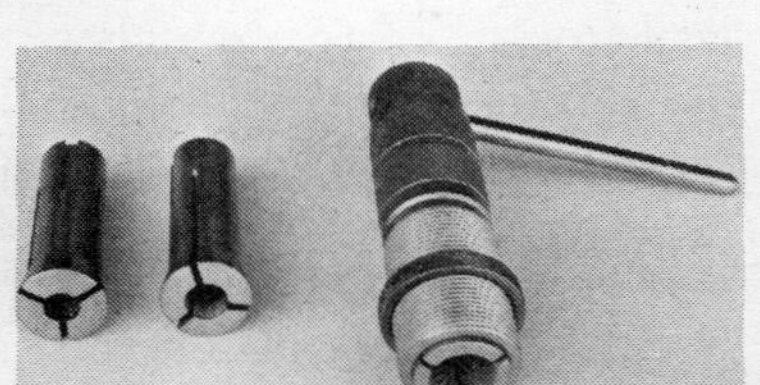

BULLET PULLER

Comes with one collet 7/8x14 thread. Extra collets in .22 through .375.
Price: Puller and one collet $12; extra collet $5.
From Whitney Sales.

See the Directory for complete company addresses.

SHOTSHELL FLUROSCOPE

The Beco Shell-Scope allows the shooter/handloader to internally inspect a shotshell for proper powder/wad/shot position. Called the Shell-Scope, this handy unit might help stop an accident before it happens.

Price: $27.50 complete; $37.50 with walnut cabinet. (Both units run off normal house current.)

From Ballistics Engineering Company.

PORTABLE/UNIVERSAL RELOADING STAND

This stand consists of an iron upright post and four folding steel legs. Allows the handloader to work in a limited-space situation. Finished in textured black enamel.

Price: $74.95

From Republic Mfg. Co.

PSI CALCULATOR

Slide rule type instrument enables you to quickly determine the maximum pressures in centerfire rifles. (To be used in conjunction with the Powley Computer for handloaders.)

Price: $4.

From Hutton Rifle Ranch.

HANDLOADING COMPUTER

Slide chart gives the user the most efficient powder selection possible. Works with any combination of modern centerfire cartridge components to find the best charge, and closest velocity estimate. Comes with complete instruction manual.

Price: $5.50 or $9 complete with PSI calculator.

From Hutton Rifle Ranch.

CHRONOGRAPH

The Telepacific TPB-03-E chronograph features direct readout (digital) and rechargeable Ni-Cad batteries. Helps the reloader accurately determine the velocity of any particular loading.

Price: $355 including electroscreens (they work on ambient light); $295 for the chronograph alone.

From Telepacific Electronics.

CHRONOGRAPH

Oehler's Model 33 "Chronotach" operates with the new Skyscreen II detectors. It instantly displays projectile velocity in FPS, or, time in microseconds. The 33 automatically resets itself in .6 seconds after the shot is fired, but the velocity and readout figures stay displayed till the next shot is fired. It's powered by 6 standard "D" flashlight batteries.

Price: Complete with Skyscreen II system and batteries $299.95.

From Oehler Research, Inc.

CHRONOGRAPH

This unit (the Model 42 Chronotach) could be described as Oehler's "Cadillac" of chronographs for the handloader. Provides velocity, pressure readings along with push-button statistical summary and enter/forget features. At the risk of being flippant, the Model 42 does just about everything but give change and spit nickels. This one's for the advanced handloader or custom loading shop. (Would suggest a potential buyer contact Oehler direct for a complete summary of what this unit can do.)

Price: $2,800.

From Oehler Research, Inc.

AUTO CASE FEEDER FOR STAR RELOADERS

The Hulme Automatic Case Feeder has been specifically designed for the progressive Star reloading press. The unit itself is gravity fed and easily attaches to the Star press. The Mark III feeder handles .38 ACP, .45 ACP, .45 AR, .38 Spl. and .44 Spl. The Mark III-A handles .38 ACP, .45 ACP, .45 AR, .357 Mag., .41 Mag, .44 Mag., .45 Long Colt and .30-M1 carbine. (Both units come with 3 transparent magazines.)

Price: $102.75 for the Mark III; $104.75 for the Mark III-A.

From Hulme Firearm Service.

CUSTOM BULLET TRAJECTORY SERVICE

You receive a complete computer rundown on your particular loading trajectory. Computer run trajectories, custom matched to any firearm, with any bullet (including roundball at any muzzle velocity) can be provided. Any combination of wind, altitude and angle of fire may be specified by the shooter.

Price: Minimum charge $9 per bullet. Write direct for full description of service.

From John Tovey Exterior Ballistics.

Prices shown are subject to change.

Section 19

Gun Book Publishers

Below are listed the principal gun book publishers in the United States, Canada, and England, along with their areas of specialization (if any). In addition to the larger, better-known houses, we also listed a number of individuals who've published their own gun books and are handling their own distribution.

Many gun shops do handle the more popular gun books, and quite a few bookstores will have a section devoted to gun or sports books. In addition, several gun book specialists carry exceptional stocks of current (and sometimes out-of-print) gun books. Their addresses appear at the bottom end of this section; their catalogs or listings are highly recommended.

American Ordnance Publications
1020 Central Ave.
Charlotte, NC 28204
Books on High Standard pistols.

Arms & Armour Press
2-6 Hampstead High St.
London NW 31 PR, England
Collector arms & militaria books.

Barlow Book Co.
942 Raleigh
Mundelein, IL 60060
Reproductions of early U.S. gun catalogs.

Bianchi Holsters/Leather Products
100 Calle Cortez
Temecula, CA 92390
Books on holsters.

Borden Publishing Co.
1855 W. Main St.
Alhambra, CA 91801
Collector oriented books.

Beinfeld Publishing, Inc.
13222 Saticoy St.
North Hollywood, CA 91605
Collector oriented books.

Brownell's, Inc.
Rte. 2, Box 1
Montezuma, IA 50171
Collector, engraving, gunsmithing books.

Collector Books
Box 3009
Paducah, KY 42001
Collector oriented books.

Sam Costanzo
5838 Mayfield Rd.
Mayfield Heights, OH 44124
Books on Luger pistols.

DBI Books
540 Frontage Rd.
Northfield, IL 60093
Books on all phases of guns, hunting.

Delta Press
Box 5093
Shreveport, LA 71105
Survival oriented books.

Dixie Gun Works
Gunpowder Lane
Union City, TN 38261
Books on antique arms, black powder shooting.

Empire Press
Box 2902
Santa Fe, N.M. 87501
Reprints of old catalogs.

Follett Publishing Co.
1010 W. Washington St.
Chicago, IL 60607
Books on all phases of guns, hunting.

Fortress Publications, Inc.
P.O. Box 241
Stoney Creek, Ontario L8G 3X9, Canada
Collectors arms and militaria books.

Gun Hill Publishing Co.
Box 187C
Yazoo City, MS 39194
Powder horn book.

Handgun Press
5832 S. Green St.
Chicago, IL 60621
Books on Luger, Mauser pistols, Bergmann

Fred L. Honeycutt, Jr.
5282 Ridan Way
Lake Park, FL 33410
Books on Japanese long arms.

Jackson Arms
6209 Hillcrest Ave.
Dallas, TX 75205
Books on antique Colts.

Jolex Books (John Olson Co.)
294 West Oakland Ave.
Oakland, NJ 07436
Collecting, militaria, shooting books.

William H. Jordan
Box 4072
Shreveport, LA 71106
Books on combat shooting.

John A. Kopec
P.O. Box 218
La Puenta, CA 91747
Single action Colt book.

H. Lueders
7013 Schley
Houston, TX 77087
Books on Ruger arms.

Lyman Products for Shooters
Route 147,
Middlefield, CT 06455
Reloading, black powder shooting books.

Gerald Marcello
8421 Beaver Lake Drive
San Diego, CA 92119
Books on .30-06 cartridge history.

Doug Murray
20 Polo Lane
Westbury, LI, NY 11590
Savage 99 book.

Museum Restoration Service
Bloomfield, Ont K0K 1G0, Canada
Booklets on collector guns.

National Rifle Association
1600 Pennsylvania Ave. NW
Washington, DC 20036
Books on various phases of guns, shooting.

Paladin Press
P.O. Box 1307
Boulder, CO 80302
Military reprints, survival, tactics books.

James Rankin
3615 Anderson Road
Coral Gables, FL 33134
Books on Walther PP, PPK.

Rutgers Book Center
127 Raritan Ave.
Highland Park, NJ 08904
Collector and hunter oriented books.

Stackpole Books
Cameron and Kelker Sts.
Harrisburg, PA 17105
Books on all phases of guns, shooting.

Stoeger Publishing Co.
55 Ruta Court
South Hackensack, NJ
Books on shooting, guns in general.

TBN Enterprises
P.O. Box 55
Alexandria, VA 22313
Books on military small arms.

Charles C. Thomas
301-327 East Lawrence Ave.
Springfield, IL
Gun reference books, criminologist oriented.

Ucross Books
Box 764
Los Alamos, NM 87544
Books on Walther P. 38.

Don Wilkerson
14160 Garrett Ave.
Apple Valley MN 55124
Post-war Colt SAA book.

Winchester Press
1421 South Sheridan Rd.
P.O. Box 1260
Tulsa, OK 74101
Books on hunting, shooting and collecting.

The following are specialists in gun books, maintaining very complete selections of almost all current gun books in print—including many published in other countries. Contact any of them regarding your specific needs in both current and out-of-print gun books.

Fairfield Book Co.
Box 289
Brookfield Center, CT 06805
Catalog, $2.00 (refundable)

Ray Riling Arms Book Co.
6844 Gorsten St.
Box 18925
Philadelphia, PA 19119
1 year mailings, $1.00

Rutgers Book Center
127 Raritan Ave.
Highland Park, N.J. 08904
Catalog, 50¢

PERIODICAL PUBLICATIONS

Air Gun (M)
The American Air Gun Assn. Inc., P.O. Box 226, Depew, NY 14043.

Airgun World
10 Sheet St., Windsor, Berks., SL4 1BG, England. $17 for 12 issues. Monthly magazine catering exclusively to the airgun enthusiast.

Alaska Magazine
Alaska Northwest Pub. Co., Box 4-EEE, Anchorage, AK 99509. $15.00 yr. Hunting and fishing articles.

The American Blade*
Beinfeld Publishing, Inc., 12767 Saticoy St., No. Hollywood, CA 91605. $9.00 yr. Add $6 f. foreign subscription. A magazine for all enthusiasts of the edged blade.

American Field†
222 W. Adams St., Chicago, IL. 60606. $12.00 yr. Field dogs and trials, occasional gun and hunting articles.

American Firearms Industry
Nat'l. Assn. of Federally Licensed Firearms Dealers, 7001 No. Clark St., Chicago, IL 60626. $10 yr. For firearms dealers & distributors.

The American Handgunner
591 Camino de la Reina, San Diego, CA 92108. $9.95 yr. Articles for handgun enthusiasts, collectors and hunters.

The American Hunter (M)
Natl. Rifle Assn., 1600 Rhode Island Ave. N.W., Washington, DC 20036. $15.00 yr. Wide scope of hunting articles.

The American Rifleman (M)
National Rifle Assn., 1600 Rhode Island Ave., N.W., Wash., DC 20036. $15.00 yr. Firearms articles of all kinds.

The American Shotgunner
P.O. Box 3351, Reno, NV 89505. $12.00 yr. Shotgun articles of all kinds.

The American West*
Amer. West Publ. Co., 20380 Town Center Lane, Suite 160, Cupertino, CA 95014. $15.00 yr.

Arms Gazette
Beinfeld Publ., Inc., 12767 Saticoy St., No. Hollywood, CA 91605. $15.00 yr.; add $5 foreign subscr. Excellent brief articles for the collector of antique and modern firearms.

Australian Shooters' Journal
P. O. Box 154, Punchbowl 2196, New Southwales, Australia. $15.00 yr. locally; $20.00 yr. overseas. Hunting and shooting articles.

Black Powder Times
P.O. Box 842, Mount Vernon, WA 98273. $8.00 for 12 issues.

Canada GunSport
P.O. Box 201, Willowdale, Ont., Canada M2N 2S9. $9.95 yr. Articles on guns, hunting, shooting, plus gun ads of all kinds.

Canadian Journal of Arms Collecting (Q)
Museums Restoration Service P.O. Drawer 390, Bloomfield, Ont., Canada KOK IGO. $5.00 yr.

Deer Unlimited*
P.O. Box 509, Clemson, SC 29631. $12.00 yr.

Deutsches Waffen Journal
Journal-Verlag Schwend GmbH, Postfach 100340, D7170 Schwabisch Hall, Germany. DM48.00 yr. plus DM10.80 postage. Antique and modern arms. German text.

Ducks Unlimited, Inc. (M)
P.O. Box 66300, Chicago, IL 60666.

Enforcement Journal (Q)
Natl. Police Officers Assn., 239 S. Fifth St., Suite 602, Louisville, KY 40202 $6.00 yr.

The Field†
The Harmsworth Press Ltd., 8 Stratton St., London W.I., England. $40.80 yr. Hunting and shooting articles, and all country sports.

Field & Stream
CBS Publications, 1515 Broadway, New York, N.Y. 10036. $9.94 yr. Articles on firearms plus hunting and fishing.

Fur-Fish-Game
A. R. Harding Pub. Co., 2878 E. Main St., Columbus, OH 43209. $6.00 yr. "Gun Rack" column by Maurice H. Decker.

Gray's Sporting Journal*
Gray's Sporting Journal Co., 1330 Beacon St., Brookline, MA 02146 $19.50 f. 7 Issues. Hunting and fishing journals.

The Gun Report
World Wide Gun Report, Inc., Box 111, Aledo, IL 61231. $12.00 yr. For the gun collector.

Gun Week
Amos Press, Inc., P.O. Box 150, Sidney, OH 45367. $12.00 yr. U.S. and possessions; $16.00 yr. other countries. Tabloid paper on guns, hunting, shooting.

Gun World
Gallant Publishing Co., 34249 Camino Capistrano, Capistrano Beach, CA 92624. $8.00 yr. For the hunting, reloading and shooting enthusiast.

Guns & Ammo
Petersen Pub. Co., 8490 Sunset Blvd., Los Angeles, CA 90069. $10.95 yr. Guns, shooting, and technical articles.

Guns
Guns Magazine, 591 Camino de la Reina, San Diego, CA 92108. $11.95 yr. Articles for gun collectors, hunters and shooters.

Guns Review
Ravenhill Pub. Co. Ltd., Standard House, Bonhill St., London E.C. 2A 4DA, England. $15.00 USA & Canada yr. For collectors and shooters.

Handloader*
Wolfe Pub. Co. Inc., Box 3030, Prescott, AZ 86302 $10.00 yr. The journal of ammunition reloading.

International Shooting Sport*
Union Internationale de Tir, 62 Wiesbaden, Webergasse 7, Germany. (Deutsche Mark) DM24.00 yr., p.p. For the International target shooter.

The Journal of the Arms & Armour Society (M)
F. Wilkinson (Secy.), 40 Great James St., Holborn, London WC1, N 3HB, England. $4.00 yr. Articles for the collector.

Journal of the Historical Breechloading Smallarms Assn.
Publ. annually, Imperial War Museum, Lambeth Road, London SE1 6HZ, England. $8 yr. Articles for the collector plus mailings of lecture transcripts, short articles on specific arms, reprints, etc.

Knife World
Knife World Publications, P.O. Box 3395, Knoxville, TN 37917. $7.00 yr. The monthly publication f. knife enthusiasts and collectors.

Law and Order
Law and Order Magazine, 37 W. 38th St., New York, NY 10018. $9.00 yr. Articles on weapons for law enforcement, etc.

Man At Arms*
222 West Exchange St., Providence, RI 02903. $15.00 yr. The magazine of arms collecting-investing.

Muzzle Blasts (M)
National Muzzle Loading Rifle Assn. P.O. Box 67, Friendship, IN 47021. $10.00 yr. For the black powder shooter.

The Muzzleloader Magazine*
Rebel Publishing Co., Inc., Route 5, Box 347-M, Texarkana, TX 75503. $7.50 yr. The publication for black powder shooters.

National Defense (M)*
American Defense Preparedness Assn., 740—15th St., N.W., Wash., DC 20005. $15.00 yr. Articles on military-related topics, including weapons, materials, technology, management and policy.

National Rifle Assn. Journal (British)
Natl. Rifle Assn. (BR.), Bisley Camp, Brookwood, Woking, Surrey, England. GU24 OPB.

National Wildlife*
Natl. Wildlife Fed., 1412 16th St. N.W., Washington, DC 20036. $8.50 yr. (6 issues); *International Wildlife*, 6 issues, $8.50 yr. Both, $12.50 yr., plus membership benefits.

New Zealand Wildlife (Q)
New Zealand Deerstalkers Assoc. Inc., P.O. Box 6514, Wellington, N.Z. $3.00 U.S. and Canada, elsewhere on application. Hunting and shooting articles.

Point Blank
Citizens Committee for the Right to Keep and Bear Arms (sent to contributors) 1601 114th S.E., Suite 151, Bellevue, WA 98004

The Police Marksman (Q)
217 S. Hull St., Montgomery, AL 36140. $15.00 yr.

Police Times (M)
1100 N.E. 125th St., No. Miami, Fla. 33161.

Precision Shooting
Precision Shooting, Inc., Box 6, Athens, PA 18810. $6.00 yr. Journal of the International Benchrest Shooters and target shooting in general.

Rifle*
Wolfe Publishing Co. Inc., Box 3030, Prescott, AZ 86302. $10.00 yr. Journal of the NBRSA. The magazine for shooters.

Second Amendment Reporter
Second Amendment Fdn., Bellefield Off. Pk., 1601—114th St. SE, Suite 157, Bellevue, WA 98004. $15.00 yr. (non-contributors).

The Shooting Industry
Publisher's Dev. Corp., 591 Camino de la Reina, San Diego, CA 92108. $25.00 yr. To the trade $12.50.

Shooting Magazine
10 Sheet St., Windsor, Berksh., SL4 1BG England. $16.50 for 12 issues. Monthly journal catering exclusively to claypigeon shooters.

The Shooting Times & Country Magazine (England) †
10 Sheet St., Windsor, Berkshire SL4 1BG, England. $42.60 yr. (52 issues). Game shooting, wild fowling, hunting, game fishing and firearms articles.

Shooting Times
PJS Publications, News Plaza, P.O. Box 1790, Peoria, IL 61656. $11.95 yr. Guns, shooting, reloading; articles on every gun activity.

The Shotgun News‡
Snell Publishing Co., Box 669, Hastings, NB 68901. $7.50 yr. Sample copy $2.00. Gun ads of all kinds.

Shotgun West
2052 Broadway, Santa Monica, CA 90404. $8.50 yr. Trap, Skeet and international shooting, scores, articles, schedules.

The Skeet Shooting Review
National Skeet Shooting Assn., P.O. Box 28188, San Antonio, TX 78228. $12.00 yr. (Assn. membership of $15.00 includes mag.) Scores, averages, skeet and hunting articles.

Sporting Goods Business
Gralla Publications, 1515 Broadway, New York, NY 10036. Trade journal.

The Sporting Goods Dealer
1212 No. Lindbergh Blvd., St. Louis, Mo. 63166. $6.00 yr. The sporting goods trade journal.

Sporting Gun
Bretton Court, Bretton, Peterborough PE3 8DZ, England. $13.50 yr. For the game and clay enthusiasts.

Trap & Field
1100 Waterway Blvd., Indianapolis, IN 46202. $12.00 yr. Official publ. Amateur Trapshooting Assn. Scores, averages, trapshooting articles.

The U.S. Handgunner (M)
U.S. Revolver Assn., 59 Alvin St., Springfield, MA 01104. $5.00 yr. General handgun and competition articles.

* Published bi-monthly † Published weekly ‡ Published twice per month. All others are published monthly.
M Membership requirements; write for details. Q Published Quarterly.

Section 20

Directory of Suppliers

A

A.C./D.C. ELECTRONICS
5912 Main; Morton Grove, IL 60053

A & A SHEET METAL
P.O. Box 2052; Michigan City, IN 46360; 219-872-7957

A & K MFG. CO., INC.
1651 N. Nancy Rose Ave.; Tucson, AZ 85712; 602-327-9275

ACCOKEEK SPORTS
Box 986; Waldorf, MD. 20601

ACCURACY SYSTEMS, INC.
2105 S. Hardy Dr.; Tempe, AZ 85282

ACCURA-SITE CO., INC.
Box 193; Neenah, WI 54956; 414-725-7267

P. O. ACKLEY GUN BARRELS
Rt. 1, Box 24; American Fork, UT 84003; 801-756-3810

LUTHER ADKINS
P.O. Box 281, Shelbyville, IN 46176

AIMPOINT U.S.A.
29351 Stonecrest Rd.; Rancho Palos Verdes, CA 90274

AIR RIFLE HEADQUARTERS
247 Court St.; Grantsville, WV 26147; 304-354-6193

ALBRIGHT PROD. CO.
P.O. Box 1144; Portola, CA 96122; 916-832-4395

ALCO CARRYING CASES, INC.
601 W. 26th St.; New York, N.Y. 10001; 212-675-5820

ALLEN CO., INC.
2330 Midway Blvd.; Broomfield, CO 80020; 303-469-1857

BOB ALLEN SPORTSWEAR
P.O. Box 477; Des Moines, IA 50302; 515-283-1988

DON ALLEN
Rte. 1; Northfield, MN 55057; 507-654-9216

ALPHA CENTAURI, INC.
P.O. Box 966; Afton, WY 83110

AMERICAN GAS & CHEMICAL CO., LTD.
5 Tenakill Park; Cresskil, NJ 07626

AMERICAN SALES & MFG. CO.
P.O. Box 677; Laredo, TX 78040; 512-723-6893

ANDERSON MFG. CO. (Storm King Lens Caps)
P.O. Box 3120; Yakima, WA 98903; 509-453-9793

ANDERSON MFG. CO. (Shotshell Trimmer)
R.R.; Royal, IA 51357; 712-933-5542

ANTIQUE GUN PARTS, INC.
1118 S. Braddock Ave.; Pittsburgh, PA 15218; 412-241-1811

R. J. ANTON
874 Olympic Dr.; Waterloo, IA 50701; 319-233-3666

ARMS INGENUITY CO.
P.O. Box 1; Weatogue, CT 06089; 203-658-5624

ARMSPORT, INC.
2811 N.W. 75th Ave.; Miami, FL 33122; 305-592-7850

ART JEWEL ENTERPRISES
P.O. Box 817; Berkley, IL 60163

ATKINSON GUN CO. (H-S Precision)
P.O. Box 512; Prescott, AZ 86301; 602-445-0607

B

B.D.U. ENTERPRISES
77 W. Villa Pl.; Ft. Thomas, KY 41075

B-SQUARE CO.
Box 11281; Ft. Worth, TX 76109

BAIN & DAVIS SPORTING GOODS
559 W. Las Tunas Dr.; San Gabriel, CA 91776; 213-284-2264

STAN BAKER
5303 Roosevelt Way NE; Seattle, WA 98105; 206-522-4575

BALLARD CUTLERY
P.O. Box 97; Golf, IL 60029

BILL BALLARD
830 Miles Ave.; Billings, MT 59101; 406-245-7502

BALLISTEK, WEAPONS SYSTEMS DIV.
Box 1813; Kearney, NB 68847

BALLISTIC PRODUCTS, INC.
16230 Fifth Ave., No.; Wayzata, MN 55391; 612-473-1550

BALLISTICS ENGINEERING CO.
P.O. Box 32 Dabel Sta.; Dayton, OH 45420

BARAMI CORP.
6250 E. 7-Mile Rd.; Detroit, MI 48234; 313-891-2536

BARBER'S AMMUNITION CO., INC.
2 Curtis Ave.; Essex Jct., VT 05452; 802-878-5797

BARNES BULLETS
P.O. Box 215; American Fork, UT 84003; 801-756-4222

JACK BARRETT
2122 Peach Orchard Rd.; Augusta, GA 30906

BAR-STO PRECISION MACHINE
633 S. Victory Blvd.; Burbank, CA 91502; 213-846-7717

EDDIE BAUER
15010 NE 36th St.; Redmond, WA 98052; 206-885-4422

BAUSCH & LOMB INC.
1400 N. Goodman St.; Rochester, NY 14602; 716-338-6289

BEAL'S BULLETS
170 W. Marshall Rd.; Lansdowne, PA 19050; 215-259-1220

BECK KNIVES
1504 Hagood Ave.; Barnewell, SC 29812; 803-259-5959

BEEMAN'S PRECISION AIRGUNS
47 Paul Drive, Bldg. 6, San Rafael, CA 94903; 415-472-7120

BEHLERT CUSTOM GUNS, INC.
725 Lehigh Ave.; Union, N.J. 07083; 201-687-3350

BELDING & MULL
P.O. Box 428; Philipsburg, PA 16866; 814-342-0607

SID BELL ORIGINALS
R.D. 2; Tully, NY 13159

BIANCHI GUNLEATHER
100 Calle Cortez; Temecula, CA 92390; 714-676-5621

AL BIESEN
W. 2039 Sinto Ave.; Spokane, WA 99201; 509-328-6818

BIG GAME
20551 Sunset; Detroit, MI 48234; 313-366-4100

BIG HORN TRADING CO.
1707 14th St.; Boulder, CO 80302; 303-449-7040

STEPHEN L. BILLEB
Rt. 3, Box 163; Bozeman, MT 59715

BIRCHWOOD CASEY
7900 Fuller Rd.; Eden Prairie, MN 55344; 612-927-1733

E.C. BISHOP & SON, INC.
Box 7; Warsaw, MO 65355; 816-438-5121

BITTERROOT BULLET CO.
P.O. Box 412; Lewiston, ID 83501; 208-743-5635

BLUE & GRAY PRODUCTS, INC.
817 E. Main St.; Bradford, PA 16701; 814-368-5333

BOB'S GUN SHOP
P.O. Box 2332; Hot Springs, AR 71901

BO-MAR TOOL & MFG. CO.
Box 168; Carthage, TX 75633; 214-693-5220

BONANZA SPORTS MFG. CO.
412 Western Av.; Faribault, MN 55021; 507-332-7153

HENRY BONHAM
218 Franklin Ave.; Seaside Heights, NJ 08751

VICTOR BORTUGNO
Atlantic & Pacific Arms Co.; 4859 Virginia Beach Blvd.; Virginia Beach, VA 23462

BOYT
Div. of Welsh Sporting Goods; Box 1108; Iowa Falls, IA 50126; 515-381-7542

BRAUER BROS. MFG. CO.
817 N. 17th; St. Louis, MO 63106

BRENIK, INC.
925 W. Chicago Ave.; Chicago, IL 60622; 312-243-2110

BRYAN BRIDGES
6350 East Pasco San Andres; Tucson, AZ 85710

BROOKSTONE CO.
125 Vose Farm Rd.; Peterborough, NH 03458; 603-924-7181

BROWN PRECISION CO.
5869 Indian Ave.; San Jose CA 95123; 408-226-4036

L.E. "RED" BROWN
3203 Del Amo Blvd.; Lakewood, CA 90712; 213-531-3994

BROWNELL'S, INC.
Rte. 2, Box 1; Montezuma, IA 50171; 515-623-5401

LENARD M. BROWNELL
Box 25; Wyarno, WY 82845; 307-737-2468

WILLIAM E. BROWNELL
1852 Alessandro Trail; Vista, CA 92083; 714-724-8305

BROWNING
Rt. 4, Box 624-B; Arnold, MO 63010; 314-287-6800

MILTON BRYNIN
Box 162, Fleetwood Station; Mount Vernon, NY 10552; 914-667-6549

J. M. BUCHEIMER CO.
P.O. Box 280; Frederick, MD 21701; 301-622-6101

BUCK KNIVES, INC.
1717 N. Magnolia Ave.; El Cajon, CA 92022; 714-449-1100

BUCK STOP
3015 Grow Rd.; Stanton, MI 48888; 517-762-5091

MAYNARD P. BUEHLER INC.
17 Orinda Highway; Orinda, CA 94563; 415-254-3201

BUENGER ENTERPRISES (Golden Rod Dryer)
P.O. Box 5286; Oxnard, CA 93030; 805-487-1802

BULLET INDUSTRIES
1617 E. 17th #30; Santa Ana, CA 92701

JACK BURRES
10333 San Fernando Rd.; Pacoima, CA 91331; 213-899-8000

BURRIS COMPANY
331 E. 8th St.; Greeley, CO 80631; 303-356-1670

BUSHNELL OPTICAL CORP.
2828 E. Foothill Blvd.; Pasadena, CA 91107; 213-577-1500

LEO BUSTANI
P.O. Box 8125; West Palm Beach, FL 33407; 305-622-2710

BUTLER CREEK CORP.
Box GG; Jackson, WY 83001; 307-733-3599

C

CCI
Box 856; Lewiston, ID 83501; 208-746-2351

C-H TOOL & DIE CORP.
Box "L"; Owen, WI 54460; 715-229-2146

C & T CABINETRY, INC.
1409 Penn Ave.; Scranton, PA 18509

C.W. CARTRIDGE CO.
71 Hackensack St.; Wood-Ridge, NJ 07075; 201-438-5111

CACHE LAPOUDRE RIFLEWORKS
168 N. College Ave.; Ft. Collins, CO 80524; 303-482-6913

CAMDEX, INC.
23880 Hoover Rd.; Warren, MI 48089; 313-756-5810

CAMILLUS CUTLERY CO.
Main St.; Camillus, NY 13031; 315-672-8111

R.C. CAMPBELL
365 W. Oxford Ave.; Englewood, CO 80110; 303-789-3104

M.H. CANJAR CO.
500 E. 45th Ave.; Denver, CO 80216; 303-623-5777

LARRY W. CARPENTER
Box 1173; Kingsport, TN 37662; 615-247-1446

CARRY-LITE DECOYS
5203 W. Clinton Ave.; Milwaukee, WI 53223; 414-355-3520

RALPH L. CARTER
Rt. 1, Box 92; Fountain, CO 80817; 303-382-7962

W. R. CASE & SONS CUTLERY CO.
20 Russell Blvd.; Bradford, PA 16701; 814-368-4124

CASWELL EQUIPMENT CO.
1221 Marshall St., N.E.; Minneapolis, MN 55413; 612-333-1511

CATCO-AMBUSH, INC.
P.O. Box 300; Corte Madera, CA 94926; 415-388-4322

CENTOFANTE KNIVES
P.O. Box 17587; Tampa, FL 33682; 813-961-0637

CENTRAL PRODUCTS FOR SHOOTERS
435 Route 18; E. Brunswick, NJ 08816

CENTRAL SPECIALTIES CO.
6030 Northwest Highway; Chicago, IL 60631; 312-774-5000

CHACE LEATHER PRODUCTS
507 Alden St., Fall River, MA 02722; 617-678-7556

CHEVRON CASE MASTER
R.R. 1, Ottawa, IL 61350; 815-433-2471

CHICAGO WHEEL & MFG. CO.
1101 W. Monroe St.; Chicago, IL 60607; 312-226-8155

CHOATE MACHINE & TOOL CO.
Box 218; Firearms Div.; Bald Knob, AR 72010; 501-724-3138

CHRISTY GUN WORKS
875 57th St.; Sacramento, CA 95819; 916-452-5447

WINSTON CHURCHILL
20 Mile Stream Rd.; Rt. 1, Box 29B, Proctorsville, VT 05153; 802-226-7772

JAMES E. CLARK
Rte. 2, Box 22A; Keithville, LA 71047; 318-925-0836

KENNETH E. CLARK
18738 Highway 99; Madera, CA 93637; 209-674-6016

CLASSIC ARMS LTD
20 Wilbraham; Palmer, MA 01069; 413-283-9729

CLEARVIEW MFG. CO.
20821 Grand River Ave.; Detroit, MI 48219

CLENZOIL CORP.
P.O. Box 1226, Sta. C; Canton, OH 44708; 216-833-9758

CLOWARD'S GUN SHOP (Dick Cloward)
4023 Aurora Ave., N., Seattle, WA 98103; 206-632-2072

CLOYCE'S GUN STOCKS
Box 1133, Twin Falls, ID 83301; 208-734-7746

CLYMER MANUFACTURING CO.
14241 W. 11 Mile Rd.; Oak Park, MI 48237; 313-541-5533

LESTER COATS
416 Simpson St.; North Bend, OR 97459; 503-756-6995

COBRA
Box 167; Brady, TX 76825; 915-463-5322

COLEMAN COMPANY, INC.
250 N. St. Francis St.; Wichita, KS 67201; 316-261-3348

COLT INDUSTRIES
Firearms Div.; 150 Huyshope Ave.; Hartford, CT 06102; 203-278-1500

COLUMBIA PRECISION WOODWORKING
715 Camden; San Antonio, TX 78215

COMMANDO ARMS, INC.
P.O. Box 10214; Knoxville, TN 37919; 615-523-3393

COMPASS INDUSTRIES
104 E. 25th St.; New York, N.Y. 10010; 212-473-2614

CONETROL SCOPE MOUNTS
Hwy. 123 South; Seguin, TX 78155; 512-379-3030

CONNECTICUT VALLEY ARMS CO.
Saybrook Rd.; Haddam, CT 06438; 203-345-8511

DAVE COOK
720 Hancock Ave.; Hancock, MI 49930; 906-482-2814

COOPER-WOODWARD
P.O. Box 972; Riverside, CA 92502; 714-683-5952

CORBIN MFG. & SUPPLY, INC.
P.O. Box 758; Phoenix, OR 97535; 503-826-5211

HAROLD CORBY (Knives by Corby)
1714 Brandonwood Dr.; Johnson City, TN 37601; 615-926-9781

CRANE CREEK GUN STOCK CO., INC.
25 Shepard Terr.; Madison, WI 53705; 608-233-9119

GEO. S. CRANE SALES CO.
P.O. Box 385; Van Nuys, CA 91408; 213-786-4086

CRAVENER'S GUN SHOP
1627 - 5th Ave.; Ford City, PA 16226; 412-763-8312

CROSMAN AIRGUNS
980 Turk Hill Rd.; Fairport, NY 14450; 716-223-6000

CROSMAN SHOOTING GAMES
Box 290; Rochester, NY 14601

CROWN CITY ARMS
Box 1126; Cortland, NY 13045; 607-753-0194

CUMBERLAND ARMS
Rt. 1, Shafer Rd.; Blantons Chapel, Manchester, TN 37355; 615-728-0688

EARL T. CURETON
Rt. 2, Box 388; Willoughby Rd.; Bullsgap, TN 37711

CUSTOM CHRONOGRAPH CO.
Rt. 1, Box 193A; Tonasket, WA 98855

CUSTOM GUNS WEST
1378 Lakewood Circle; Salt Lake City, UT 84117; 801-272-4126

THE CUSTOM GUNSMITH
475 Truckey St.; St. Ignace, MI 49781

CUSTOM KNIFEMAKER'S SUPPLY
P.O. Box 308; Emory, TX 75440; 214-328-2453

D

D&E MAGAZINES MFG.
P.O. Box 4579; Downey, CA 90242

D&H PRODUCTS
P.O. Box 22; Glenshaw, PA 15116

DAISY MFG. CO.
Box 220; Rogers, AR 72756; 501-636-1200

DARA-NES DIVISION
Nesci-Enterprises; P.O. Box 119; East Hampton, CT 06424; 203-267-4175

DAVE'S GUN SHOP
720 Hancock Ave.; Hancock, MI 49930; 906-482-2814

K.J. DAVID & CO.
P.O. Box 923; Oak Brook, IL 60521

DAVIDSON PRODUCTS FOR SHOOTERS
2020 Huntington Dr.; Las Cruces, NM 88001; 505-524-6929

DAVIS GUN SHOP
7213 Lee Highway; Falls Church, VA 22046; 703-534-8222

G. WM. DAVIS
P.O. Box 446; Arcadia, CA 91006

R.J. DAVIS & SON, INC.
758 College Ave.; Adrian, MI 49221; 517-263-1329

DAYTON-TRAISTER CO.
P.O. Box 593; Oak Harbor, WA 98277; 206-675-5375

J. DeCHRISTOPHER
P.O. Box 457, Feasterville, PA 19047

DECKER SHOOTING PRODUCTS
1729 Laguna Ave.; Schofield, WI 54476; 715-359-5873

DEER ME PRODUCTS CO.
Box 345; Anoka, MN 55303; 612-421-8971

DEL REY PRODUCTS
P.O. Box 91561; Los Angeles, CA 90009; 213-823-0494

DEL-SPORTS, INC.
Main St.; Margaretville, NY 12455; 914-586-4103

DEN-RUS PARTS
P.O. Box 267; Cut & Shoot, TX 77302

STAN de TREVILLE
Box 33021; San Diego, CA 92103; 714-298-3393

DEVEL CORP.
3441 W. Brainard Rd.; Cleveland, OH 44122

JACK B. DEVER
8520 N.W. 90; Oklahoma City, OK 73132; 405-721-6393

R.H. DEVEREAUX
475 Truckey St.; St. Ignace, MI 49781

DIANA CO.
842 Vallejo St.; San Francisco, CA 94133; 415-989-7033

DOMINIC DiSTEFANO
4303 Friar Lane; Colorado Springs, CO 80907; 303-599-3366

DIXIE GUN WORKS
Hwy. 51, South; Union City, TN 38261; 901-885-0561

DOSKOCIL MFG. CO.
P.O. Box 1246; Arlington, TX 76010

DOUGLAS BARRELS, INC.
5504 Big Tyler Rd.; Charleston, WV 25312; 304-776-1341

T.M. DOWELL
139 N.W. Saint Helens Pl.; Bend, OR 97701; 503-382-8924

BILL DOWTIN
P.O. Box 72; Celina, TX 75009; 213-233-8903

DRI-SLIDE, INC.
Industrial Park, 1210 Locust St.; Fremont, MI 49412; 616-924-3950

DROVEL IND.
37 Potter St.; Farmingdale, NY 11735; 516-249-2801

DAVID R. DUNLOP
Route 1, Box 199; Rolla, ND 58367

DuPONT SMOKELESS POWDERS
10th & Market Sts.; Wilmington, DE 19898; 302-774-8825

DURANGO U.S.A.
P.O. Box 1029; Durango, CO 81301; 303-247-5296

BILL DYER
P.O. Box 75255; Oklahoma City, OK 73107; 405-941-4110

E

E-Z MOUNT CORP. (Gun Racks)
120 W. 4th; San Angelo, TX 76902

E-Z MOUNT, INC. (Taxidermy)
5050 Excelsior Blvd.; Suite 209; Minneapolis, MN 55416; 612-927-7066

EZE-LAP DIAMOND PROD.
Box 2229; Westminster, CA 92683; 714-847-1555

EASTERN SPORTS INTERNATIONAL
Savage Rd.; Milford, NH 03055; 603-673-4967

JOHN H. EATON
8516 James St.; Upper Marlboro, MD 20870; 301-868-6819

EDMISTEN CO., INC.
P.O. Box 298; Boone, NC 28607

EDWARDS RECOIL REDUCER (Jessie B. Edwards)
269 Herbert St.; Alton, IL 62002; 618-462-3257

EFEMES ENTERPRISES
P.O. Box 122M; Bay Shore, NY 11706

EL DORADO LEATHER CO.
1045 Vernon Way; El Cajon, CA 92020; 714-449-4920

ELECTRO BALLISTIC LABORATORY
1900 Embarcadero Rd., Suite 209; Palo Alto, CA 94303; 415-326-5227

ELK MOUNTAIN SHOOTERS SUPPLY
1719 Marie; Pasco, WA 99301; 803-648-9288

F. K. ELLIOTT
P.O. Box 785; Ramona, CA 92065; 714-789-0173

EMSCO CHOKES
101 Second Ave., SE.; Waseca, MN 56093; 507-835-1481

WILTON L. ENGLISH
12009-B Barksdale Dr.; Omaha, NB 68123; 402-291-3960

ENSIGN CO. (Knives by Ensign)
Gunnison, UT 84634

EPCO PUBLISHING CO.
75-24 64th St.; Glendale, NY 11227

NORBERT ERTEL
Box 1150; Des Plaines, IL 60018; 312-824-2315

THE EUTAW CO.
U.S. Highway 176W; Holly Hill, SC 29059; 803-496-3341

KEN EYSTER (Heritage Gunsmiths, Inc.)
6441 Bishop Rd.; Centerburg, OH 43011; 614-625-6131

F

FTL MARKETING CORP.
11100 Cumpston St.; North Hollywood, CA 91601; 213-985-2939

REINHART FAJEN, INC.
Box 338; Warsaw, MO 65355; 816-438-5111

FALLING BLOCK WORKS
P.O. Box 22; Troy, MI 48084; 313-689-5816

FANTA AIR RIFLES
Box 8122; La Crescenta, CA 91214; 213-248-6227

FARMER BROS.
1102 Washington St.; Eldora, IA 50627; 515-858-3651

N. B. FASHINGBAUER
Box 366; Lac du Flambeau, WI 54538; 715-588-7116

FEDERAL CARTRIDGE CORP.
2700 Foshay Tower; Minneapolis, MN 55402; 612-333-8255

FEDERAL FIREARMS CO., INC.
145 Thoms Run Rd.; Oakdale, PA 15071; 412-221-9700

FEDERAL ORDNANCE INC.
9643 Alpaca St.; So. El Monte, CA 91733; 213-283-3880

JACK FIRST DISTRIBUTORS, INC.
44633 Sierra Highway; Lancaster, CA 93534; 805-942-2016

MARSHALL R. FISH
Rt. 22 North, Westport, NY 12993; 518-962-4897

JERRY FISHER
1244 - 4th Ave., W.; Kalispell, MT 59901; 406-755-7093

FITZ
653 N. Hagar St.; San Fernando, CA 91340; 213-399-0212

FLAIG'S, INC.
Babcock Blvd. & Thompson Run Rd.; Millvale, PA 15209; 411-811-1717

TOM FORREST, INC.
2785 Kurtz St. No. 7, San Diego, CA 92110

LARRY L. FORSTER
Box 212; Gwinner, ND 58040; 701-678-2475

KEITH FRANCIS
8515 Wagner Creek Rd.; Talent, OR 97540; 503-535-1569

FRAZIER'S CUSTOM GUNS
Box 8644; Bird Creek, AK 99540

FREELAND'S SCOPE STANDS, INC.
3737 14th Ave.; Rock Island, IL 61201; 309-788-7449

J. R. FRENCH
2633 Quail Valley; Irving, TX 75060; 214-253-4057

GEO. M. FULLMER
2499 Mavis St.; Oakland, CA 94601; 415-533-4193

G

G & H DECOY MFG. CO.
P.O. Box 937; Henryetta, OK 74437; 918-652-3314

GRS CORP.
Box 1157; Boulder, CO 80302; 303-447-2154

J. L. GALEF & SON, INC.
85 Chambers St.; New York, NY 10007; 212-267-6727

GAME-WINNER, INC.
Kinston Hwy; Opp, AL 36467; 404-588-0401

GAULT PRESENTATION KNIVES
Rte. 1, Box 184; Lexington, TX 78947

GERBER LEGENDARY BLADES
14200 S.W. 72nd St.; Portland, OR 97223; 503-639-6161

GLENDO CORPORATION (Gravermeister)
Box 1153; Emporia, KS 66801; 316-343-1084

DALE GOENS
Box 224; Cedar Crest, NM 87008; 505-281-5419

GOLDEN AGE ARMS CO.
14 W. Winter St.; Delaware, OH 43015; 614-548-5451

GOLDEN EAGLE FIREARMS
P.O. Box 42139; Houston, TX 77042; 713-776-6854

RAMON B. GONZALEZ
P.O. Box 370; RFD #1; Monticello, NY 12701; 914-794-4515

GARY GOUDY
263 Hedge Rd.; Menlo Park, CA 44025

GRACE METAL PRODUCTS
115 Ames St.; Elk Rapids, MI 49629; 616-264-8133

HOWARD V. GRANT
P.O. Box 396; Lac Du Flambeau, WI 54538; 715-588-3586

GREAT LAKES AIRGUNS
S6175 S. Park Ave.; Hamburg, NY 14075; 716-649-3825

GREEN BAY BULLETS
233 N. Ashland Ave.; Green Bay, WI 54303; 414-432-9003

GREEN RIVER FORGE, LTD.
P.O. Box 884; Springfield, OR 97477; 503-726-1246

GREG'S WINCHESTER PARTS
P.O. Box 8125; West Palm Beach, FL 33407

GRIFFIN & HOWE INC.
589 Broadway - 4th FL; New York, NY 10019; 212-966-5323

H. L. GRISEL
61400 S. Hwy. 97; Bend, OR 97701; 503-382-8197

GUN-HO CASE MFG. CO.
110 E. 10th St.; St. Paul, MN 55101; 612-224-5381

GUN HOUSE
54 Stearns St.; Waltham, MA 02154; 617-893-3050

GUNLINE TOOLS, INC.
719 N. East St.; Anaheim, CA 92805; 714-535-3385

THE GUN ROOM
1201 Burlington Dr.; Muncie, IN 47302

GUSSERT BULLET & CARTRIDGE CO., INC.
P.O. Box 3945; Green Bay, WI 54303; 414-434-3227

GUTMAN CO., INC.
900 S. Columbus Ave., Mt. Vernon, NY 10550

H

H & M TOOL CO.
24062 Orchard Lake Rd.; Box 258; Farmington, MI 48024; 313-474-4604

H-S PRECISION
P.O. Box 512; Prescott, AZ 86301; 602-445-0607

HARDIN SPECIALTY DISTRIBUTORS
P.O. Box 338; Radcliff, KY 40160; 502-351-6649

HARRINGTON & RICHARDSON
Industrial Rowe; Gardner, MA 01440; 617-632-9600

HARRIS ENGINEERING, INC.
Barlow, KY 42024; 502-334-3633

ROBERT W. HART & SON, INC. (Hart Products)
401 Montgomery St.; Nescopeck, PA 18635; 717-752-3481

HARTFORD REAMER CO.
Box 134; Lathrup Village, MI 48075

HAYES GUNSTOCK SERVICE
914 E. Turner St.; Clearwater, FL 33516; 813-446-0726

THE HAWKEN SHOP
3028 N. Lindbergh Blvd.; St. Louis, MO 63074; 314-739-7300

HEATBATH CORP.
P.O. Box 2978; Springfield, MA 01101

HUBERT J. HECHT
55 Rose Mead Circle; Sacramento, CA 95831; 916-421-4429

EDWARD O. HEFTI
300 Fairview; College Station, TX 77840

STEVE HENIGSON
2049 Kerwood Ave. #3; Los Angeles, CA 90025

HENRIKSEN TOOL CO., INC.
P.O. Box 668; Phoenix, OR 97535; 503-535-2309

HENSLEY & GIBBS
P.O. Box 10; Murphy, OR 97533; 503-862-2341

HERITAGE CUSTOM KNIVES
2895 Seneca St.; Buffalo, NY 14224; 716-822-0272

HERITAGE GUNSMITHS, INC.
6441 Bishop Rd.; Centerburg, OH 43011

HERRETT'S STOCKS, INC.
Box 741; Twin Falls, ID 83301; 208-733-1498

HERTER'S INC.
Waseca, MN 56093; 507-835-4011

TONY HIDALGO
6 Capp St.; Carteret, NJ 07008

HIGH STANDARD SPORTING FIREARMS
31 Prestige Park Circle; E. Hartford, CT 06108; 203-289-9531

HI PER CARTRIDGE CORP.
133 Blue Bell Rd.; Greensboro, NC 27406

WM. H. HOBAUGH, THE RIFLE SHOP
Box M; Philipsburg, MT 59858; 406-859-3515

RICHARD HOCH
The Gun Shop; 62778 Spring Creek Rd.; Montrose, CO 81401; 303-249-3625

HODGON POWDER CO., INC.
7710 W. 50 Hiway; Shawnee-Mission, KS 66202; 913-362-5410

HOENIG-RODMAN
6521 Morton Dr.; Boise, ID 83705; 208-375-1116

HOFFMANN PRODUCTS
P.O. Box 853; Lake Forest, IL 60045; 312-234-4075

J. B. HOLDEN CO.
295 W. Pearl; Plymouth, MI 48170; 313-455-4850

HOPKINS & ALLEN ARMS
#1 Melnick Rd.; Monsey, NY 10952

FRANK A. HOPPE DIV.
P.O. Box 97; Parkesburg, PA 19365; 215-384-6000

HORNADY MFG. CO.
P.O. Box 1848; Grand Island, NB 68801; 308-382-1390

N. E. HOUSE CO.
Middletown Rd.; RR 4, Box 68; E. Hampton, CT 06424; 203-267-2133

HUDSON OPTICS
842 Broadway; New York, NY 10003; 800-221-3520

MARVIN HUEY
Box 98; Reed's Spring, MO 65737

HULME FIREARM SERVICE
P.O. Box 83; Millbrae, CA 94030; 415-697-5160

DON HUME LEATHER GOODS
Box 351; Miami, OK 74354; 918-542-6604

THE HUNTER CO.
3300 W. 71st Ave.; Westminster, CO 80030; 303-427-4626

THE HUTSON CORP.
P.O. Box 1127; Arlington, TX 76010; 817-261-4927

HUTTON RIFLE RANCH
1802 S. Oak Park Dr.; Rolling Hills, Tucson, AZ 85710

HYDROSORBENT CO.
Box 675; Rye, N.Y. 10580

I

RALPH W. INGLE
#4 Missing Link; Rossville, GA 30741; 404-866-5589

INTERNATIONAL ARMS
23239 Doremus Ave.; St. Clair Shores, MI 48080

IRON AGE CRAFTWORKS
P.O. Box 518; Preston, WA 98050; 206-222-5854

J

JJJJ RANCH, GUN & MACHINE SHOP
Rte. 1; Ironton, OH 45638; 614-532-5298

JACKASS LEATHER CO.
7383 N. Rodgers Ave., Chicago, IL 60626; 312-338-2800

JACOB & TIFFIN, INC. (Jafin Products)
P.O. Box 547; Clanton, AL 35045; 205-755-6925

PAUL JAEGER, INC.
211 Leedom St.; Jenkintown, PA 19046; 215-884-6920

JAFIN PRODUCTS (Light Load)
Box 547; Clanton, AL 35045

KEN JANTZ
Rt. 1; Sulphur, OK 73086; 405-622-3790

JASCO
J. A. Somers; P.O. Box 49750; Los Angeles, CA 90049; 213-828-7676

JASON EMPIRE, INC.
9200 Cody; Overland Park, KS 66214; 913-888-0220

J. J. JENKINS
375 Pine Ave., No. 25; Goleta, CA 93017; 805-967-1366

JERROW'S INLETTING BLACK
452 5th Ave., East North; Kalispell, MT 59901; 406-756-4756

JET-AER CORP.
100 Sixth Ave.; Paterson, NJ 07524; 201-278-8300

S. R. JOBS
1513 Martin Chapel Rd.; Murray, KY 42071

BILL JOHNS
2217 N. 10th; McAllen, TX 78501; 512-682-6606

JOHNSON WOOD PRODUCTS
Route 1; Strawberry Point, IA 52076; 319-933-4930

LaDOW JOHNSTON
2322 W. Country Club Parkway; Toledo, OH 43614; 419-382-3283

JONAS BROTHERS, INC.
1037 Broadway; Denver, CO 80203; 303-543-7400

JACK JONAS SAFARIS, INC.
800 E. Girard, Suite 118; Denver, CO 80231; 303-750-9802

BRUCE JONES BARREL RESTORATION
389 Calla Ave.; Imperial Beach, CA 92032

NEIL A. JONES (Custom Products)
686 Baldwin St.; Meadville, PA 16335; 814-724-7045

PHIL JUDD
83 East Park St.; Butte, MT 59701; 406-723-3802

JOSEPH JURJEVIC
605 Main St.; Marble Falls, TX 78654

K

KTW, INC.
710 Foster Park Rd.; Lorain, OH 44053; 216-233-6919

KASENITE CO., INC.
3 King St., Box K; Mahwah, NJ 07430; 201-529-3663

KASSNAR IMPORTS
5480 Linglestown Rd.; Harrisburg, PA 17110; 717-238-9547

R. H. KEELER
P. O. Box 536; Port Angeles, WA 98362; 206-457-4702

KELLOG'S PROFESSIONAL PRODUCTS, INC.
321 Pearl St.; Sandusky, OH 44870; 419-625-6551

LANCE KELLY
4226 Lamar St.; Decatur, GA 30036; 404-284-6418

JIM KELSO
P.O. Box 518; Preston, WA 98050; 206-222-5854

KEN'S METAL FINISHING
2333 Emerson Ave.; N. Minneapolis, MN 55411

KINGS GUN WORKS
1837 W. Glenoaks Blvd; Glendale, CA 91201; 211-244-6811

JON KIRK KNIVES
800 North Olive St.; Fayetteville, AR 72701

KIRKPATRICK LEATHER CO.
P.O. Box 3150; Laredo, TX 78041

K. W. KLEINENDORST
48 Taylortown RD.; Montville, NJ 07045; 201-334-8662

KOGOT
410 College Ave.; Trinidad, CO 81082; 303-846-9406

KOLPIN MFG. INC.
Box 231; Berlin, WI 54923; 414-361-0400

JOHN KOPEC
P.O. Box 218; La Puente, CA 91747; 213-336-3933

J. KORZINEK
RD #2, Box R; Canton, PA 17724; 717-673-8512

KRIS MOUNTS
108 Lehigh St.; Johnstown, PA 15905; 814-536-1272

KWIK-SITE
5555 Treadwell; Wayne, MI 48185; 313-326-1500

L

L.E.M. GUN SPECIALTIES
P.O. Box 31; College Park, GA 30337; 404-761-9054

LPS RESEARCH LABORATORIES, INC.
2050 Cotner Ave.; Los Angeles, CA 90025; 213-478-0095

L & W CASTING CO.
5014 Freeman Rd. East; Puyallup, WA 98371

LAC-CUM BULLET PULLER
Star Route, Box 242; Apollo, PA 15613; 412-478-1794

LAKEVIEW GUN SHOP
1018 Lloyd; Latrobe, PA 15650; 412-539-9221

RON L. LAMPERT
Rt. 1, Box 61; Guthrie, MN 56451; 218-854-7345

BETH LANE
815 N. Ladd St.; Pontiac, IL 61764; 815-842-2402

GEORGE LAWRENCE CO.
306 S.W. 1st Ave.; Portland, OR 97204; 503-228-8246

HARRY LAWSON CO.
3328 N. Rickey Blvd.; Tucson, AZ 85176; 602-326-1117

JOHN G. LAWSON (The Sight Shop)
1802 E. Columbia Ave.; Tacoma, WA 98404; 206-474-5465

LeCLEAR INDUSTRIES
P.O. Box 484; Royal Oak, MI 48068; 313-588-1025

LEE CUSTOM ENGINEERING, INC.
46 E. Jackson St.; Hartford, WI 53027; 414-673-3060

LEE PRECISION, INC.
Highway U; Hartford, WI 53027; 414-673-3075

T. K. LEE CO.
2830 S. 19th St., off. #4; Birmingham, AL 35209; 205-871-6065

TOM LEE
Rte. 2, Box 463; Gaffey, SC 29340

LEE'S RED RAMPS
7552 E. Ave. V-3; Littlerock, CA 93543; 805-944-4487

LeFEVER ARMS CO., INC.
R.D. 1; Lee Center Stroke, NY 13363; 315-337-2465

PHILIP D. LETIECQ
RD 2; Homer, NY 13077; 607-749-4698

LEUPOLD & STEVENS, INC.
P.O. Box 688; Beaverton, OR 97005

FRANK LIGGAT
1730 Crooked Oak Dr.; Lancaster, PA 17601

AL LIND
7821 - 76th Ave. S.W.; Tacoma, WA 98498; 206-584-6361

LINO CUSTOM CASE MFG. CO.
Box 9460; Colorado Springs, CO 80932

LOCK, STOCK & BARREL
Box 1173; Kingsport, TN 37662

WALTER H. LODEWICK
2816 N.E. Halsey; Portland, OR 97232

JIM LOFLAND
2275 Larkin Rd.; Boothwyn, PA 19061

LOHMAN MFG. CO.
320 East Spring St.; Neosho, MO 64850

LOMONT PRECISION BULLETS
4421 S. Wayne Ave.; Ft. Wayne, IN 46807

LONDON GUNS
1528 - 20th St.; Santa Monica, CA 90404

LONER PRODUCTS: INC.
P.O. Box 219; Yorktown Heights, NY 10598

LORAY SHARPENERS
2032 N. Main St. Ex 1; Butler, PA 16001

LYMAN PRODUCTS FOR SHOOTERS CORP.
Route 147; Middlefield, CT 06455

Mc

H. O. McBURNETT, JR.
Route 4, Box 337; Piedmont, AL 36272; 205-492-6344

BILL McGUIRE
1600 N. Eastmont Ave.; East Wenatchee, WA 98801; 509-884-6021

ARTHUR McKEE
121 Eaton's Neck; Northport, NY 11768

McKEOWN'S GUNS
R.R. #1; Pekin, IL 61554; 309-347-3559

McKILLEN & HEYER
Box 627; Willoughby, OH 44094; 216-942-2491

JAMES McLEMORE
16005 S. Grove Rd.; Hebron, IN 46341

GALE McMILLAN
28638 N. 42nd St.; Box 7870 Cave Creek Stage; Phoenix, AZ 85020; 602-992-4473

M

M. SPORTING ARMS CO.
Route 4; Pekin, IL 61554

MTM MOLDED PRODUCTS CO.
5680 Webster St.; Dayton, OH 45414; 513-890-7461

MAG-NA-PORT ARMS, INC.
30016 S. River Rd.; Mt. Clemens, MI 48043; 313-469-6727

WILLIAM H. MAINS
3212 B. Wynn Rd., Suite 214; Las Vegas, NV 89102; 702-876-6278

MALLARDTONE GAME CALLS
2901 16th St.; Moline, IL 61265; 309-762-8089

MANDALL SHOOTING SUPPLIES CORP.
3616 N. Scottsdale Rd.; Scottsdale, AZ 85251; 602-945-2553

MARATHON RUBBER PRODUCTS CO.
510 Sherman St.; Wausau, WI 54401; 715-845-2255

MARBLE ARMS CORP.
420 Industrial Park; Gladstone, MI 49837; 906-425-2841

MARKSMAN PRODUCTS
Div. of L & R Industries, Inc.; P. O. Box 2983; Torrance, CA 90509; 213-775-8847

MARMEL PRODUCTS
P.O. Box 97; Utica, MI 48087; 313-731-8029

MARQUART PRECISION CO.
Box 1740; Prescott, AZ 86301; 602-445-5646

MARSHAL'S
Rte #3, Box 729; Preston, ID 83263; 208-852-2437

SEELY MASKER
261 Washington Ave; Pleasantville, NY 10570; 914-769-2627

MASTER LOCK COMPANY
2600 N. 32nd St.; Milwaukee, WI 53245; 414-444-2800

MATCHPOINT INDUSTRIES, INC.
3111 Gardenbrook Dr.; Dallas, TX 75234; 214-243-4999

MAURER ARMS
2366 Frederick Dr.; Cuyahoga Falls, OH 44221; 216-928-4288

MAYVILLE ENGINEERING CO.
715 South St.; Mayville, WI 53050; 414-387-4500

MEADOW INDUSTRIES
Dept. 92; Meadows Lands, PA 15347

BOB MEECE CO., INC.
1602 Stemmons, Suite C; Carrollton, TX 75006; 214-245-7911

RAY MELLEN
Box 101; Winston, GA 30187

TOM MENCK
5703 S. 77th St.; Ralston, NB 68127

MERIT GUNSIGHT CO.
P.O. Box 995; Sequin, WA 98382; 206-683-6127

MICHAELS OF OREGON CO.
P.O. Box 13010; Portland, OR 97213; 503-255-6890

MICRO AMMUNITION
Box 213; Las Cruces, NM 88001

MILL RUN PRODUCTS
6118 Kinsman Rd; Cleveland, OH 44104; 216-431-8575

MILLER SINGLE TRIGGER MFG. CO.
RD 1 on Rte. 209; Millersburg, PA 17061; 717-692-3704

C. D. MILLER GUNS
Purl St.; St. Onge, SD 57779; 605-578-1790

MINIATURE MACHINE CO.
210 E. Poplar; Deming, NM 88030; 505-546-2151

MIRROR LUBE
P.O. Box 693; San Juan Capistrano, CA 92675; 714-493-3771

FRANK MITTERMEIER, INC.
3577 E. Tremont Ave.; New York, NY 10465; 212-828-3843

MODERNTOOLS CORP. (Carl Niese, Inc.)
Box 407; Woodside, NY 11377; 212-446-7799

WILLIAM LARKIN MOORE & CO.
31360 Via Colinas, Suite 109; Westlake Village, CA 91361; 213-889-4160

MORTON INTERNATIONAL ENTERPRISES
Tom Morton; (RR2); Knoxville, MD 21758; 301-834-8071

MOUNTAIN STATE MUZZLELOADING SUPPLIES
Box 154-1 H.; Williamstown, WV 26187

LARRY MROCK
4165 Middlebelt; Orchard Lake, MI 48033; 313-626-0136

MULTI-SCALE CHARGE LTD.
3269 Niagara Falls Blvd.; No. Tonawanda, NY 14120

TOMMY MUNSCH
Prior Lake, MN 55372

MUZZLELOADERS ETC., INC.
9901 Lyndale Ave., So.; Bloomington, MN 55420; 612-884-1161

S. D. MYRES SADDLE CO.
5530 E. Paisano; El Paso, TX 79905; 915-778-4467

N

NATIONAL TARGET CO.. INC.
4960 Wyaconda Rd., Rockville, MD 20852; 301-770-7060

NAVY ARMS CO.
689 Bergen Blvd.; Ridgefield, NJ 07657; 201-945-2500

KARL A. NEISE, INC. (Moderntools)
56-02 Roosevelt Ave.; Woodside, NY 11377; 212-446-7799

ROBERT H. NEWELL
55 Coyote; Los Alamos, NM 87544; 505-662-7135

NEW METHOD MFG. CO.
76 South Avenue, Box 175; Bradford, PA 16701; 814-362-6611

NEWPORT PLASTICS
Costa Mesa, CA 92626

NITTAN U.S.A. INC.
4901 Morena Blvd., Suite 307; San Diego, CA 92117; 714-272-6113

NON-FERROUS METALS, INC.
2905 15th Ave., S.W.; Seattle, WA 98134

NORMA-PRECISION
Auburn Rd.; Lansing, NY 14882; 607-273-2993

NORTEX CO.
Safety Products Div.; P. O. Box 7500; Cerfitos, CA 90701

NORTHERN INSTRUMENTS, INC.
6680 North Highway 49; Lino Lakes, MN 55014; 612-784-1250

NORTON SAFETY PRODUCTS
16624 Edwards Road; Cerritos, CA 90701; 213-926-0545

NOSLER BULLETS
P.O. Box 688; Beaverton, OR 97005; 503-646-9171

NUMRICH ARMS CORP.
West Hurley, NY 12491; 914-679-2417

O

OEHLER RESEARCH
P.O. Box 9135; Austin, TX 78756; 512-251-4110

OGG CUSTOM KNIVES
Rte 1, Box 230; Paris, AR 72855

OKER'S ENGRAVING
280 Illinois St.; Crystal Lake, IL 60014; 815-459-8640

OLD WEST INC. LEATHER PRODUCTS
P.O. Box 2030; Chula Vista, CA 92012; 714-429-8050

OLSEN KNIFE CO., INC.
7 Joy St.; Howard City, MI 49329; 616-931-4373

OLSEN'S
2528 Nye Highway; Charlotte, MI 48813

OLT GAME CALLS
Pekin, IL 61554

OMARK-CCI, INC.
Box 856; Lewiston, ID 83501; 208-746-2351

OMEGA SALES
P.O. Box 1066; Mt. Clemens, MI 48043

OLYMPIC OPTICAL CO.
P.O. Box 18334; Memphis, TN 38118; 901-794-3890

ORDNANCE PARK CORP.
P.O. Box 217; Grand Junction, CO 81501

ORIGINAL MINK OIL
Box 20191; 10652 N.E. Holman St.; Portland, OR 97220; 503-255-2814

MAURICE OTTMAR
Box 657; Coulee City, WA 99115; 509-632-5717

OUTERS LABORATORIES, INC.
P.O. Box 37; Onalaska, WI 54650; 608-783-1515

OX-YOKE ORIGINALS
130 Griffin Rd.; West Suffield, CT 06093

P

PACHMAYR GUN WORKS
1220 S. Grand Ave.; Los Angeles, CA 90015; 213-748-7271

PACIFIC TOOL CO.
P.O. Drawer 2048; Ordnance Plant Rd.; Grand Island, NB 68801; 308-384-2308

PAK-TOOL CO.
4411 S. W. 100th; Seattle, WA 98146

PALMGREN PRODUCTS (Chicago Tool & Engineering Co.)
8383 S. Chicago Ave.; Chicago, IL 60617; 312-721-9675

MELVIN M. PARDUE
P.O. Box 14357; Tampa, FL 33690; 813-879-2570

PATCH BOX ARMS
3598 Helendora Ave.; Millersport, OH 43046; 614-467-2429

PAULSEN GUNSTOCKS
Rte. 71, Box 11; Chinook, MT 59529; 406-357-3403

BOB PEASE ACCURACY
P.O. Box 787; New Braunfels, TX 78130; 512-625-1342

PENGUIN INDUSTRIES
P.O. Box 97; Parkesburg, PA 19365; 215-384-6000

PENN'S WOODS PRODUCTS, INC.
19 West Pittsburgh St.; Delmont, PA 15626; 412-468-8311

PEPPLERS SMALL ARMS
Star Rte. Box 240; Apollo, PA 15613

PERRY'S AMMO SLING CO.
Route 1, Box 277; McDonough, GA 30253

PETERSON'S LABELS
P.O. Box 186; Redding Ridge, CT 06876; 203-938-2349

PHANTOM LEATHER
P.O. Box 33; Colorado Springs, CO 80901

PHILLIP PILKINGTON
P.O. Box 2284; University Station; Enid, OK 73701; 405-242-0025

FERRIS PINDELL
R.R. 3, Box 205; Connersville, IN 37331; 317-825-3759

PIONEER PRODUCTS (King & Priest)
1033 W. Amity Rd.; Boise, ID 83705; 208-345-9600

PLUM CITY BALLISTICS RANGE
Rte. 1, Box 29A; Plum City, WI 54761; 715-647-2539

POLY CHOKE CO., INC.
P.O. Box 296; Hartford, CT 06101; 203-289-2743

PONSNESS-WARREN, INC.
Box 8; Rathdrum, ID 83858; 208-687-1331

POTTER ENG. CO.
1410 Santa Ana Dr.; Dunedin, FL 33528; 813-733-1434

MARIAN POWLEY
Petra Lane, R.R. 1; Eldridge, IA 52748

PRECISE (PIC)
3 Chestnut; Suffern, NY 10901

PRECISION REFLEX, INC.
P.O. Box 95; New Bremen, OH 45869; 419-829-0701

WAYNE PRESTON, INC.
3444 Northhaven Rd.; Dallas, TX 75229; 214-358-4477

PRIME LEATHER FINISHES CO.
205 S. 2nd St.; Milwaukee, WI 53204; 414-276-1668

PROTECTO PLASTICS, INC.
201 Alpha Road; Wind Gap, PA 18091; 215-863-6997

PROVO STEEL & SUPPLY CO.
P.O. Box 977; Provo, UT 84601; 801-373-2385

E. C. PRUDHOMME
513 Ricou-Brewster Bldg.; Shreveport, LA 71101; 318-425-8421

PUGH KNIVES
P.O. Box 711; Azle, TX 76020

Q

QUINETICS Corp.
Box 13237; San Antonio, TX 78213; 512-684-8561

R

RCBS, INC.
P.O. Box 1919; Oroville, CA 95965; 916-533-5191

RANDALL-MADE KNIVES
Box 1988; Orlando, FL 32802

RANGER LEATHER PRODUCTS
Box 3198; East Camden, AR 71701; 501-574-1502

RANGING, INC.
90 No. Lincoln Rd.; East Rochester, NY 14445; 716-385-1250

REDDING-HUNTER, INC.
114 Starr Rd.; Cortland, NY 13045; 607-753-3331

REDFIELD CO.
5800 East Jewell Ave.; Denver, CO 80222; 303-757-6411

REFRIGIWEAR, INC.
71 Inip Dr.; Inwood, L.I., NY 11696; 516-239-7022

RELIANCE BULLETS
Box 2128W; Peabody, MA 01960

REMINGTON ARMS CO., INC.
939 Barnum Ave.; Bridgeport, CT 06602; 203-333-1112

REMOTE SURVIVAL CO.
P.O. Box 523; New Haven, CT 06503; 203-488-1914

REPLICA MODELS, INC.
610 Franklin St.; Alexandria, VA 22314; 703-549-0772

REPUBLIC TOOL MFG. CO.
P.O. Box 1121, Caldwell, NJ 07006

RESEARCH PRODUCTS DISTRIBUTORS (Exammo)
North 311 Walnut Road; Spokane, WA 99206; 509-928-0604

RICE GUN COATINGS
1521 - 43rd St.; West Palm Beach, FL 33407; 305-848-2228

RICHARDS MICRO-FIT STOCKS
P.O. Box 1066; Sun Valley, CA 91352; 213-767-6097

RICHLAND ARMS CO.
321 W. Adrian St.; Blissfield, MI 49228; 517-486-2102

PETE RICKARD INC.
Box 1250; Cobleskill, NY 12043; 518-234-2731

THE RIFLE RANCH
Rte 5; Prescott, AZ 86301

RIFLE SHOP
Box M; Philipsburg, MT 59858

RIG PRODUCTS DIV. OF MITANN INDUSTRIES
21320 Deering Ct.; Canoga Park, CA 91304

RIGID KNIVES
P.O. Box 460; Santee, CA 92071; 714-449-5775

WILLIAM A. ROBERTS
Rte. 4, Box 34; Athens, AL 35611; 205-232-7027

ROCHESTER LEAD WORKS
76 Anderson Ave.; Rochester, NY 14607; 716-442-8500

ROCKY MOUNTAIN TARGET CO. (Data - Targ)
P.O. Box 30291; Billings, MT 59107; 406-259-4847

ROCKY MOUNTAIN WILDLIFE PROD.
4620 Moccasin Circle; LaPorte, CO 80535

ROGCHILD, INC.
P.O. Box 1336; Clarksburg, WV 26301; 304-623-2901

ROGERS HOLSTERS
10601 Theresa Dr.; Jacksonville, FL 32216

JOHN & HANS ROHNER
Sunshine Canyon; Boulder, CO 80302; 303-447-2154

ROMAN PRODUCTS
15400 W. 44th Ave.; Golden, CO 80401; 303-279-6959

ROY'S CUSTOM LEATHER GOODS
P.O. Box 852; Magnolia, AR 71753; 501-234-1566

ROYAL ARMS, INC.
10064 Bert Acosta St.; Santee, CA 92071; 714-448-5466

ROYAL GAME CALL
435 Edgewater Dr.; Mishawaka, IN 46544; 219-255-5208

ROYAL SPORTING BOOTS/RED BALL
8530 Page Ave.; St. Louis, MO 63114; 314-429-6952

MURRAY F. RUFFINO
Rte. 2; Milford, ME 04461; 207-827-2688

RUSTEPRUFE LABS
Sparta, WI 54656; 608-269-6403

S

S & K MFG. CO.
Box 247; Pittsfield, PA 16340; 814-563-7808

S & S FIREARMS
88-21 Aubrey Ave.; Glendale, NY 11227; 212-497-1100

SWMS (SOUTHWEST METALLIC SILHOUETTE)
P.O. Box 476; Uvalde, TX 78801; 512-278-5454

SAECO RELOADING, INC.
P.O. Box 778; Carpinteria, CA 93013; 805-684-5656

SAFETY DIRECT
23 Snider Way; Sparks, NV 89431; 702-359-4451

SAF-T-BAK, INC.
5200 Sixth Ave.; Altoona, PA 16603; 814-944-9427

ANTHONY F. SAILER AMMUNITION
Third St., P.O. Box L; Owen, WI 54460; 715-229-2516

JEAN ST. HENRI
6525 Dume Dr.; Malibu, CA 90265

SALISH HOUSE, INC.
P.O. Box 27; Rollins, MT 59931

SARCO, INC.
323 Union St.; Stirling, NJ 07980; 201-647-3800

SAN ANGELO CO., INC.
P.O. Box 984; San Angelo, TX 76901; 715-655-7126

SAN/BAR CORP.
P.O. Box 11787; 17422 Pullman St., Santa Ana, CA 92711; 714-546-6500

SANDIA DIE AND CARTRIDGE CO.
Rte. 5, Box 5400; Albuquerque, NM 87123; 505-298-5729

SAVAGE ARMS
Springdale Rd.; Westfield, MA 01085; 413-562-2361

SCHIERMEIER
Box 704; Twin Falls, ID 83301; 208-733-7682

D. SCHNEIDER HORNS, INC.
7411 Gallop Dr., Box G; San Antonio, TX 78227

SCHULTEA'S GUN STRING
67 Burress, Houston, TX 77022; 713-697-5659

SCOTCH GAME CALL
60 Main St.; Oakfield, NY 14125; 716-948-5242

SE-CUR-AL GUN CABINETS
P.O. Box 2052; Michigan City, IN 46360; 219-872-7957

L. W. SEECAMP CO.
Box 255; New Haven, CT 06502; 203-877-3429

SERVICE ARMAMENT CO.
689 Bergen Blvd.; Ridgefield, NJ 07657; 201-945-2500

SHASSERE
P.O. Box 25218; Houston, TX 77005; 713-780-7041

SHAW-LEIBOWITZ
Rt. 1, Box 421; New Cumberland, WV 26047; 304-564-3108

SHERIDAN PRODUCTS, INC.
3205 Sheridan; Racine, WI 53403; 414-633-5424

SHERWOOD DISTRIBUTORS, INC.
18714 Parthenia St.; Northridge, CA 91324; 213-349-7600

GEORGE SHERWOOD
Box 735; Winchester, OR 97495; 503-672-3159

SHILEN RIFLES INC.
205 Metropark Blvd.; Ennis, TX 75119; 214-875-5318

SHILOH PRODUCTS
37 Potter St.; Farmingdale, NY 11735

HAROLD H. SHOCKLEY
204 E. Farmington Rd.; Hanna City, IL 61536; 309-565-4524

BEN SHOSTLE (The Gun Room)
1201 Burlington Dr.; Muncie, IN 47302; 317-282-9073

SIEGRIST GUN SHOP
2689 McLean Rd., Whittemore, MI 48770; 517-873-4435

SIERRA BULLETS
P.O. Box 3104; Santa Fe Springs, CA 90670; 213-941-0251

THE SIGHT SHOP
1802 E. Columbia Ave.; Tacoma, WA 98404; 206-474-5465

SIGMA SCIENTIFIC INC.
1830 South Baker Ave.; Ontario, CA 91761; 714-983-8200

CORBET R. SIGMAN
Rte. 1, Box 212A; Liberty, WV 25124; 304-586-9131

SILE DISTRIBUTORS, INC.
7 Centre Market Pl.; New York, NY 10013; 212-925-4111

C. E. SILER LOCKS
Rt. 6, Box 5; Candler, NC 28715; 704-667-2376

JERRY SIMMONS
713 Middlebury St.; Goshen, IN 46526; 219-533-8546

SIMMS HARDWARE CO.
2801 J. St.; Sacramento, CA 95816; 916-442-3894

SIX ENTERPRISES
6564 Hidden Creek Dr.; San Jose, CA 95120; 408-268-8296

SLUG SITE CO.
Whitetails Wilds; Lake Hubert, MN 56459; 218-963-4617

SMALL ARMS ENGINEERING (John Kaufield)
7698 Garden Prairie Rd.; Garden Prairie, IL 61038; 815-597-3981

JOHN T. SMITH
8404 Cedar Crest Dr.; So. Haven, MS 38671; 601-393-7061

SMITH & WESSON
Box 2208; Springfield, MA 01101

SNAPP'S GUNSHOP
6911 E. Washington Rd., Clare, MI 48617; 517-386-9226

W. J. SONNEVILLE KNIVES
1050 Chalet Dr. W.; Mobile, AL 36608; 205-342-5447

SOUTHERN PRECISION INSTRUMENT CO.
3419 E. Commerce St.; San Antonio, TX 78219; 512-224-5801

SOUTHWEST METALLIC SILHOUETTES (SWMS)
P.O. Box 476; Uvalde, TX 78801; 512-278-5454

BERNARD SPARKS (Knives)
Box 32; Dingle, ID 83233; 208-847-1883

SPEER PRODUCTS
P.O. Box 896; Lewiston, ID 83501; 208-743-8574

FRED D. SPEISER
2229 Dearborn; Missoula, MT 59801; 406-549-8133

SPORT LORE, INC.
1757 Cherry St.; Denver, CO 80220; 303-377-0206

SPORTS HAVEN, INC.
P.O. Box 88231; Seattle, WA 98188; 206-575-3686

SPORTS INNOVATIONS
Box 385; Wichita Falls, TX; 817-766-1463

SPORTS SPECIALTIES
Box 744; Sunnyvale, CA 94088

SPORTSMEN'S LABORATORIES, INC.
P.O. Box 732; Anoka, MN 55303; 612-427-1569

SPRINGFIELD SPORTERS
RD 1; Penn Run, PA 15765; 412-254-2626

STAR MACHINE WORKS OF SAN DIEGO, INC.
418 10th Ave.; San Diego, CA 92101; 714-232-3216

STEARNS MFG. CO.
P.O. Box 1498; St. Cloud, MN 56301; 612-252-1642

GLEN STEARNS
5318 Brophy Drive; Toledo, OH 43611; 419-729-3540

JOHNNY STEWART GAME CALLS, INC.
Box 7594; Waco, TX 76710; 817-772-3261

C. H. STOCKING
Rt. 3, Box 195; Hutchinson, MN 55350; 612-879-5810

STOWLINE RIFLE SAFE
P.O. Box 3760; Kent, WA 98031; 206-242-1330

VICTOR W. STRAWBRIDGE (Vic's Gun Refinishing)
6 Pineview Dr.; Dover Point; Dover, NH 03820; 603-742-0013

W. C. STRUTZ
Rte. #1, Woodland; Eagle River, WI 54521; 715-479-4766

SUGAR CREEK GUN CO.
Hwy 34 East, Box 808; Ottumwa, IA 52501

SURE-SHOT GAME CALLS, INC.
P.O. Box 816; Groves, TX 77619; 713-962-1636

SURVIVAL SYSTEMS
1830 S. Baker Ave.; Ontario, CA 91761

SWENSON'S 45 SHOP
P.O. Box 606; Fallbrook, CA 92028; 714-728-5319

SWIFT INSTRUMENTS, INC.
952 Dorchester Ave.; Boston, MA 02125; 617-436-2960

SWISS ARMY KNIVES, INC.
P.O. Box 824; Shelton; CT 06484; 800-243-6041

T

T.E.S., INC.
2807 N. Prospect St.; Colorado Springs, CO 80907; 303-633-5937

DAVE TALLEY, GUNSMITH
124 Whitehaven Dr.; Greenville, SC 29611

T-MAGIC CO.
33 Burnside Ave.; East Hartford, CT 06108

TAMARACK PRODUCTS, INC.
Box 224; Barrington, IL 60010

TASCO, INC.
1075 N.W. 71st St.; Miami, FL 33138; 305-836-3551

TAYLOR & ROBBINS
Box 164; Rixford, PA 16745; 814-966-3233

TELEPACIFIC ELECTRONICS CO., INC.
P.O. Box 2210; Escondido, CA 92025; 713-744-4415

10-X MFG. CO.
1745 S. Acoma St.; Denver, CO 80223; 303-778-0324

TENNESSEE VALLEY ARMS CO.
P.O. Box 461; Union City, TN 38261

TESTING SYSTEMS, INC.
#5 Tenakill Pk.; Cresskill, NJ 07626; 201-569-5200

TEXAS PLATERS SUPPLY CO.
2453 W. Five Mile Parkway; Dallas, TX 75233; 214-330-7168

THOMPSON-CENTER ARMS
P.O. Box 2405; Rochester, NH 03867; 603-332-2394

THE 3-D COMPANY
Box 142; Doniphan, NB 68832; 402-845-2285

GORDON TIBBITTS
1378 Lakewood Circle; Salt Lake City, UT 84117; 801-272-4126

TIMNEY MFG. CO.
2847 E. Siesta Lane; Phoenix, AZ 85024; 602-992-6067

TITUS BARREL & GUN CO.
RFD #1, Box 23; Heber City, UT 84032; 801-654-2933

JOHN TOVEY
4710 104th Ln. N. E.; Circle Pines, MN 55014

DWIGHT L. TOWELL
Rte. 1; Midvale, ID 83645; 208-355-2419

TRAIL GUNS ARMORY
1634 E. Main St.; League City, TX 77573; 713-332-5833

TREADLOK SECURITY CHEST (Tread Corp.)
P.O. Box 13207; Roanoke, VA 24012; 703-982-6881

TREVALLION GUNSTOCKS
6524 N. Carrollton Ave.; Indianapolis, IN 46220; 317-257-9581

TRIKTRUK, INC.
P.O. Box 3760; Kent, WA 98301; 206-242-1330

TRIPLE-K MFG. CO.
568 Sixth Ave.; San Diego, CA 92101; 714-232-2066

TRIUS PRODUCTS
Box 25; Cleves, OH 45002; 513-941-5682

TRU-BALANCE KNIFE CO.
2155 Tremont Blvd. NW; Grand Rapids, MI 49504; 616-543-3679

TUFF-LITE DECOY CO.
P.O. Box 1232-Himlet Hangar; Ketchum, ID 83340; 208-726-3161

TULLER & CO.
29 Germania St.; Galeton, PA 16922; 814-435-2442

TWIN CITY STEEL TREATING CO., INC.
1114 S. Third St.; Minneapolis, MN 55415; 612-332-4849

U

JOHN UNERTL OPTICAL CO.
3551-5 East St.; Pittsburgh, PA 15214

UNIROYAL SPECIAL MARKETS
Box 455; Naugatuck, CT 06770

UPPER MISSOURI TRADING CO.
3rd & Harold Sts.; Crofton, NB 68730; 402-388-4844

V

ROBERT VALADE
Rte. 1, Box 30-A; Cove, OR 97824

J. W. VAN PATTEN
Box 145, Foster Hill; Milford, PA 18337; 717-296-7069

JOHN VEST
6715 Shasta Way; Klamath Falls, OR 97601; 503-884-5585

VIC'S GUN REFINISHING
6 Pineview Dr., Dover Point; Dover, NH 03820; 603-742-0013.

VITT & BOOS
11 Sugar Loaf Dr.; Wilton, CT 06897

W

WD-40 CO.
1061 Cudahy Pl.; San Diego, CA 92110; 714-275-1400

W.K. KNIVES
P.O. Box 327; Pioneer, OH 43554; 419-737-2627

VERNON G. WAGONER
P.O. Box 18234; Fountain Hills, AZ 85268

HERMAN WALDRON
Box 475; Pomeroy, WA 99347; 509-843-1404

WALTERS INDUSTRIES
6226 Park Lane; Dallas, TX 75225; 214-691-6973

WAYNE PRODUCTS CO.
P.O. Box 247; Camp Hill, PA 17011; 717-761-6120

WEATHERBY, INC.
2781 Firestone Blvd.; South Gate, CA 90280

WEATHER SHIELD SPORTS EQUIPMENT, INC.
P.O. Box 227; Charlevoix, MI 49720

W. R. WEAVER COMPANY
7125 Industrial Ave.; El Paso, TX 79915; 915-778-5281

C. H. WEISZ
P.O. Box 311; Arlington, VA 22210; 703-243-9161

WELLS LAMONT CORP.
6640 W. Touhy Ave.; Chicago, IL 60648

ROBERT G. WEST
27211 Huey Ave.; Eugene, OR 97402; 503-689-6610

WEST COAST SECOA
3915 U.S. Hwy. 98S; Lakeland, FL 33801; 813-665-1734

WESTERN CUTLERY CO.
1800 Pike Rd., Longmont, CO 80501; 303-772-5900

WHITNEY SALES, INC.
P.O. Box 875; Reseda, CA 91335; 213-345-4212

WICHITA ENGINEERING & SUPPLY, INC.
P.O. Box 11371; Wichita, KS 67202; 316-265-0661

WIDE VIEW SCOPE MOUNT CORP.
26110 Michigan Ave.; Inkster, MI 48141; 313-274-1238

WILL-BURT COMPANY
169 S. Main; Orrville, OH 44667; 216-682-7015

WILLIAMS GUN SIGHT CO.
7389 Lapeer Rd.; Davison, MI 48423; 313-653-2131

DICK WILLIS
141 Shady Creek Rd.; Rochester, NY 14623; 716-334-0319

WILSON ARMS CO.
63 Leetes Island Rd.; Branford, CT 06405

WINCHESTER SUTLER
Bloomery Star Route Box 61; Winchester, VA 22601

WINCHESTER-WESTERN
275 Winchester Ave.; New Haven, CT 06504; 203-777-7911

W. C. WOLFF CO.
Box 232; Ardmore, PA 19003; 213-647-3461

LESTER WOMACK
P.O. Box 17210; Tucson, AZ 85710; 602-298-2036

WOOD DIE SHOP
Box 386; Florence, OR 97439

MEL WOOD
3901 Crestmont Dr.; Santa Maria, CA 93454; 805-937-2777

DAVE WOODRUFF
Box 5; Bear, DE 19701; 302-328-5766

WOODSTREAM CORP.
P.O. Box 327; Lititz, PA 17543; 717-626-2125

DWAIN WRIGHT
The Muffin House; 67168 Central; Bend, OR 97701; 503-389-5558

STAN WRIGHT
64 Merchants Row; Swanton; VT 05488

Z

CARL ZEISS, INC.
444 Fifth Ave.; New York, NY 10018; 212-736-6070

ZERO BULLET CO.
P.O. Box 1012; Cullman, AL 35055; 205-739-1606